A TREASURY OF SCIENCE

A TREASURY OF SCIENCE

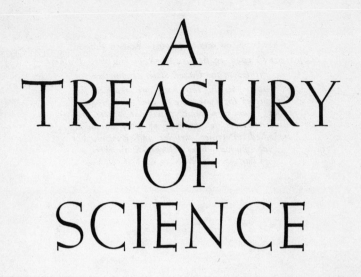

Edited by HARLOW SHAPLEY

SAMUEL RAPPORT and HELEN WRIGHT

With an Introduction by Dr. Shapley

FOURTH REVISED EDITION

*New material on
Radio Astronomy, Measurement of Geologic Time,
The Origin of Life and Man's Ancestral Past.
New sections on Rocketry and Space Travel, and Atomic Energy*

HARPER & BROTHERS PUBLISHERS
NEW YORK

Library of Congress catalog card number: 58-7974

TABLE OF CONTENTS

C. MATTER, ENERGY, PHYSICAL LAW

Part Four: THE WORLD OF LIFE

A. THE RIDDLE OF LIFE

B. THE SPECTACLE OF LIFE

C. THE EVOLUTION OF LIFE

Part Five: THE WORLD OF MAN

A. FROM APE TO CIVILIZATION

B. THE HUMAN MACHINE

C. THE CONQUEST OF DISEASE

D. MAN'S MIND

Part Six: THE ROCKET AND THE ATOM

A. ROCKETS, MISSILES, SPACE

B. THE POWER OF THE ATOM:
AN END OR A BEGINNING?

Preface

THE READER OF THIS BOOK MAY BE INTERESTED IN the methods used in preparing it. We envisaged the audience as the person without specialized knowledge; we accepted as our purpose to give some realization of how the scientist works, of the body of knowledge that has resulted and of the excitement of the scientist's search. One of us has endeavored to convey some of that excitement in his Introduction, *On Sharing in the Conquests of Science.*

We realized that a group of random selections, however good in themselves, would suggest little of the unity, the architectural quality of science. We spent some months therefore in organizing the material before we adopted a definite plan. The plan is evident from the titles of the major Parts: Science and the Scientist, The Physical World, The World of Life and The World of Man. The subdivisions carry through the plan in what seems a logical sequence.

There followed a period of over a year during which several thousand books and articles were examined in the light of this general scheme. In making our selections we have tried to emphasize especially the status and the contributions of modern science, to the end that the reader can bring himself abreast of current progress. But in a few cases, we have gone back the better part of a century to find the right discussion. We have incorporated a number of biographical sketches of important scientists, among them Pasteur, Madame Curie, Leeuwenhoek, in order to give a glimpse of the personalities of scientific explorers. Also we have reached generously into the past and selected classics of science, which not only add flavor but also exhibit the work and workers who have done so much to guide and inspire our civilization.

It has been found possible to avoid translations almost completely, since the whole range of modern science has been explored assiduously by English-writing people. Much assistance in the preparation of a volume of this sort comes from the American standard magazines, and the semi-popular scientific monthlies. They have provided for scientific writers an incentive to summarize their work or the special field concerning which they write, in a fashion that is comprehensive, and comprehensible to the layman.

We are also especially indebted to certain skillful scientific interpreters, among them the English school of writers which includes the Huxleys, Sir J. A. Thomson, Sir James Jeans, and J. B. S. Haldane. More than once we have turned to their writings in preference to the scattered, technical, fragmentary originals from which their synthetic pictures are compounded.

Many important scientists are of course not represented in this collection, either because their writings have not been on the appropriate level, or because in our judgment the reader can do better with another writer. Limitations of space have also shortened and compressed many of the selections. And since the volume is designed for the general reader and not for the specialist, except when he is also a general reader, the addition of references, technical footnotes and the similar apparatus of the serious student are omitted.

We hope that the volume will justify itself in interest, and in instructional value, whether it is opened at random, or is methodically read from beginning to end. For the reader who wishes to understand the full meaning of any selection in relation to its context, we suggest a perusal of the brief introductory notes at the beginnings of the main Parts.

As a general reference book this volume should have definite value. For example, the attentive reading of Moulton, Jeans, and Eddington will provide an authoritative picture of the fundamentals as well as the recent advances of astronomy; and in short space the reader can obtain from Langewiesche a fair understanding of modern weather prediction. Several contributors make atomic structure or the past of man a well-rounded story. And in a single essay subjects such as the Metagalaxy, earthquakes, parasitism or Freudianism are each clearly summarized.

Nevertheless, the reader should realize that this work does not aim to be encyclopedic in presentation. It is our hope that he will go further into the vast stores of available writings to get specialized knowledge of any branch of science that may interest him.

A contribution toward the integration of science is, as we have said, one goal of this volume. We hope that it may be of particular value to the scientific worker himself. No one works effectively in more than one or two of the special fields. The average specialist is just as uninformed about science remote from his speciality as is the general reader. A familiarity with other disciplines should not only be good entertainment, but instructive as to techniques and attitudes. But of most importance, the scientific specialist, while reading abroad, is informing himself on the inter-fields of science, or at least on the possibility and merit of inter-field study. If this volume can assist in however small a way in the integration that seems essential to man's intelligent control of his own fabrications, it will have attained the desired end.

Preface to the Fourth Edition

A S IN THE TWO PRECEDING EDITIONS OF *A Treasury of Science*, we are compelled, by the rapid uncovering of new treasures, to report on important advances in several fields. Radio astronomy (by Lovell), the origin of life (Wald), artificial satellites (Isakov and Howe), and the genetic dangers of atomic bomb fall-out (Weaver) are among the additions. The recent experiments and discoveries relative to biogenesis—that is, the emergence of the living from the inanimate —affects so directly our philosophies that it seems appropriate to point out in this Preface the relevance of methane, the amino acids, sunlight, and the expanding universe to man's self-evaluation and to his orientation in the material world. For the scattering of galaxies, the habits of giant molecules, and the astounding abundance of stars are forcing those who ponder such matters to a further adjustment (the fourth) of their understanding of the place and functioning of man in the physical universe.

The philosophers and priests of the early tribes of men gradually realized that the universe is not simply anthropocentric—centered on man himself. The geocentric concept became common doctrine; but in the sixteenth century, through the agency of the Copernican revolution, it was replaced by the sun-center or heliocentric hypothesis. Thereafter for nearly four centuries our star, the sun, was held to be the center not only of the local planetary system but of the whole sidereal world.

That second adjustment made no great philosophic disturbance, but less than forty years ago came the need for a third shift, one that is destined to affect deeply man's religious and philosophical thinking. This third adjustment deflates his pride and self-assurance; it introduces the "galactocentric" universe, and puts man and all his works in the outer star-fields of one galaxy in a universe of billions of galaxies. His sun is but one average star in a galaxy containing a hundred billion other stars.

This downgrading of the sun and earth, and the elevation of the galaxies, is not the end of the progress of scientific pilgrims through philosophic fields. The need for a further jolting adjustment now arises—not wholly unexpected by workers in science. This new concern is the spread of life throughout the universe.

To the ancients, only a few thousand stars were known; to the early telescopes, however, the number was a million; and that astounding number has increased spectacularly with every telescopic advance. We now accept the existence of more than 10^{20} stars in the explorable part of the universe.

The significance of this discovery, or rather of this uncovering, is that the universe contains more than one hundred million million million sources of light and warmth for whatever planets accompany the radiant stars.

We now accept the observational evidence for a rapidly expanding universe of galaxies. The expansion implies an increasingly greater concentration of these cosmic units (galaxies) as we go back in time. A few thousand million years ago the average density of matter in space must have been so great that collisions, near encounters, and gravitational disruptions were necessarily frequent. And here is a highly important coincidence: the crust of the earth, radioactively measured, is also a few thousand million years old, and therefore the earth and the other planets of our sun's family were "born" in those days of mighty turbulence. At that time countless millions of other planetary systems must have developed, for our sun is of a very common stellar variety.

Other ways in which planets may form are recognized. The contraction of proto-stars out of the hypothetical primeval gas, giving birth on the way to protoplanets, is an evolutionary process now widely favored for our own solar system. It would imply the existence of countless planets. In fact, whatever the method of their origin, planets must be the common heritage of all stars except those so constituted (e.g. double stars) that planetary materials would be swallowed or cast out through gravitational action.

(In passing we note that our kinds of chemistry and physics prevail throughout the universe we explore. There is nothing uncommon here or now.)

Remembering our 10^{20} stars and the high probability of millions of planets with suitable chemistry, dimensions and distance from their nutrient stars, we are ready for the question: On some of these planets is there actually life? Are there biochemical operations elsewhere? Or are they all strangely limited to our little planet, to No. 3 in the family of the sun, which is a run-of-the-mill star located in the outer part of a galaxy that contains a hundred thousand million other stars—and this galaxy but one of millions already on the records?

Is life thus restricted? Of course not.

In his article on the origin of life George Wald has presented details of natural biogenesis. To put it briefly: biochemistry and microbiology, with the assistance of geophysics, astronomy, and other sciences, have gone so far in bridging the gap between the inanimate and the living that we can no longer doubt but that whenever the physics, chemistry and climates are right on a planet's surface, life will emerge and persist.

The many researches of the past few years in the fields of viruses and macro-molecules have made it unnecessary to postulate miracles or the supernatural for the origin of life.

We cannot reasonably doubt that great numbers of planets have had both long and varied experience with biochemical evolution. Here on the earth thousands of kinds of animals are known to develop neurotic complexes of the sort we call "intelligence." It comes naturally. Could it be otherwise on another life-bearing planet?

It is indeed a magnificent universe and we are properly proud to be a part of it. But humbly we should observe that there is no reason in the world to believe that our own mental stature has not been excelled by sentient beings elsewhere. I am not suggesting, however, that *Homo* is repeated. There are millions of variations on the animal theme.

HARLOW SHAPLEY

PART ONE

INTRODUCTION

On Sharing in the Conquests of Science

HARLOW SHAPLEY

IT'S A WONDER I CAN STAND IT! TRAMPING FOR HOURS through the damp woods back of Walden Pond with Henry Thoreau, checking up on the food preferences of the marsh hawk, and the spread of sumach and goldenrod in old abandoned clearings. It requires stamina to match his stride as he plunges through swamps and philosophy, through underbrush, poetry, and natural history; it takes agility of body and mind if one does a full share of the day's measuring and speculation.

But no sooner have I left the Walden Woods than I am scrambling up the fossil-rich Scottish cliffs with Hugh Miller, preparing the groundwork of the immortal history of The Old Red Sandstone. With the wonderment of pioneers we gaze at the petrified ripple-marks that some shallow receding sea, in ancient times, has left as its fluted memorial—its monument built on the sand and of the sand, but nevertheless enduring. We break open a stony ball—this Scottish stonemason and I—a nodular mass of blue limestone, and expose beautiful traces of an extinct world of animals and plants; we find fossilized tree ferns, giant growths from the Carboniferous Period of two hundred and fifty million years ago—and forthwith we lose ourselves in conjecture.

And then I am off on another high adventure, higher than the moon this time; I am entering the study of the Frauenburg Cathedral to help Nicholas Copernicus do calculations on the hypothetical motions of the planets. He is, of course, deeply bemused with that rather queer notion that it might be the Sun that stands still—not the Earth. Perhaps he can demonstrate that the planets go around the Sun, each in its own course. Fascinated, I peer over his shoulder at the archaic geometry, watch his laborious penning of the great book, and listen to his troubled murmuring about the inaccuracies of the measured coördinates of Saturn. "There are, you know, two other big ones further out," I put in; "and a system of many moons around Jupiter, which makes it all very clear and obvious." It must startle him no end to have me interrupt

3

in such a confident way. But he does nothing about it. More planets? An incredible idea! Difficulties enough in trying to explain the visible, without complicating the complexities further by introducing invisible planets. My assistance ignored, I experience, nevertheless, a carefree exhilaration; for I have, as it were, matched my wits with the wisdom of the greatest of revolutionaries, and come off not too badly!

Now that I am fully launched in this career of working with the great explorers, and of coöperating in their attacks on the mysteries of the universe, I undertake further heroic assignments. I labor in the laboratories of the world; I maintain fatiguing vigils in the mountains and on the sea, try dangerous experiments, and make strenuous expeditions to Arctic shores and to torrid jungles—all without moving from the deep fireside chair.

Benjamin Franklin has a tempting idea, and I am right there to lend him a hand. We are having a lot of trouble in keeping that cantankerous kite in the thunder-cloud, from which the electric fluid should flow to charge and animate the house key. "Before long, Sir, we shall run printing presses with this fluid, and light our houses, and talk around the world"—but he does not put it in the *Autobiography*. I am clearly a century ahead of my time!

Youthful Charles Darwin is in the Galapagos. The good brig *Beagle* stands offshore. He has with him the collecting kit, the notebooks, and his curiosity. He is making records of the slight variations among closely similar species of plants and animals. He is pondering the origin of these differences, and the origin of species, and the whole confounding business of the origin of plants and animals. I sit facing him, on the rocks beside the tide pool, admiring the penetration and grasp of this young dreamer. The goal of his prolonged researches is a revolution in man's conception of life; he is assembling the facts and thoughts, and in this work I am a participant! Nothing could be more exciting. Also I have an advantage. I know about Mendel and Mendelian laws, and genes and chromosomes. I know that X-rays (unknown to Darwin), and other agents, can produce mutations and suddenly create living forms that Nature has not attained. This posterior knowledge of mine enhances the pleasure of my collaboration with the great naturalist; and I need have no fear that my information, or my ethereal presence, might bother him.

There is so much scientific work of this sort for me to do before some tormenting duty draws me out of my strategic chair. The possibilities are nearly endless. Like a benign gremlin, I sit on the brim of a test tube in Marie Curie's laboratory and excitedly speculate with her on that radioactive ingredient in the pitchblende; I help name it radium.

With Stefansson and the Eskimos I live for months on a scanty menu, and worry with him about the evils of civilization. And when young Evariste Galois, during his beautiful, brief, perturbed life in Paris, sits down to devise sensationally new ideas and techniques in pure mathematics, I am right there with applause and sympathy.

Whenever I pause to appreciate how simple it is for me to take an active part in unravelling the home life of primitive man, or observing the voracity of a vampire bat; how simple for me, in company with the highest authorities, to reason on the theory of relativity or explore with a cyclotron the insides of atoms, it is then that I call for additional blessings on those artisans who invented printing. They have provided me with guide lines to remote wonders—highly conductive threads that lead me, with a velocity faster than that of light itself, into times long past and into minds that biologically are long extinct. Through the simple process of learning how to interpret symbols, such as those that make this sentence, I can take part in most of the great triumphs of the human intellect. Blessings and praises, laurel wreaths and myrtle, are due those noble spirits who made writing and reading easily accessible, and thus opened to us all the romance of scientific discovery.

Have you ever heard an ox warble? Probably not. Perhaps it goes through its strange life-cycle silent to our gross ears. But I have seen ox warbles, and through the medium of the printed page I have followed their gory careers. The ox warbles to which I refer are, of course, not bovine melodies, but certain flies that contribute to the discomfort of cattle, to the impoverishment of man's property, and to the enrichment of his knowledge of the insect world.[1]

It required a declaration of war on this entomological enemy, by some of the great nations of the planet, in order to discover him completely and entrench mankind against his depredations. It took a century of detective work on the part of entomologists to lay bare the ox warble's secret life. Now that I have the story before me, I can go along with the scientists and experience again their campaigns, their misadventures, and their compensating discoveries. I can see how to connect a number of separate phenomena that long were puzzling—those gay pasture flies that look like little bumblebees; those rows of tiny white eggs on the hairs above the hoofs of cattle; the growing larvae, guided mysteriously by ancestral experience to wind their way for months through the flesh of the legs and bodies of their unknowing hosts; the apparently inactive

[1] The full story of the ox warble is buried in various technical government reports. But see a brief chapter on the subject in *Insects—Man's Chief Competitors*, by W. P. Flint and C. L. Metcalf (Williams & Wilkins, 1932).

worms in the cattle's throats; the large midwinter mounds, scattered
subcutaneously along the spines of the herd; and eventually those ruin-
ous holes in the leather, which have forced governments into aggressive
action—into defense-with-pursuit tactics for the protection of their economic frontiers. It is all clear now. During the millennia of recent geological periods a little fly has learned how to fatten its offspring on a fresh
beef diet, and prepare its huge grub for that critical moment when it
crawls out, through the hole it has made in the ox hide, and drops to
the earth for its metamorphosis—the change from a headless, legless,
eyeless, dark childhood to a maturity of wings and sunlight.

The curiosity the scientist strives to satisfy is thus sometimes impelled by economics; more often by the pure desire to know. Our
black-on-white guiding threads, which you may call printed books, or
recorded history, not only transmit the stories of ancient and modern
inquisitiveness and the inquiries it has inspired, but they also report, to
the discerning recipient, the inevitability of practiced internationalism.
They transmit the message that all races of mankind are curious about
the universe, and that, when free and not too depressed by hunger, men
instinctively question and explore, analyze and catalogue. They have done
it in all ages, in all civilized countries. They work singly, in groups,
and increasingly in world-wide organizations. Science recognizes no
impossible national boundaries, and only temporary barriers of language.
It points the way to international coöperation.

To more than the art of printing, however, do we owe the successes
and pleasures of our vicarious adventures in science. We are also greatly
indebted to those who can write and will write in terms of our
limited comprehension. Not all the scientists have the facility. Sometimes the talk is too tough for us, or too curt. They have not the time
to be lucid on our level and within our vocabulary, or perhaps their
mental intensity has stunted the faculty of sympathetic explanation.
When such technical barriers shut us from the scientific workshop, it is
then we like to consult with a clear-spoken and understanding inter-
preter. We sit on the back porch of the laboratory, while he, as middle-
man, goes inside to the obscurities and mysteries, to return occasionally
with comprehensible reports. In listening to him we hear not only his
voice, but the overtones of the master he interprets. I like these men of
understanding who play Boswell to the specialist. They often have a
gift greater than that of the concentrated workers whom they soften
up for us. For they have breadth and perspective, which help us to
get at the essence of a problem more objectively than we could even if
we were fully equipped with the language and knowledge of the fact-

bent explorer and analyst. The scientific interpreters frequently enhance our enjoyment in that they give us of themselves, as well as of the discoverers whose exploits they recount. We are always grateful to them, moreover, for having spared us labor and possibly discouragement.

Perhaps the greatest satisfaction in reading of scientific exploits and participating, with active imagination, in the dull chores, the brave syntheses, the hard-won triumphs of scientific work, lies in the realization that ours is not an unrepeatable experience. Tomorrow night we can again go out among the distant stars. Again we can drop cautiously below the ocean surface to observe the unbelievable forms that inhabit those salty regions of high pressure and dim illumination. Again we can assemble the myriad molecules into new combinations, weave them into magic carpets that take us into strange lands of beneficent drugs and of new fabrics and utensils destined to enrich the process of everyday living. Again we can be biologist, geographer, astronomer, engineer, or help the philosopher evaluate the nature and meaning of natural laws.

We can return another day to these shores, and once more embark for travels over ancient or modern seas in quest of half-known lands— go forth as dauntless conquistadores, outfitted with the maps and gear provided through the work of centuries of scientific adventures.

But we have done enough for this day. We have much to dream about. Our appetites may have betrayed our ability to assimilate. The fare has been irresistibly palatable. It is time to disconnect the magic threads; time to wind up the spiral galaxies, roll up the Milky Way and lay it aside until tomorrow.

1943

PART TWO

SCIENCE AND THE SCIENTIST

Synopsis

MANY STORIES OF JOURNEYS TO UNKNOWN LANDS HAVE been written. Many tales of wonder have been told by the great writers of the world. Yet it is common knowledge that the reality of modern science is more wonderful than the imaginative world of a Poe, a Wells or a Jules Verne. It is therefore unfortunate that the story has usually been told in long words, written down in forbidding tomes. Like Agassiz's monumental work on turtles, Contributions to the Natural History of the United States, described by Dallas Lore Sharp in the following pages, they are "massive, heavy, weathered as if dug from the rocks." Yet there is amusement in science, excitement, profound satisfaction. It is fitting that our first selection should be an attempt to describe that feeling, The Wonder of the World by Sir J. Arthur Thomson and Patrick Geddes.

Nor is science something esoteric, something mysterious and incomprehensible to the average person. We are all scientists, as T. H. Huxley shows clearly, whether we are concerned with the properties of green apples or with finding the burglar who stole our spoons. And we are led to our conclusions by "the same train of reasoning which a man of science pursues when he is endeavoring to discover the origin and laws of the most occult phenomena." One of the great scientists of the nineteenth century, as well as its greatest scientific writer, Huxley is well qualified to instruct us.

The quality that sets the scientist apart is perhaps the persistence of his curiosity about the world. That is what causes him to bury himself in his laboratory or travel to a remote corner of the globe. Like Oliver La Farge, in Scientists Are Lonely Men, he may spend months or even years on some quest, seeming trivial yet destined perhaps to prove a clue to the origin of a race. Or like Mr. Jenks of Middleboro, in Turtle Eggs for Agassiz, he may spend countless hours beside a murky pond, waiting for a turtle to lay her eggs. In both these tales there is much of the excitement, the emotional and intellectual spirit of the scientific quest.

It is not possible in brief space to describe all the aspects of that quest. But in The Aims and Methods of Science, a group of thinkers illuminate a few of its many complexities. A passage from Roger Bacon shows why he is considered one of the originators of scientific method. Albert Einstein asks and answers the question, "Why does this magnificent applied science, which saves work and makes life easier, bring us so little happiness?" Sir Arthur Eddington shows that again and again the scientist must fly like Icarus, before he finally reaches the sun. The passion of work and research is Ivan Pavlov's theme. In a final selection, written for a Report of the Atomic Energy Commission, Alan Gregg, Chairman of the AEC Advisory Committee on Biology and Medicine, examines the possibilities for good and evil of the frightening new discoveries in nuclear physics.

The Wonder of the World

SIR J. ARTHUR THOMSON AND PATRICK GEDDES

From *Life: Outlines of General Biology*

ARISTOTLE, WHO WAS NOT UNACCUSTOMED TO resolute thinking, tells us that throughout nature there is always something of the wonderful—*thaumaston*. What precisely is this "wonderful"? It cannot be merely the startling, as when we announce the fact that if we could place in one long row all the hair-like vessels or capillaries of the human body, which connect the ends of the arteries with the beginnings of the veins, they would reach across the Atlantic. It would be all the same to us if they reached only half-way across. Nor can the wonderful be merely the puzzling, as when we are baffled by the "sailing" of an albatross round and round our ship without any perceptible strokes of its wings. For some of these minor riddles are being read every year, without lessening, however, the fundamental wonderfulness of Nature. Indeed, the much-abused word "wonderful" is properly applied to any fact the knowledge of which greatly increases our appreciation of the significance of the system of which we form a part. *The truly wonderful makes all other things deeper and higher.* Science is always dispelling mists— the minor marvels; but it leaves us with intellectual blue sky, sublime mountains, and deep sea. Their wonder appears—and remains.

There seems to be a rational basis for wonder in the abundance of power in the world—the power that keeps our spinning earth together as it revolves round the sun, that keeps our solar system together as it journeys through space at the rate of twelve miles a second towards a point in the sky, close to the bright star Vega, called "the apex of the sun's way." At the other extreme there is the power of a fierce little world within the complex atom, whose imprisoned energies are set free to keep up the radiant energies of sun and star. And between these extremes of the infinitely great and the infinitely little are the powers of life—the power of winding up the clock almost as fast as it runs down, the power of a fish that has better engines than those of a *Mauretania*, life's power of multiplying itself, so that in a few hours an invisible microbe may become a fatal million.

Another, also old-fashioned, basis for wonder is to be found in the immensities. It takes light eight minutes to reach us from the sun, though it travels at the maximum velocity—of about 186,300 miles per second. So we see the nearest star by the light that left it four years ago, and Vega as it was twenty-seven years ago, and most of the stars that we see without a telescope as they were when Galileo Galilei studied them in the early years of the seventeenth century. In any case it is plain that we are citizens of no mean city.

A third basis for rational wonder is to be found in the intricacy and manifoldness of things. We get a suggestion of endless resources in the creation of individualities. Over two thousand years ago Aristotle knew about five hundred different kinds of animals; and now the list of the named and known includes twenty-five thousand different kinds of back-boned animals, and a quarter of a million—some insist on a minimum of half a million—backboneless animals, each itself and no other. For "all flesh is not the same flesh, but there is one kind of flesh of men, another flesh of beasts, another of fishes, and another of birds." The blood of a horse is different from that of an ass, and one can often identify a bird from a single feather or a fish from a few scales. One is not perhaps greatly thrilled by the fact that the average man has twenty-five billions of oxygen-capturing red blood corpuscles, which if spread out would occupy a surface of 3,300 square yards; but there is significance in the calculation that he has in the cerebral cortex of his brain, the home of the higher intellectual activities, some nine thousand millions of nerve cells, that is to say, more than five times the present population of the globe—surely more than the said brain as yet makes use of.

So it must be granted that we are fearfully and wonderfully made! Our body is built up of millions of cells, yet there is a simplicity amid the multitudinousness, for each cell has the same fundamental structure. Within the colloid cell-substance there floats a kernel or nucleus, which contains forty-seven (or in woman forty-eight) chromosomes, each with a bead-like arrangement of smaller microsomes, and so on, and so on. Similarly, while eighty-nine different elements have been discovered out of the theoretically possible ninety-two, we know that they differ from one another only in the number and distribution of the electrons and protons that make up their microcosmic planetary system. What artistry to weave the gorgeously varied tapestry of the world out of two kinds of physical thread—besides, of course, Mind, which eventually searches into the secret of the loom.

A fourth basis for rational wonder is in the orderliness of Nature, and that is almost the same thing as saying its intelligibility. What implications there are in the fact that man has been able to make a science of Nature! Given three good observations of a comet, the astronomer can predict its return to a night. It is not a phantasmagoria that we live in, it is a rational-isable cosmos. The more science advances the more the fortuitous shrivels, and the more the power of prophecy grows. Two astronomers foretold the discovery of Neptune; the chemists have anticipated the discovery of new elements; the biologist can not only count but portray his chickens before they are hatched. The Order of Nature is the largest of all certainties; and leading authorities in modern physics tell us that we cannot think of it as emerging from the fortuitous. It is time that the phrase "a fortuitous con-course of atoms" was buried. Even the aboriginal nebula was not *that*! No doubt there have been diseases and tragedies among men, cataclysms and volcanic eruptions upon the earth, and so on—no one denies the shadows; but even these disturbances are not disorderly; the larger fact is the ab-sence of all caprice. To refer to the poet's famous line, no one any longer supposes that gravitation can possibly cease when he goes by the avalanche. Nor will a microbe's insurgence be influenced by the social importance of the patient.

Corresponding to the intelligibility of Nature is the pervasiveness of beauty—a fifth basis of rational wonder, appealing to the emotional side of our personality. Surely Lotze was right, that it is of high value to look upon beauty not as a stranger in the world, nor as a casual aspect of cer-tain phenomena, but as "the fortunate revelation of that principle which permeates all reality with its living activity."

A sixth basis of rational wonder is to be found in the essential character-istics of living creatures. We need only add the caution that the marvel of life is not to be taken at its face value; as Coleridge wisely said, the first wonder is the child of *ignorance*; we must attend diligently to all that biochemistry and biophysics can discount; we must try to understand all that can be formulated in terms of colloids, and so on. Yet when all that is said, there seem to be large residual phenomena whose emergence in living creatures reveal a new depth in Nature. Life is an enduring, in-surgent activity, growing, multiplying, developing, enregistering, varying, and above all else evolving.

For this is the seventh wonder—Evolution. It is not merely that all things flow; it is that life flows uphill. Amid the ceaseless flux there is not only conservation, there is advancement. The changes are not those of a kaleidoscope, but of "an onward advancing melody." As the unthinkably long ages passed the earth became the cradle and home of life; nobler and finer kinds of living creatures appeared; there was a growing victory of life over things and of "mind" over "body"; until at last appeared Man, who is Life's crowning wonder, since he has given to everything else a higher and deeper significance. And while we must consider man in the light of evolution, as most intellectual combatants admit, there is the even more difficult task of envisaging evolution in the light of Man. *Finis coronat opus*—a wise philosophical axiom; and yet the scientist must qualify it by asking who can say Finis to Evolution.

1931

We Are All Scientists

T. H. HUXLEY

From *Darwiniana*

SCIENTIFIC INVESTIGATION IS NOT, AS MANY PEOPLE seem to suppose, some kind of modern black art. You might easily gather this impression from the manner in which many persons speak of scientific inquiry, or talk about inductive and deductive philosophy, or the principles of the "Baconian philosophy." I do protest that, of the vast number of cants in this world, there are none, to my mind, so contemptible as the pseudo-scientific cant which is talked about the "Baconian philosophy."

To hear people talk about the great Chancellor—and a very great man he certainly was,—you would think that it was he who had invented science, and that there was no such thing as sound reasoning before the time of Queen Elizabeth! Of course you say, that cannot possibly be true; you perceive, on a moment's reflection, that such an idea is absurdly wrong. . . .

The method of scientific investigation is nothing but the expression of the necessary mode of working of the human mind. It is simply the mode at which all phenomena are reasoned about, rendered precise and exact. There is no more difference, but there is just the same kind of difference, between the mental operations of a man of science and those of an ordinary person, as there is between the operations and methods of a baker or of a butcher weighing out his goods in common scales, and the operations of a chemist in performing a difficult and complex analysis by means of his balance and finely-graduated weights. It is not that the action of the scales in the one case, and the balance in the other, differ in the principles of their construction or manner of working; but the beam of one is set on an infinitely finer axis than the other, and of course turns by the addition of a much smaller weight.

You will understand this better, perhaps, if I give you some familiar example. You have all heard it repeated, I dare say, that men of science work by means of induction and deduction, and that by the help of these operations, they, in a sort of sense, wring from Nature certain other things, which are called natural laws, and causes, and that out of these, by some cunning skill of their own, they build up hypotheses and theories. And it is imagined by many, that the operations of the common mind can be by no means compared with these processes, and that they have to be acquired by a sort of special apprenticeship to the craft. To hear all these large words, you would think that the mind of a man of science must be constituted differently from that of his fellow men; but if you will not be frightened by terms, you will discover that you are quite wrong, and that all these terrible apparatus are being used by yourselves every day and every hour of your lives.

There is a well-known incident in one of Molière's plays, where the author makes the hero express unbounded delight on being told that he had been talking prose during the whole of his life. In the same way, I trust, that you will take comfort, and be delighted with yourselves, on the discovery that you have been acting on the principles of inductive and deductive philosophy during the same period. Probably there is not one who has not in the course of the day had occasion to set in motion a complex train of reasoning, of the very same kind, though differing of course in degree, as that which a scientific man goes through in tracing the causes of natural phenomena.

A very trivial circumstance will serve to exemplify this. Suppose you go into a fruiterer's shop, wanting an apple,—you take up one, and, on biting it, you find it is sour; you look at it, and see that it is hard and green. You take up another one, and that too is hard, green, and sour. The shopman offers you a third; but, before biting it, you examine it, and find that it is hard and green, and you immediately say that you will not have it, as it must be sour, like those that you have already tried.

Nothing can be more simple than that, you think; but if you will take the trouble to analyse and trace out into its logical elements what has been done by the mind, you will be greatly surprised. In the first place, you have performed the operation of induction. You found that, in two experiences, hardness and greenness in apples went together with sourness. It was so in the first case, and it was confirmed by the second. True, it is a very small basis, but still it is enough to make an induction from; you generalise the facts, and you expect to find sourness in apples where you get hardness and greenness. You found upon that a general law, that all hard and green apples are sour; and that, so far as it goes, is a perfect induction. Well, having got your natural law in this way, when you are offered another apple which you find is hard and green, you say, "All hard and green apples are sour; this apple is hard and green, therefore this apple is sour." That train of reasoning is what logicians call a syllogism, and has all its various parts and terms—its major premiss, its minor premiss, and its conclusion. And, by the help of further reasoning, which, if drawn out, would have to be exhibited in two or three other syllogisms, you arrive at your final determination, "I will not have that apple." So that, you see, you have, in the first place, established a law by induction, and upon that you have founded a deduction, and reasoned out the special conclusion of the particular case. Well now, suppose, having got your law, that at some time afterwards, you are discussing the qualities of apples with a friend: you will say to him, "It is a very curious thing,—but I find that all hard and green apples are sour!" Your friend says to you, "But how do you know that?" You at once reply, "Oh, because I have tried them over and over again, and have always found them to be so." Well, if we were talking science instead of common sense, we should call that an experimental verification. And, if still opposed, you go further, and say, "I have heard from the people in Somersetshire and Devonshire, where a large number of apples are grown, that they have observed the same thing. It is also found to be the case in Normandy, and in North America. In short, I find it to be the universal experience of mankind wherever attention has been directed to the subject." Whereupon, your friend, unless he is a very unreasonable man, agrees with you, and is convinced that you are quite right in the conclusion you have drawn. He believes, although perhaps he does not know he believes it, that the more extensive verifications are,—that the more frequently experiments have been made, and results of the same kind arrived at,—that the more varied the conditions under which the same results are attained, the more certain is the ultimate conclusion, and he disputes the question no further. He sees that the experiment has been tried under all sorts of conditions, as to time, place, and people, with the same result; and he says with you, therefore, that the law you have laid down must be a good one, and he must believe it.

In science we do the same thing;—the philosopher exercises precisely the same faculties, though in a much more delicate manner. In scientific inquiry it becomes a matter of duty to expose a supposed law to every possible kind of verification, and to take care, moreover, that this is done intentionally, and not left to a mere accident, as in the case of the apples. And in science, as in common life, our confidence in a law is in exact proportion to the absence of variation in the result of our experimental verifications. For instance, if you let go your grasp of an article you may have in your hand, it will immediately fall to the ground. That is a very common verification of one of the best established laws of nature—that of gravitation. The method by which men of science establish the existence of that law is exactly the same as that by which we have established the trivial proposition about the sourness of hard and green apples. But we believe it in such an extensive, thorough, and unhesitating manner because the universal experience of mankind verifies it, and we can verify it ourselves at any time; and that is the strongest possible foundation on which any natural law can rest.

So much, then, by way of proof that the method of establishing laws in science is exactly the same as that pursued in common life. Let us now turn to another matter (though really it is but another phase of the same question), and that is, the method by which, from the relations of certain phenomena, we prove that some stand in the position of causes towards the others.

I want to put the case clearly before you, and I will therefore show you what I mean by another familiar example. I will suppose that one of you, on coming down in the morning to the parlour of your house, finds that a tea-pot and some spoons which had been left in the room on the previous evening are gone,—the window is open, and you observe the mark of a dirty hand on the window-frame, and perhaps, in addition to that, you notice the impress of a hob-nailed shoe on the gravel outside. All these phenomena have struck your attention instantly, and before two seconds have passed you say, "Oh, somebody has broken open the window, entered the room, and run off with the spoons and the tea-pot!" That speech is out of your mouth in a moment. And you will probably add, "I know there has; I am quite sure of it!" You mean to say exactly what you know;

but in reality you are giving expression to what is, in all essential particulars, an hypothesis. You do not *know* it at all; it is nothing but an hypothesis rapidly framed in your own mind. And it is an hypothesis founded on a long train of inductions and deductions.

What are those inductions and deductions, and how have you got at this hypothesis? You have observed, in the first place, that the window is open; but by a train of reasoning involving many inductions and deductions, you have probably arrived long before at the general law—and a very good one it is—that windows do not open of themselves; and you therefore conclude that something has opened the window. A second general law that you have arrived at in the same way is, that tea-pots and spoons do not go out of a window spontaneously, and you are satisfied that, as they are not now where you left them, they have been removed. In the third place, you look at the marks on the window-sill, and the shoe-marks outside, and you say that in all previous experience the former kind of mark has never been produced by anything else but the hand of a human being; and the same experience shows that no other animal but man at present wears shoes with hob-nails in them such as would produce the marks in the gravel. I do not know, even if we could discover any of those "missing links" that are talked about, that they would help us to any other conclusion! At any rate the law which states our present experience is strong enough for my present purpose. You next reach the conclusion, that as these kinds of marks have not been left by any other animals than men, or are liable to be formed in any other way than by a man's hand and shoe, the marks in question have been formed by a man in that way. You have, further, a general law, founded on observation and experience, and that, too, is, I am sorry to say, a very universal and unimpeachable one,—that some men are thieves; and you assume at once from all these premises—and that is what constitutes your hypothesis—that the man who made the marks outside and on the window-sill, opened the window, got into the room, and stole your tea-pot and spoons. You have now arrived at a *vera causa*;—you have assumed a cause which, it is plain, is competent to produce all the phenomena you have observed. You can explain all these phenomena only by the hypothesis of a thief. But that is a hypothetical conclusion, of the justice of which you have no absolute proof at all; it is only rendered highly probable by a series of inductive and deductive reasonings.

I suppose your first action, assuming that you are a man of ordinary common sense, and that you have established this hypothesis to your own satisfaction, will very likely be to go for the police, and set them on the track of the burglar, with the view to the recovery of your property. But just as you are starting with this object, some person comes in, and on learning what you are about, says, "My good friend, you are going on a great deal too fast. How do you know that the man who really made the marks took the spoons? It might have been a monkey that took them, and the man may have merely looked in afterwards." You would probably reply, "Well, that is all very well, but you see it is contrary to all experience of the way tea-pots and spoons are abstracted; so that, at any rate, your hypothesis is less probable than mine." While you are talking the thing over in this way, another friend arrives. And he might say, "Oh, my dear sir, you are certainly going on a great deal too fast. You are most presumptuous. You admit that all these occurrences took place when you were fast asleep, at a time when you could not possibly have known anything about what was taking place. How do you know that the laws of Nature are not suspended during the night? It may be that there has been some kind of supernatural interference in this case." In point of fact, he declares that your hypothesis is one of which you cannot at all demonstrate the truth and that you are by no means sure that the laws of Nature are the same when you are asleep as when you are awake.

Well, now, you cannot at the moment answer that kind of reasoning. You feel that your worthy friend has you somewhat at a disadvantage. You will feel perfectly convinced in your own mind, however, that you are quite right, and you say to him, "My good friend, I can only be guided by the natural probabilities of the case, and if you will be kind enough to stand aside and permit me to pass, I will go and fetch the police." Well, we will suppose that your journey is successful, and that by good luck you meet with a policeman; that eventually the burglar is found with your property on his person, and the marks correspond to his hand and to his boots. Probably any jury would consider those facts a very good experimental verification of your hypothesis, touching the cause of the abnormal phenomena observed in your parlour, and would act accordingly.

Now, in this suppositious case, I have taken phenomena of a very common kind, in order that you might see what are the different steps in an ordinary process of reasoning, if you will only take the trouble to analyse it carefully. All the operations I have described, you will see, are involved in the mind of any man of sense in leading him to a conclusion as to the course he should take in order to make good a robbery and punish the offender. I say that you are led, in that case, to your conclusion by exactly the same train of reasoning as that which a man of science pursues when he is endeavouring to discover the origin and laws of the most occult phenomena. The process is, and always must be, the same; and precisely the same mode of reasoning was employed by Newton and Laplace in their endeavours to discover and define the causes of the movements of the heavenly bodies, as you, with your own common sense, would employ to detect a burglar. The only difference is, that the nature of the inquiry being more abstruse, every step has to be most carefully watched, so that there may not be a single crack or flaw in your hypothesis. A flaw or crack in many of the hypotheses of daily life may be of little or no moment as affecting the general correctness of the conclusions at which we may arrive; but, in a scientific inquiry, a fallacy, great or small, is always of importance, and is sure to be in the long run constantly productive of mischievous, if not fatal results.

Do not allow yourselves to be misled by the common notion that an hypothesis is untrustworthy simply because it is an hypothesis. It is often urged, in respect to some scientific conclusion, that, after all, it is only an hypothesis. But what more have we to guide us in nine-tenths of the most important affairs of daily life than hypotheses, and often very ill-based ones? So that in science, where the evidence of an hypothesis is subjected to the most rigid examination, we may rightly pursue the same course. You may have hypotheses and hypotheses. A man may say, if he likes, that the moon is made of green cheese: that is an hypothesis. But another man, who has devoted a great deal of time and attention to the subject, and availed himself of the most powerful telescopes and the results of the observations of others, declares that in his opinion it is probably composed of materials very similar to those of which our own earth is made up: and that is also only an hypothesis. But I need not tell you that there is an enormous difference in the value of the two hypotheses. That one which is based on sound scientific knowledge is sure to have a corresponding value; and that which is a mere hasty random guess is likely to have but little value. Every great step in our progress in discovering causes has been made in exactly the same way as that which I have detailed to you. A person observing the occurrence of certain facts and phenomena asks, naturally enough, what process, what kind of operation known to occur in Nature applied to the particular case, will unravel and explain the mystery? Hence you have the scientific hypothesis; and its value will be proportionate to the care and completeness with which its basis has been tested and verified. It is in these matters as in the commonest affairs of practical life: the guess of the fool will be folly, while the guess of the wise man will contain wisdom. In all cases, you see that the value of the result depends on the patience and faithfulness with which the investigator applies to his hypothesis every possible kind of verification. . . .

1863

Scientists Are Lonely Men

OLIVER LA FARGE

IT IS NOT SO LONG AGO THAT, EVEN IN MY DILETTANTE
study of the science of ethnology, I corresponded with men in Ireland,
Sweden, Germany, France, and Yucatán, and had some discussion with
a Chinese. One by one these interchanges were cut off; in some countries
the concept of science is dead, and even in the free strongholds of Britain
and the Americas pure science is being—must be—set aside in favor of
what is immediately useful and urgently needed. It must hibernate now;
for a while all it means is likely to be forgotten.

It has never been well understood. Scientists have never been good at
explaining themselves and, frustrated by this, they tend to withdraw into
the esoteric, refer to the public as "laymen," and develop incomprehensible
vocabularies from which they draw a naïve, secret-society feeling of
superiority.

What is the special nature of a scientist as distinguished from a soda-
jerker? Not just the externals such as his trick vocabulary, but the human
formation within the man? Most of what is written about him is rot; but
there is stuff there which a writer can get his teeth into, and it has its vivid,
direct relation to all that we are fighting for.

The inner nature of science within the scientist is both emotional and
intellectual. The emotional element must not be overlooked, for without
it there is no sound research on however odd and dull-seeming a subject.
As is true of all of us, an emotion shapes and forms the scientist's life;
at the same time an intellectual discipline molds his thinking, stamping
him with a character as marked as a seaman's although much less widely
understood.

To an outsider who does not know of this emotion, the scientist suggests
an ant, putting forth great efforts to lug one insignificant and apparently
unimportant grain of sand to be added to a pile, and much of the time his

struggle seems as pointless as an ant's. I can try to explain why he does it and what the long-term purpose is behind it through an example from my own work. Remember that in this I am not thinking of the rare, fortunate geniuses like the Curies, Darwin, or Newton, who by their own talents and the apex of accumulated thought at which they stood were knowingly in pursuit of great, major discoveries. This is the average scientist, one among thousands, obscure, unimportant, toilsome.

I have put in a good many months of hard work, which ought by usual standards to have been dull but was not, on an investigation as yet unfinished to prove that Kanhobal, spoken by certain Indians in Guatemala, is not a dialect of Jacalteca, but that, on the contrary, Jacalteca is a dialect of Kanhobal. Ridiculous, isn't it? Yet to me the matter is not only serious but exciting. Why?

There is an item of glory. There are half a dozen or so men now living (some now, unfortunately, our enemies) who will pay me attention and respect if I prove my thesis. A slightly larger number, less interested in the details of my work, will give credit to La Farge for having added to the linguistic map of Central America the name of a hitherto unnoted dialect. But not until I have told a good deal more can I explain—as I shall presently—why the notice of so few individuals can constitute a valid glory.

There's the nature of the initial work. I have spent hours, deadly, difficult hours, extracting lists of words, paradigms of verbs, constructions, idioms, and the rest from native informants, often at night in over-ventilated huts while my hands turned blue with cold. (Those mountains are far from tropical.) An illiterate Indian tires quickly when giving linguistic information. He is not accustomed to thinking of words in terms of other words; his command of Spanish is so poor that again and again you labor over misunderstandings; he does not think in our categories of words. Take any schoolchild and ask him how you say, "I go." Then ask him in turn, "Thou goest, he goes, we go." Even the most elementary schooling has taught him, if only from the force of staring resentfully at the printed page, to think in terms of the present tense of a single verb—that is, to conjugate. He will give you, in Spanish for instance, "*Me voy, te vas, se va, nos vamos,*" all in order. Try this on an illiterate Indian. He gives you his equivalent of "I go," follows it perhaps with "thou goest," but the next question reminds him of his son's departure that morning for Ixtatán, so he answers "he sets out," and from that by another mental leap produces "we are traveling." This presents the investigator with a magnificently irregular verb. He starts checking back, and the Indian's mind being set in the new channel, he now gets "I travel" instead of "I go."

There follows an exhausting process of inserting an alien concept into the mind of a man with whom you are communicating tenuously in a language which you speak only pretty well and he quite badly.

Then of course you come to a verb which really is irregular and you mistrust it. Both of you become tired, frustrated, upset. At the end of an hour or so the Indian is worn out, his friendship for you has materially decreased, and you yourself are glad to quit.

Hours and days of this, and it's not enough. I have put my finger upon the village of Santa Eulalia and said, "Here is the true, the classic Kanhobal from which the other dialects diverge." Then I must sample the others; there are at least eight villages which must yield me up fairly complete word-lists and two from which my material should be as complete as from Santa Eulalia. More hours and more days, long horseback trips across the mountains to enter strange, suspicious settlements, sleep on the dirt floor of the schoolhouse, and persuade the astonished yokelry that it is a good idea, a delightful idea, that you should put "The Tongue" into writing. Bad food, a bout of malaria, and the early-morning horror of seeing your beloved horse's neck running blood from vampire bats ("Oh, but, yes, señor, everyone knows that here are very troublesome the vampire bats"), to get the raw material for proving that Jacalteca is a dialect of Kanhobal instead of ...

You bring your hard-won data back to the States and you follow up with a sort of detective-quest for obscure publications and old manuscripts which may show a couple of words of the language as it was spoken a few centuries ago, so that you can get a line on its evolution. With great labor you unearth and read the very little that has been written bearing upon this particular problem.

By now the sheer force of effort expended gives your enterprise value in your own eyes. And you still have a year's work to put all your data in shape, test your conclusions, and demonstrate your proof.

Yet the real emotional drive goes beyond all this. Suppose I complete my work and prove, in fact, that Kanhobal as spoken in Santa Eulalia is a language in its own right and the classic tongue from which Jacalteca has diverged under alien influences, and that, further, I show just where the gradations of speech in the intervening villages fit in. Dear God, what a small, dull grain of sand!

But follow the matter a little farther. Jacalteca being relatively well-known (I can, offhand, name four men who have given it some study), from it it has been deduced that this whole group of dialects is most closely related to the languages spoken south and east of these mountains. If my theory is correct, the reverse is true—the group belongs to the Northern Division of the Mayan Family. This fact, taken along with others regarding physical appearance, ancient remains, and present culture, leads to a new conclusion about the direction from which these tribes came into the mountains: a fragment of the ancient history of what was once a great, civilized people comes into view. So now my tiny contribution begins to be of help to men working in other branches of anthropology than my own, particularly to the archaeologists; it begins to help toward an eventual understanding of the whole picture in this area: the important question of, not what these people are to-day, but how they got that way and what we can learn from that about all human behavior including our own.

Even carrying the line of research as far as this assumes that my results have been exploited by men of greater attainments than I. Sticking to the linguistic line, an error has been cleared away, an advance has been made in our understanding of the layout and interrelationship of the many languages making up the Mayan Family. With this we come a step nearer to working out the processes by which these languages became different from one another and hence to determining the archaic, ancestral roots of the whole group.

So far as we know at present, there are not less than eight completely unrelated language families in America north of Panama. This is unreasonable: there are hardly that many families among all the peoples of the Old World. Twenty years ago we recognized not eight, but forty. Some day perhaps we shall cut the total to four. The understanding of the Mayan process is a step toward that day; it is unlikely that Mayan will remain an isolated way of speech unconnected with any other. We know now that certain tribes in Wyoming speak languages akin to those of others in Panama; we have charted the big masses and islands of that group of tongues and from the chart begin to see the outlines of great movements and crashing historical events in the dim past. If we should similarly develop a relationship between Mayan and, let's say, the languages of the Mississippi Valley, again we should offer something provocative to the archaeologist, the historian, the student of mankind. Some day we shall show an unquestionable kinship between some of these families and certain languages of the Old World and with it cast a new light on the dim subject of the peopling of the Americas, something to guide our minds back past the Arctic to dark tribes moving blindly from the high plateaus of Asia.

My petty detail has its place in a long project carried out by many men which will serve not only the history of language but the broad scope of history itself. It goes farther than that. The humble Pah-Utes of Nevada speak a tongue related to that which the subtle Montezuma used, the one narrow in scope, evolved only to meet the needs of a primitive people, the other sophisticated, a capable instrument for poetry, for an advanced governmental system, and for philosophical speculation. Men's thoughts make language and their languages make thought. When the matter of the speech of mankind is fully known and laid side by side with all the other knowledges, the philosophers, the men who stand at the gathering-together point of science, will have the means to make man understand himself at last.

Of course no scientist can be continuously aware of such remote possible consequences of his labors; in fact the long goal is so remote that if he kept his eyes on it he would become hopelessly discouraged over the half inch of progress his own life's work will represent. But it was the vision of this which first made him choose his curious career, and it is an emotional sense of the great structure of scientific knowledge to which his little grain will be added which drives him along.

II

I spoke of the item of glory, the half dozen colleagues who will appreciate one's work. To understand that one must first understand the *isolation* of research, a factor which has profound effects upon the scientist's psyche.

The most obvious statement of this is in the public attitude and folk-literature about "professors." The titles and subjects of Ph.D. theses have long been sources of exasperated humor among us; we are all familiar with the writer's device which ascribes to a professorial character an intense interest in some such matter as the development of the molars in pre-Aurignacian man or the religious sanctions of the Levirate in northeastern Australia, the writer's intention being that the reader shall say "Oh God!", smile slightly, and pigeonhole the character. But what do you suppose is the effect of the quite natural public attitude behind these devices upon the man who is excitedly interested in pre-Aurignacian molars and who knows that this is a study of key value in tracing the evolution of *Homo sapiens*?

Occasionally some line of research is taken up and made clear, even fascinating, to the general public, as in Zinsser's *Rats, Lice and History*, or de Kruif's rather Sunday-supplement writings. Usually, as in these cases, they deal with medicine or some other line of work directly resulting in findings of vital interest to the public. Then the ordinary man will consent to understand, if not the steps of the research itself, at least its importance, will grant the excitement, and honor the researcher. When we read Eve Curie's great biography of her parents our approach to it is colored by our knowledge, forty years later, of the importance of their discovery to every one of us. It would have been quite possible at the time for a malicious or merely ignorant writer to have presented that couple as archetypes of the "professor," performing incomprehensible acts of self-immolation in pursuit of an astronomically unimportant what's-it.

Diving to my own experience like a Stuka with a broken wing, I continue to take my examples from my rather shallow linguistic studies because, in its very nature, the kind of thing a linguist studies is so beautifully calculated to arouse the "Oh God!" emotion.

It happened that at the suggestion of my letters I embarked upon an ambitious, general comparative study of the whole Mayan Family. The farther in I got the farther there was to go and the more absorbed I became. Puzzle piled upon puzzle to be worked out and the solution used for getting after the next one, the beginning of order in chaos, the glimpse of understanding at the far end. Memory, reasoning faculties, realism, and imagination were all on the stretch; I was discovering the full reach of whatever mental powers I had. When I say that I became absorbed I mean absorbed; the only way to do such research is to roll in it, become soaked in it, live it, breathe it, have your system so thoroughly permeated with it that at the half glimpse of a fugitive possibility everything you have learned so far and everything you have been holding in suspension is in order and ready to prove or disprove that point. You do not only think about your subject while the documents are spread before you; everyone knows that some of our best reasoning is done when the surface of the mind is occupied with something else and the deep machinery of the brain is free to work unhampered.

One day I was getting aboard a trolley car in New Orleans on my way to Tulane University. As I stepped up I saw that if it were possible to prove that a prefixed s- could change into a prefixed y- a whole series of troublesome phenomena would fall into order. The transition must come through u- and, thought I with a sudden lift of excitement, there may be a breathing associated with u- and that may make the whole thing possible. As I paid the conductor I thought that the evidence I needed might exist in Totonac and Tarascan, non-Mayan languages with which I was not familiar. The possibilities were so tremendous that my heart pounded and I was so preoccupied that I nearly went to sit in the Jim Crow section. Speculation was useless until I could reach the University and dig out the books, so after a while I calmed myself and settled to my morning ration of Popeye, who was then a new discovery too. As a matter of fact, the idea was no good, but the incident is a perfect example of the "professor mind."

Of course, if as I stepped on to the car it had dawned upon me that the reason my girl's behavior last evening had seemed odd was that she had fallen for the Englishman we had met, the incident would not have seemed so funny, although the nature of the absorption, subconscious thinking, and realization would have been the same in both cases.

I lived for a month with the letter k. If we have three words in Quiché, one of the major Mayan languages, beginning with k, in Kanhobal we are likely to find that one of these begins with ch. Moving farther west and north, in Tzeltal one is likely to begin with k, one with ch, and the one which began with ch in Kanhobal to begin with ts. In Hausteca, at the extreme northwest, they begin with k, ts, and plain s respectively. Why don't they all change alike? Which is the original form? Which way do these changes run, or from which point do they run both ways? Until those questions can be answered we cannot even guess at the form of the mother tongue from which these languages diverged, and at that point all investigation halts. Are these $k's$ in Quiché pronounced even faintly unlike? I noticed no difference between the two in Kanhobal, but then I wasn't listening for it. I wished someone properly equipped would go and listen to the Quiché Indians, and wondered if I could talk the University into giving me money enough to do so.

This is enough to give some idea of the nature of my work, and its uselessness for general conversation. My colleagues at Tulane were archaeologists. Shortly after I got up steam they warned me frankly that I had to stop trying to tell them about the variability of k, the history of Puctun t^y, or any similar matter. If I produced any results that they could apply, I could tell them about it; but apart from that I could keep my damned sound-shifts and intransitive infixes to myself; I was driving them nuts. My other friends on the faculty were a philosopher and two English professors; I was pursuing two girls at the time but had not been drawn to either because of intellectual interests in common; my closest friends were two painters and a sculptor. The only person I could talk to was myself.

The cumulative effect of this non-communication was terrific. A strange, mute work, a thing crying aloud for discussion, emotional expression, the check and reassurance of another's point of view, turned in upon myself to boil and fume, throwing upon me the responsibility of being my own sole check, my own impersonal, external critic. When finally I came to New York on vacation I went to see my Uncle John. He doesn't know Indian languages but he is a student of linguistics, and I shall never forget the relief, the reveling pleasure, of pouring my work out to him.

Thus at the vital point of his life-work the scientist is cut off from communication with his fellow-men. Instead, he has the society of two, six, or twenty men and women who are working in his specialty, with whom he corresponds, whose letters he receives like a lover, with whom when he meets them he wallows in an orgy of talk, in the keen pleasure of conclusions and findings compared, matched, checked against one another—the pure joy of being really understood.

The praise and understanding of those two or six become for him the equivalent of public recognition. Around these few close colleagues is the larger group of workers in the same general field. They do not share with one in the steps of one's research, but they can read the results, tell in a general way if they have been soundly reached, and profit by them. To them McGarnigle "has shown" that there are traces of an ancient, dolichocephalic strain among the skeletal remains from Pusilhá, which is something they can use. Largely on the strength of his close colleagues' judgment of him, the word gets round that McGarnigle is a sound man. You can trust his work. He's the fellow you want to have analyze the material if you turn up an interesting bunch of skulls. All told, including men in allied fields who use his findings, some fifty scientists praise him; before them he has achieved international reputation. He will receive honors. It is even remotely possible that he might get a raise in salary.

McGarnigle disinters himself from a sort of fortress made of boxes full of skeletons in the cellar of Podunk University's Hall of Science, and emerges into the light of day to attend a Congress. At the Congress he delivers a paper entitled *Additional Evidence of Dolichocephaly among the Eighth Cycle Maya* before the Section on Physical Anthropology. In the audience are six archaeologists specializing in the Maya field, to whom these findings have a special importance, and twelve physical anthropologists including Gruenwald of Eastern California, who is the only other man working on Maya remains.

After McGarnigle's paper comes Gruenwald's turn. Three other physical anthropologists, engaged in the study of the Greenland Eskimo, the Coastal Chinese, and the Pleistocene Man of Lake Mojave respectively, come in. They slipped out for a quick one while McGarnigle was speaking because his Maya work is not particularly useful to them and they can read the paper later; what is coming next, with its important bearing on method and theory, they would hate to miss.

Gruenwald is presenting a perfectly horrible algebraic formula and a diagram beyond Rube Goldberg's wildest dream, showing *A Formula for Approximating the Original Indices of Artificially Deformed Crania.* (These titles are not mere parodies; they are entirely possible.) The archaeologists depart hastily to hear a paper in their own section on *Indications of an Early Quinary System at Uaxactún.* The formula is intensely

exciting to McGarnigle because it was the custom of the ancient Mayas
to remodel the heads of their children into shapes which they (erroneously) deemed handsomer than nature's. He and Gruenwald have been
corresponding about this; at one point Gruenwald will speak of his colleague's experience in testing the formula; he has been looking forward
to this moment for months.

After the day's sessions are over will come something else he has been
looking forward to. He and Gruenwald, who have not seen each other in
two years, go out and get drunk together. It is not that they never get
drunk at home, but that now when in their cups they can be uninhibited,
they can talk their own, private, treble-esoteric shop. It is an orgy of
release.

III

In the course of their drinking it is likely—if an archaeologist or two
from the area joins them it is certain—that the talk will veer from femoral
pilasters and alveolar prognathism to personal experiences in remote sections of the Petén jungle. For in my science and a number of others there
is yet another frustration.

We go into the field and there we have interesting experiences. The
word "adventure" is taboo and "explore" is used very gingerly. But the
public mind has been so poisoned by the outpourings of bogus explorers
that it is laden with claptrap about big expeditions, dangers, hardships,
hostile tribes, the lighting of red flares around the camp to keep the savages at bay, and God knows what rot. (I can speak freely about this because my own expeditions have been so unambitious and in such easy
country that I don't come into the subject.) As a matter of fact it is generally true that *for a scientist on an expedition to have an adventure is
evidence of a fault in his technique.* He is sent out to gather information,
and he has no business getting into "a brush with the natives."

The red-flare, into-the-unknown, hardship-and-danger boys, who manage to find a tribe of pink-and-green Indians, a lost city, or the original,
handpainted descendants of the royal Incas every time they go out, usually
succeed in so riling the natives and local whites upon whom scientists
must depend if they are to live in the country as to make work in the
zones they contaminate difficult for years afterward. The business of their
adventures and discoveries is sickening. . . .

These men by training express themselves in factual, "extensional"
terms, which don't make for good adventure stories. They understand-
ably lean over backward to avoid sounding even remotely like the frauds,

the "explorers." And then what they have seen and done lacks validity to them if it cannot be told in relation to the purpose and dominant emotion which sent them there. McGarnigle went among the independent Indians of Icaiché because he had heard of a skull kept in one of their temples which, from a crude description, seemed to have certain important characteristics. All his risks and his maneuverings with those tough, explosive Indians centered around the problem of gaining access to that skull. When he tries to tell an attractive girl about his experiences he not only understates, but can't keep from stressing the significance of a skull with a healed, clover-leaf trepan. The girl gladly leaves him for the nearest broker. . . .

It is too bad both for the scientists and the public that they are so cut off from each other. The world needs now not the mere knowledges of science, but the way of thought and the discipline. It is the essence of what Hitler has set out to destroy; against it he has waged total war within his own domain. It is more than skepticism, the weighing of evidence more even than the love of truth. It is the devotion of oneself to an end which is far more important than the individual, the certainty that the end is absolutely good, not only for oneself but for all mankind, and the character to set personal advantage, comfort, and glory aside in the devoted effort to make even a little progress toward it.

1942

Turtle Eggs for Agassiz

DALLAS LORE SHARP

IT IS ONE OF THE WONDERS OF THE WORLD THAT SO few books are written. With every human being a possible book, and with many a human being capable of becoming more books than the world could contain, is it not amazing that the books of men are so few? And so stupid!

I took down, recently, from the shelves of a great public library, the four volumes of Agassiz's *Contributions to the Natural History of the United States*. I doubt if anybody but the charwoman, with her duster, had touched those volumes for twenty-five years. They are an excessively learned, a monumental, an epoch-making work, the fruit of vast and heroic labors, with colored plates on stone, showing the turtles of the United States, and their embryology. The work was published more than half a century ago (by subscription); but it looked old beyond its years—massive, heavy, weathered, as if dug from the rocks. It was difficult to feel that Agassiz could have written it—could have built it, grown it, for the laminated pile had required for its growth the patience and painstaking care of a process of nature, as if it were a kind of printed coral reef. Agassiz do this? The big, human, magnetic man at work upon these pages of capital letters, Roman figures, brackets, and parentheses in explanation of the pages of diagrams and plates! I turned away with a sigh from the weary learning, to read the preface.

When a great man writes a great book he usually flings a preface after it, and thereby saves it, sometimes, from oblivion. Whether so or not, the best things in most books are their prefaces. It was not, however, the quality of the preface to these great volumes that interested me, but rather the wicked waste of durable book material that went to its making. Reading down through the catalogue of human names and of thanks for help received, I came to a sentence beginning:—

"In New England I have myself collected largely; but I have also received valuable contributions from the late Rev. Zadoc Thompson of Burlington . . . from Mr. D. Henry Thoreau of Concord . . . and from Mr. J. W. P. Jenks of Middleboro." And then it hastens on with the thanks in order to get to the turtles, as if turtles were the one and only thing of real importance in all the world.

Turtles no doubt are important, extremely important, embryologically, as part of our genealogical tree; but they are away down among the roots of the tree as compared with the late Rev. Zadoc Thompson of Burlington. I happen to know nothing about the Rev. Zadoc, but to me he looks very interesting. Indeed any reverend gentleman of his name and day who would catch turtles for Agassiz must have been interesting. And as for Henry Thoreau, we know he was interesting. The rarest wood turtle in the United States was not so rare a specimen as this gentleman of Walden Woods and Concord. We are glad even for this line in the preface about him; glad to know that he tried, in this untranscendental way, to serve his day and generation. If Agassiz had only put a chapter in his turtle book about it! But this is the material he wasted, this and more of the same human sort, for the Mr. "Jenks of Middleboro" (at the end of the quotation) was, years later, an old college professor of mine, who told me some of the particulars of his turtle contributions, particulars which Agassiz should have found a place for in his big book. The preface says merely that this gentleman sent turtles to Cambridge by the thousands—brief and scanty recognition. For that is not the only thing this gentleman did. On one occasion he sent, not turtles, but turtle *eggs* to Cambridge— *brought* them, I should say; and all there is to show for it, so far as I could discover, is a sectional drawing of a bit of the mesoblastic layer of one of the eggs!

Of course, Agassiz wanted to make that mesoblastic drawing, or some other equally important drawing, and had to have the fresh turtle egg to draw it from. He had to have it, and he got it. A great man, when he wants a certain turtle egg, at a certain time, always gets it, for he gets someone else to get it. I am glad he got it. But what makes me sad and impatient is that he did not think it worth while to tell about the getting of it, and so made merely a learned turtle book of what might have been an exceedingly interesting human book.

It would seem, naturally, that there could be nothing unusual or interesting about the getting of turtle eggs when you want them. Nothing at all, if you should chance to want the eggs as you chance to find them. So with anything else—good copper stock, for instance, if you should chance to want it, and should chance to be along when they chance to be giving it away. But if you want copper stock, say of C & H quality, *when* you want it, and are bound to have it, then you must command more than a college professor's salary. And likewise, precisely, when it is turtle eggs that you are bound to have.

Agassiz wanted those turtle eggs when he wanted them—not a minute over three hours from the minute they were laid. Yet even that does not seem exacting, hardly more difficult than the getting of hen eggs only three hours old. Just so, provided the professor could have had his private turtle coop in Harvard Yard; and provided he could have made his turtles lay. But turtles will not respond, like hens, to meat scraps and the warm mash. The professor's problem was not to get from a mud turtle's nest in the back yard to the table in the laboratory; but to get from the laboratory in Cambridge to some pond when the turtles were laying, and back to the laboratory within the limited time. And this, in the days of Darius Green, might have called for nice and discriminating work—as it did.

Agassiz had been engaged for a long time upon his *Contributions*. He had brought the great work nearly to a finish. It was, indeed, finished but for one small yet very important bit of observation: he had carried the turtle egg through every stage of its development with the single exception of one—the very earliest—that stage of first cleavages, when the cell begins to segment, immediately upon its being laid. That beginning stage had brought the *Contributions* to a halt. To get eggs that were fresh enough to show the incubation at this period had been impossible.

There were several ways that Agassiz might have proceeded: he might have got a leave of absence for the spring term, taken his laboratory to some pond inhabited by turtles, and there camped until he should catch the reptile digging out her nest. But there were difficulties in all of that—as those who are college professors and naturalists know. As this was quite out of the question, he did the easiest thing—asked Mr. "Jenks of Middleboro" to get him the eggs. Mr. Jenks got them. Agassiz knew all about his getting of them; and I say the strange and irritating thing is that Agassiz did not think it worth while to tell us about it, a least in the preface to his monumental work.

It was many years later that Mr. Jenks, then a gray-haired college professor, told me how he got those eggs to Agassiz.

"I was principal of an academy, during my younger years," he began, "and was busy one day with my classes, when a large man suddenly filled the doorway of the room, smiled to the four corners of the room, and called out with a big, quick voice that he was Professor Agassiz.

"Of course he was. I knew it, even before he had had time to shout it to me across the room.

"Would I get him some turtle eggs? he called. Yes, I would. And would

I get them to Cambridge within three hours from the time they were laid? Yes, I would. And I did. And it was worth the doing. But I did it only once.

"When I promised Agassiz those eggs I knew where I was going to get them. I had got turtle eggs there before—at a particular patch of sandy shore along a pond, a few miles distant from the academy.

"Three hours was the limit. From the railroad station to Boston was thirty-five miles; from the pond to the station was perhaps three or four miles; from Boston to Cambridge we called about three miles. Forty miles in round numbers! We figured it all out before he returned, and got the trip down to two hours—record time: driving from the pond to the station; from the station by express train to Boston; from Boston by cab to Cambridge. This left an easy hour for accidents and delays.

"Cab and car and carriage we reckoned into our time-table; but what we didn't figure on was the turtle." And he paused abruptly.

"Young man," he went on, his shaggy brows and spectacles hardly hiding the twinkle in the eyes that were bent severely upon me, "young man, when *you* go after turtle eggs, take into account the turtle. No! no! That's bad advice. Youth never reckons on the turtle—and youth seldom ought to. Only old age does that; and old age would never have got those turtle eggs to Agassiz.

"It was in the early spring that Agassiz came to the academy, long before there was any likelihood of the turtles laying. But I was eager for the quest, and so fearful of failure that I started out to watch at the pond fully two weeks ahead of the time that the turtles might be expected to lay. I remember the date clearly: it was May 14.

"A little before dawn—along near three o'clock—I would drive over to the pond, hitch my horse near by, settle myself quietly among some thick cedars close to the sandy shore, and there I would wait, my kettle of sand ready, my eye covering the whole sleeping pond. Here among the cedars I would eat my breakfast, and then get back in good season to open the academy for the morning session.

"And so the watch began.

"I soon came to know individually the dozen or more turtles that kept to my side of the pond. Shortly after the cold mist would lift and melt away they would stick up their heads through the quiet water; and as the sun slanted down over the ragged rim of tree tops the slow things would float into the warm, lighted spots, or crawl out and doze comfortably on the hummocks and snags.

"What fragrant mornings those were! How fresh and new and un-breathed! The pond odors, the woods odors, the odors of the ploughed fields—of water lily, and wild grape, and the dew-laid soil! I can taste them yet, and hear them yet—the still, large sounds of the waking day— the pickerel breaking the quiet with his swirl; the kingfisher dropping anchor; the stir of feet and wings among the trees. And then the thought of the great book being held up for me! Those were rare mornings!

"But there began to be a good many of them, for the turtles showed no desire to lay. They sprawled in the sun, and never one came out upon the sand as if she intended to help on the great professor's book. The embryology of her eggs was of small concern to her; her contribution to the Natural History of the United States could wait.

"And it did wait. I began my watch on the fourteenth of May; June first found me still among the cedars, still waiting, as I had waited every morning, Sundays and rainy days alike. June first saw a perfect morning, but every turtle slid out upon her log, as if egg laying might be a matter strictly of next year.

"I began to grow uneasy—not impatient yet, for a naturalist learns his lesson of patience early, and for all his years; but I began to fear lest, by some subtle sense, my presence might somehow be known to the creatures; that they might have gone to some other place to lay, while I was away at the schoolroom.

"I watched on to the end of the first week, on to the end of the second week in June, seeing the mists rise and vanish every morning, and along with them vanish, more and more, the poetry of my early morning vigil. Poetry and rheumatism cannot long dwell together in the same clump of cedars, and I had begun to feel the rheumatism. A month of morning mists wrapping me around had at last soaked through to my bones. But Agassiz was waiting, and the world was waiting, for those turtle eggs; and I would wait. It was all I could do, for there is no use bringing a china nest egg to a turtle; she is not open to any such delicate suggestion.

"Then came a mid-June Sunday morning, with dawn breaking a little after three: a warm, wide-awake dawn, with the level mist lifted from the level surface of the pond a full hour higher than I had seen it any morning before.

"This was the day: I knew it. I have heard persons say that they can hear the grass grow; that they know by some extra sense when danger is nigh. That we have these extra senses I fully believe, and I believe they can be sharpened by cultivation. For a month I had been watching, brooding over this pond, and now I knew. I felt a stirring of the pulse of things that the cold-hearted turtles could no more escape than could the clods and I.

"Leaving my horse unhitched, as if he too understood, I slipped eagerly into my covert for a look at the pond. As I did so, a large pickerel ploughed a furrow out through the spatter-docks, and in his wake rose the head of an enormous turtle. Swinging slowly around, the creature headed straight for the shore, and without a pause scrambled out on the sand.

"She was about the size of a big scoop shovel; but that was not what excited me, so much as her manner, and the gait at which she moved; for there was method in it, and fixed purpose. On she came, shuffling over the sand toward the higher open fields, with a hurried, determined seesaw that was taking her somewhere in particular, and that was bound to get her there on time.

"I held my breath. Had she been a dinosaurian making Mesozoic footprints, I could not have been more fearful. For footprints in the Mesozoic mud, or in the sands of time, were as nothing to me when compared with fresh turtle eggs in the sands of this pond.

"But over the strip of sand, without a stop, she paddled, and up a narrow cow path into the high grass along a fence. Then up the narrow cow path, on all fours, just like another turtle, I paddled, and into the high wet grass along the fence.

"I kept well within sound of her, for she moved recklessly, leaving a trail of flattened grass a foot and a half wide. I wanted to stand up,—and I don't believe I could have turned her back with a rail,—but I was afraid if she saw me that she might return indefinitely to the pond; so on I went, flat to the ground, squeezing through the lower rails of the fence, as if the field beyond were a melon patch. It was nothing of the kind, only a wild, uncomfortable pasture, full of dewberry vines, and very discouraging. They were excessively wet vines and briery. I pulled my coat sleeves as far over my fists as I could get them, and, with the tin pail of sand swinging from between my teeth to avoid noise, I stumped fiercely, but silently, on after the turtle.

"She was laying her course, I thought, straight down the length of this dreadful pasture, when, not far from the fence, she suddenly hove to, warped herself short about, and came back, barely clearing me, at a clip that was thrilling. I warped about, too, and in her wake bore down across the corner of the pasture, across the powdery public road, and on to a fence along a field of young corn.

"I was somewhat wet by this time, but not so wet as I had been before, wallowing through the deep dry dust of the road. Hurrying up behind a large tree by the fence, I peered down the corn rows and saw the turtle stop, and begin to paw about in the loose soft soil. She was going to lay!

"I held on to the tree and watched, as she tried this place, and that place, and the other place—the eternally feminine! But *the* place, evidently, was hard to find. What could a female turtle do with a whole field of possible nests to choose from? Then at last she found it, and, whirling about, she backed quickly at it, and, tail first, began to bury herself before my staring eyes.

"Those were not the supreme moments of my life; perhaps those moments came later that day; but those certainly were among the slowest, most dreadfully mixed of moments that I ever experienced. They were hours long. There she was, her shell just showing, like some old hulk in the sand alongshore. And how long would she stay there? And how should I know if she had laid an egg?

"I could still wait. And so I waited, when, over the freshly awakened fields, floated four mellow strokes from the distant town clock.

"Four o'clock! Why, there was no train until seven! No train for three hours! The eggs would spoil! Then with a rush it came over me that this was Sunday morning, and there was no regular seven o'clock train—none till after nine.

"I think I should have fainted had not the turtle just then begun crawling off. I was weak and dizzy; but there, there in the sand, were the eggs! And Agassiz! And the great book! And I cleared the fence, and the forty miles that lay between me and Cambridge, at a single jump. He should have them, trains or no. Those eggs should go to Agassiz by seven o'clock, if I had to gallop every mile of the way. Forty miles! Any horse could cover it in three hours, if he had to; and, upsetting the astonished turtle, I scooped out her round white eggs.

"On a bed of sand in the bottom of the pail I laid them, with what care my trembling fingers allowed; filled in between them with more sand; so with another layer to the rim; and, covering all smoothly with more sand, I ran back for my horse.

"That horse knew, as well as I, that the turtle had laid, and that he was to get those eggs to Agassiz. He turned out of that field into the road on two wheels, a thing he had not done for twenty years, doubling me up before the dashboard, the pail of eggs miraculously lodged between my knees.

"I let him out. If only he could keep this pace all the way to Cambridge! Or even halfway there; and I should have time to finish the trip on foot. I shouted him on, holding to the dasher with one hand, the pail of eggs with the other, not daring to get off my knees, though the bang on them, as we pounded down the wood road, was terrific. But nothing must happen to the eggs; they must not be jarred, or even turned over in the sand before they came to Agassiz.

"In order to get out on the pike it was necessary to drive back away from Boston toward the town. We had nearly covered the distance, and were rounding a turn from the woods into the open fields, when, ahead of me, at the station it seemed, I heard the quick sharp whistle of a locomotive.

"What did it mean? Then followed the *puff, puff, puff* of a starting train. But what train? Which way going? And, jumping to my feet for a longer view, I pulled into a side road that paralleled the track, and headed hard for the station.

"We reeled along. The station was still out of sight, but from behind the bushes that shut it from view rose the smoke of a moving engine. It was perhaps a mile away, but we were approaching, head-on, and, topping a little hill, I swept down upon a freight train, the black smoke pouring from the stack, as the mighty creature pulled itself together for its swift run down the rails.

"My horse was on the gallop, going with the track, and straight toward the coming train. The sight of it almost maddened me—the bare thought of it, on the road to Boston! On I went; on it came, a half—a quarter of a mile between us, when suddenly my road shot out along an unfenced field with only a level stretch of sod between me and the engine.

"With a pull that lifted the horse from his feet, I swung him into the field and sent him straight as an arrow for the track. That train should carry me and my eggs to Boston!

"The engineer pulled the rope. He saw me standing up in the rig, saw my hat blow off, saw me wave my arms, saw the tin pail swing in my teeth, and he jerked out a succession of sharp halts! But it was he who should halt, not I; and on we went, the horse with a flounder landing the carriage on top of the track.

"The train was already grinding to a stop; but before it was near a stand-still I had backed off the track, jumped out, and, running down the rails with the astonished engineers gaping at me, had swung aboard the cab.

"They offered no resistance; they hadn't had time. Nor did they have the disposition, for I looked strange, not to say dangerous. Hatless, dew-soaked, smeared with yellow mud, and holding, as if it were a baby or a bomb, a little tin pail of sand.

" 'Crazy,' the fireman muttered, looking to the engineer for his cue.

"I had been crazy, perhaps, but I was not crazy now.

" 'Throw her wide open,' I commanded. 'Wide open! These are fresh turtle eggs for Professor Agassiz of Cambridge. He must have them before breakfast.'

"Then they knew I was crazy, and, evidently thinking it best to humor me, threw the throttle wide open, and away we went.

"I kissed my hand to the horse, grazing unconcernedly in the open field, and gave a smile to my crew. That was all I could give them, and hold myself and the eggs together. But the smile was enough. And they smiled through their smut at me, though one of them held fast to his shovel, while the other kept his hand upon a big ugly wrench. Neither of them spoke to me, but above the roar of the swaying engine I caught enough of their broken talk to understand that they were driving under a full head of steam, with the intention of handing me over to the Boston police, as perhaps the easiest way of disposing of me.

"I was only afraid that they would try it at the next station. But that station whizzed past without a bit of slack, and the next, and the next; when it came over me that this was the through freight, which should have passed in the night, and was making up lost time.

"Only the fear of the shovel and the wrench kept me from shaking hands with both men at this discovery. But I beamed at them; and they at me. I was enjoying it. The unwonted jar beneath my feet was wrinkling my diaphragm with spasms of delight. And the fireman beamed at the engineer, with a look that said, 'See the lunatic grin; he likes it!'

"He did like it. How the iron wheels sang to me as they took the rails! How the rushing wind in my ears sang to me! From my stand on the fireman's side of the cab I could catch a glimpse of the track just ahead of the engine, where the ties seemed to leap into the throat of the mile-devouring monster. The joy of it! Of seeing space swallowed by the mile!

"I shifted the eggs from hand to hand and thought of my horse, of Agassiz, of the great book, of my great luck,—luck,—luck,—until the multitudinous tongues of the thundering train were all chiming 'luck! luck! luck!' They knew! They understood! This beast of fire and tireless wheels was doing its very best to get the eggs to Agassiz!

"We swung out past the Blue Hills, and yonder flashed the morning sun from the towering dome of the State House. I might have leaped from the cab and run the rest of the way on foot, had I not caught the eye of the engineer watching me narrowly. I was not in Boston yet, nor in Cambridge either. I was an escaped lunatic, who had held up a train, and forced it to carry me to Boston.

"Perhaps I had overdone my lunacy business. Suppose these two men should take it into their heads to turn me over to the police, whether I would or no? I could never explain the case in time to get the eggs to Agassiz. I looked at my watch. There were still a few minutes left, in which I might explain to these men, who, all at once, had become my captors. But it was too late. Nothing could avail against my actions, my appearance, and my little pail of sand.

"I had not thought of my appearance before. Here I was, face and clothes caked with yellow mud, my hair wild and matted, my hat gone, and in my full-grown hands a tiny tin pail of sand, as if I had been digging all night with a tiny tin shovel on the shore! And thus to appear in the decent streets of Boston of a Sunday morning!

"I began to feel like a hunted criminal. The situation was serious, or might be, and rather desperately funny at its best. I must in some way have shown my new fears, for both men watched me more sharply.

"Suddenly, as we were nearing the outer freight yard, the train slowed down and came to a stop. I was ready to jump, but I had no chance. They had nothing to do, apparently, but to guard me. I looked at my watch again. What time we had made! It was only six o'clock, with a whole hour to get to Cambridge.

"But I didn't like this delay. Five minutes—ten—went by.

"'Gentlemen,' I began, but was cut short by an express train coming past. We were moving again, on—into a siding; on—on to the main track; and on with a bump and a crash and a succession of crashes, running the length of the train; on at a turtle's pace, but on, when the fireman, quickly jumping for the bell rope, left the way to the step free, and—the chance had come!

"I never touched the step, but landed in the soft sand at the side of the track, and made a line for the yard fence.

"There was no hue or cry. I glanced over my shoulder to see if they were after me. Evidently their hands were full, and they didn't know I had gone.

"But I had gone; and was ready to drop over the high board fence, when it occurred to me that I might drop into a policeman's arms. Hanging my pail in a splint on top of a post, I peered cautiously over—a very wise thing to do before you jump a high board fence. There, crossing the open square toward the station, was a big, burly fellow with a club— looking for me.

"I flattened for a moment, when someone in the yard yelled at me. I preferred the policeman, and, grabbing my pail, I slid over to the street. The policeman moved on past the corner of the station out of sight. The square was free, and yonder stood a cab!

"Time was flying now. Here was the last lap. The cabman saw me coming, and squared away. I waved a paper dollar at him, but he only stared the more. A dollar can cover a good deal, but I was too much for one dollar. I pulled out another, thrust them both at him, and dodged into the cab, calling, 'Cambridge!'

"He would have taken me straight to the police station had I not said, 'Harvard College. Professor Agassiz's house! I've got eggs for Agassiz'; and pushed another dollar up at him through the hole.

"It was nearly half past six.

" 'Let him go!' I ordered. "Here's another dollar if you make Agassiz's house in twenty minutes. Let him out; never mind the police!'

"He evidently knew the police, or there were none around at that time on a Sunday morning. We went down the sleeping streets as I had gone down the wood roads from the pond two hours before, but with the rattle and crash now of a fire brigade. Whirling a corner into Cambridge Street, we took the bridge at a gallop, the driver shouting out something in Hibernian to a pair of waving arms and a belt and brass buttons.

"Across the bridge with a rattle and jolt that put the eggs in jeopardy, and on over the cobblestones, we went. Half standing, to lessen the jar, I held the pail in one hand and held myself in the other, not daring to let go even to look at my watch.

"But I was afraid to look at the watch. I was afraid to see how near to seven o'clock it might be. The sweat was dropping from my nose, so close was I running to the limit of my time.

"Suddenly there was a lurch, and I dived forward, ramming my head into the front of the cab, coming up with a rebound that landed me across the small of my back on the seat, and sent half of my pail of eggs helter-skelter over the floor.

"We had stopped. Here was Agassiz's house; and without taking time to pick up the scattered eggs I tumbled out, and pounded at the door.

"No one was astir in the house. But I would stir them. And I did. Right in the midst of the racket the door opened. It was the maid.

" 'Agassiz,' I gasped, 'I want Professor Agassiz, quick!' And I pushed by her into the hall.

" 'Go 'way, sir. I'll call the police. Professor Agassiz is in bed. Go 'way, sir!'

" 'Call him—Agassiz—instantly, or I'll call him myself.'

"But I didn't; for just then a door overhead was flung open, a great white-robed figure appeared on the dim landing above, and a quick loud voice called excitedly:—

" 'Let him in! Let him in! I know him. He has my turtle eggs!'

"And the apparition, slipperless, and clad in anything but an academic gown, came sailing down the stairs.

"The maid fled. The great man, his arms extended, laid hold of me with both hands, and, dragging me and my precious pail into his study, with a swift, clean stroke laid open one of the eggs, as the watch in my trembling hands ticked its way to seven—as if nothing unusual were happening to the history of the world."

"You were in time, then?" I said.

"To the tick. There stands my copy of the great book. I am proud of the humble part I had in it."

1910

The Aims and Methods of Science

THE METHODS OF ACQUIRING KNOWLEDGE

ROGER BACON

THERE ARE TWO METHODS IN WHICH WE ACQUIRE knowledge—argument and experiment. Argument allows us to draw conclusions, and may cause us to admit the conclusion; but it gives no proof, nor does it remove doubt, and cause the mind to rest in the conscious possession of truth, unless the truth is discovered by way of experience, e.g. if any man who had never seen fire were to prove by satisfactory argument that fire burns and destroys things, the hearer's mind would not rest satisfied, nor would he avoid fire; until by putting his hand or some combustible thing into it, he proved by actual experiment what the argument laid down; but after the experiment has been made, his mind receives certainty and rests in the possession of truth which could not be given by argument but only by experience. And this is the case even in mathematics, where there is the strongest demonstration. For let anyone have the clearest demonstration about an equilateral triangle without experience of it, his mind will never lay hold of the problem until he has actually before him the intersecting circles and the lines drawn from the point of section to the extremities of a straight line.

1214-1294

ADDRESS BEFORE THE STUDENT BODY CALIFORNIA INSTITUTE OF TECHNOLOGY

ALBERT EINSTEIN

MY DEAR YOUNG FRIENDS:
I am glad to see you before me, a flourishing band of young people who have chosen applied science as a profession.

I could sing a hymn of praise with the refrain of the splendid progress in applied science that we have already made, and the enormous further progress that you will bring about. We are indeed in the era and also in the native land of applied science.

But it lies far from my thought to speak in this way. Much more, I am reminded in this connection of the young man who had married a *not* very attractive wife and was asked whether or not he was happy. He answered thus: "If I wished to speak the truth, then I would have to lie."

So it is with me. Just consider a quite uncivilized Indian, whether his experience is less rich and happy than that of the average civilized man. I hardly think so. There lies a deep meaning in the fact that the children of all civilized countries are so fond of playing "Indians."

Why does this magnificent applied science, which saves work and makes life easier, bring us so little happiness? The simple answer runs—because we have not yet learned to make a sensible use of it.

In war, it serves that we may poison and mutilate each other. In peace it has made our lives hurried and uncertain. Instead of freeing us in great measure from spiritually exhausting labor, it has made men into slaves of machinery, who for the most part complete their monotonous long day's work with disgust, and must continually tremble for their poor rations.

You will be thinking that the old man sings an ugly song. I do it, however, with a good purpose, in order to point out a consequence.

It is not enough that you should understand about applied science in order that your work may increase man's blessings. *Concern for man himself and his fate must always form the chief interest of all technical endeavors, concern for the great unsolved problems of the organization of labor and the distribution of goods*—in order that the creations of our mind shall be a blessing and not a curse to mankind. Never forget this in the midst of your diagrams and equations.

1938

ICARUS IN SCIENCE

SIR ARTHUR EDDINGTON

From *Stars and Atoms*

IN ANCIENT DAYS TWO AVIATORS PROCURED TO themselves wings. Daedalus flew safely through the middle air and was duly honored on his landing. Icarus soared upwards to the sun till the wax melted which bound his wings and his flight ended in fiasco. In weighing their achievements, there is something to be said for Icarus. The classical authorities tell us that he was only "doing a stunt," but I prefer to think of him as the man who brought to light a serious constructional defect in the flying machines of his day. So, too, in science, cautious Daedalus will apply his theories where he feels confident they will safely go; but by his excesses of caution their hidden weaknesses remain undiscovered. Icarus will strain his theories to the breaking point till the weak points gape. For the mere adventure? Perhaps partly; that is human nature. But if he is destined not yet to reach the sun and solve finally the riddle of its constitution we may hope at least to learn from his journey some hints to build a better machine.

1927

BEQUEST TO THE ACADEMIC YOUTH OF HIS COUNTRY

IVAN PAVLOV

—————

WHAT SHALL I WISH FOR THE YOUNG STUDENTS OF my country? First of all, sequence, consequence and again consequence. In gaining knowledge you must accustom yourself to the strictest sequence. You must be familiar with the very groundwork of science before you try to climb the heights. Never start on the "next" before you have mastered the "previous." Do not try to conceal the shortcomings of your knowledge by guesses and hypotheses. Accustom yourself to the roughest and simplest scientific tools. Perfect as the wing of a bird may be, it will never enable the bird to fly if unsupported by the air. Facts are the air of science. Without them the man of science can never rise. Without them your theories are vain surmises. But while you are studying, observing, experimenting, do not remain content with the surface of things. Do not become a mere recorder of facts, but try to penetrate the mystery of their origin. Seek obstinately for the laws that govern them. And then—modesty. Never think you know all. Though others may flatter you, retain the courage to say, "I am ignorant." Never be proud. And lastly, science must be your passion. Remember that science claims a man's whole life. Had he two lives they would not suffice. Science demands an undivided allegiance from its followers. In your work and in your research there must always be passion.

1936

BIOLOGY AND MEDICINE

ALAN GREGG

—————

THE PHILOSOPHER SANTAYANA HAS REMARKED THAT he who feels prepared to ignore history is doomed to repeat it. In the history of scientific discovery there are lessons that the Atomic Energy

Commission *is* heeding, deliberately and energetically, lest the frustrations and futilities that attend other discoveries repeat themselves in the study and development of atomic energy.

Sulphuric ether was discovered by Valerius Cordus in 1540. For over three hundred years it remained a chemical commonplace, dangerously inflammable, almost unused, though employed playfully by students as a brisk and potent intoxicant. Then Crawford Long and W. T. G. Morton in 1842-44 found and showed its wonderful value as an anesthetic. It may take long years to make a substance that is known to science useful to man. Think of the sum total of unnecessary pain during three hundred years of the failure to explore the effect of ether on man. Once a new substance is made, or a new process invented, years—even centuries—may elapse before all its properties or uses have been discovered and put in practice.

Roentgen discovered X-rays in 1895. The immediately obvious application in the detection and correction of fractured bones was made rather promptly. In 1902 Cannon, by using X-ray photographs of barium swallowed by experimental animals, defined one of the effects of strong emotions on the stomach and intestines. He thus laid one of the foundations for psychosomatic medicine—a far cry from classical physics. Still later in the use of hard X-rays upon tumors and soft X-rays upon the skin and hair, physicists and physicians found uses of X-rays not dreamed of by Roentgen or his contemporaries. The uses a new substance may possess are as unpredictable and as yet as certain as the future shape of a tree lying invisible in its seed.

Gasoline—at first a worthless and dangerous byproduct of distilling kerosene from crude petroleum—was thrown away by the millions of barrels, until its value was shown when used in engines designed to turn its explosive energy into mechanical work. As both result and cause of developments of the internal combustion engine, came the automobile, the tractor, and the airplane—long after gasoline was first produced and thrown away.

However, with energetic and alert study the gap between a discovery and its major application may not last long. Only fourteen years elapsed between Fleming's discovery of the antibiotic effects of a common mold and the production of penicillin in significant quantities for use in human therapy.

But we cannot safely overlook the possibility of danger lurking in any activity that leads to discovery. Research experiments may create substances or unleash forces so powerful in their effects on living tissues that investigation of their properties is no idle curiosity or speculative diversion.

It is an impelling necessity. We cannot afford to be casual or careless. The appalling burns from the ignorant and casual use in the early days of X-rays and radium stand on the record as a somber warning.

If scientific research offers unimaginable opportunities for good, it imposes unexampled obligations to protect ourselves against equally unforeseeable dangers. Thanks to examples (from other fields) of wasteful waiting and reckless inadvertence, the Atomic Energy Commission is devoting extensive and unflagging attention to the biological and medical effects of radiant energy—both those that may prove to be beneficent and those that may maim or kill. When man first discovered fire he began a long apprenticeship to caution in dealing with what is both useful and dangerous—and the end is not yet.

The story of the Garden of Eden and the myth of the Promethean fire find uncanny parallels in the huge responsibilities of the Atomic Energy Commission to control the unprecedented forces of atomic energy for the welfare of man. To control the use of this power, to explore its nature, its implications and potential applications, and at the same time to protect us all against its dangers—these responsibilities set a series of tasks that also are without precedent and all but immeasurable. . . .

Perhaps the kernel of the situation lies in the fact that the greater man's knowledge of the laws of nature the more substances he can create that have never actually been found in nature. We can thus not only make completely unfamiliar substances but also release forces that in quality or intensity are not to be found in the natural world. Virtually a second world for study and exploration comes thus into being as a result of profoundly understanding the laws that govern the phenomena of the world about us—the first world we studied and explored. Nor is this the end of the possibilities before us. There is almost an infinity of possible applications of new substances and new forces. Indeed the case for finding the uses of new substances for human needs, the harnessing of new forms of energy to serve human purposes, rests in the phrase of Protagoras the Sophist: *homo mensura*—"man is the measure of all things." And what is to measure the needs and purposes of man?

1949

PART THREE

THE PHYSICAL WORLD

Synopsis

A. THE HEAVENS

ON THE TWENTY-THIRD OF MAY, FOUR HUNDRED YEARS
ago, Nicholas Copernicus received on his death bed the first copy of his im-
mortal book, De Revolutionibus Orbium Coelestium (Concerning the Revo-
lutions of the Heavenly Bodies), in which he expressed his belief that the
earth moves around the sun. A few hours later he closed his eyes on a
medieval world that still believed in Ptolemy's geocentric universe.

Sixty-seven years later, in 1610, Galileo Galilei watched four small bodies
which appeared in the field of his telescope. Night after night he observed
them as they moved around the planet Jupiter. Here was a miniature solar
system similar to our own. Here was proof of the Copernican theory. Thus,
one of the greatest revolutions in the history of the human race took place.
Man was no longer the center of the world; he had assumed a subordinate
place in a larger universe.

In the following pages this story of Copernicus and Galileo is told in their
own words. As we read, some of the excitement and wonder which they
must have felt comes to us across the centuries.

Since that day, our knowledge of astronomy has greatly increased. We
know more about the planets; much more about the composition and even
the internal constitution of the stars; and we have discovered realms far be-
yond the range of Galileo's little telescope. This Orderly Universe extends
from our familiar satellite, the moon, to those exterior galaxies which are
visible only in the largest telescopes. To tell us about it, we chose Forest Ray
Moulton, who with T. C. Chamberlin is responsible for the modern theory
that the solar system was formed by the passage of a star near our own sun.
His description is an astronomical education in brief—a bird's-eye view of
modern astronomy.

Our own galaxy, consisting of thousands of millions of stars, is merely one of innumerable groups which together make up the universe. The study of these external galaxies has resulted in numerous discoveries and theories. In The Milky Way and Beyond, Sir Arthur Eddington, who was responsible for many developments in the field, tells why he believes the universe is expanding. It is a fascinating hypothesis and there is much disagreement among astronomers about the causes of the observed phenomena. The 200-inch telescope at Palomar threw new light on the problem. And now the new science of radio astronomy, which the noted British astronomer A. C. B. Lovell discusses in Radio Stars, gives us a tool undreamed of as recently as the past decade, for probing what is perhaps the greatest of all scientific problems—the way in which the world began.

B. THE EARTH

From outer space to A Young Man Looking at Rocks is a long jump to more familiar ground. It is easier to contemplate the sculptured heart of a fossil than the arms of a spiral nebula. Yet for that very reason, we are apt to take the "commonest things" for granted. We forget that rocks, like everything else, have a history. Old rocks hold the key to the age of the earth; younger ones the clue to the origin of species. With Hugh Miller we observe the history of the earth's crust spread before us, in massive blocks of gneiss and hornblende and sedimentary beds of sandstone and shale. It is charming autobiography from one of the classics of geology.

In the different types of rocks, Sir Archibald Geike can trace the story of bygone ages. In the remarkable Geological Change, this famous nineteenth century scientist describes the fundamentals of geology. He tells of the rhythmic cycles caused by alternate erosion and uplifting of land. He tells of the catastrophic changes which give rise to Earthquakes described by Father Macelwane, or ferocious volcanic eruptions like that which doomed forty thousand lives in St. Pierre, ironically saving the one man who was in jail.

In the organic remains, the fossils, laid down in stratified rock, Geike discerns forms now extinct—the ferns and conifers of which Peattie writes in a later part; the scales of fishes found by Hugh Miller; the remains of dinosaurs that once roamed the earth; even the fragments of prehistoric man, the missing links about which you may read in Part Five.

Geike also watches the effects of erosion on the land. Here is a clue to the decay of those civilizations which permit man to take everything from the earth, giving nothing in return.

Geike was one of the participants in the celebrated nineteenth-century controversy between the physicists and the geologists about the age of the earth. The age set by the physicists, led by Lord Kelvin, was far too short for the very slow and gradual changes the geologists envisaged. That controversy was settled by the discovery of radium. Its disintegration furnished a source of energy the physicists had not taken into their calculations. And its slow change into a unique type of lead has furnished a new geological clock. Examination of radioactive substances now leads us to assign a period of 4.5 billion years as the age of the earth.

Other forms of radioactivity, more recently discovered, also play their part in the study of geological time. Carbon 14 has proved an extremely accurate tool in measuring the time which has elapsed since fossils like tree stumps and animal bones became extinct. Richard Foster Flint, Professor of Geology at Yale, explains the technique in Pin-pointing the Past with the Cosmic Clock.

If we would understand the wind and the rain, we must know What Makes the Weather. In aviation and agriculture and a thousand other activities, it is a problem of vital importance. In long range history, it may mean climatic change that can alter the surface of a hemisphere. Here are the modern theories about cold fronts and air masses. Here are the ideas which help the weatherman become a successful prophet.

C. MATTER, ENERGY, PHYSICAL LAW

In 1642, when Galileo died an old and disillusioned man, he had already learned a great deal about the mathematical meaning of motion. But he still did not understand why the planets moved around the sun. He could not know that in that same year a baby would be born who would create a world conforming to both mathematical and physical law.

On Christmas Day, 1642, Isaac Newton was born in the village of Woolsthorpe in Lincolnshire, a premature, frail baby, the posthumous son of a yeoman farmer. Despite expectations to the contrary, he lived, and became the greatest scientist in history. He was to discover the law of gravitation, the laws of motion, the principles of optics, the composite nature of light, and with Leibnitz to invent the calculus. He of course owed a great debt to Galileo and to two other astronomers who lived in this same extraordinary period: Tycho Brahe, who first recorded accurately the motions of the planets; and Johann Kepler whose laws of planetary motion showed how these planets moved with relation to their central sun. On the foundations laid by these three, Newton built a conception of the world and the forces that guide it that was destined to hold undisputed place until the beginning of the twentieth century, and even at that distant date to undergo but minor modification.

Newtoniana tells us something of the man; while Discoveries gives us all too brief glimpses of the work that made him what he was.

The Physical Laws of the world are not easy to comprehend. Mathematics, physics and chemistry are so bound up with mysterious symbolism, not difficult in itself but unintelligible to those who have not learned its secret, that words cannot give their full meaning. Yet meaning they do have, even for the layman. Much of it is conveyed in the selections that follow.

First, let us consider mathematics, the foundation of physical law, the indispensable tool of the scientist. It transforms indefinite thoughts into specific theories. With its advance has come the advance of civilization. In remote ages primitive man learned to count; later to measure; finally to calculate. So we come to the modern world of science, where man must be a "calculating animal" if he is to understand physical and even biological science. Hogben tells something of the story in Mathematics, the Mirror of Civilization.

From mathematics we turn to physics. But before we do so, let us consider the Experiments and Ideas of that protean American Ben Franklin. He is best known for his work with electricity, with kites and lightning rods. Few remember his bifocal glasses, his discovery of the origin of northeast storms, his extraordinary prophecy of aerial invasion.

In physics, we run squarely against one of the fundamental scientific problems of the century: what goes on inside the atom? In Exploring the Atom, Sir James Jeans describes this strange world which all of us have heard about yet few understand. He shows how our nineteenth century concept of the atom as a sort of indestructible brick has been changed completely; he makes the new picture of the atom really clear. And in doing so, he gives us the basic knowledge which we must have to understand atomic fission and the atomic bomb.

The basic research which culminated in the bomb was, in fact, no new thing. Actually, it had had its beginnings nearly half a century before, when Henri Becquerel observed a fogging of a carefully wrapped photographic plate which had accidentally been placed near a fragment of the same substance, uranium, which was to play a dominant part in later events. The next development, which came as a sequence to Becquerel's observation, was the work of that extraordinary woman, Marie Curie, who kept house, brought up a family, and discovered radium. The Discovery of Radium, written by her daughter Eve, is a story which gains new meaning when it is related to the course of modern physics. From Becquerel's studies, to Marie Curie's discovery, through numberless experiments by men and women of many nationalities, to the final release of nuclear energy in the bomb, we can trace the development of one of the most intricately constructed edifices in science.

The science of nucleonics, which deals with what goes on inside the atomic nucleus, is in its infancy, but the work of harnessing the electron has already had great influence on the everyday world of science and industry. In Electronics Everywhere, the Past President and Fellow of the British Institute of Radio Engineers, Professor A. M. Low, tells what electrons are capable of doing and how a large part of our activity depends on these modern slaves. In one direction, the science of electronics has resulted in a development which laymen are inclined to look on with awe—the mechanical brain. The fundamental concepts which resulted in its creation are discussed in Giant Brains, by Edmund Callis Berkeley. Mr. Berkeley has participated in the development of large-scale automatic computers, and in the following article, Machines That Think, he writes amusingly and illuminatingly about these modern Frankensteins.

As physics and chemistry continue to advance, it becomes harder to decide where one begins and the other ends. In the eighteenth century, when men first began to comprehend the distinction between the various elements and how they combined, there was little connection. In Some Early Pioneers in Chemistry, the British scientists Stephen and L. M. Miall, tell something about the early discoverers and discoveries and relate them to the thousands of experiments which have resulted in our chemical civilization. On chemical reactions depend practically all modern industrial processes. How they do so is discussed by the former director of the Du Pont laboratories, Robert E. Rose, in The Foundations of Chemical Industry. The story of chemistry is brought up to date in the authentic and believable Man's Synthetic Future by Roger Adams, a leading synthetic chemist and a past President of the American Association for the Advancement of Science.

It was from his work on the theory of relativity that Einstein drew his famous equation on the equivalence of matter and energy, $E=mc^2$. In 1940, the relationship seemed incomprehensible to all but a handful of specialists, yet it has since revolutionized man's most fundamental concepts of the world. The relativity theory remains deep water indeed. Yet in Space, Time and Einstein, Dr. Heyl, the man who weighed the earth, says interesting things about it which are not too difficult for the informed layman to understand.

A. THE HEAVENS

A Theory that the Earth Moves Around the Sun

NICHOLAS COPERNICUS

From *Concerning the Revolutions of the Heavenly Bodies*

THAT THE UNIVERSE IS SPHERICAL

FIRST OF ALL WE ASSERT THAT THE UNIVERSE IS spherical; partly because this form, being a complete whole, needing no joints, is the most perfect of all; partly because it constitutes the most spacious form, which is thus best suited to contain and retain all things; or also because all discrete parts of the world, I mean the sun, the moon and the planets, appear as spheres; or because all things tend to assume the spherical shape, a fact which appears in a drop of water and in other fluid bodies when they seek of their own accord to limit themselves. Therefore no one will doubt that this form is natural for the heavenly bodies.

THAT THE EARTH IS LIKEWISE SPHERICAL

That the earth is likewise spherical is beyond doubt, because it presses from all sides to its center. Although a perfect sphere is not immediately recognized because of the great height of the mountains and the depression of the valleys, yet this in no wise invalidates the general spherical form of the earth. This becomes clear in the following manner: To people who travel from any place to the North, the north pole of the daily revolution rises gradually, while the south pole sinks a like amount. Most of the stars in the neighborhood of the Great Bear appear not to set, and in the South some stars appear no longer to rise. Thus Italy does not see Canopus, which is visible to the Egyptians. And Italy sees the outermost star of the River, which is unknown to us of a colder zone. On the other hand, to people who travel toward the South, these stars rise higher in the heavens, while those stars which are higher to us

become lower. Therefore, it is plain that the earth is included between
the poles and is spherical. Let us add that the inhabitants of the East do
not see the solar and lunar eclipses that occur in the evening, and people
who live in the West do not see eclipses that occur in the morning, while
those living in between see the former later, and the latter earlier.

That even the water has the same shape is observed on ships, in that
the land which can not be seen from the ship can be spied from the tip
of the mast. And, conversely, when a light is put on the tip of the mast,
it appears to observers on land gradually to drop as the ship recedes until
the light disappears, seeming to sink in the water. It is clear that the
water, too, in accordance with its fluid nature, is drawn downwards, just
as is the earth, and its level at the shore is no higher than its convexity
allows. The land therefore projects everywhere only as far above the
ocean as the land accidentally happens to be higher. . . .

WHETHER THE EARTH HAS A CIRCULAR MOTION, AND CONCERNING
THE LOCATION OF THE EARTH

Since it has already been proved that the earth has the shape of a
sphere, I insist that we must investigate whether from its form can be
deduced a motion, and what place the earth occupies in the universe.
Without this knowledge no certain computation can be made for the
phenomena occurring in the heavens. To be sure, the great majority of
writers agree that the earth is at rest in the center of the universe, so that
they consider it unbelievable and even ridiculous to suppose the contrary.
Yet, when one weighs the matter carefully, he will see that this question
is not yet disposed of, and for that reason is by no means to be considered
unimportant. Every change of position which is observed is due either
to the motion of the observed object or of the observer, or to motions,
naturally in different directions, of both; for when the observed object
and the observer move in the same manner and in the same direction,
then no motion is observed. Now the earth is the place from which we
observe the revolution of the heavens and where it is displayed to our
eyes. Therefore, if the earth should possess any motion, the latter would
be noticeable in everything that is situated outside of it, but in the
opposite direction, just as if everything were traveling past the earth.
And of this nature is, above all, the daily revolution. For this motion
seems to embrace the whole world, in fact, everything that is outside of
the earth, with the single exception of the earth itself. But if one should
admit that the heavens possess none of this motion, but that the earth
rotates from west to east; and if one should consider this seriously with
respect to the seeming rising and setting of the sun, of the moon and

the stars; then one would find that it is actually true. Since the heavens which contain and retain all things are the common home of all things, it is not at once comprehensible why a motion is not rather ascribed to the thing contained than to the containing, to the located rather than to the locating. This opinion was actually held by the Pythagoreans Heraklid and Ekphantus and the Syracusean Nicetas (as told by Cicero), in that they assumed the earth to be rotating in the center of the universe. They were indeed of the opinion that the stars set due to the intervening of the earth, and rose due to its receding. . . .

REFUTATION OF THE ARGUMENTS, AND THEIR INSUFFICIENCY

It is claimed that the earth is at rest in the center of the universe and that this is undoubtedly true. But one who believes that the earth rotates will also certainly be of the opinion that this motion is natural and not violent. Whatever is in accordance with nature produces effects which are the opposite of what happens through violence. Things upon which violence or an external force is exerted must become annihilated and cannot long exist. But whatever happens in the course of nature remains in good condition and in its best arrangement. Without cause, therefore, Ptolemy feared that the earth and all earthly things if set in rotation would be dissolved by the action of nature, for the functioning of nature is something entirely different from artifice, or from that which could be contrived by the human mind. But why did he not fear the same, and indeed in much higher degree, for the universe, whose motion would have to be as much more rapid as the heavens are larger than the earth? Or have the heavens become infinite just because they have been removed from the center by the inexpressible force of the motion; while otherwise, if they were at rest, they would collapse? Certainly if this argument were true the extent of the heavens would become infinite. For the more they were driven aloft by the outward impulse of the motion, the more rapid would the motion become because of the ever increasing circle which it would have to describe in the space of 24 hours; and, conversely, if the motion increased, the immensity of the heavens would also increase. Thus velocity would augment size into infinity, and size, velocity. But according to the physical law that the infinite can neither be traversed, nor can it for any reason have motion, the heavens would, however, of necessity be at rest.

But it is said that outside of the heavens there is no body, nor place, nor empty space, in fact, that nothing at all exists, and that, therefore, there is no space in which the heavens could expand; then it is really strange that something could be enclosed by nothing. If, however, the heavens were infinite and were bounded only by their inner concavity, then we have, perhaps, even better confirmation that there is nothing outside of the heavens, because everything, whatever its size, is within them; but then the heavens would remain motionless. The most important argument, on which depends the proof of the finiteness of the universe, is motion. Now, whether the world is finite or infinite, we will leave to the quarrels of the natural philosophers; for us remains the certainty that the earth, contained between poles, is bounded by a spherical surface. Why should we hesitate to grant it a motion, natural and corresponding to its form; rather than assume that the whole world, whose boundary is not known and cannot be known, moves? And why are we not willing to acknowledge that the *appearance* of a daily revolution belongs to the heavens, its *actuality* to the earth? The relation is similar to that of which Virgil's *Æneas* says: "We sail out of the harbor, and the countries and cities recede." For when a ship is sailing along quietly, everything which is outside of it will appear to those on board to have a motion corresponding to the movement of the ship, and the voyagers are of the erroneous opinion that they with all that they have with them are at rest. This can without doubt also apply to the motion of the earth, and it may appear as if the whole universe were revolving. . . .

CONCERNING THE CENTER OF THE UNIVERSE

. . . Since nothing stands in the way of the movability of the earth, I believe we must now investigate whether it also has several motions, so that it can be considered one of the planets. That it is not the center of all the revolutions is proved by the irregular motions of the planets, and their varying distances from the earth, which cannot be explained as concentric circles with the earth at the center. Therefore, since there are several central points, no one will without cause be uncertain whether the center of the universe is the center of gravity of the earth or some other central point. I, at least, am of the opinion that gravity is nothing else than a natural force planted by the divine providence of the Master of the World into its parts, by means of which they, assuming a spherical shape, form a unity and a whole. And it is to be assumed that the impulse is also inherent in the sun and the moon and the other planets, and that by the operation of this force they remain in the spherical shape in which they appear; while they, nevertheless, complete their revolutions in diverse ways. If then the earth, too, possesses other motions besides that around its center, then they must be of such a character as to become apparent in many ways and in appropriate manners; and among such possible effects we recognize the yearly revolution.

1543

Proof that the Earth Moves

GALILEO GALILEI

From *The Sidereal Messenger*

ABOUT TEN MONTHS AGO A REPORT REACHED MY ears that a Dutchman had constructed a telescope, by the aid of which visible objects, although at a great distance from the eye of the observer, were seen distinctly as if near; and some proofs of its most wonderful performances were reported, which some gave credence to, but others contradicted. A few days after, I received confirmation of the report in a letter written from Paris by a noble Frenchman, Jaques Badovere, which finally determined me to give myself up first to inquire into the principle of the telescope, and then to consider the means by which I might compass the invention of a similar instrument, which after a little while I succeeded in doing, through deep study of the theory of Refraction; and I prepared a tube, at first of lead, in the ends of which I fitted two glass lenses, both plane on one side, but on the other side one spherically convex, and the other concave. Then bringing my eye to the concave lens I saw objects satisfactorily large and near, for they appeared one-third of the distance off and nine times larger than when they are seen with the natural eye alone. I shortly afterwards constructed another telescope with more nicety, which magnified objects more than sixty times. At length, by sparing neither labour nor expense, I succeeded in constructing for myself an instrument so superior that objects seen through it appear magnified nearly a thousand times, and more than thirty times nearer than if viewed by the natural powers of sight alone.

FIRST TELESCOPIC OBSERVATIONS

It would be altogether a waste of time to enumerate the number and importance of the benefits which this instrument may be expected to confer, when used by land or sea. But without paying attention to its use for terrestrial objects, I betook myself to observations of the heavenly bodies; and first of all, I viewed the Moon as near as if it was scarcely two semidiameters of the Earth distant. After the Moon, I frequently observed other heavenly bodies, both fixed stars and planets, with incredible delight. . . .

DISCOVERY OF JUPITER'S SATELLITES

There remains the matter, which seems to me to deserve to be considered the most important in this work, namely, that I should disclose and publish to the world the occasion of discovering and observing four planets, never seen from the very beginning of the world up to our own times, their positions, and the observations made during the last two months about their movements and their changes of magnitude. . . .

On the 7th day of January in the present year, 1610, in the first hour of the following night, when I was viewing the constellations of the heavens through a telescope, the planet Jupiter presented itself to my view, and as I had prepared for myself a very excellent instrument, I noticed a circumstance which I had never been able to notice before, owing to want of power in my other telescope, namely, that three little stars, small but very bright, were near the planet; and although I believed them to belong to the number of the fixed stars, yet they made me somewhat wonder, because they seemed to be arranged exactly in a straight line, parallel to the ecliptic, and to be brighter than the rest of the stars, equal to them in magnitude. The position of them with reference to one another and to Jupiter was as follows:

Ori.   *   *   O   *   Occ.

On the east side there were two stars, and a single one towards the west. The star which was furthest towards the east, and the western star, appeared rather larger than the third.

I scarcely troubled at all about the distance between them and Jupiter, for, as I have already said, at first I believed them to be fixed stars; but when on January 8th, led by some fatality, I turned again to look at the same part of the heavens, I found a very different state of things, for there were three little stars all west of Jupiter, and nearer together than on the previous night, and they were separated from one another by equal intervals, as the accompanying figure shows.

Ori.   O   *   *   *   Occ.

At this point, although I had not turned my thoughts at all upon the approximation of the stars to one another, yet my surprise began to be excited, how Jupiter could one day be found to the east of all the aforesaid fixed stars when the day before it had been west of two of them; and forthwith I became afraid lest the planet might have moved differently from the calculation of astronomers, and so had passed those stars by its own proper motion. I, therefore, waited for the next night with the most intense longing, but I was disappointed of my hope, for the sky was covered with clouds in every direction.

But on January 10th the stars appeared in the following position with regard to Jupiter, the third, as I thought, being

Ori.   *   *   O   Occ.

hidden by the planet. They were situated just as before, exactly in the same straight line with Jupiter, and along the Zodiac.

When I had seen these phenomena, as I knew that corresponding changes of position could not by any means belong to Jupiter, and as, moreover, I perceived that the stars which I saw had always been the same, for there were no others either in front or behind, within a great distance, along the Zodiac—at length, changing from doubt into surprise, I discovered that the interchange of position which I saw belonged not to Jupiter, but to the stars to which my attention had been drawn, and I thought therefore that they ought to be observed henceforward with more attention and precision.

Accordingly, on January 11th I saw an arrangement of the following kind:

Ori.   *   *   O   Occ.

namely, only two stars to the east of Jupiter, the nearer of which was distant from Jupiter three times as far as from the star further to the east; and the star furthest to the east was nearly twice as large as the other one; whereas on the previous night they had appeared nearly of equal magnitude. I, therefore, concluded, and decided unhesitatingly, that there are three stars in the heavens moving about Jupiter, as Venus and Mercury round the Sun; which at length was established as clear as daylight by numerous other subsequent observations. These observations also established that there are not only three, but four, erratic sidereal bodies performing their revolutions round Jupiter. . . .

These are my observations upon the four Medicean planets, recently discovered for the first time by me; and although it is not yet permitted me to deduce by calculation from these observations the orbits of these bodies, yet I may be allowed to make some statements, based upon them, well worthy of attention.

ORBITS AND PERIODS OF JUPITER'S SATELLITES

And, in the first place, since they are sometimes behind, sometimes before Jupiter, at like distances, and withdraw from this planet towards the east and towards the west only within very narrow limits of divergence, and since they accompany this planet alike when its motion is retrograde and direct, it can be a matter of doubt to no one that they perform their revolutions about this planet while at the same time they all accomplish together orbits of twelve years' length about the centre of the world. Moreover, they revolve in unequal circles, which is evidently the conclusion to be drawn from the fact that I have never been permitted to see two satellites in conjunction when their distance from Jupiter was great, whereas near Jupiter two, three, and sometimes all four, have been found closely packed together. Moreover, it may be detected that the revolutions of the satellites which describe the smallest circles round Jupiter are the most rapid, for the satellites nearest to Jupiter are often to be seen in the east, when the day before they have appeared in the west, and contrariwise. Also, the satellite moving in the greatest orbit seems to me, after carefully weighing the occasions of its returning to positions previously noticed, to have a periodic time of half a month. Besides, we have a notable and splendid argument to remove the scruples of those who can tolerate the revolution of the planets round the Sun in the Copernican system, yet are so disturbed by the motion of one Moon about the Earth, while both accomplish an orbit of a year's length about the Sun, that they consider that this theory of the universe must be upset as impossible; for now we have not one planet only revolving about another, while both traverse a vast orbit about the Sun, but our sense of sight presents to us four satellites circling about Jupiter, like the Moon about the Earth, while the whole system travels over a mighty orbit about the Sun in the space of twelve years.

1610

The Orderly Universe

FOREST RAY MOULTON

ON THE CLEAR VAULT OF THE HEAVENS MANY
shining objects are seen—the sun by day, the moon and numerous
stars at night. In comparison with the enormous earth beneath our feet,
they all appear to be insignificant bodies. Indeed, the sun and the moon
are often hidden from our view by a passing cloud, while the stars are
only scintillating points of light. Not only do the heavenly bodies appear
to be relatively small, but men in all ages almost down to our own have
believed that they are small. The general conception of the relative importance of the various bodies in the cosmos is illustrated by the story of
creation in Genesis. According to this account, after the earth had been
created, "God made two great lights" in the sky above, "the greater light
to rule the day, and the lesser light to rule the night." And then, almost
as if it were an afterthought, "he made the stars also."

Often in the history of science it has been found that "things are not
what they seem." It has been so in the history of astronomy to a marked
degree. Perhaps in no other field of exploration have the differences
between appearances and realities been so great. On the one hand, this
apparently limitless planet on which we dwell has been reduced relatively
to a particle of dust floating in the immensity of space; while, on the
other hand, "the greater light," hanging like a lamp in the sky, has been
expanded to a flaming mass of gas a million times greater in volume than
the earth. More remarkable still, the tiny twinkling stars, instead of being
fireflies of the heavens, are in reality other suns, many greater than our
own, whose glories are dimmed only by their enormous distances from
us; and the soft circle of light which we know as the Milky Way has
been found to be a vast cosmic system of twenty thousand million stars.

Amazing are the differences between what the heavenly bodies appear
to be and what they actually are. Equally amazing are the differences
between the intervals of time within the range of direct human experience

and the enormous periods covered by the cosmic processes. Historians speak of the civilizations which long ago flourished in the valleys of the Nile and the Euphrates as being ancient, and from the standpoint of human history they are ancient. Yet all the written records which archeologists have recovered from the buried ruins of long-forgotten cities date back less than ten thousand years, which is only a moment in comparison with the millions of years of the geological eras or with the three thousand million years during which the earth has existed as a separate body. Even the great age of the earth is only a small fraction of the enormous lifetime of a star.

Great distances, prodigious masses, and long intervals of time are not merely interesting. They stir our imaginations, exercise our reasoning powers, expand our spirits, and change our perspective with respect to all the experiences of life. But they do not include all the important consequences of astronomical investigations. Indeed, they do not directly include that which is most important, the supreme discovery of science—*the orderliness of the universe*.

What do we mean by "the orderliness of the universe"? Astronomers found from painstaking and long-continued observations of the heavenly bodies that celestial phenomena recur in regular sequences. Though the order of the succession of events in the heavens is often somewhat complex, it is nevertheless systematic and invariable. The running of no clock ever approached in precision the motions of the sun, the moon, and the stars. In fact, to this day clocks are corrected and regulated by comparing them with the apparent diurnal motions of the heavenly bodies. Since not merely a few but hundreds of celestial phenomena were long ago found to be perfectly orderly, it was gradually perceived that majestic order prevails universally in those regions in which, before the birth of science, capricious gods and goddesses were believed to hold dominion. . . .

THE MOON

For a few days each month the crescent moon may be seen after sunset in the western sky. In a week it changes to a semicircle of light directly south on the meridian at the same hour; in another week, at the full phase, it rises in the east as the sun sets. If observations are continued through the night, the full moon is found directly south at midnight, and setting in the west as the sun rises. Year after year and century after century this shining body goes through its cycles of changes, each cycle being generally similar to the others but no two of them being exactly alike. It is not surprising that primitive peoples should have regarded it with awe and determined the times of their religious ceremonies by its phases. Indeed, most of the calendars of antiquity were based upon the phases of the moon.

Regularities in the motions of the moon and in the succession of its phases have always been found by those who have carefully followed celestial phenomena. But these approximations to cyclical repetitions are only crude hints of the perfect orderliness which accurate and long-continued astronomical observations have proved to exist. Every apparent departure from some simple theory has been found to be a part of a greater and more complicated order. The observed motion of the moon is compounded out of more than a thousand cycles whose magnitudes and phases are now accurately known. The theory of the motion of the moon is so perfect that its position can be computed for any instant in the future, even for a thousand years. Indeed, it is obvious that if it were not possible for mathematicians to compute accurately the motions of the moon, they could not unerringly predict all the circumstances of eclipses many years in advance of their occurrence.

Astronomers have not simply worked out the properties of the motion of the moon from observations of its positions over long intervals of time. They have discovered the underlying reason for all the complexities of its path about the earth, and that reason is that it moves subject to the gravitational attraction of the earth and, to a lesser degree, of the more distant sun. This force which prevents the moon from flying away from the earth is sufficient to break a steel cable nearly three hundred miles in diameter. Yet invisibly, like the force between a magnet and a piece of iron, it acts across the 240,000 miles between the earth and the moon. With extraordinary exactness it varies inversely as the square of the distance between these bodies. Together with the attraction of the sun on the earth and the moon, it forms an infallible basis for explaining all the peculiarities of the motion of our satellite. Indeed, in numerous instances it has enabled mathematicians to anticipate experience and to predict phenomena which observations later confirmed.

Mere words cannot do justice to the marvelous agreement between theory and the actual motions of the moon. No machine ever ran with such accuracy; no predictions of terrestrial phenomena were ever so perfectly fulfilled. If we are entitled to conclude that we understand anything whatever, we may claim that we understand how the moon moves around the earth under the attractions of the earth and the sun. . . .

Evidently the moon is above the level of the highest clouds and far away from the earth. It is easy to understand that if two astronomers are at two different points, they will see the moon in somewhat different directions from their points of observation: and it is almost as easy to understand that from the distance between the astronomers and the angle at which the moon is observed its altitude above the earth can be computed. From such observations and calculations, astronomers have found that the distance from the center of the earth to the center of the moon varies between 225,000 and 252,000 miles, with an average of 238,857 miles. This distance is known with nearly the same percentage of accuracy as the diameter of the earth. The moon moves at an average speed of 3,350 feet per second in an orbit so large that in going this distance it deviates from a straight line only about one twentieth of an inch.

After the distance to the moon has been determined, its diameter can be computed from its apparent size. This shining object which even a small button held at arm's length will hide from view is actually 2,160 miles in diameter, or more than one fourth the diameter of the earth. Its exterior area is approximately thirty million square miles, or ten times the area of the United States. Consequently, there is abundant room on its surface for mountains and valleys and plains and lakes and seas. There are, indeed, many mountains on the moon's surface, both isolated peaks and long ranges, and there are valleys and plains, but no lakes or seas. In fact, there is no water whatever upon its surface, nor is there even an atmosphere surrounding it.

There is no real mystery respecting the lack of air and water on the moon. The surface gravity of this small world (about one sixth that of the earth) is not sufficient to hold the swiftly darting molecules of an atmosphere from escaping away into space. Its surface is a desert, unprotected by clouds or an atmosphere from the burning rays of the sun during its day, or from the rapid escape of heat during its night. Both extremes of its surface temperature are particularly severe, because its period of rotation is about 29.5 times that of the earth. For nearly fifteen of our days a point on its surface is subjected to a temperature above the boiling point of water on the earth; for an equal interval of time it freezes in a temperature which descends far toward the absolute zero (about −460° Fahrenheit). Evidently it cannot be the abode of life. . . .

THE PLANETS

From a certain point of view the earth is for us a very important body, more important than every celestial body except the sun. It has been the home of the life stream of which we are a part for more than a thousand million years. It will be the home of our successors until our race becomes extinct. Our very existence depends upon it.

From another point of view, which we shall now take, the earth is not very important. It is only one of nine known planets which revolve around the sun, each of them held in its orbit by the attraction of the great central mass. Thus, the very brilliant silvery object which we see in the western evening sky (and eastern morning sky) every nineteen months is the planet Venus, a world in size and in most other respects similar to our earth. The wandering conspicuous red body which appears in the evening sky every twenty-six months is the planet Mars, and the brighter yellowish object which returns every thirteen months is Jupiter. These bodies and two others, Mercury and Saturn, were called *planets* (or wanderers) by the ancients because they are constantly moving with respect to the stars. . . .

It was not until the first decades of the seventeenth century that Kepler worked out from the observations of Tycho Brahe the properties of the planetary orbits; it was not until the latter part of the same century that Newton proved the law of gravitation and explained by means of it the motions of the planets and of the moon, the oblateness of the earth, and the ebb and flow of the tides. These great achievements mark the closing of an epoch in the history of the thought of the world and the beginning of a new, for they entirely overthrew earlier views respecting the nature of the cosmos and established others which were entirely different. They permanently removed man from his proud position at the center of creation and placed him on a relatively insignificant body; but, as a compensation, they rescued him from a universe of chance and superstition and gave him one of unfailing and majestic orderliness.

There have been many impressive illustrations of the orderliness of the universe and of our understanding of that order, but none has been more dramatic than the discovery of Neptune. This remarkable story opened in 1781 with the discovery of the planet Uranus (the first one discovered in historic times) by William Herschel; it closed with the discovery of Neptune in 1846.

After Uranus had been observed for a few months, mathematicians computed its orbit and directed observers where to point their telescopes in order to see this planet, for it is too faint to be observable with the unaided eye. For nearly forty years Uranus was always found precisely where the mathematicians said it would be seen. Then there began to be an appreciable difference between theory and the observations. By 1830 the discrepancies had become serious; by 1840 they were intolerably large. Although the discrepancies were intolerably large to scientists they would have been negligible to anyone else in the world. During the sixty years following the discovery of Uranus it did not depart from its predicted positions by an amount large enough to be observable without the aid of a telescope. Since mankind had never even known of the existence of Uranus until 1781, it at first seems absurd that scientists should have been disturbed by very minute unexplained peculiarities in its motions— variations from theory so slight that they were not observable until the lapse of about forty years. The theories, however, were believed to be very perfect. Hence the discrepancies called into question their exactness, or perhaps even the soundness of mathematical reasoning. In fact, the unexplained difference between theory and observation threw a doubt on our ability to discover and to apply the laws of nature. For this reason the motion of Uranus became one of the most important problems in science.

In 1846 order was restored by a brilliant discovery. Some years earlier it had been suggested that Uranus was departing slightly from its pre-dicted orbit as the consequence of the attraction of an unknown world. The problem was to find the unknown body from its minute effects on Uranus. No brief statement can give any adequate realization of the difficulties of the problem. The leading mathematicians of the time thought it could not be solved. But two young men, J. C. Adams, of England, and U. J. Leverrier, of France, inspired with the optimism and energy of youth, calculated where the unknown world would be found. Their predictions were brilliantly fulfilled by the discovery of Neptune on February 23, 1846, by J. G. Galle, a young German astronomer. With this discovery, the motion of Uranus again was fully explained, the laws of nature and our reasoning powers were no longer in question, and the universe was once more orderly. . . .

No experiences give us a better understanding of distances than those obtained from long journeys. Consequently, let us in imagination board some miraculous skyship, of which everyone has often dreamed, and travel from the sun to the various planets.

Obviously our skyship must fly rapidly or we shall not live long enough to cross the great distance from one planet to another. On the other hand, if it travels at too great speed we shall not be able to descend safely upon the surface of a planet. So let us suppose our skyship can traverse the interplanetary spaces at the rate of a thousand miles per hour, a speed of travel at which one might eat breakfast in the eastern part of the United States and luncheon in Europe. Let us start from the surface of the sun. Perhaps before directing our way toward Mercury we should circle around this great center of attraction. Jauntily we set out and travel continuously, but we do not complete the circuit of the sun and get back to our point of departure until 113 days, or nearly four months, have elapsed.

With some trepidation at leaving the sun and plunging into the inter-planetary spaces, we depart for Mercury, which we reach in four years and one month. In three and one half years we are at the distance of Venus; in three more at the orbit of the earth, ten years and seven months after we left the sun. Since five years and seven months more are required to reach Mars from the orbit of the earth, it takes our skyship sixteen years and two months to fly from the sun to this planet. Obviously the intervals of time required for these sky voyages are so great that they fail to give us any real understanding of the enormous distances we traverse. Yet let us continue on our way.

We arrive at Jupiter in fifty-five years after we left the sun; at Saturn in 101 years; at Uranus in 203 years; and at Neptune in 318 years. If we should continue to distant and inconspicuous Pluto, we should arrive there in 420 years. And yet at the rate of our travel we could eat breakfast in New York, luncheon in London, and return to New York for dinner and the theater. . . .

COMETS

Since the dawn of history and, indeed, for millions of years before the origin of man, the sun and the moon have not changed appreciably in appearance. But there are celestial visitors, the *comets*, which do not possess these qualities of permanence and uniformity from which the orderliness of the universe was first perceived. These objects often come quite unexpectedly out of the depths of space for a brief visit to the interior of the solar system, and then they recede back into the night from which they came. They are not of fixed shape or constant dimensions like the planets. The typical comet consists of a small nucleus, generally starlike in appearance, surrounded by a vast gaseous envelope which varies enormously in volume, sometimes being as large as the sun; while from its head there streams out a tail, perhaps fifty millions of miles in length, which in exceptional cases appears to reach a third of the way across the sky.

It is not strange that primitive peoples and, indeed, all men until only two or three centuries ago regarded comets with superstitious fear. Our predecessors believed that these bizarre-appearing objects are malignant spirits prowling through our atmosphere, or at least that they are portents of wars and pestilences. After centuries of belief in these superstitions, accepted alike by the ignorant and the learned, by theologians and scientists, observations led finally to the truth.

Tycho Brahe (1571-1630), the greatest and last observer before the invention of the telescope, comparing the different apparent directions of the comet of 1577 as seen simultaneously from various places in Europe, proved that this terrifying object was far beyond our atmosphere and at least as distant as the moon. By this demonstration he removed comets from the apparent vagaries of atmospheric phenomena to the orderly domains of the celestial bodies.

It should not be thought that comets and their motions were at once completely understood. The phenomena they present are far too complicated for an easy explanation. In fact, the determination of the properties of their paths through the solar system had to await Newton's discovery of the law of gravitation in 1686 and his use of it in explaining the celestial motions. He devised methods of determining the orbits of comets, however elongated they might be.

A lifelong friend of Newton, Edmund Halley, applied Newton's methods to computing the orbit of a great comet which had been observed in 1682. After an enormous amount of work on this and earlier comets, he proved that it revolves in a very elongated path, returning to the neighborhood of the sun about every seventy-five years. He concluded that it was identical with comets which had been observed in 1456, 1301, 1145, 1066, and at various other times; he boldly predicted it would return in 1759, and it did. It came again according to predictions in 1835, and most recently in 1910. Now it is far out in its long orbit. It has been invisible for twenty-five years and will not be seen again for forty years in the future. Yet mathematicians can follow it with perfect certainty, and long before its next return they will compute the very day when it will arrive at the point of its orbit nearest the sun.

. . . Comets differ enormously from one another in brightness, volume, length of tails, and internal activity. From three to eleven comets are observed each year, nearly all of them being so faint as to be invisible without optical aid. Occasionally one appears which is bright enough to be easily visible to the unaided eye; about three or four times a century a very great one becomes the most conspicuous object in the night sky. The tails of comets develop and increase in length as these objects approach the sun and diminish and disappear as they recede again. While a comet is approaching the sun, its tail streams out behind; as it recedes, its tail projects out ahead of it. . . .

THE SUN

In comparison with the universe in general, only one object in the solar system is worth mentioning, and that object is the sun. It is a million times greater than the earth in volume and a thousand times greater in mass than all the planets combined. It holds the little planets under its gravitative control, it lights and warms them with its abundant rays, it takes them with it in its enormous excursions among the stars.

How brilliant the light of the noonday sun is! In comparison with it all artificial lights are feeble and dull. How intensely it warms the surface of the earth on a summer's day! This general impression is not erroneous, for accurate measurements prove that when its rays fall perpendicularly upon the surface of the earth radiant energy is received from it at the rate of 1.5 horsepower per square yard. Under the same condition of perpendicular rays, a square mile of surface receives radiant energy from the sun at the rate of 4,646,400 horsepower, or at the rate of 330 million million (330,000,000,000,000) horsepower on the whole earth. If this energy were divided equally among the two billion human beings now living on the earth, each of them would have more than a hundred thousand horsepower for his use.

As enormous as is the energy received by the earth *from* the sun, it is trivial compared with the amount radiated *by* the sun, for the earth as seen from the sun would appear to be only a point, somewhat smaller than Venus appears to us when it is the bright evening star. It is evident that such a distant and apparently insignificant object would intercept only a very small fraction of the solar energy streaming out from it in every direction. It is found by computation that the earth intercepts only one two-billionth of the energy radiated by the sun. Otherwise expressed, the sun radiates more energy in a second than the earth receives in sixty years.

Obviously the sun must be very hot, for otherwise it would not radiate energy at an enormous rate. By several methods it is found that the temperature of its exterior radiating layers is about ten thousand degrees Fahrenheit, or far beyond the temperature required for melting and volatilizing iron and other similar substances. In its deep interior the temperatures are enormously higher, mounting to at least several million degrees.

The temperature of the sun's interior has not, of course, been measured by any direct means, for the depths of the sun are quite inaccessible to us. But science often penetrates inaccessible regions by reasoning, as it does in this case. The general principles underlying the method used in this problem are as follows: Each layer of the sun weighs down upon the one directly beneath it and tends to compress it. This tendency to compression of a layer is balanced by the expansive forces due to its temperature. Now the rates of increase downward in both density and temperature can be determined by the condition that the entire mass of the sun shall be in equilibrium. The results are subject to some uncertainties, however, because of our lack of knowledge of the properties of matter under the extreme conditions of pressure and temperature prevailing deep in the sun.

When we recall the terrestrial storms that are produced by unequal heating of different portions of the earth's atmosphere, we naturally expect extremely violent disturbances on the sun. The wildest flights of our imagination, however, never approach the realities, for often masses of enormously heated gases a hundred times greater than the earth in volume shoot upward from its surface, sometimes farther than from the earth to the moon. Particularly in intermediate latitudes on each side of the solar equator there are storm zones in which great whirling sun spots appear. These sun-spot disturbances, ranging from a few thousand up to more than a hundred thousand miles in diameter, have centers which appear dark in contrast to the surrounding bright surface, though they are more luminous than the filament of an electric light. In them incandescent gases surge and billow, and from their borders eruptions to great altitudes are particularly abundant. If our earth were placed on the surface of the sun it would be tossed about like a pebble in a whirlpool; it would be melted and dissipated like a snowflake in a seething lake of lava. . . .

If the sun were dissipating its mass into space, scientists would naturally inquire how it is restored, but until about 1850 they did not ask the same question respecting the energy it radiates. Until that time they did not realize that energy is something quantitative and measurable, and hence that its origin requires explanation. The sun cannot be a body which was once much hotter than at present and which is slowly cooling off, for if this were all there is to its heat it would not have lasted a thousandth of the long periods of the geological ages. It cannot be simply burning, for the heat produced by its combustion, even if it were composed of pure coal and oxygen, would last only a few thousand years. If it were contracting, the heat generated in the process would maintain its radiation only a few million years, which is less than one per cent of the interval during which it has shed its warm rays upon the earth at approximately the present rate.

Recently very conclusive reasons have been found for believing that the energy the sun radiates is due to transformations of its elements, particularly of hydrogen, into heavier elements, and probably to the transformation of matter into energy in accordance with Einstein's principle of the fundamental equivalence of mass and energy. These sources of energy are of an entirely different and higher order of magnitude than any heretofore considered by scientists. Although the mass equivalent of the energy radiated by the sun in a second is over 4,000,000 tons, the mass of the sun is so enormous that it will not be reduced through radiation by so much as one per cent in 150,000,000,000 years. Consequently, it is not surprising that the geological evidence is conclusive that the earth has received solar energy at substantially the present rate for perhaps a thousand million

years. Even this long interval of time is only a very small fraction of the
period during which the earth will continue in the future to be lighted
and warmed by the sun almost precisely as it is at present. The fears once
held that in a few million years the light of the sun will fail have proved
groundless, and scientists no longer look forward to a time when the earth,
cold and lifeless, will circulate endlessly around a dark center of attraction.

One of the miracles of science has been the determination of the composition of the sun. . . . The normal ear has the ability to distinguish separately
a mixture of a considerable number of tones. The eye has no corresponding power—a mixture of blue and yellow, for example, appears as a
single color (green) and not as a combination of two colors. Fortunately,
a very remarkable instrument, the *spectroscope*, separates a mixture of light
into its component colors, or wave lengths, and enables the astronomer
to determine precisely what wave lengths are present in the radiation
from the sun, or, indeed, from any other celestial body from which
sufficient radiant energy is received. . . .

Of the ninety elements known on the earth, at least fifty have been found
to exist in the atmosphere of the sun in the gaseous state, and the presence
of several others is probable. The elements found in considerable abundance in the sun include hydrogen, helium, oxygen, magnesium, iron,
silicon, sodium, potassium, calcium, aluminum, nickel, manganese,
chromium, cobalt, titanium, copper, vanadium, and zinc. Some of the
heaviest elements, such as gold and uranium, have not been found in the
sun's atmosphere, perhaps because they lie at low levels. . . .

THE STARS

As the sun rises, all the sparkling stars which sprinkle the clear night
sky pale into insignificance and totally disappear. Yet actually they are suns,
most of those which are visible to the unaided eye being much greater
than our own. Indeed, some of them radiate thousands of times as much
light, and a few are known which are millions of times greater in volume.
Their apparent insignificance is due to their incomprehensibly enormous
distances.

In order to bring within the range of our understanding the distance
from the sun to the earth, we computed the time necessary for an
imaginary skyship to travel from one of these bodies to the other at the rate
of a thousand miles per hour. We found that if it continued on its way
night and day, without pausing, it would require ten years and seven
months to traverse the ninety-three million miles between the center of
our system and this little planet of ours. Even with the aid of this calculation we do not grasp the significance of the distances in the solar system.

Perhaps we shall improve our understanding of the distances in the solar system by noting that the velocity we assumed for our skyship was more than 30 per cent greater than that of sound in our atmosphere, for sounds travels at the rate of only 736 miles per hour. Let us assume that sound could come from the sun to us at this speed. Then, if we should see some tremendous solar explosion and should expectantly await its thunders, we should be held in suspense before hearing it for more than fourteen years.

If we fail to comprehend the great distances between the members of our solar system, we naturally shall fall far short of grasping as realities the enormously greater distances to the stars. Yet we must attempt to do so, and we shall find that our understanding of these distances increases as we struggle with them. Let us start with the nearest star visible without optical aid from northern latitudes, the brilliant Sirius, the brightest star in all the sky. This beautiful bluish-white object is on the southern meridian at eight o'clock in the evening about the first of March each year. Astronomers have found by measurements that its distance is 51,700,-000,000,000 miles, or more than 550,000 times the distance from the sun to the earth. Therefore, more than 6,000,000 years would be required for our imaginary skyship to fly from the solar system to Sirius.

In view of the enormous distances to even the nearest of the stars, we naturally wonder how astronomers have measured them and whether, after all, they are not merely conjectures resting upon no substantial foundation. The method of determining the distances of the relatively near stars is essentially the same as that used in determining the distance to the moon, namely, measuring the differences in their directions as seen from two different points. At some convenient time in the year the star Sirius, for example, is observed to be in a certain direction from the earth. A few months later, after the earth has moved many millions of miles in its orbit, Sirius is found to be in a slightly different direction. From this change in direction and the distance apart of the two points of observation the distance of Sirius is readily computed. Obviously, the method is entirely sound, and in the case of a star no more distant than Sirius it is known that the results are not uncertain to more than about one per cent of their value.

Although the direct method of measuring stellar distances is relatively simple, the difficulties of putting it into effect are in general enormous because of the remoteness of the stars. Indeed, the greatest observed difference in direction of Sirius as observed from the earth from two points in its orbit separated by as great a distance as even that from the earth to the sun is extremely small. It is as small as the difference in direction of an object twenty-two miles away when viewed first with one eye and then with the other. Moreover, only four or five other known stars, all of which except one are so faint as to be invisible without optical aid, are as near to us as Sirius. Indeed, all except a few hundred stars out of the millions which can be photographed through large telescopes are so very remote that their distances cannot be measured by the direct method which has been outlined. Nevertheless, our knowledge of the distances of the stars does not stop with this limited number, for astronomers with extraordinary skill have used their knowledge of the distances and other properties of these nearer stars as a basis for several other methods which reach enormously farther into space.

Before taking up the characteristics of the stars we shall define a more convenient unit for stellar distances which we shall often have occasion to use. It is the distance light travels in interstellar space in a year, known as the *light-year*. Since light travels in a vacuum at the rate of about 186,000 miles per second, the light-year is 5,880,000,000,000 miles, or about 60,000 times the distance from the sun to the earth. The star Sirius is distant 8.8 light-years; the stars of the Big Dipper are distant 70 to 80 light-years; the Pleiades, about 200 light-years; the brighter stars in Orion, about 500 light-years; and the star clouds which make up the Milky Way thousands of light-years.

In spite of the enormous distances of the stars a great deal has been learned about them as individual bodies. In the first place, they consist of a number of classes depending upon the properties of the light they radiate as determined by the spectroscope. At one extreme are the blue Class B stars, of which a number of the brighter stars in Orion are examples. These stars, which radiate many thousand times as much light as our sun, are enormous bodies whose exterior atmospheres are at temperatures ranging from 80,000 to 100,000 degrees Fahrenheit. In their atmospheres are spectral evidences of only hydrogen, helium, oxygen, and nitrogen.

Next come the Class A stars, which are not quite so hot or brilliant as the Class B stars. Sirius is a splendid example of this class. Its surface temperature is nearly twice that of the sun, and it radiates twenty-seven times as much light. Then follow the Class F stars, of which Canopus and Procyon are illustrations. These stars approach in temperature, brilliance, and composition the Class G stars to which Capella and the sun belong. Nearly half of all the stars in the catalogues of stellar spectra are closely related to the sun. Only a few are giants of Class A, and a still smaller number are supergiants of Class B.

Beyond the stars in the spectral sequence of class G, to which the sun belongs, come the cooler and ruddier stars of Class K, of which Arcturus and Aldebaran are notable examples. So far the stars of each spectral class connect by insensible gradations with those of the next class. But at the stars of Class K there is a discontinuity. The next class in the order in which they are usually given are those of Class M, of which Betelgeuse and Antares are examples. The atmospheres of these stars are at relatively low temperatures, as would naturally be inferred from their colors, and they contain many compounds as well as individual chemical elements. There are three other classes of stars, classes N, R, and S, which have no well-defined relationship to the other classes. They are all faint, with one or two exceptions being far beyond the range of the unaided eye, they are very few in number, and they are deep red in color. . . .

In 1650, forty years after the invention of the telescope by Galileo, the star at the bend of the handle of the Big Dipper, which theretofore looked like an ordinary star, was found to consist of two stars apparently almost touching each other. It is now known, however, that these two stars are hundreds of times as far apart as are the earth and the sun. The discovery of this pair has been followed by the discovery of nearly 20,000 other *double stars*. Probably a few of these double pairs consist of two unrelated stars which happen to be for a time almost in the same direction from us, but in nearly all cases they are actually twin suns revolving around their center of gravity. The periods of revolution of most of them are so long, however, that they have not been determined from observations in the relatively short intervals since their discovery. . . .

In certain cases the plane of revolution of a double star passes through or near the present position of the solar system. It is clear that when the two stars of such a pair are in a line with the earth, one wholly or partially eclipses the other, and at such times the light received from the pair is temporarily reduced. If the two stars are equal in volume and equally bright, the light received by the earth at the time of eclipse is one half its normal value. If one star is totally dark, it may entirely eclipse the luminous star. It is evident that many cases are theoretically possible, and it is an interesting fact that nearly all of them have been observed.

It is clearly not difficult to determine the periods of revolution of these *variable stars*, as they are called, for their periods are defined by the intervals between their eclipses. But to determine the distance between the components of such a pair is quite another matter, for they are so close together that they appear to be a single star. Fortunately, a remarkable application of the spectroscope, which cannot be explained here, enables the astronomer to measure the relative velocity of a pair in their orbit;

and from this velocity and the period of revolution of a pair he computes the perimeter of their orbit, and then their distance apart. . . .

Many stars, however, are variables as a consequence of change in the rates of their radiation. In certain cases the variations in brightness are nearly as regular as those of eclipsing variables, though the changes are otherwise quite different. In other cases the variations in brightness are irregular and through wide ranges. For example, the star Omicron Ceti is at least ten thousand times brighter at its highest maxima than at its lowest minima. . . .

The extreme limit in variable stars is reached by the temporary stars, or *novae*. These stars blaze out suddenly from obscurity to great brilliance, in some cases increasing their radiation a hundred-thousandfold in a day or two, only gradually to sink back to relative obscurity within a few months. A number of these remarkable temporary stars have played important roles in the history of astronomy. For example, the Greek philosopher and astronomer Hipparchus (about 160-105 B.C.) made the earliest known catalogue of stars, 1080 in number, in order to determine whether all stars are as transitory as the nova which he observed. Another temporary star inspired Tycho Brahe (1546-1601) to become an observer, and another which appeared in 1572 aroused the interest of Kepler in astronomy.

We do not know the cause of the remarkable outbursts of the novae, which are more violent phenomena on a stellar scale than any of the little explosions which ever take place on the earth or even than the much greater ones on the sun. If our sun should ever become a temporary star, our earth and the other planets would be quickly destroyed. It seems probable, however, that only certain stars are subject to these mighty outbursts, and that they occur again and again, separated by long intervals. These cataclysmic phenomena teach us how little we know of violent forces, even when we observe enormous volumes of incandescent gases shoot up hundreds of thousands of miles from the surface of the sun.

NEBULAE

There are among the stars many faint, hazy patches called *nebulae*, or little clouds. Some of them, such as that around the central star in the Sword of Orion, are faintly visible to the unaided eye, but most of them are found only with telescopic aid or by photography. They look like tenuous gaseous masses, and for a long time they were thought to be gaseous in nature, perhaps primordial world stuff out of which stars evolve in the course of enormous periods of time. With more powerful telescopes, however, a few of them were resolved into separate stars.

Then for a time it was supposed that probably all nebulae are swarms of stars which can be resolved by sufficiently powerful instruments. But toward the close of the nineteenth century this conjecture was proved by the spectroscope to be false, for when their light was examined by this instrument it was found to have the properties of light radiated by luminous gases rather than by relatively dense stars. Consequently, we now know that the nebulae, except those which are now classed differently, are tenuous gases. . . .

OUR STELLAR SYSTEM

We have found that our earth is a member of a family of planets. Now we inquire whether our sun is similarly a member of a family of stars.

When we attempt to determine whether the stars are the components of some vast organism, we are at once confronted with serious difficulties because of their great distances apart. For example, the distance between our solar system and the nearest known star, the far southern Alpha Centauri, is 4.3 light-years, or more than 25,000,000,000,000 miles. The nearest bright star visible from northern latitudes is Sirius at a distance of 8.8 light-years. Most of the stars within the range of the unaided eye are many times as far away as Sirius, while most of those photographed with large telescopes are distant more than a thousand light-years. . . .

Let us first consider the stellar density near the present position of the solar system where the results are most trustworthy. Since it is possible with modern instruments and photographic processes to measure with much precision the distances of stars within thirteen light-years (76,000,-000,000,000 miles) of the sun, we shall first examine this region around the sun. Within this sphere of thirteen light-years in radius there are thirty known stars, five of which are doubles and one of which is a triple. It would be natural to expect that these relatively near stars would be included among the hundred brightest stars in the sky. As a matter of fact, only six of them, besides the sun, are bright enough to be visible without optical aid, while several of them are of such low luminosity that they are very faint in spite of their small distance from us, astronomically speaking. Since several of these near faint stars are of recent discovery, it is probable that there are a few others, at present unknown, which are within thirteen light-years of our sun. For the sake of having a definite number to serve as a basis for our calculations, we shall assume that there are thirty-five stars within this sphere. . . .

It should not be understood that the thirty-five stars we are considering form a system in any special sense. They are simply a small sample out of an ocean of stars and give us some idea respecting what the general stellar system is like. At present the stars in this sphere are near one another, but their neighborliness is only transitory, for they are moving in various directions at various velocities, and their mutual gravitation lacks much of being sufficient to hold them together. In a million years they will be far from one another and will have formed entirely different close associates.

There are, however, families of stars in the sense that they permanently, or at least for millions of millions of years, form a dynamical system of mutually interacting bodies. The best-known of such families is the Hyades stars in the constellation Taurus. About eighty of these stars are moving together through the celestial regions like a flock of migratory birds across the sky. Their spectra prove that they are similar in constitution, they undoubtedly had a common origin, and they are undergoing parallel evolutions. . . .

There are several hundred other known clusters of stars besides the Hyades family. Some of them are open groups like the Big Dipper and the Sickle in Leo. Others are more closely related families like the Pleiades, and in a few clusters the stars appear to be actually crowded together, although those which are nearest each other are rarely separated by less than a light-year. . . .

Our sun does not appear to be a member of a compact (in the astronomical sense) family of stars, but it is a member of an enormous star cloud containing millions of stars. In these larger organizations the stars do not exhibit the similarities which are found among the stars of such compact families as the Hyades. Nor are they moving in parallel lines at the same speed. They consist, rather, of stars of all classes and kinds, moving around among one another somewhat like bees in a swarm, doubtless held loosely together by their mutual gravitation. These great star clouds largely make up the Milky Way. Even with the unaided eye they loom up conspicuously, under favorable conditions, in Cygnus, Sagittarius and Scorpius. With a photographic telescope their soft mist is resolved into myriads of stars. . . .

When we pass beyond the star cloud of which the sun is a member, we arrive at our entire Milky Way system, or *galaxy*. It is composed of vast clouds of stars and millions of individual stars spread out in the form of a disk, the diameter of which is of the order of 60,000 light-years and the thickness of which is perhaps one eighth as great. It is not to be understood that our galaxy is homogeneous with well-defined exterior surfaces. It is, rather, a somewhat irregular assemblage of star clouds and individual stars, with vast regions of relatively high steller density, always decreasing, however, toward its borders. If the average stellar density of the galactic system were as great as it is within thirteen light-years of the sun, there would be in our galaxy more than 50,000,000,000 stars. Although this number may be somewhat too large, it is probable that there are several billion stars in our Milky Way system, and the number of them may exceed even fifty billions. It is interesting that heretofore estimates of astronomers have always fallen short of the actualities, as have conjectures in other fields of science.

If the solar system were at the center of the galaxy, the stars would be symmetrically distributed around the Milky Way. The stars are, however, much more numerous in the direction of Sagittarius and Scorpius than in the opposite part of the heavens. This fact means that the galactic center is in the direction of these constellations, perhaps at a distance of a few thousand light-years. Moreover, the sun is some distance, perhaps a few hundred light-years, north of the central plane of the galaxy, a result which is inferred from the observed fact that stars are somewhat more numerous on the south side than they are on the north side of the great circle representing, at least generally, its central line. This is the position of the solar system at present, but the sun is moving obliquely northward from the galactic plane at the rate of a light-year in fifteen or twenty thousand years. Consequently, if it maintains its velocity and direction of motion for a million years, it will then be in a substantially different part of our galaxy.

Our stellar system owes its disklike shape to its rotation, an inference which is based on dynamical principles and which has been verified by observations. Astronomers long ago proved the revolution of the earth around the sun by observations of the distant stars. Now they are proving the rotation of the enormous galaxy by measurements of velocities toward or from systems of stars far beyond its borders. . . . In spite of all the variety in the motions of its stars and star clouds, it on the whole is involved in an immense gyration. At the distance of the sun from its center the velocity of its rotation is probably of the order of one or two hundred miles per second, and the period of its rotation between fifty and two hundred million years. It follows that during the long intervals of the geological eras our earth in its motion with the sun has traveled widely throughout our galactic system. . . .

GLOBULAR CLUSTERS

Somewhat outside of our galactic system, at distances ranging from 25,000 to 160,000 light-years, there are approximately a hundred great aggregations of stars which are called *globular clusters* because they are almost exactly spherical in form. At the distances of these clusters only giant and supergiant stars are separately visible even through large tele-scopes. Consequently, those of their stars which are observed or photo-graphed as separate objects are only a very small fraction of all the stars which they contain. Yet the separately observed stars in the globular clusters are numbered by thousands and tens of thousands, and the fainter ones almost certainly number hundreds of thousands and probably millions.

One of the few globular clusters visible to the unaided eye is the Great Cluster in Hercules. At its distance of 33,000 light-years the combined light of 400,000 stars, each equal to our sun in luminosity, would be hardly visible to the unaided eye. Hence this cluster must be composed of an enormous number of stars and many of high luminosity. Indeed, on a photograph of it taken with one of the great telescopes on Mount Wilson, the images of 40,000 stars were counted, the faintest of these stars being approximately a hundred times as luminous as our sun. Consequently, there can be little doubt that this immense system contains at least a million stars as great as our sun, and probably many millions of lower luminosity. Yet it is so far away in the depths of space that we receive from all its millions of suns less than one sixth as much light as we receive from the North Star.

. . . Assume that the Hercules cluster contains a hundred thousand giant and supergiant stars and a million stars altogether. We find from its distance and its apparent diameter that its actual diameter is about one hundred light-years. Hence it follows that if its hundred thousand great stars were uniformly distributed throughout its volume, the average distance between those which are adjacent would be more than two light-years, or about 140,000 times the distance from the sun to the earth. If we include the million stars in our computation, we find that the average distance between neighbors is about one light-year. . . . Even the giant stars in the clusters are no brighter as seen from one another than Venus is as observed from the earth.

The globular clusters are dynamically mature; that is, they have arrived at a state in which as a whole they remain unchanged, although their individual stars are in ceaseless motion. Since many other aggre-gations of stars, such as our galaxy and its star clouds, are very irregular in structure, it does not seem probable that the globular clusters have always had their present perfect symmetries. Perhaps better support for our opinion that the stars in them were once irregularly distributed is found in the exterior galaxies which are usually, but not always, far from symmetrical.

If the present nearly spherical forms of the globular clusters are due to dynamical evolutions, we may inquire how great must have been the interval of time between some earlier heterogeneous state and their present conditions. We first find the astonishing result that the period of the circuit of a star around the Hercules cluster, or from near its exterior deep into its interior and out again somewhere else, is of the order of ten million years. We next note that the dynamical evolution which we are considering is due primarily to the near approaches of the stars, just as the uniform distribution of molecules of various kinds in a gas is due primarily to their collisions which occur with great frequency; indeed, on the average, five thousand million times a second.

The distances between the stars in the clusters are so great that, on the average, a star will make ten thousand circuits before it will pass near enough another star to have the direction of its motion changed by as much as twenty degrees. That is, on the average it moves for a hundred thousand million years (ten thousand times ten million years) as though the mass of the cluster were not concentrated into stars. Then it passes so near one of these concentrations of mass (one of the stars) that the direction of its motion is appreciably changed. After a very large number, perhaps a million, of these adventures all the earlier heterogeneities are smoothed out with a resulting globular cluster of stars. That is, the very organization of the globular clusters proves that these spherical masses of stars have been undergoing independent evolutions for at least millions of millions of years. In the course of time, however, these symmetrical structures may pass near or through somewhat similar aggregations and be transformed into spinning irregular spirals similar to our galaxy.

EXTERIOR GALAXIES

We have often called the Milky Way system of stars "our" galaxy, as though it were something we possess, or which is at least in our immediate neighborhood. From the standpoint of the earth or even of the whole solar system our language has been presumptuous, for we have explored tens of thousands of light-years, or hundreds of millions of times the distance from our planet to the sun. . . . But all these objects are of secondary importance and interest in comparison with the enormous galaxy known as the *Great Nebula in Andromeda*. Until within a few years astronomers gazed up at this hazy patch of light, which is just within the range of the unaided eye, and thought they were looking only at a tenuous nebula lying out toward the borders of our stellar system. Now they know that what they have been seeing is a great exterior galaxy, which in magnitude, in number of stars, and in structure is similar to our own.

The distance from our present position to the Great Nebula in Andromeda is about 900,000 light-years. Consequently, we see this galaxy not as it is now but as it was before our ancestors evolved to the level of men. . . . The so-called Andromeda nebula is actually a galaxy in every essential respect similar to our own, a much flattened disk of many billions of stars, having a diameter of something like 80,000 light-years and rotating in a period of perhaps 150,000,000 years.

There are within a million light-years of the solar system six known galaxies, including our own. But outside of this great sphere there are hundreds of thousands of other galaxies within easy reach of large photographic telescopes. . . .

From atoms to galaxies each physical unit is made up of smaller units—atoms of protons and electrons, molecules of atoms, stars of molecules, galaxies of stars. We naturally inquire whether the galaxies we observe are not components of still greater cosmic units; whether our Milky Way system, for example, the Magellanic Clouds, the Andromeda galaxy and others which are relatively near are not the constituents of a supergalaxy enormously greater than any one of them, and perhaps millions of light-years in diameter. Although the field which we are considering is relatively new, astronomers have already found numerous aggregations of galaxies into supergalaxies. For example, Harlow Shapley has described a supergalaxy in the direction of Centaurus, but a hundred and fifty million light-years beyond the stars of this constellation, which is composed of more than three hundred galaxies, all of which are probably comparable to our own steller system. The space occupied by this supergalaxy is an oval about seven million light-years in length and two million light-years in diameter. It is so vast that the average distance between those of its galaxies which are adjacent is approximately a million light-years.

What is beyond the supergalaxies? There is no observational evidence bearing upon the question. There are good theoretical reasons, however, for concluding that they do not extend on through an infinite space with the approximate frequency which is found within a few hundred million light-years of our own galaxy. According to certain deductions from the theory of relativity they are limited in number, and space itself is limited in extent. On the other hand, the supergalaxies which we now know may be the component units of enormously greater supergalaxies of the second order. And these supergalaxies of the second order may be the constituents of supergalaxies of the third order, and so on upward in an unending sequence.

1937

The Milky Way and Beyond

SIR ARTHUR EDDINGTON

IN ONE OF JULES VERNE'S STORIES THE ASTRONOMER begins his lecture with the words "Gentlemen, you have seen the moon —or at least heard tell of it." I think I may in the same way presume that you are acquainted with the Milky Way, which can be seen on any clear dark night as a faintly luminous band forming an arch from horizon to horizon. The telescopes show that it is composed of multitudes of stars. One is tempted to say "countless multitudes"; but it is part of the business of an astronomer to count them, and the number is not uncountable though it amounts to more than ten thousand millions. The number of stars in the Milky Way is considerably greater than the number of human beings on the earth. Each star, I may remind you, is an immense fiery globe of the same general nature as our sun.

There is no sharp division between the distant stars which form the Milky Way and the brighter stars which we see strewn over the sky. All these stars taken together form one system or galaxy; its extent is enormous but not unlimited. Since we are situated inside it we do not obtain a good view of its form; but we are able to see far away in space other galaxies which also consist of thousands of millions of stars, and presumably if we could see our own galaxy from outside, it would appear like one of them. These other galaxies are known as "spiral nebulae." We believe that our own Milky Way system is more or less like them. If so, the stars form a flat coil—rather like a watch-spring—except that the coil is double.

When we look out in directions perpendicular to the plane of the coil, we soon reach the limit of the system; but in the plane of the coil we see stars behind stars until they become indistinguishable and fade into the hazy light of the Milky Way. It has been ascertained that we are a very long way from the centre of our own galaxy, so that there are many more stars on one side of us than on the other.

Looking at one of these galaxies, it is impossible to resist the impression that it is whirling round—like a Catherine Wheel. It has, in fact, been possible to prove that some of the spiral nebulae are rotating, and to measure the rate of rotation. Also by studying the motions of the stars in our own galaxy, it has been found that it too is rotating about a centre. The centre is situated a long way from us in the constellation Ophiuchus near a particularly bright patch of the Milky Way; the actual centre is, however, hidden from us by a cloud of obscuring matter. My phrase, "whirling round," may possibly give you a wrong impression. With these vast systems we have to think in a different scale of space and time, and the whirling is slow according to our ordinary ideas. It takes about 300 million years for the Milky Way to turn round once. But after all that is not so very long. Geologists tell us that the older rocks in the earth's crust were formed 1300 million years ago; so the sun, carrying with it the earth and planets, has made four or five complete revolutions round the centre of the galaxy within geological times.

The stars which form our Milky Way system show a very wide diversity. Some give out more than 10,000 times as much light and heat as the sun; others less than 1/100th. Some are extremely dense and compact; others are extremely tenuous. Some have a surface temperature as high as 20,000 or 30,000° C.; others not more than 3000° C. Some are believed to be pulsating—swelling up and deflating within a period of a few days or weeks; these undergo great changes of light and heat accompanying the expansion and collapse. It would be awkward for us if our sun behaved that way. A considerable proportion (about 1/3 of the whole number) go about in pairs, forming "double stars"; the majority, however, are bachelors like the sun.

But in spite of this diversity, the stars have one comparatively uniform characteristic, namely their mass, that is, the amount of matter which goes to form them. A range from 1/5 to 5 times the sun's mass would cover all but the most exceptional stars; and the general run of the masses is within an even narrower range. Among a hundred stars picked at random the diversity of mass would not be greater proportionately than among a hundred men, women and children picked at random from a crowd.

Broadly speaking, a big star is big, not because it contains an excessive amount of material, but because it is puffed out like a balloon; and a small star is small because its material is highly compressed. Our sun, which is intermediate in this, as in most respects, has a density rather greater than that of water. (The sun is in every way a typical middle-class star.) The two extremes—the extremely rarefied and the extremely dense stars—are especially interesting. We find stars whose material is as tenuous as a gas. The well-known star Capella, for example, has an average density about equal to that of air; to be inside Capella would be like being surrounded by air, as we ordinarily are, except that the temperature (which is about 5,000,000° C) is hotter than we are accustomed to. Still more extreme are the red giant stars Betelgeuse in Orion and Antares in Scorpio. To obtain a star like Betelgeuse, we must imagine the sun swelling out until it has swallowed up Mercury, Venus and the Earth, and has a circumference almost equal to the orbit of Mars. The density of this vast globe is that of a gas in a rather highly exhausted vessel. Betelgeuse could be described as "a rather good vacuum."

At the other extreme are the "white dwarf" stars, which have extravagantly high density. I must say a little about the way in which this was discovered.

Between 1916 and 1924 I was very much occupied trying to understand the internal constitution of the stars, for example, finding the temperature in the deep interior, which is usually ten million degrees, and making out what sort of properties matter would have at such high temperatures. Physicists had recently been making great advances in our knowledge of atoms and radiation; and the problem was to apply this new knowledge to the study of what was taking place inside a star. In the end I obtained a formula by which, if you knew the mass of a star, you could calculate how bright it ought to be. An electrical engineer will tell you that to produce a certain amount of illumination you must have a dynamo of a size which he will specify; somewhat analogously I found that for a star to give a certain amount of illumination it must have a definite mass which the formula specified. This formula, however, was not intended to apply to all stars, but only to diffuse stars with densities corresponding to a gas, because the problem became too complicated if the material could not be treated as a perfect gas.

Having obtained the theoretical formula, the next thing was to compare it with observation. That is where the trouble often begins. And there was trouble in this case; only it was not of the usual kind. The observed masses and luminosities agreed with the formulae all right; the trouble was that they would not stop agreeing! The dense stars for which the formula was *not* intended agreed just as well as the diffuse stars for which the formula was intended. This surprising result could only mean that, although their densities were as great as that of water or iron, the stellar material was nevertheless behaving like a gas; in particular, it was compressible like an ordinary gas.

We had been rather blind not to have foreseen this. Why is it that we can compress air, but cannot appreciably compress water? It is because in air the ultimate particles (the molecules) are wide apart, with plenty of empty space between them. When we compress air we merely pack the molecules a bit closer, reducing the amount of vacant space. But in water the molecules are practically in contact and cannot be packed any closer. In all substances the ordinary limit of compression is when the molecules jam in contact; after that we cannot appreciably increase the density. This limit corresponds approximately to the density of the solid or liquid state. We had been supposing that the same limit would apply in the interior of a star. We ought to have remembered that at the temperature of millions of degrees there prevailing the atoms are highly ionized, i.e. broken up. An atom has a heavy central nucleus surrounded by a widely extended but insubstantial structure of electrons—a sort of crinoline. At the high temperature in the stars this crinoline of electrons is broken up. If you are calculating how many dancers can be accommodated in a ball-room, it makes a difference whether the ladies wear crinolines or not. Judging by the crinolined terrestrial atoms we should reach the limit of compression at densities not much greater than water; but the uncrinolined stellar atoms can pack much more densely, and do not jam together until densities far beyond terrestrial experience are reached.

This suggested that there might exist stars of density greater than any material hitherto known, which called to mind a mystery concerning the Companion of Sirius. The dog-star Sirius has a faint companion close to it, visible in telescopes of moderate power. There is a method of finding densities of stars which I must not stop to explain. The method is rather tentative; and when it was found to give for the Companion of Sirius a density 50,000 times greater than water, it was naturally assumed that it had gone wrong in its application. But in the light of the foregoing discussion, it now seemed possible that the method had not failed, and that the extravagantly high density might be genuine. So astronomers endeavoured to check the determination of density by another method depending on Einstein's relativity theory. The second method confirmed the high density, and it is now generally accepted. The stuff of the Companion of Sirius is 2000 times as dense as platinum. Imagine a match-box filled with this matter. It would need a crane to lift it—it would weigh a ton.

I am afraid that what I have to say about the stars is largely a matter of facts and figures. There is only one star near enough for us to study its surface, namely our sun. Ordinary photographs of the sun show few features, except the dark spots which appear at times. But much more interesting photographs are obtained by using a spectro-heliograph, which is an instrument blind to all light except that of one particular wave length—coming from one particular kind of atom.

Now let us turn to the rest of the universe which lies beyond the Milky Way. Our galaxy is, as it were, an oasis of matter in the desert of emptiness, an island in the boundless ocean of space. From our own island we see in the far distance other islands—in fact a whole archipelago of islands one beyond another till our vision fails. One of the nearest of them can actually be seen with the naked eye; it is in the constellation Andromeda, and looks like a faint, rather hazy, star. The light which we now see has taken 900,000 years to reach us. When we look at that faint object in Andromeda we are looking back 900,000 years into the past. Some of the telescopic spiral nebulae are much more distant. The most remote that has yet been examined is 300,000,000 light-years away.

These galaxies are very numerous. From sample counts it is found that more than a million of them are visible in our largest telescopes; and there must be many more fainter ones which we do not see. Our sun is just one star in a system of thousands of millions of stars; and that whole system is just one galaxy in a universe of thousands of millions of galaxies.

Let us pause to see where we have now got to in the scale of size. The following comparative table of distances will help to show us where we are:

	Kilometres
Distance of the sun	150,000,000
Limit of the solar system (Orbit of Pluto)	5,800,000,000
Distance of the nearest star	40,000,000,000,000
Distance of nearest external galaxy	8,000,000,000,000,000,000,000
Distance of furthest galaxy yet observed	3,000,000,000,000,000,000,000,000

Some people complain that they cannot realize these figures. Of course they cannot. But that is the last thing one wants to do with big numbers—to "realize" them. In a few weeks time our finance minister in England will be presenting his annual budget of about £900,000,000. Do you suppose that by way of preparation, he throws himself into a state of trance in which he can visualize the vast pile of coins or notes or commodities that it represents? I am quite sure he cannot "realize" £900,000,000. But he can spend it. It is a fallacious idea that these big numbers create a difficulty in comprehending astronomy; they can only do so if you are seeking the wrong sort of comprehension. They are not meant to be gaped at, but to be manipulated and used. It is as easy to use millions

and billions and trillions for our counters as ones and twos and threes.
What I want to call attention to in the above table is that since we are
going out beyond the Milky Way we have taken a very big step up in the
scale of distance.

The remarkable thing that has been discovered about these galaxies is
that (except three or four of the nearest of them) they are running away
from our own galaxy; and the further they are away, the faster they go.
The distant ones have very high speeds. On the average the speed is
proportional to the distance.

Why are they all running away from us? If we think a little, we shall
see that the aversion is not especially directed against us; they are running
away from us, but they are also running away from each other. If this
room were to expand 10 per cent in its dimensions, the seats all separating
in proportion, you would at first think that everyone was moving away
from you; the man 10 metres away has moved 1 metre further off; the
man 20 metres away has moved 2 metres further off; and so on. Just
as with the galaxies, the recession is proportional to the distance. This
law of proportion is characteristic of a uniform expansion, not directed
away from any one centre, but causing a general scattering apart. So we
conclude that recession of the nebulae is an effect of uniform expansion.

The system of the galaxies is all the universe we know, and indeed
we have strong reason to believe that it is the whole physical universe.
The expansion of the system, or scattering apart of the galaxies, is therefore commonly referred to as the expansion of the universe; and the
problem which it raises is the problem of the "expanding universe."

The expansion is proceeding so fast that, at the present rate, the nebulae
will recede to double their present distances in 1300 million years. Astronomers will have to double the apertures of their telescopes every 1300
million years in order to keep pace with the recession. But seriously 1300
million years is not a long period of cosmic history; I have already mentioned it as the age of terrestrial rocks. It comes as a surprise that the
universe should have doubled its dimensions within geological times.
It means that we cannot go back indefinitely in time; and indeed the
enormous time-scale of billions [The English "billion" is equivalent to
the American "trillion."] of years, which was fashionable ten years ago,
must be drastically cut down. We are becoming reconciled to this speeding up of the time-scale of evolution, for various other lines of evidence
have convinced us that it is essential. It seems clear now that we must

take an upper limit to the age of the stars not greater than 10,000 million years; previously, an age of a thousand times longer was commonly adopted.

For reasons which I cannot discuss fully we believe that along with the expansion of the material universe there is an expansion of space itself. The idea is that the island galaxies are scattered throughout a "spherical space." Spherical space means that if you keep going straight on in any direction you will ultimately find yourself back at your starting point. This is analogous to what happens when you travel straight ahead on the earth; you reach your starting point again, having gone round the world. But here we apply the analogy to an extra dimension—to *space* instead of to a *surface*. I realize, of course, that this conception of a closed spherical space is very difficult to grasp, but really it is not worse than the older conception of infinite open space which no one can properly imagine. No one can conceive infinity; one just uses the term by habit without trying to grasp it. If I may refer to our English expression, "out of the frying-pan into the fire," I suggest that if you feel that in receiving this modern conception of space you are falling into the fire, please remember that you are at least escaping from the frying-pan.

Spherical space has many curious properties. I said that if you go straight ahead in any direction you will return to your starting point. So if you look far enough in any direction and there is nothing in the way, you ought to see—the back of your head. Well, not exactly—because light takes at least 6000 million years to travel round the universe and your head was not there when it started. But you will understand the general idea. However, these curiosities do not concern us much. The main point is that if the galaxies are distributed over the spherical space more or less in the same way that human beings are distributed over the earth, they cannot form an expanding system—they cannot all be receding from one another—unless the space itself expands. So the expansion of the material system involves, and is an aspect of, an expansion of space.

This scattering apart of the galaxies was not unforeseen. As far back as 1917, Professor W. de Sitter showed that there was reason to expect this phenomenon and urged astronomers to look for it. But it is only recently that radial velocities of spiral nebulae have been measured in sufficient numbers to show conclusively that the scattering occurs. It is one of the deductions from relativity theory that there must exist a force, known as "cosmical repulsion," which tends to produce this kind of scattering in which every object recedes from every other object. You know the theory of relativity led to certain astronomical consequences —a bending of light near the sun detectable at eclipses, a motion of the perihelion of Mercury, a red-shift of spectral lines—which have been more or less satisfactorily verified. The existence of cosmical repulsion is an equally definite consequence of the theory, though this is not so widely known—partly because it comes from a more difficult branch of the theory and was not noticed so early, and perhaps partly because it is not so directly associated with the magic name of Einstein.

I can see no reason to doubt that the observed recession of the spiral nebulae is due to cosmical repulsion, and is the effect predicted by relativity theory which we were hoping to find. Many other explanations have been proposed—some of them rather fantastic—and there has been a great deal of discussion which seems to me rather pointless. In this, as in other developments of scientific exploration, we must recognize the limitations of our present knowledge and be prepared to consider revolutionary changes. But when, as in this case, observation agrees with what our existing knowledge had led us to expect, it is reasonable to feel encouraged to pursue the line of thought which has proved successful; and there seems little excuse for an outburst of unsupported speculation.

. . . Now we have been all over the universe. If my survey has been rather inadequate, I might plead that light takes 6000 million years to make the circuit that I have made in an hour. Or rather, that was the original length of the circuit; but the universe is expanding continually, and whilst I have been talking the increase of the circuit amounts to one or two more days' journey for the light. Anyhow, the time has come to leave this nightmare of immensity and find again, among the myriads of orbs, the tiny planet which is our home.   *1937*

Editors' Note:—

The preceding article by the great English astronomer, Sir Arthur Eddington, was written twenty-one years ago. Since that time, and especially since the dedication of the 200-inch Hale telescope on Mount Palomar in California in 1948, our ideas of the size of the universe and the speed of recession of the distant galaxies have changed. While the methods and processes described by Eddington are still considered valid, some of his figures, especially on distances, need revision. Thus, largely from studies of globular clusters in the Magellanic Clouds and on the Andromeda Nebula, it is possible that the Andromeda Nebula (described on earlier pages by Moulton and Eddington) may be nearly three million light years away from us and three times as large as originally estimated— larger, therefore, than our own galaxy, the Milky Way. Spectroscopic observations with the 200-inch telescope indicate also that the most distant measurable galaxies are receding at a speed of about 75,000 miles per second. It is possible that current research may alter these results still further. It is also possible that research in the embryonic field of radio astronomy may aid in the solution of these and other problems.

One of the ablest investigators in this new field in which rapid advances are already being made is the English astronomer, A. C. B. Lovell, professor of radio astronomy at the University of Manchester and director of the observatory at Jodrell Bank. In our next article, "Radio Stars," he describes some of the developments and looks forward to future advances which may revolutionize our knowledge of the universe. With the huge radio telescopes which have been set up, astronomers look forward to penetrating the depths of the universe far beyond the range of the Hale telescope. In this way they hope to find the answers to such age-old questions as: "What is the size and shape of the universe? How did it originate? How does it evolve? What is its destiny?"

As Eddington has shown in "The Milky Way and Beyond" we see the most distant galaxies as they were a billion years ago when their light left them on its long, long journey to us, and we see the nearest galaxies as they were only a few million years ago—provided, of course, that nothing has happened to alter the nature of that light on its journey. With the Hale telescope we have been able to reach out more than two billion light years on the new distance scale. With new and greater radio telescopes, we should be able to penetrate even farther. Will observations continue to show, as it now appears, that the population of radio stars increases with distance from the earth? Will they confirm recent tentative observations made with the Hale telescope which indicate that the rate of expansion of the universe is slowing down? Shall we be able to identify additional nonluminous matter in intergalactic space now invisible with optical telescopes? How will answers to these and other questions help us in our understanding of the origin of the universe? How will they help us to choose between the two presently outstanding theories of that origin—between the one which holds that the universe was created in a single cataclysmic birth from a small but highly concentrated mass of matter (from which the whole has evolved), and the other advocated by a group of English scientists which holds that the universe is the result of a process of continuous creation without beginning or any evident end?

If the rate of expansion is actually slowing down and the density of matter increases with increasing distance, both these facts would suggest an evolutionary universe and would argue against theories of continuous creation which postulate a more or less uniform distribution of matter in space. We return then to the question of the exact kind of evolutionary universe with which we are dealing—and to the questions already propounded by Eddington in "The Milky Way and Beyond."

Radio Stars

A. C. B. LOVELL

W HEN A COUNTRY THAT IS STRUGGLING WITH A
financial crisis and shortages of raw materials decides to spend a
million dollars and 2,000 tons of steel on a single instrument for fundamental research, big dividends must be expected. Great Britain is now
making such an investment in a new kind of gigantic telescope.[1] It will be
concerned with what may seem a visionary enterprise—the exploration of
the universe—but Britain anticipates a rich harvest of discovery from the
investment.

The story behind the decision to build this instrument is a thrilling
chapter in the history of research. It is the story of radio astronomy. Until
20 years ago our only window into space was the visual region of the
electromagnetic spectrum. We knew that our vision was somewhat obscured by dust and vapors clouding the starlight, but it seemed unlikely
that outer space had many secrets which our great optical telescopes would
not eventually reveal. Then quite by accident a new window was discovered in another part of the electromagnetic spectrum. While studying
atmospheric radio disturbances Karl G. Jansky, an electrical engineer at
the Bell Telephone Laboratories, picked up radio signals which he
decided must be coming from outer space. His now famous discovery was
confirmed by the radio engineer Grote Reber, who built in his garden a
30-foot parabolic aerial with which he plotted the first radio map of the
sky.

Reber's survey showed that the signals were strongest from the direction
of the Milky Way, and that in general the regions of space with the
thickest clusters of visible stars emitted the strongest radio waves. But
Reber was not able to connect the radio signals with any specific object.
He pointed his aerial in the direction of bright stars, extragalactic nebulae

[1] [It went into operation in the summer of 1957. Eds.]

and other strong emitters of light, but none of them seemed to be the cause of the radio signals! Reber concluded that the radio waves probably were generated by atomic processes in the hydrogen gas in interstellar space. It was an interesting theory, but apparently not destined to lead to any startling revelations about the universe.

Astronomers at first took little account of the radio experiments. In 1948, however, there came a new development which decidedly quickened their interest. Reber's difficulty had been that his radio telescope had very poor resolution: it could not separate small objects in the sky because it received radiation in a beam several degrees wide. To focus on a small object a telescope must look into space in a narrow beam, and this requires that the reflector or other radiation receiver be very much larger than the wavelength of the radiation. The wavelength of the light waves collected by an optical telescope is only a few hundred thousandths of an inch. But the radio signals received by Reber's telescope had a wavelength of about six feet, and his 30-foot antenna could receive only a broad beam. In 1948 two experimenters on opposite sides of the world found a way to get better resolution of the sources of the radio signals. They were J. G. Bolton in Sydney, Australia, and Martin Ryle in Cambridge, England. They used a combination of two antennas, placed several hundred yards apart and connected to a single radio receiver. Radio waves coming in obliquely from space reached one aerial slightly before the other and therefore produced an interference effect, either reinforcing or opposing each other. As the earth rotates, this radio "interferometer" sweeps the sky with a fan of fine lobes, thus making it possible to get some idea of the size of the radio-broadcasting region in space; a source smaller than the space between the lobes would produce sharp maxima and minima in the strength of the received signal. To the great astonishment of astronomers, Bolton and Ryle found that at least some of the radio waves were coming from sources small enough to be called "radio stars." Bolton found one in the constellation of Cygnus, and Ryle discovered an even stronger one in Cassiopeia. Subsequently many more radio stars were located.

The strangest feature of these discoveries was that none of the radio stars seemed to coincide with a bright star or any other visible object. The belief soon arose that the radio stars represented a hitherto unknown type of stellar object—dark or only faintly luminous, but with the facility of emitting intense radio waves. There seem to be a great number of these radio stars: more than 200 are now known, and it is very likely that vastly greater numbers will be found as radio telescopes are improved. In fact, there are grounds for believing that radio stars may be as numerous as the common visible stars.

In 1950 a large radio telescope was built at the Jodrell Bank station of the University of Manchester in England. It is similar in shape to the one originally used by Reber, but 220 feet in diameter, so that it can receive radio signals in a beam only two degrees wide. Its antenna is fixed, however, and it can survey only a small part of the sky. With this telescope R. Hanbury Brown succeeded in recording radio waves emanating from the great spiral nebula in Andromeda and from more distant galaxies. Thus it became evident that radio stars must be common not only in the Milky Way but also throughout the universe.

Determined efforts have been made to unravel this strange mystery of a universe filled with radio-emitting bodies which have no obvious connection with the common stars, and in the last few months a little progress has been made. Among the radio stars detected by Bolton is one in the constellation of Taurus which coincides with an outstanding celestial object known as the Crab nebula. This nebula is believed to be the hot, expanding, gaseous shell of a supernova which exploded in 1054. The position and size of the radio star, the third most intense in the sky, coincide well with the position and size of that gaseous shell. Last summer Brown discovered a radio star in the position of another supernova—the one observed by Tycho Brahe in 1572, the remnants of which are no longer visible in telescopes. Hence it now seems well established that the remains of a great stellar explosion are capable of generating intense radio waves. One more check is needed to place the matter beyond doubt: detection of radio waves from the remains of the third known supernova, observed by Johannes Kepler in 1604. Unfortunately Kepler's object is outside the field of view of the fixed radio telescope at Jodrell Bank, and no other instrument of sufficient size is available to study it.

These three supernovae would account for three radio stars, but what about all the others? To study the situation more closely the astronomers on Palomar Mountain trained their 200-inch telescope on the region of sky containing the two most intense radio stars in Cassiopeia and Cygnus. This search, which began early in 1952, has been very fruitful. Near the Cassiopeia radio star the telescope has revealed a region of diffuse gaseous nebulosity with some strange and still unexplained properties. The result of the investigation of the Cygnus region is even more startling. The Palomar observers Walter Baade and R. Minkowski believe that the Cygnus radio star is caused by the collision of two galaxies!

The general findings so far are indeed remarkable. Of the three strongest radio stars in the sky, one seems to be the remains of a star which suffered a violent death, another appears to represent whole galaxies in collision, and the strongest of all seems to be a very faint region of gas in violent motion.

As the sky has been plotted in greater and greater detail with radio telescopes of improved resolving power, it has become clear that the regions with the greatest concentrations of stars generate the most intense radio waves. Even in our present state of uncertainty regarding the source of the radio waves, this relationship is of the utmost importance to astronomy. Our view of the star-rich central regions of the Milky Way is badly obscured by clouds of minute dust particles in interstellar space. In fact, it has been estimated that this dust must hide over 90 per cent of the stars in the Milky Way from visual detection by even our most powerful telescopes. Naturally this is a severe impediment to the study of the structure of our galaxy. Radio waves, however, can penetrate the dust without absorption and bring to the radio telescopes details of the hidden regions. The radio plotting of the sky is, therefore, a most important task. The work needs high resolution, and we have seen that this requires very large radio telescopes. That is the reason for undertaking the new telescope at Jodrell Bank.

Its design is based on the radio telescope which has been in use there for several years, but it will be much bigger, and instead of being fixed in one position it will be movable, so that it can be trained on any part of the sky. Some 500 tons of steel and concrete are now being sunk into the ground as the foundation for the instrument. The foundation will support a superstructure of 1,500 tons, mounted on a circular railway and driven by motors which will enable it to track automatically any object in the heavens. Its great antenna will be a steel bowl 250 feet in diameter and 60 feet deep at the center; the 300-ton aerial will pivot on an axis 180 feet above ground level.

The primary assignment of this great telescope will be to survey the heavens, but it will also be equipped for all other types of work in radio astronomy, including radar tracking of meteors.

The telescope will operate over a wide range of radio wavelengths. Until recently most of the work in radio astronomy was done in the range of wavelengths between one and 20 meters. But there has been increasing interest in the use of shorter wavelengths, and in 1951 this field was given a tremendous stimulus by one of those spectacular discoveries that have been so characteristic of work in radio astronomy. It had been suggested that the hydrogen atoms in interstellar space might, as the result of a certain change in energy state, emit radio energy at a wavelength of 21 centimeters. In 1951 radiation of this wavelength was actually detected, first by Harold I. Ewen and E. M. Purcell at Harvard University and then by others. Thus for the first time astronomers had a specific spectral line to work with in the radio spectrum. The lines in the visible spectra of the stars have been, as everyone knows, of enormous value to astronomy; for one thing, they have been the basis of the studies of the red shift in the light from distant stars and led to the theory of the expanding universe. In the same way studies of slight Doppler-effect shifts in the 21-centimeter radio line will make it possible to determine the relative motion of the earth and the clouds of hydrogen gas in space.

Astronomy has marched forward with the growth in size of its telescopes. The need is always for more light-gathering power and more resolving power. In radio astronomy history will doubtless repeat itself; the building of radio telescopes with more sensitivity and more resolving power should yield striking advances in our knowledge of the universe. High hopes are entertained for the great engineering enterprise now under construction at Jodrell Bank. In combination with visual [and photographic] observations through the giant optical telescopes on the California mountains, it may well open a new era for astronomy.

1953

B. THE EARTH

A Young Man Looking at Rocks

HUGH MILLER

From *The Old Red Sandstone*

MY ADVICE TO YOUNG WORKING MEN DESIROUS OF bettering their circumstances, and adding to the amount of their enjoyment, is a very simple one. Do not seek happiness in what is misnamed pleasure; seek it rather in what is termed study. Keep your consciences clear, your curiosity fresh, and embrace every opportunity of cultivating your minds. You will gain nothing by attending Chartist meetings. The fellows who speak nonsense with fluency at these assemblies, and deem their nonsense eloquence, are totally unable to help either you or themselves: or, if they do succeed in helping themselves, it will be all at your expense. Leave them to harangue unheeded, and set yourselves to occupy your leisure hours in making yourselves wiser men. Learn to make a right use of your eyes; the commonest things are worth looking at—even stones and weeds, and the most familiar animals.

It was twenty years last February since I set out, a little before sunrise to make my first acquaintance with a life of labour and restraint: and I have rarely had a heavier heart than on that morning. I was but a slim, loose-jointed boy at the time, fond of the pretty intangibilities of romance, and of dreaming when broad awake; and, woeful change! I was now going to work at what Burns has instanced, in his "Twa Dogs" as one of the most disagreeable of all employments,—to work in a quarry. Bating the passing uneasiness occasioned by a few gloomy anticipations, the portion of my life which had already gone by had been happy beyond the common lot. I had been a wanderer among rocks and woods, a reader of curious books when I could get them, a gleaner of old traditionary stories: and now I was going to exchange all my day-dreams. and all my amusements, for the kind of life in which men toil every day that they may be enabled to eat, and eat every day that they may be enabled to toil!

The quarry in which I wrought lay on the southern shore of a noble inland bay, or frith rather, with a little clear stream on the one side, and a thick fir wood on the other. It had been opened in the Old Red Sandstone of the district, and was overtopped by a huge bank of diluvial clay, which rose over it in some places to the height of nearly thirty feet, and which at this time was rent and shivered, wherever it presented an open front to the weather, by a recent frost. A heap of loose fragments, which had fallen from above, blocked up the face of the quarry, and my first employment was to clear them away. The friction of the shovel soon blistered my hands, but the pain was by no means very severe, and I wrought hard and willingly, that I might see how the huge strata below, which presented so firm and unbroken a frontage, were to be torn up and removed. Picks, and wedges, and levers, were applied by my brother-workers; and, simple and rude as I had been accustomed to regard these implements, I found I had much to learn in the way of using them. They all proved inefficient, however, and the workmen had to bore into one of the inferior strata, and employ gunpowder. The process was new to me, and I deemed it a highly amusing one; it had the merit, too, of being attended with some such degree of danger as a boating or rock excursion, and had thus an interest independent of its novelty. We had a few capital shots: the fragments flew in every direction; and an immense mass of the diluvium came toppling down, bearing with it two dead birds, that in a recent storm had crept into one of the deeper fissures, to die in the shelter. I felt a new interest in examining them. The one was a pretty cock goldfinch, with its hood of vermilion, and its wings inlaid with the gold to which it owes its name, as unsoiled and smooth as if it had been preserved for a museum. The other, a somewhat rarer bird, of the woodpecker tribe, was variegated with light blue and a grayish yellow. I was engaged in admiring the poor little things, more disposed to be sentimental, perhaps, than if I had been ten years older, and thinking of the contrast between the warmth and jollity of their green summer haunts, and the cold and darkness of their last retreat, when I heard our employer bidding the workmen lay by their tools. I looked up, and saw the sun sinking behind the thick fir wood beside us, and the long dark shadows of the trees stretching downwards towards the shore.

This was no very formidable beginning of the course of life I had so much dreaded. To be sure, my hands were a little sore, and I felt nearly as much fatigued as if I had been climbing among the rocks; but I had wrought and been useful, and had yet enjoyed the day fully as much as usual. It was no small matter, too, that the evening, converted, by a rare transmutation, into the delicious "blink of rest" which Burns so truthfully describes, was all my own. I was as light of heart next morning as any of my brother-workmen. There had been a smart frost during the night, and the rime lay white on the grass as we passed onwards through the fields; but the sun rose in a clear atmosphere, and the day mellowed, as it advanced, into one of those delightful days of early spring which give so pleasing an earnest of whatever is mild and genial in the better half of the year.

The gunpowder had loosened a large mass in one of the interior strata, and our first employment, on resuming our labours, was to raise it from its bed. I assisted the other workmen in placing it on edge, and was much struck by the appearance of the platform on which it had rested. The entire surface was ridged and furrowed like a bank of sand that had been left by the tide an hour before. I could trace every bend and curvature, every cross hollow and counter ridge, of the corresponding phenomena; for the resemblance was no half resemblance,—it was the thing itself; and I had observed it a hundred and a hundred times, when sailing my little schooner in the shallows left by the ebb. But what had become of the waves that had thus fretted the solid rock, or of what element had they been composed? I felt as completely at fault as Robinson Crusoe did on his discovering the print of the man's foot on the sand. The evening furnished me with still further cause of wonder. We raised another block in a different part of the quarry, and found that the area of a circular depression in the stratum below was broken and flawed in every direction, as if it had been the bottom of a pool recently dried up, which had shrunk and split in the hardening. Several large stones came rolling down from the diluvium in the course of the afternoon. They were of different qualities from the sandstone below, and from one another; and, what was more wonderful still, they were all rounded and water-worn, as if they had been tossed about in the sea or the bed of a river for hundreds of years. There could not, surely, be a more conclusive proof that the bank which had enclosed them so long could not have been created on the rock on which it rested. No workman ever manufactures a half-worn article, and the stones were all half-worn! And if not the bank, why then the sandstone underneath? I was lost in conjecture, and found I had food enough for thought that evening, without once thinking of the unhappiness of a life of labour.

The immense masses of diluvium which we had to clear away rendered the working of the quarry laborious and expensive, and all the party quitted it in a few days, to make trial of another that seemed to promise better. The one we left is situated, as I have said, on the southern shore of an inland bay,—the Bay of Cromarty; the one to which we removed has been opened in a lofty wall of cliffs that overhangs the northern shore of the Moray Frith. I soon found I was to be no loser by the change. Not the united labours of a thousand men for more than a thousand years could have furnished a better section of the geology of the district than this range of cliffs. It may be regarded as a sort of chance dissection on the earth's crust. We see in one place the primary rock, with its veins of granite and quartz, its dizzy precipices of gneiss, and its huge masses of horneblend; we find the secondary rock in another, with its beds of sandstone and shale, its spars, its clays, and its nodular limestones. We discover the still little-known but highly interesting fossils of the Old Red Sandstone in one deposition; we find the beautifully preserved shells and lignites of the Lias in another. There are the remains of two several creations at once before us. The shore, too, is heaped with rolled fragments of almost every variety of rock,—basalts, ironstones, hyperstenes, porphyries, bituminous shales, and micaceous schists. In short, the young geologist, had he all Europe before him could hardly choose for himself a better field. I had, however, no one to tell me so at the time, for Geology had not yet travelled so far north; and so, without guide or vocabulary, I had to grope my way as I best might, and find out all its wonders for myself. But so slow was the process, and so much was I a seeker in the dark, that the facts contained in these few sentences were the patient gatherings of years.

In the course of the first day's employment I picked up a nodular mass of blue limestone, and laid it open by a stroke of the hammer. Wonderful to relate, it contained inside a beautifully finished piece of sculpture,—one of the volutes, apparently, of an Ionic capital; and not the far-famed walnut of the fairy tale, had I broken the shell and found the little dog lying within, could have surprised me more. Was there another such curiosity in the whole world? I broke open a few other nodules of similar appearance,—for they lay pretty thickly on the shore,—and found that there might be. In one of these there were what seemed to be the scales of fishes, and the impressions of a few minute bivalves, prettily striated; in the centre of another there was actually a piece of decayed wood. Of all Nature's riddles, these seemed to me to be at once the most interesting and the most difficult to expound. I treasured them carefully up, and was told by one of the workmen to whom I showed them, that there was a part of the shore about two miles farther to the west where curiously-shaped stones, somewhat like the heads of boarding-pikes, were occasionally picked up; and that in his father's days the country people called them thunderbolts, and deemed them of sovereign efficacy in curing bewitched cattle. Our employer, on quitting the quarry for the building on which we were to be engaged, gave all the workmen a half-holiday. I employed it in visiting the place where the thunderbolts had fallen so thickly, and found it a richer scene of wonder than I could have fancied in even my dreams.

What first attracted my notice was a detached group of low-lying skerries, wholly different in form and colour from the sandstone cliffs above or the primary rocks a little farther to the west. I found them composed of thin strata of limestone, alternating with thicker beds of a black slaty substance, which, as I ascertained in the course of the evening, burns with a powerful flame, and emits a strong bituminous odour. The layers into which the beds readily separate are hardly an eighth part of an inch in thickness, and yet on every layer there are the impressions of thousands and tens of thousands of the various fossils peculiar to the Lias. We may turn over these wonderful leaves one after one, like the leaves of a herbarium, and find the pictorial records of a former creation in every page: scallops, and gryphites, and ammonites, of almost every variety peculiar to the formation, and at least some eight of ten varieties of belemnite; twigs of wood, leaves of plants, cones of an extinct species of pine, bits of charcoal, and the scales of fishes; and, as if to render their pictorial appearance more striking, though the leaves of this interesting volume are of a deep black, most of the impressions are of a chalky whiteness. I was lost in admiration and astonishment, and found my very imagination paralysed by an assemblage of wonders that seemed to outrival in the fantastic and the extravagant even its wildest conceptions. I passed on from ledge to ledge, like the traveller of the tale through the city of statues, and at length found one of the supposed aerolites I had come in quest of firmly imbedded in a mass of shale. But I had skill enough to determine that it was other than what it had been deemed. A very near relative, who had been a sailor in his time on almost every ocean, and had visited almost every quarter of the globe, had brought home one of these meteoric stones with him from the coast of Java. It was of a cylindrical shape and vitreous texture, and it seemed to have parted in the middle when in a half-molten state, and to have united again, somewhat awry, ere it had cooled enough to have lost the adhesive quality. But there was nothing organic in its structure; whereas the stone I had now found was organized very curiously indeed. It was of a conical form and filamentary texture, the filaments radiating in straight lines from the centre to the circumference. Finely-marked veins like white threads ran transversely through these in its upper half to the point; while the space below was occupied by an internal cone, formed of plates that lay parallel to the base, and which, like watch-glasses, were concave on the under side and convex on the upper. I learned in time to call this stone a belemnite, and became acquainted with enough of its history to know that it once formed part of a variety of cuttle-fish, long since extinct.

My first year of labour came to a close, and I found that the amount of my happiness had not been less than in the last of my boyhood. My knowledge, too, had increased in more than the skill of at least the common mechanic, I had fitted myself for independence. The additional experience of twenty years has not shown me that there is any necessary connection between a life of toil and a life of wretchedness; and when I have found good men anticipating a better and a happier time than either the present or the past, the conviction that in every period of the world's history the great bulk of mankind must pass their days in labour, has not in the least inclined me to scepticism. . . .

One important truth I would fain press on the attention of my lowlier readers: there are few professions, however humble, that do not present their peculiar advantages of observation; there are none, I repeat, in which the exercise of the faculties does not lead to enjoyment. I advise the stone-mason, for instance, to acquaint himself with Geology. Much of his time must be spent amid the rocks and quarries of widely-separated localities. The bridge or harbour is no sooner completed in one district than he has to remove to where the gentleman's seat or farm-steading is to be erected in another; and so, in the course of a few years, he may pass over the whole geological scale, even when restricted to Scotland, from the Grauwacke of the Lammermuirs, to the Wealden of Moray or the Chalk-flints of Banffshire and Aberdeen; and this, too, with opportunities of observation at every stage which can be shared with him by only the gentleman of fortune who devotes his whole time to the study. Nay, in some respects his advantages are superior to those of the amateur himself. The latter must often pronounce a formation unfossiliferous when, after the examination of at most a few days, he discovers ir it nothing organic; and it will be found that half the mistakes of geologists have arisen from conclusions thus hastily formed. But the working man, whose employments have to be carried on in the same formation for months, perhaps years, together, enjoys better opportunities for arriving at just decisions. There are, besides, a thousand varieties of accident which lead to discovery,—floods, storms, landslips, tides of unusual height, ebbs of extraordinary fall; and the man who plies his labour at all seasons in the open air has by much the best chance of profiting by these. There are formations which yield their organisms slowly to the discoverer, and the proofs which establish their place in the geological scale more tardily still. I was acquainted with the Old Red Sandstone of Ross and Cromarty

for nearly ten years ere I had ascertained that it is richly fossiliferous,—
a discovery which, in exploring this formation in those localities, some of
our first geologists had failed to anticipate: I was acquainted with it for
nearly ten years more ere I could assign to its fossils their exact place in
the scale.

... Should the working man be encouraged by my modicum of success
to improve his opportunities of observation, I shall have accomplished the
whole of it. It cannot be too extensively known, that nature is vast and
knowledge limited, and that no individual, however humble in place
or acquirement, need despair of adding to the general fund.

1841

Geological Change

SIR ARCHIBALD GEIKE

IT WAS A FUNDAMENTAL DOCTRINE OF HUTTON
[James Hutton, 1726-1797] and his school that this globe has not
always worn the aspect which it bears at present; that on the contrary,
proofs may everywhere be culled that the land which we now see has
been formed out of the wreck of an older land. Among these proofs, the
most obvious are supplied by some of the more familiar kinds of rocks,
which teach us that, though they are now portions of the dry land, they
were originally sheets of gravel, sand, and mud, which had been worn
from the face of long-vanished continents, and after being spread out
over the floor of the sea were consolidated into compact stone, and
were finally broken up and raised once more to form part of the dry
land. This cycle of change involved two great systems of natural processes. On the one hand, men were taught that by the action of running
water the materials of the solid land are in a state of continual decay and
transport to the ocean. On the other hand, the ocean floor is liable from
time to time to be upheaved by some stupendous internal force akin

to that which gives rise to the volcano and the earthquake. Hutton further perceived that not only had the consolidated materials been disrupted and elevated, but that masses of molten rock had been thrust upward among them, and had cooled and crystallized in large bodies of granite and other eruptive rocks which form so prominent a feature on the earth's surface.

It was a special characteristic of this philosophical system that it sought in the changes now in progress on the earth's surface an explanation of those which occurred in older times. Its founder refused to invent causes or modes of operation, for those with which he was familiar seemed to him adequate to solve the problems with which he attempted to deal. Nowhere was the profoundness of his insight more astonishing than in the clear, definite way in which he proclaimed and reiterated his doctrine, that every part of the surface of the continents, from mountain top to seashore, is continually undergoing decay, and is thus slowly travelling to the sea. He saw that no sooner will the sea floor be elevated into new land than it must necessarily become a prey to this universal and unceasing degradation. He perceived that as the transport of disintegrated material is carried on chiefly by running water, rivers must slowly dig out for themselves the channels in which they flow, and thus that a system of valleys, radiating from the water parting of a country, must necessarily result from the descent of the streams from the mountain crests to the sea. He discerned that this ceaseless and wide-spread decay would eventually lead to the entire demolition of the dry land, but he contended that from time to time this catastrophe is prevented by the operation of the under-ground forces, whereby new continents are upheaved from the bed of the ocean. And thus in his system a due proportion is maintained between land and water, and the condition of the earth as a habitable globe is preserved.

A theory of the earth so simple in outline, so bold in conception, so full of suggestion, and resting on so broad a base of observation and reflection, ought (we think) to have commanded at once the attention of men of science, even if it did not immediately awaken the interest of the outside world; but, as Playfair sorrowfully admitted, it attracted notice only very slowly, and several years elapsed before any one showed himself publicly concerned about it, either as an enemy or a friend. Some of its earliest critics assailed it for what they asserted to be its irreligious tendency,—an accusation which Hutton repudiated with much warmth. The sneer levelled by Cowper a few years earlier at all inquiries into the history of the universe was perfectly natural and intelligible from that poet's point of view. There was then a wide-spread belief that this world came into existence some six thousand years ago, and that any attempt greatly to increase that antiquity was meant as a blow to the authority of Holy Writ. So far, however, from aiming at the overthrow of orthodox beliefs, Hutton evidently regarded his "Theory" as an important contribution in aid of natural religion. He dwelt with unfeigned pleasure on the multitude of proofs which he was able to accumulate of an orderly design in the operations of Nature, decay and renovation being so nicely balanced as to maintain the habitable condition of the planet. But as he refused to admit the predominance of violent action in terrestrial changes, and on the contrary contended for the efficacy of the quiet, continuous processes which we can even now see at work around us, he was constrained to require an unlimited duration of past time for the production of those revolutions of which he perceived such clear and abundant proofs in the crust of the earth. The general public, however, failed to comprehend that the doctrine of the high antiquity of the globe was not inconsistent with the comparatively recent appearance of man,—a distinction which seems so obvious now.

Hutton died in 1797, beloved and regretted by the circle of friends who had learned to appreciate his estimable character and to admire his genius, but with little recognition from the world at large. Men knew not then that a great master had passed away from their midst, who had laid broad and deep the foundations of a new science; that his name would become a household word in after generations, and that pilgrims would come from distant lands to visit the scenes from which he drew his inspiration. . . .

Clear as was the insight and sagacious the inferences of the great masters [of the Edinburgh school] in regard to the history of the globe, their vision was necessarily limited by the comparatively narrow range of ascertained fact which up to their time had been established. They taught men to recognize that the present world is built of the ruins of an earlier one, and they explained with admirable perspicacity the operation of the processes whereby the degradation and renovation of land are brought about. But they never dreamed that a long and orderly series of such successive destructions and renewals had taken place and had left their records in the crust of the earth. They never imagined that from these records it would be possible to establish a determinate chronology that could be read everywhere and applied to the elucidation of the remotest quarter of the globe. It was by the memorable observations and generalizations of William Smith that this vast extension of our knowledge of the past history of the earth became possible. While the Scottish philosophers were building up their theory here, Smith was quietly ascertaining by extended journeys that the stratified rocks of the west of England occur in a definite sequence, and that each well-marked group of them can be discriminated from the others and identified across the country by means of its inclosed organic remains. It is nearly a hundred years since he made known his views, so that by a curious coincidence we may fitly celebrate on this occasion the centenary of William Smith as well as that of James Hutton. No single discovery has ever had a more momentous and far-reaching influence on the progress of a science than that law of organic succession which Smith established. At first it served merely to determine the order of the stratified rocks of England. But it soon proved to possess a world-wide value, for it was found to furnish the key to the structure of the whole stratified crust of the earth. It showed that within that crust lie the chronicles of a long history of plant and animal life upon this planet, it supplied the means of arranging the materials for this history in true chronological sequence, and it thus opened out a magnificent vista through a vast series of ages, each marked by its own distinctive types of organic life, which, in proportion to their antiquity, departed more and more from the aspect of the living world.

Thus a hundred years ago, by the brilliant theory of Hutton and the fruitful generalization of Smith, the study of the earth received in our country the impetus which has given birth to the modern science of geology. . . .

From the earliest times the natural features of the earth's surface have arrested the attention of mankind. The rugged mountain, the cleft ravine, the scarped cliff, the solitary bowlder, have stimulated curiosity and prompted many a speculation as to their origin. The shells embedded by millions in the solid rocks of hills far removed from the seas have still further pressed home these "obstinate questionings." But for many long centuries the advance of inquiry into such matters was arrested by the paramount influence of orthodox theology. It was not merely that the church opposed itself to the simple and obvious interpretation of these natural phenomena. So implicit had faith become in the accepted views of the earth's age and of the history of creation, that even laymen of intelligence and learning set themselves unbidden and in perfect good faith to explain away the difficulties which nature so persistently raised up, and to reconcile her teachings with those of the theologians. . . .

It is the special glory of the Edinburgh school of geology to have cast aside all this fanciful trifling. Hutton boldly proclaimed that it was no part of his philosophy to account for the beginning of things. His concern lay only with the evidence furnished by the earth itself as to its origin. With the intuition of true genius he early perceived that the only basis from which to explore what has taken place in bygone time is a knowledge of what is taking place to-day. He thus founded his system upon a careful study of the process whereby geological changes are now brought about. . . .

Fresh life was now breathed into the study of the earth. A new spirit seemed to animate the advance along every pathway of inquiry. Facts that had long been familiar came to possess a wider and deeper meaning when their connection with each other was recognized as parts of one great harmonious system of continuous change. In no department of Nature, for example, was this broader vision more remarkably displayed than in that wherein the circulation of water between land and sea plays the most conspicuous part. From the earliest times men had watched the coming of clouds, the fall of rain, the flow of rivers, and had recognized that on this nicely adjusted machinery the beauty and fertility of the land depend. But they now learned that this beauty and fertility involve a continual decay of the terrestrial surface; that the soil is a measure of this decay, and would cease to afford us maintenance were it not continually removed and renewed, that through the ceaseless transport of soil by rivers to the sea the face of the land is slowly lowered in level and carved into mountain and valley, and that the materials thus borne outwards to the floor of the ocean are not lost, but accumulate there to form rocks, which in the end will be upraised into new lands. Decay and renovation, in well-balanced proportions, were thus shown to be the system on which the existence of the earth as a habitable globe had been established. It was impossible to conceive that the economy of the planet could be maintained on any other basis. Without the circulation of water the life of plants and animals would be impossible, and with the circulation the decay of the surface of the land and the renovation of its disintegrated materials are necessarily involved.

As it is now, so must it have been in past time. Hutton and Playfair pointed to the stratified rocks of the earth's crust as demonstrations that the same processes which are at work to-day have been in operation from a remote antiquity. . . .

Obviously, however, human experience, in the few centuries during which attention has been turned to such subjects, has been too brief to warrant any dogmatic assumption that the various natural processes must have been carried on in the past with the same energy and at the same rate as they are carried on now. . . . It was an error to take for granted that no other kind of process or influence, nor any variation in the rate of activity save those of which man has had actual cognizance, has played a part in the terrestrial economy. The uniformitarian writers laid themselves open to the charge of maintaining a kind of perpetual motion in the machinery of Nature. They could find in the records of the earth's history no evidence of a beginning, no prospect of an end. . . .

The discoveries of William Smith, had they been adequately understood, would have been seen to offer a corrective to this rigidly uniformitarian conception, for they revealed that the crust of the earth contains the long record of an unmistakable order of progression in organic types. They proved that plants and animals have varied widely in successive periods of the earth's history; the present condition of organic life being only the latest phase of a long preceding series, each stage of which recedes further from the existing aspect of things as we trace it backward into the past. And though no relic had yet been found, or indeed was ever likely to be found, of the first living things that appeared upon the earth's surface, the manifest simplification of types in the older formations pointed irresistibly to some beginning from which the long procession has taken its start. If then it could thus be demonstrated that there had been upon the globe an orderly march of living forms from the lowliest grades in early times to man himself to-day, and thus that in one department of her domain, extending through the greater portion of the records of the earth's history, Nature had not been uniform, but had followed a vast and noble plan of evolution, surely it might have been expected that those who discovered and made known this plan would seek to ascertain whether some analogous physical progression from a definite beginning might not be discernible in the framework of the globe itself.

But the early masters of the science labored under two great disadvantages. In the first place, they found the oldest records of the earth's history so broken up and effaced as to be no longer legible. And in the second place, . . . they considered themselves bound to search for facts, not to build up theories; and as in the crust of the earth they could find no facts which threw any light upon the primeval constitution and subsequent development of our planet, they shut their ears to any theoretical interpretations that might be offered from other departments of science. . . .

What the more extreme members of the uniformitarian school failed to perceive was the absence of all evidence that terrestrial catastrophes even on a colossal scale might not be a part of the present economy of this globe. Such occurrences might never seriously affect the whole earth at one time, and might return at such wide intervals that no example of them has yet been chronicled by man. But that they have occurred again and again, and even within comparatively recent geological times, hardly admits of serious doubt. . . .

As the most recent and best known of these great transformations, the Ice Age stands out conspicuously before us. . . . There can not be any doubt that after man had become a denizen of the earth, a great physical change came over the Northern hemisphere. The climate, which had previously been so mild that evergreen trees flourished within ten or twelve degrees of the North Pole, now became so severe that vast sheets of snow and ice covered the north of Europe and crept southward beyond the south coast of Ireland, almost as far as the southern shores of England, and across the Baltic into France and Germany. This Arctic transformation was not an episode that lasted merely a few seasons, and left the land to resume thereafter its ancient aspect. With various successive fluctuations it must have endured for many thousands of years. When it began to disappear it probably faded away as slowly and imperceptibly as it had advanced, and when it finally vanished it left Europe and North America profoundly changed in the character alike of their scenery and of their inhabitants. The rugged rocky contours of earlier times were ground smooth and polished by the march of the ice across them, while the lower grounds were buried under wide and thick sheets of clay, gravel, and sand, left behind by the melting ice. The varied and abundant flora which had spread so far within the Arctic circle was driven away into more southern and less ungenial climes. But most memorable of all was the extirpation of the prominent large animals which, before the advent of the ice, had roamed over Europe. The lions, hyenas, wild horses, hippopotamuses, and other creatures either became entirely extinct or were driven into the Mediterranean basin and into Africa. In their place came northern forms—the reindeer, glutton, musk ox, wooly rhinoceros, and mammoth.

Such a marvellous transformation in climate, in scenery, in vegetation and in inhabitants, within what was after all but a brief portion of geological time, though it may have involved no sudden or violent convulsion, is surely entitled to rank as a catastrophe in the history of the globe. It was probably brought about mainly if not entirely by the operation of forces external to the earth. No similar calamity having befallen the continents within the time during which man has been recording his experience, the Ice Age might be cited as a contradiction to the doctrine of uniformity. And yet it manifestly arrived as part of the established order of Nature. Whether or not we grant that other ice ages preceded the last great one, we must admit that the conditions under which it arose, so far as we know them, might conceivably have occurred before and may occur again. The various agencies called into play by the extensive refrigeration of the Northern hemisphere were not different from those with which we are familiar. Snow fell and glaciers crept as they do to-day. Ice scored and polished rocks exactly as it still does among the Alps and in Norway. There was nothing abnormal in the phenomena, save the scale on which they were manifested. And thus, taking a broad view of the whole subject, we recognize the catastrophe, while at the same time we see in its progress the operation of those same natural processes which we know to be integral parts of the machinery whereby the surface of the earth is continually transformed.

Among the debts which science owes to the Huttonian school, not the least memorable is the promulgation of the first well-founded conceptions of the high antiquity of the globe. Some six thousand years had previously been believed to comprise the whole life of the planet, and indeed of the entire universe. When the curtain was then first raised that had veiled the history of the earth, and men, looking beyond the brief span within which they had supposed that history to have been transacted, beheld the records of a long vista of ages stretching far away into a dim illimitable past, the prospect vividly impressed their imagination. Astronomy had made known the immeasurable fields of space; the new science of geology seemed now to reveal boundless distances of time. . . .

The universal degradation of the land, so notable a characteristic of the earth's surface, has been regarded as an extremely slow process. Though it goes on without ceasing, yet from century to century it seems to leave hardly any perceptible trace on the landscapes of a country. Mountains and plains, hills and valleys appear to wear the same familiar aspect which is indicated in the oldest pages of history. This obvious slowness in one of the most important departments of geological activity doubtless contributed in large measure to form and foster a vague belief in the vastness of the antiquity required for the evolution of the earth.

But, as geologists eventually came to perceive, the rate of degradation of the land is capable of actual measurement. The amount of material worn away from the surface of any drainage basin and carried in the form of mud, sand, or gravel, by the main river into the sea represents the extent to which that surface has been lowered by waste in any given period of time. But denudation and deposition must be equivalent to each other. As much material must be laid down in sedimentary accumulations as has been mechanically removed, so that in measuring the annual bulk of sediment borne into the sea by a river, we obtain a clue not only to the rate of denudation of the land, but also to the rate at which the deposition of new sedimentary formations takes place. . . .

But in actual fact the testimony in favor of the slow accumulation and high antiquity of the geological record is much stronger than might be inferred from the mere thickness of the stratified formations. These sedimentary deposits have not been laid down in one unbroken sequence, but have had their continuity interrupted again and again by upheaval and depression. So fragmentary are they in some regions that we can easily demonstrate the length of time represented there by still existing sedimentary strata to be vastly less than the time indicated by the gaps in the series.

There is yet a further and impressive body of evidence furnished by the successive races of plants and animals which have lived upon the earth and have left their remains sealed up within its rocky crust. No universal destructions of organic life are chronicled in the stratified rocks. It is everywhere admitted that, from the remotest times up to the present day, there has been an onward march of development, type succeeding type in one long continuous progression. As to the rate of this evolution precise data are wanting. There is, however, the important negative argument furnished by the absence of evidence of recognizable specific variations of organic forms since man began to observe and record. We know that within human experience a few species have become extinct, but there is no conclusive proof that a single new species have come into existence, nor are appreciable variations readily apparent in forms that live in a wild state. The seeds and plants found with Egyptian mummies, and the flowers and fruits depicted on Egyptian tombs, are easily identified with the vegetation of modern Egypt. The embalmed bodies of animals found in that country show no sensible divergence from the structure or proportions of the same animals at the present day. The human races of Northern Africa and Western Asia were already as distinct when portrayed by the ancient Egyptian artists as they are now, and they do not seem to have undergone any perceptible change since then. Thus a lapse of four or five thousand years has not been accompanied by any recognizable variation in such forms of plant and animal life as can be tendered in evidence. Absence of sensible change in these instances is, of course, no proof that considerable alteration may not have been accomplished in other forms more exposed to vicissitudes of climate and other external influences. But it furnishes at least a presumption in favor of the extremely tardy progress of organic variation.

If, however, we extend our vision beyond the narrow range of human history, and look at the remains of the plants and animals preserved in those younger formations which, though recent when regarded as parts of the whole geological record, must be many thousands of years older than the very oldest of human monuments, we encounter the most impressive proofs of the persistence of specific forms. Shells which lived in our seas before the coming of the Ice Age present the very same peculiarities of form, structure, and ornament which their descendants still possess. The lapse of so enormous an interval of time has not sufficed seriously to modify them. So too with the plants and the higher animals which still survive. Some forms have become extinct, but few or none which remain display any transitional gradations into new species. We must admit that such transitions have occurred, that indeed they have been in progress ever since organized existence began upon our planet, and are doubtless taking place now. But we can not detect them on the way, and we feel constrained to believe that their march must be excessively slow. . . .

If the many thousands of years which have elapsed since the Ice Age have produced no appreciable modification of surviving plants and animals, how vast a period must have been required for that marvellous scheme of organic development which is chronicled in the rocks! . . .

I have reserved for final consideration a branch of the history of the earth which, while it has become, within the lifetime of the present generation, one of the most interesting and fascinating departments of geological inquiry, owed its first impulse to the far-seeing intellects of Hutton and Playfair. With the penetration of genius these illustrious teachers perceived that if the broad masses of land and the great chains of mountains owe their origin to stupendous movements which from time to time have convulsed the earth, their details of contour must be mainly due to the eroding power of running water. They recognized that as the surface of the land is continually worn down, it is essentially by a process of sculpture that the physiognomy of every country has been developed, valleys being hollowed out and hills left standing, and that these inequalities in topographical detail are only varying and local accidents in the progress of the one great process of the degradation of the land.

1892

Earthquakes—What Are They?

THE REVEREND JAMES B. MACELWANE, S.J.

ROUND ABOUT THIS EARTH OF OURS THERE RUN certain belts in which earthquakes occur more often than in other parts of the world. Why should this be the case? We read from time to time of destructive earthquakes in Japan. But many lesser shocks occur there of which we never hear. In fact, there is an earthquake, large or small, somewhere in Japan practically every day. Similarly, the Kurile Islands, the Aleutian Islands, Alaska and the Queen Charlotte Islands are subject to frequent earth shocks. Continuing around the Pacific circle, we meet with many earthquakes in California, Mexico, Central America, Venezuela, Colombia, Ecuador, Bolivia, Peru and Chili. And on the other side of the Pacific Ocean, the earthquake belt continues from Japan southward through Formosa and the Philippine Deep to New Zealand. Another somewhat less striking earthquake zone runs from Mexico and the Antilles through the northern Mediterranean countries and Asia Minor into the Pamirs, Turkestan, Assam and the Indian Ocean. In other parts of the earth, destructive earthquakes also occur, but as more or less isolated phenomena. Examples in this country are the Mississippi Valley earthquakes of 1811 and of the following year, and the Charleston earthquake of 1886.

Now why should destructive earthquakes occur more frequently in such a zone or belt as the border of the Pacific Ocean? What is an earthquake? Centuries ago, many people, and even scientific men, thought that earthquakes were caused by explosions down in the earth; and there have not been wanting men in our own time who held this view. Others, like Alexander von Humboldt, thought that earthquakes were connected with volcanoes; that the earth is a ball of molten lava covered by a thin shell of rock and that the volcanoes were a sort of safety valve. As long as the volcanoes are active, they said, the pressure within the molten lava of the earth is held down, but when the volcanoes

113

cease their activity, thus closing the safety valves, so to speak, the increasing pressure eventually causes a fracture in the earth's crust. Another theory supposed that the lava occupied passageways in a more or less solid portion of the earth underneath the crust and that the movement of lava within these passages caused such pressure as to burst their walls, thus causing an earthquake.

Quite a different point of view was taken by those who held the theory that earthquakes occurred within the uppermost crust of the earth. This crust was supposed to be honeycombed with vast caves. Even the whole mountain chain of the Alps was thought to be an immense arch built up over a cavern. When the arch should break, thus allowing the overlying rocks to drop somewhat, we would have an earthquake. In many cases, those who held this theory believed that the entire roof would collapse and that earthquakes are generally due to the impact of the falling mass of rocks on the floor of the cavern.

But it has been shown, since the discovery of the passage of earthquake waves through the earth and their registration by means of seismographs, that the outer portion of the earth down to a depth of at least five elevenths of the earth's radius is not only solid, but, with the exception of the outer layers, is more than twice as rigid as steel in the laboratory. It has also been shown that volcanoes are a purely surface phenomenon; that they have no connection with each other, even when they are but a few miles apart. Hence it is clear that earthquakes connected with volcanoes must be of very local character, if they are to be caused by the movement of lava. This is found to be actually the case. It is also clear that some other cause must operate in producing earthquakes, since destructive earthquakes often occur very far from volcanoes. In fact, some regions where there are frequent earthquakes have no volcanoes at all.

In the California earthquake of 1906, there occurred a fracture of the earth's crust which could be followed at the surface for a distance of more than 150 miles, extending from the Gualala River Valley on the northern coast of California southeastward through Tomales Bay and outside the Golden Gate to the old mission of San Juan Bautista. The rocks on the east side of this fracture moved southeastward relatively to those on the west side, so that every road, fence or other structure which had been built across the line of fracture was offset by varying amounts up to twenty-one feet. A study of this earthquake led scientific men to the conclusion that the mechanism of the earthquake was an elastic rebound. It was thought that the rocks in the portion of the earth's crust west of the fracture had been dragged northward until the ultimate strength of the rocks was reached along this zone of weakness. When the fracture occurred, the rocks, like bent springs, sprang back to an unstrained position. But this did not occur in one continuous throw, but in a series of jerks, each of which set up elastic vibrations in the rocks. These vibrations traveled out in all directions and constituted the earthquake proper. The zone of weakness in which the California earthquake occurred is a valley known as the San Andreas rift. It is usually quite straight and ignores entirely the physiography of the region, passing indifferently over lowlands and mountains and extending more than 300 miles beyond the end of the fracture of 1906 until it is lost in the Colorado desert east of San Bernardino. The entire floor of the valley has been broken up by earthquakes occurring through the ages into small blocks and ridges and even into rock flour.

The San Andreas rift is only one of the many features which parallel the Pacific Coast in California. There are other lesser rifts on which earthquakes have occurred. Similar to these rifts in some respects are the ocean deeps, along the walls of which occur some of the world's most violent earthquakes.

Why do these features parallel the Pacific shore? And why are earthquakes associated with them? Both seem to be connected in some way with the process of mountain-building, for many of the features in this circum-Pacific belt are geologically recent. Many have thought that mountain-building in general and the processes going on around the Pacific in particular are due to a shortening of the earth's crust caused by gradual cooling of the interior and the consequent shrinkage, but this is not evident. While the earth is surely losing heat by radiation into space, it is being heated by physical and chemical processes connected with radioactivity at such a rate that, unless the radioactive minerals are confined to the uppermost ten miles or so of the earth's crust, the earth must be getting hotter instead of cooler, because the amount of heat generated must exceed that which is conducted to the surface and radiated away.

Another suggested cause of earthquakes is isostatic compensation. If we take a column of rock extending downward from the top of a mountain chain to a given level within the earth's crust and compare it with another column extending to the same level under a plain, the mountain column will be considerably longer than the other and consequently will contain more rock. Hence it should weigh more, unless the rocks of which it is composed are lighter than those under the plain, but geodesists tell us that the two columns weigh the same. Hence the rocks under the plain must be the heavier of the two. But even if this is the case, we should expect the conditions to change; for rain and weather are continually removing rocks from the tops of the mountains and distributing the materials of which they are composed over the plain. Nevertheless, according to the geodesists, the columns continue to weigh the same. Hence we must conclude that compensation in some form must be taking place. There must be an inflow of rock into the mountain column and an outflow from the plain column. But the cold flow of a portion of a mass of rock must place enormous strain on the surrounding portions. When the stress reaches the ultimate strength of the rocks, there must be fracture and a relief of strain, thus causing an earthquake.

It has recently been found that earthquakes occur at considerable depth in the earth. Hence they can not be caused by purely surface strains. There are a few earthquakes which seem to have occurred at depths up to 300 miles. This is far below the depth of compensation of the geodesists. It is also below the zone of fracture of the geologists, and far down in what they call the zone of flow. Can an earthquake be generated by a simple regional flow? We do not know, but it would seem that sudden release of strain is necessary to cause the vibrations which we call an earthquake. It may be that a strain is produced and gradually grows in such a way as to produce planes of shear such as occur when a column is compressed lengthwise. These planes of maximum shear usually form an angle of about forty-five degrees with the direction of the force. Recent investigation into the failure of steel indicates that under certain conditions it will retain its full strength up to the moment of failure when the steel becomes as plastic as mud along the planes of maximum shear. The two portions of the column then glide over each other on the plastic zone until the strain is relieved, whereupon the steel within the zone becomes hard and rigid as before. It may be that a process somewhat similar to this may take place deep down in the earth, and that the sheared surface may be propagated upwards through the zone of flow to the zone of fracture and even to the surface of the earth. In that case, the plastic shear would give way to true fracture near the surface.

It is only by a careful study, not only of the waves produced by earthquakes and of the permanent displacements which occur in them, but of the actual movement along the planes of fracture, that we shall be able to discover what an earthquake really is. For the present, we must be satisfied with knowing that it is an elastic process; that it is usually destructive only within a very restricted belt, and that it is probably produced by the sudden release of a regional strain within the crust of the earth.

1933

Last Days of St. Pierre

FAIRFAX DOWNEY

From *Disaster Fighters*

I

THE PLANTER

HOW GRACIOUSLY HAD FORTUNE SMILED ON FERNAND Clerc. Little past the age of forty, in this year of 1902, he was the leading planter of the fair island of Martinique. Sugar from his broad cane fields, molasses, and mellow rum had made him a man of wealth, a millionaire. All his enterprises prospered.

Were the West Indies, for all their beauty and their bounty, sometimes powerless to prevent a sense of exile, an ache of homesickness in the heart of a citizen of the Republic? Then there again fate had been kind to Fernand Clerc. Elected a member of the Chamber of Deputies, it was periodically his duty and his pleasure to embark and sail home to attend its sessions—home to France, to Paris.

Able, respected, good-looking, blessed with a charming wife and children, M. Clerc found life good indeed. With energy undepleted by the tropics, he rode through the island visiting his properties. Tall and thick grew the cane stalks of his plantation at Vivé on the slopes of Mont Pelée. Mont Pelée—Naked Mountain—well named when lava erupting from its cone had stripped it bare of its verdure. But that was long ago. Not since 1851 had its subterranean fires flared up and then but insignificantly. Peaceful now, its crater held the lovely Lake of Palms, whose wooded shores were a favorite picnic spot for parties from St. Pierre and Fort-de-France. Who need fear towering Mont Pelée, once mighty, now mild, an extinct volcano?

Yet this spring M. Clerc and all Martinique received a rude shock. The mountain was not dead, it seemed. White vapors veiled her summit, and by May 2nd she had overlaid her green mantle with a gown

117

of gray cinders. Pelée muttered and fumed like an angry woman told her day was long past. Black smoke poured forth, illumined at night by jets of flame and flashes of lightning. The grayish snow of cinders covered the countryside, and the milky waters of the Rivière Blanche altered into a muddy and menacing torrent.

Nor was Pelée uttering only empty threats. On May 5th, M. Clerc at Vivé beheld a cloud rolling from the mountain down the valley. Sparing his own acres, the cloud and the stream of smoking lava which it masked, enveloped the Guerin sugar factory, burying its owner, his wife, overseer, and twenty-five workmen and domestics.

Dismayed by this tragedy, M. Clerc and many others moved from the slopes into St. Pierre. The city was crowded, its population of 25,000 swollen to 40,000, and the throngs that filled the market and the cafés or strolled through the gorgeously luxuriant Jardin des Plantes lent an air of added animation, of almost hectic gaiety. When M. Clerc professed alarm at the behavior of Pelée to his friends, he was answered with shrugs of shoulders. Danger? On the slopes perhaps, but scarcely here in St. Pierre down by the sea.

Thunderous, scintillant, Mont Pelée staged a magnificent display of natural fireworks on the night of May 7th. Whites and negroes stared up at it, fascinated. Some were frightened but more took a child-like joy in the vivid spectacle. It was as if the old volcano were celebrating the advent of tomorrow's fête day.

M. Fernand Clerc did not sleep well that night. He breakfasted early in the household where he and his family were guests and again expressed his apprehensions to the large group of friends and relatives gathered at the table. Politely and deferentially—for one does not jeer a personage and man of proven courage—they heard him out, hiding their scepticism.

The voice of the planter halted in mid-sentence; and he half rose, his eyes fixed on the barometer. Its needle was actually fluttering!

M. Clerc pushed back his chair abruptly and commanded his carriage at once. A meaning look to his wife and four children, and they hastened to make ready. Their hosts and the rest followed them to the door. *Non, merci,* none would join their exodus. *Au revoir. A demain.*

From the balcony of their home, the American Consul, Thomas Prentis, and his wife waved to the Clerc family driving by. "Stop," the planter ordered and the carriage pulled up. Best come along, the planter urged. His American friends thanked him. There was no danger, they laughed, and waved again to the carriage disappearing in gray dust as racing hoofs and wheels sped it out of the city of St. Pierre.

THE GOVERNOR

Governor Mouttet, ruling Martinique for the Republic of France, glared up at rebellious Mont Pelée. This *peste* of a volcano was deranging the island. There had been no such crisis since its captures by the English, who always relinquished it again to France, or the days when the slaves revolted. A great pity that circumstances beyond his control should damage the prosperous record of his administration, the Governor reflected.

That miserable mountain was disrupting commerce. Its rumblings drowned out the band concerts in the Savane. Its pyrotechnics distracted glances which might far better have dwelt admiringly on the proverbial beauty of the women of Martinique. . . . Now attention was diverted to a cruder work of Nature, a sputtering volcano. *Parbleu!* It was enough to scandalize any true Frenchman.

Governor Mouttet sighed and pored over the reports laid before him. He had appointed a commission to study the eruption and get at the bottom of *l'affaire Pelée*, but meanwhile alarm was spreading. People were fleeing the countryside and thronging into St. Pierre, deserting that city for Fort-de-France, planning even to leave the island. Steamship passage was in heavy demand. The *Roraima*, due May 8th, was booked solid out of St. Pierre, one said. This would never do. Steps must be taken to prevent a panic which would scatter fugitives throughout Martinique or drain a colony of France of its inhabitants.

A detachment of troops was despatched by the Governor to St. Pierre to preserve order and halt the exodus. His Excellency, no man to send others where he himself would not venture, followed with Mme. Mouttet and took up residence in that city. Certainly his presence must serve to calm these unreasoning, exaggerated fears. He circulated among the populace, speaking soothing words. *Mes enfants*, the Governor avowed, Mont Pelée rumbling away there is only snoring soundly in deep slumber. Be tranquil.

Yet, on the ominous night of May 7th, as spurts of flame painted the heavens, the Governor privately confessed to inward qualms. What if the mountain should really rouse? Might it not then cast the mortals at its feet into a sleep deeper than its own had been, a sleep from which they would never awaken?

THE CHIEF OFFICER

Ellery S. Scott, chief officer of the Quebec Line steamship *Roraima*, stood on the bridge with Captain Muggah as the vessel bore down on Martinique. A column of smoke over the horizon traced down to the

4,500-foot summit of Mont Pelée. So the old volcano was acting up! Curiosity on the bridge ran high as anchor was dropped in the St. Pierre roadstead about 6 o'clock on the morning of May 8th. But all seemed well ashore. The streets, twisting and climbing between the bright-colored houses, were filled with crowds in gay holiday attire.

Promptly the agents came aboard. The volcano? But certainly it was erupting and causing inconvenience. But there was no danger, regardless of the opinion of that Italian skipper yesterday who had said that had he seen Vesuvius looking like Pelée, he would have departed from Naples as fast as he was going to leave St. Pierre. Although the authorities refused him clearance and threatened penalties, he had sailed in haste, with only half his cargo.

By the way, the agents continued, the passenger list was to be considerably augmented: sixty first-class anxious to leave St. Pierre. Here they were boarding now with bag and baggage. Could they be humored, and the *Roraima* sail for St. Lucia at once, returning to discharge its Martinique cargo? the agents inquired of Captain Muggah.

Chief Officer Scott, ordered below to inspect the stowage, thought of his boy in the forecastle. A good lad this eldest son of his. Used to say he'd have a ship of his own some day and keep on his father as first mate. No, his father planned a better career than the sea for him. The boy was slated to go to college and be a lawyer. This would be his last voyage.

Stowed shipshape and proper as Scott knew he would find it, the cargo plainly could not be shifted without a good deal of difficulty. The Martinique consignment lay above that for St. Lucia, and it would be a heavy task to discharge at the latter port first. Scott so reported.

The agents hesitated briefly. To be sure, sixty first-class passengers were to be obliged if possible but—ah, well, let them wait a little longer. The *Roraima* would sail as soon as the upper layer of cargo was landed.

Ship's bells tolled the passing hours. Pelée yonder growled hoarsely and belched black smoke. A little before 8, Chief Officer Scott apprehensively turned his binoculars on the summit.

THE PRISONER

It was dark in the underground dungeon of the St. Pierre prison, but thin rays of light filtered through the grated opening in the upper part of the cell door. Enough so that Auguste Ciparis could tell when it was night and when it was day.

Not that it mattered much unless a man desired to count the days until he should be free. What good was that? One could not hurry them by. Therefore Auguste stolidly endured them with the long patience of Africa. The judge had declared him a criminal and caused him to be locked up here. Thus it was settled and nothing was to be done. Yet it was hard, this being shut out of life up there in the gay city—hard when one was only twenty-five and strong and lusty.

Auguste slept and dozed all he could. Pelée was rumbling away in the distance—each day the jailer bringing him food and water seemed more excited about it—but the noise, reaching the subterranean cell only as faint thunder, failed to keep the negro awake. . . .

Glimmerings of the dawn of May 8th filtered through the grating into the cell, and Auguste stirred into wakefulness. This being a fête day, imprisonment was less tolerable. What merriment his friends would be making up there in the squares of St. Pierre! He could imagine the side-long glances and the swaying hips of the mulatto girls he might have been meeting today. Auguste stared sullenly at the cell door. At least the jailer might have been on time with his breakfast.

The patch of light in the grating winked out into blackness. *Ai! Ai!* All of a sudden it was night again.

II

On the morning of May 8th, 1902, the clocks of St. Pierre ticked on toward ten minutes of 8 when they would stop forever. Against a background of bright sunshine, a huge column of vapor rose from the cone of Mont Pelée.

A salvo of reports as from heavy artillery. Then, choked by lava boiled to white heat by fires in the depths of the earth, Pelée with a terrific explosion blew its head off.

Like a colossal Roman candle it shot out streaks of flame and fiery globes. A pall of black smoke rose thousands of feet in the air, darkening the heavens. Silhouetted by a red, infernal glare, Pelée flung aloft viscid masses which rained incandescent ashes on land and sea.

Then, jagged and brilliant as the lightning flashes, a fissure opened in the flank of the mountain toward St. Pierre. Out of it issued an immense cloud which rushed with unbelievable rapidity down on the doomed city and the villages of Carbet and Le Precheur.

In three minutes that searing, suffocating cloud enveloped them, and 40,000 people died!

Fernand Clerc, the planter, watched from Mont Parnasse, one mile east of St. Pierre, where he had so recently breakfasted. Shrouded in such darkness as only the inmost depths of a cavern afford, he reached out for the wife and children he could not see and gathered them in blessed safety into his arms. But the relatives, the many friends he had left so short a while ago, the American consul and his wife, who had waved him a gay good-by—them he would never see alive again. . . .

In that vast brazier which was St. Pierre, Governor Mouttet may have lived the instant long enough to realize that Pelée had in truth awakened and that eternal sleep was his lot and his wife's and that of all those whose flight he had discouraged. . . .

Down in that deep dungeon cell of his Auguste Ciparis blinked in the swift-fallen night. Through the grating blew a current of burning air, scorching his flesh. He leaped, writhing in agony and screaming for help. No one answered.

Leaving a blazing city in its wake, the death cloud from the volcano rolled over the docks, and the sea, hissing and seething, shrank back before it. Aboard the *Roraima*, Chief Officer Scott lowered his glasses precipitately from Pelée. One look at that cloud bearing down like a whirlwind and he snatched a tarpaulin from a ventilator and pulled it over him. The ship rolled to port, almost on her beam ends, then back to starboard. Her funnels and other superstructure and most of her small boats were swept off by the mighty blast laden with scalding ashes and stone dust. Badly scorched, Scott emerged from his refuge to catch a glimpse of the British steamer *Roddam* plunging by toward the open sea, her decks a smoking shambles. Of the other sixteen vessels which had been anchored in the roadstead there was no sign.

Staggering toward the twisted iron wreckage of the bridge, the Chief Officer beheld the swaying figure of Captain Muggah. From the hideous, blackened mask that had been his face a voice croaked:

"All hands! Heave up the anchor!"

All hands! Only Scott, two engineers, and a few members of the black gang who had been below responded. In vain Scott scanned the group for his son. He never saw the lad again.

The anchor could not be unshackled. "Save the women and children," the captain ordered. During attempts to lower a boat, the captain disappeared. Later he was pulled out of the water in a dying condition.

Now the *Roraima* was afire fore and aft. Amid the shrieks and groans of dying passengers, Scott and three more able-bodied men fought the flames, helped by a few others whose hands, burned raw, made it torture to touch anything. Between dousing the fire with bucketfuls from the sea, Scott tried to give drinks of fresh water to those who begged pitifully for it, though their seared, swollen throats would not let them swallow a drop. Tongues lolling, they dragged themselves along the deck, following him like dogs.

When the French cruiser *Suchet* steamed up to the rescue, the only survivors among the passengers were a little girl and her nurse. Twenty-eight out of a crew of forty-seven were dead.

The eyes of all aboard the *Suchet* turned toward shore. There at the foot of a broad, bare pathway, paved by death and destruction down the slope of Mont Pelée, lay the utter ruins of the city of St. Pierre.

III

Not until the afternoon of May 8th did the devastation of St. Pierre cool sufficiently to allow rescuers from Fort-de-France to enter. They could find none to rescue except one woman who died soon after she was taken from a cellar.

"St. Pierre, that city this morning alive, full of human souls, is no more!" Vicar-General Parel wrote his Bishop. "It lies consumed before us, in its windingsheet of smoke and cinders, silent and desolate, a city of the dead. We strain our eyes for fleeing inhabitants, for men returning to bury their lost ones. We see no one! There is no living being left in this desert of desolation, framed in a terrifying solitude. In the background, when the cloud of smoke and cinders breaks away, the mountain and its slopes, once so green, stand forth like an Alpine landscape. They look as if they were covered with a heavy cloak of snow, and through the thickened atmosphere rays of pale sunshine, wan, and unknown to our latitudes, illumine this scene with a light that seems to belong to the other side of the grave."

Indeed St. Pierre might have been an ancient town, destroyed in some half-forgotten cataclysm and recently partly excavated—another Pompeii and Herculaneum. Cinders, which had buried its streets six feet deep in a few minutes, were as the dust of centuries. Here was the same swift extinction Vesuvius had wrought.

Here was no slow flow of lava. That cloud disgorged by Pelée was a superheated hurricane issuing from the depths of the earth at a speed of ninety miles an hour. Such was the strength of the blast, it killed by concussion and by toppling walls on its victims. The fall of the fourteen-foot metal statue of Notre Dame de la Garde—Our Lady of Safety—symbolized the dreadful fact that tens of thousands never had a fighting chance for their lives.

But chiefly the death cloud slew with its lethal content of hot steam and dust. So swiftly did it pass that its heat did not always burn all of the light tropical clothing from its prey, but once it was inhaled into the lungs—that was the end. Some had run a few frantic steps; then dropped, hands clutched over nose and mouth. Encrusted by cement-like ashes, corpses lay fixed in the contorted postures of their last struggle.

replicas of the dead of Vesuvius preserved in the Naples museum. Fire had charred others or incinerated them to a heap of bones. A horrible spectacle was presented by bodies whose skulls and abdomens had been burst by heat and gases.

People who had been indoors when the cloud descended perished where they stood or sat, but the hand of death had marked most of them less cruelly. They seemed almost still alive, as each shattered building disclosed its denouement. There a girl lay prone, her arms about the feet of an image of the Virgin. A man bent with his head thrust into a basin from which the water had evaporated. A family was gathered around a restaurant table. A child held a doll in her arms; when the doll was touched, it crumbled away except for its china eyes. A clerk sat at his desk, one hand supporting his chin, the other grasping a pen. A baker crouched in the fire pit under his oven. In one room of a home a blonde girl in her bathrobe leaned back in a rocking-chair. Behind her stood a negro servant who apparently had been combing the girl's hair. Another servant had crawled under a sofa. Not far away lay the body of a white woman, beautiful as a Greek statue, and—like many an antique statue—headless. . . .

Then four days after the catastrophe, two negroes walking through the wreckage turned gray as they heard faint cries for help issuing from the depths of the earth.

"Who's that?" they shouted when they could speak. "Where are you?"

Up floated the feeble voice: "I'm down here in the dungeon of the jail. Help! Save me! Get me out!"

They dug down through the debris, broke open the dungeon door, and released Auguste Ciparis, the negro criminal. . . .

When the scorching air penetrated his cell that day, he smelled his own body burning but breathed as little as possible during the moment the intense heat lasted. Ignorant of what had occurred, not realizing that he was buried alive, he slowly starved for four days in his tomb of a cell. His scant supply of water was soon gone. Only echoes answered his shouts for help. When at last he was heard and freed, Ciparis, given a drink of water, managed with some assistance to walk six kilometers to Morne Rouge.

One who lived where 40,000 died! History records no escape more marvelous.

1938

Pin-pointing the Past with the Cosmic Clock

RICHARD FOSTER FLINT

I N A CHICAGO LABORATORY A RADIOCHEMIST STOOD
before an oscilloscope connected to a Geiger counter. Across the
oscilloscope screen, very much like the screen in a small television set,
jumped a never-ending ribbon of green zigzags. The zigzags were made
by the impulses coming from disintegrating atoms of radioactive carbon
within the counter. The carbon had been extracted from a piece of wood,
but the wood was by no means ordinary. In fact, it was a piece of very
old wood, part of a spruce tree that grew in a Wisconsin forest so long ago
that when the tree was alive the Ice Age still had northern United States
in its chill grip. So long ago that mastodons and mammoths still inhabited the country in force. Indeed, it is quite possible that a mastodon,
crashing through the spruce forest in the chill glacial air, brushed against
this very tree.

The wood had been sent to the laboratory for an exact determination of
its age—not the age of the living tree, which can easily be learned by
counting its growth rings, but the time elapsed since the tree was alive.
When a police surgeon examines a dead body, his medical skill tells him
about how much time has elapsed since death occurred. But only *about*.
He has no means of fixing the time exactly, even though the guilt or in-
nocence of a person accused of murder may depend upon it. The surgeon
can only look for certain signs and use his professional judgment.

Like the surgeon, geologists and archaeologists, trying to date the
events of prehistoric periods, have only been able to look for signs and
on the basis of them to make estimates which, although far better than
nothing at all, are certainly not accurate. Some geologists, for example, had
estimated the age of this particular spruce forest in Wisconsin at about
25,000 years, although they could not be sure.

The uncertainty, however, was being ended by the green zigzags that continued to jump across the oscilloscope screen. Radiocarbon, the cause of the zigzags, is a recent discovery that promises to make an accurate timetable of prehistoric events. It constitutes a kind of clock that set itself going when the forest tree died and that has been ticking ever since, at a known rate. The piece of wood was the latest of five samples, all collected from the same forest. When tested, all five gave answers very close to each other, and the average of them reads: 11,400 years ago—six times as long ago as the birth of Christ—and the date is probably accurate to within a few per cent.

This date is of tremendous importance to science, for it cuts earlier estimates and guesses more than in half and brings the extinct mastodons and mammoths (among other things) much closer to our own time than had been supposed. Thanks to radiocarbon, we can look forward to the enjoyment of talking about prehistoric dates in figures that are almost precise.

How this has been made possible is a story of research in nuclear physics and in chemistry, with important contributions from archaeology and geology. It is a story of co-operation among scientists, a pooling of knowledge in several fields. The pioneers in this unusual research are Dr. W. F. Libby and Dr. J. R. Arnold, and they did the work at the University of Chicago's Institute for Nuclear Studies.

WHAT IS RADIOCARBON?

The story of the research that has led up to this result shows the extent to which science has become integrated, with contributions from nuclear physics, chemistry, archaeology—and a few additions from geology, the field of sanitation, and antarctic exploration!

It all grew out of research on cosmic rays. These are great streams of neutrons that pour in to the Earth from outer space. They bombard the Earth's atmosphere and set up a sort of chain reaction that showers cascades of particles down through the air to the Earth's solid surface, where their arrival is pictured on the oscilloscope screen.

Many of the invading horde of neutrons, penetrating the Earth's atmosphere, collide with atoms of nitrogen, of which the atmosphere is largely composed. When one of these high-speed collisions occurs, a new nucleus is created. This disintegrates, emitting in the process an atom of a newly created element, Carbon 14. In this way great quantities of Carbon 14 are created, miles above the Earth's surface, like sparks struck by an impact. Like sparks, too, the Carbon 14 atoms do not last long, for they are radioactive, and they destroy themselves through spontaneous disintegration. Carbon 14 is "heavy" carbon. It is "heavy" because, whereas ordinary carbon has atomic weight of 12, the weight of the new carbon is 14. The new carbon isotope is familiarly called, by the scientists who study its characteristics, *radiocarbon*.

Although radiocarbon atoms may not last long, still, while they do exist, they get around. The first thing they do is combine with oxygen to form carbon dioxide. This mixes with the ordinary carbon dioxide that contains ordinary carbon and in the course of time becomes evenly mixed throughout the air that surrounds the Earth's solid surface. Wherever we may be, as we breathe we draw into our lungs heavy carbon in this form.

That doesn't mean, though, that radiocarbon is very abundant. Actually, for every trillion atoms of ordinary carbon in the atmosphere there is only one atom of the heavy Carbon 14! So, although we are constantly breathing "hot" carbon, its "hotness" is almost unbelievably faint, and we are none the worse for it.

The proportion of Carbon 14 to Carbon 12 in the atmosphere is believed to be constant. This should be so because it represents a balance between the supposedly steady rate of creation of radiocarbon and the rate of its destruction through its own disintegration.

Both plants and animals absorb carbon dioxide freely from the atmosphere. Probably, therefore, they contain just the same proportion of radiocarbon to ordinary carbon—one to about a trillion—that is present in the air. To be sure, the radiocarbon in plant and animal tissues is constantly disintegrating, but it is being renewed as constantly from the air.

A CALENDAR OF THE PAST

This continuous renewal of radiocarbon goes on as long as the plant or animal is alive. But when death occurs—in a tree, for instance—the intake of atmospheric carbon ceases abruptly, and so new radiocarbon no longer comes in to replenish what is being continuously lost by radioactive disintegration. Thus from year to year the amount of radiocarbon present in the dead wood becomes gradually less.

The rate of decrease of radiocarbon is the same everywhere, and the rate is known. Because of this it is possible, by measuring the amount of radiocarbon left in the dead wood, to calculate the time that has elapsed since the death of the tree. Actually it isn't the *amount* that is measured; it is the *rate* of disintegration, which constantly diminishes and is always proportional to the amount of radiocarbon remaining. It is the tiny disintegrations—so many per minute per gram of carbon—that produce the green zigzags on the oscilloscope. The measurement is a tricky laboratory operation, one that must be watched carefully at every stage and that must be safeguarded against possible errors of several kinds. But thanks to skillful development, it works.

HOW THE CALENDAR WAS DEVELOPED

The radiocarbon calendar is the culmination of a long train of necessary research, without which the calendar would have no value. More than fifteen years ago it occurred to Dr. A. V. Grosse, radiochemist of the Houdry Process Corporation of Pennsylvania, that bombardment by cosmic rays probably was creating new radioactive elements. Later, this idea led Dr. Libby to believe that "heavy" carbon, created in that way, must be found in living matter. To test this theory, Libby and Grosse obtained from the Department of Public Works of the City of Baltimore a sample of sewage, a pure organic product. Analyzing it, they not only found radiocarbon in it; they also found that radiocarbon was present in just about the proportion they had calculated beforehand.

The next step was to make tests to see whether this same proportion of radiocarbon is present in living matter all over the world. So they obtained samples of wood from Chicago, New Mexico, Panama, South America, a Pacific island, Australia, North Africa, and Sweden and tested them for radiocarbon. This is a pretty good geographic distribution. But seashells (calcium carbonate) from Florida and seal oil specially collected by the Ronne Antarctic Expedition were tested also; and in the whole lot, radiocarbon proved to be present in the same proportion, within the limits of experimental error.

The success of these tests made it seem possible to take any piece of ancient wood or other carbon-bearing organic substance and determine its radiocarbon date. So it was decided to check radiocarbon against historical knowledge. The method was to determine the radiocarbon dates of pieces of wood and to compare these dates with the dates already calculated by archaeologists on the basis of historical evidence. This was done with a variety of samples, and the archaeologists no doubt had an interesting time selecting them. Two of these were pieces of wood from Egyptian tombs known to be about 4600 years old. The radiocarbon dates came out within 150 years of the historians' figures.

Although it was apparently true that the proportion of radiocarbon to ordinary carbon is uniform in all living matter, regardless of its location, and although the tests on Egyptian wood seemed to show that this proportion has been the same during the last 4600 years, this was not the end. For it was not yet proved that the same held true for still more ancient times, more than 4600 years ago. To prove this it would be necessary to test still older material. But there is one difficulty about all such very old objects. Their dates are unknown; therefore, they provide nothing with which to compare the radiocarbon dates.

There was only one thing to do: get radiocarbon dates for a large number of samples, collected from many different geologic and archaeologic deposits, compare them, and see whether the dates were consistent with each other. If they were, it could be fairly concluded that the concentration of radiocarbon had been very nearly constant throughout the whole period represented by the samples.

The selection of all these samples demanded the co-operation of a number of specialists. So the American Anthropological Association and the Geological Society of America were asked to name a committee of four specialists to collaborate with Libby and Arnold in the tests. As a result, more than 200 samples were collected and dated. Their ages ranged back more than 15,000 years.

The results were so generally consistent with each other as to leave little doubt that the radiocarbon calendar is reliable for dates as far back as it can reach. Unfortunately, however, its reach is limited, and for a simple reason. The rate at which radiocarbon disintegrates is comparatively rapid —so rapid that 5568 years after a plant or animal has died, the radiocarbon it contains is half gone. Although the rate gradually diminishes with time, still the proportion of radiocarbon remaining at the end of 20,000 years is so small as to make accurate laboratory counting very difficult. It is not likely that any refinement in technique will stretch the reach of the calendar much beyond 30,000 years.

Still, we must not ask for too much; during the last 20,000 to 30,000 years a great many things have happened, the dates of which science wants very much to know.

HISTORY OF THE ANCIENT FOREST

At this point we can return to the ancient Wisconsin spruce forest from which we got the sample of wood we began with. The forest is buried beneath a thick layer of earth and stones plastered over it by the great glacial ice sheet that—not so long ago, as we have seen—flowed into the United States from Canada. Because of its burial, the forest would have been unsuspected if the ground had not been deeply cut into by the waves of Lake Michigan. In the course of time the Lake has created a bluff, or cliff, in which the ancient forest is exposed as a dark-colored layer of peat. Thanks to meticulous studies made by Professor L. R. Wilson of the University of Massachusetts, the peat has been described almost inch by inch. In it are spruce stumps still rooted in the ground beneath the peat. All the stumps are splintered. Many spruce logs lie in the peat or in the earth above it, all of them pointing southwest, the direction in which the invading glacier moved. Some of the logs are flattened, as though a great weight had pressed on them. Furthermore, their butts are splintered and twisted as only green, living wood splinters. From these facts it cannot be doubted that the trees were overwhelmed by the glacier, which snapped them off as a giant bulldozer might have done and then overrode the prostrate wreckage, smearing stony clay across its top.

When the logs were sawed through, they revealed confirmatory evidence. The oldest of the trees has 142 annual growth rings; so it is sure that the forest existed for at least 142 years before it was destroyed. The few outermost or youngest rings are closer together than the ones inside them, showing that during the last few years of their lives the trees were growing poorly. The reason for the poor growth is not far to seek. The upper part of the peat, unlike the peat layers beneath, consists only of mosses that live on wet ground or in water itself. The topmost moss plants are still upright, just as they grew, and their youngest branches are thin and scraggly. Water-laid clay overlies the plants and is packed around their stems, as could be the case only if it had been deposited while the mosses were still growing.

Clearly, what slowed the growth of the trees and what killed the mosses was a muddy lake, which must have flooded the spruce forest for several years before the final catastrophe. The lake could only have been created by the advancing glacier, which, by blocking the Strait of Mackinac, dammed up the water in the Lake Michigan basin and caused the lake gradually to rise. Meanwhile the glacier continued to flow southward, so that by the time our spruce forest had been standing in muddy water for several years, the moving wall of ice stood towering above it, ready to complete the task of destruction.

Following the track of this glacier, geologists have found the ridges of earth and stones that mark its outer limit only 25 miles southwest of the buried forest. They have traced this outer limit nearly as far south as Milwaukee, and, on the eastern side of Lake Michigan, to a point between Ludington and Muskegon. Between Milwaukee and Muskegon the glacier formed a great tongue that projected southward.

The radiocarbon calendar has given a date—11,400 years—for the destruction of the spruce forest. No buried wood has yet been found nearer than this to the outer limit of the glacier; so geologists have to resort, for the present at least, to their former method of estimating. From what is known about the rates of present-day glaciers, a reasonable estimate of the time required for the ice to flow from the forest site to its extreme and final limit is 400 years. Therefore we can say, provisionally, that the glacier stood at its final or "Milwaukee" line about 11,000 years ago, and from that line it began to melt away.

MATCHING UP ICE-AGE EVENTS

Away down near St. Charles, Missouri, close to the point where the Missouri River empties into the Mississippi, a group of geologists found, in 1949, a log of wood imbedded in the base of a terrace, the top of which stands 50 feet above the river. They recognized the terrace as the remnant of a deposit made when the Mississippi and the Missouri were choked with sand and silt poured into them by melting ice from the glacier hundreds of miles to the north. Gradually, the rivers silted up their valleys with these "melt-water" sediments, until in time their beds stood 50 feet or more above their present positions. Sediment 50 feet thick, filling a valley more than a mile wide through a distance of hundreds of miles, forms a very bulky deposit.

When the glacier melted away, it ceased to pour extra sediment into the big valleys. The two great rivers, no longer burdened with superloads of sand and silt, could then cut down into the thick sediments they had been obliged to deposit on their floors during the glacial invasion. With their great volumes of water they succeeded in flushing much of the accumulation away, but in protected places along the valley sides flat-topped terraces of sand and silt remained as witnesses to the former great fills of glacial waste. St. Charles is one of those places.

All this was apparent to the group of geologists as they examined the log projecting from the terrace sand. They realized further that the log must have been floated in and deposited as driftwood during the time when the river was choked with glacial sand. They guessed that the ice invasion was probably the one in which the ice in the Lake Michigan basin stood along the "Milwaukee line," straddled the Mississippi at Minneapolis-St. Paul, and stood in the Missouri valley at Yankton, South Dakota.

All this seemed probable, though it wasn't proved. But thanks to radiocarbon, several months later it *was* proved. A sample of wood from the log was sent to the laboratory, reduced to carbon, put into the counter, and the automatic counting was begun. Result: the log proved to be just a few hundred years older than the Wisconsin spruce forest. Clearly the choking of the rivers had begun while the ice stood somewhere north of the "Milwaukee line," before, but not long before, it overwhelmed the forest. Radiocarbon had proved a close connection between two events that occurred more than 11,000 years ago at places hundreds of miles apart.

For the group of geologists who were trying to decipher the history of the Ice Age it was a godsend. To have established by ordinary geologic methods even an approximate relation in time between the driftwood log and the buried spruce forest would have required years of difficult and painstaking measurement of the terraces along the Mississippi River between Wisconsin and Missouri.

PREHISTORIC MAN IN AMERICA

One of the important ways in which the radiocarbon calendar can add to the history of America is by dating the races of prehistoric man that lived on this continent thousands of years before the coming of white Europeans, and even before the arrival of the present-day Indians.

Since 1926, archaeologists had been finding evidence in western North America that Stone Age people once lived there. The evidence consisted of a peculiar kind of arrowhead, or rather dart-head, made of quartz and unlike any ever seen before. In contrast with the later Indian arrowheads these dart-heads had no notch at the base, but they did have a long groove down each side, and they were beautifully and delicately made. As the first ones were found near the little town of Folsom, New Mexico, they came to be called *Folsom points,* and soon archaeologists were speaking of the Stone Age people who had made them as *Folsom Man.*

More Folsom points came to light. Implements of this sort were discovered in New Mexico, Texas, Nebraska, Colorado, Wyoming, Nevada, western Canada, and even Alaska. Furthermore, they were found in the same layers with the bones of an extinct kind of bison, larger than modern buffalo and quite different from them. Indeed, one point was found imbedded in the backbone of a bison—a bison that a prehistoric hunter probably killed to secure food and clothing. Clearly western North America had been the ancient hunting ground of a skillful and wide-ranging race of early Americans.

These discoveries led to all sorts of estimates of the time when the Folsom people lived, but the estimates remained estimates—until radiocarbon came into the picture. A group of geologists and archaeologists in Texas, sensing at once that the radiocarbon calendar could solve the problem, searched for Folsom material suitable for laboratory use. At Lubbock, Texas, they found it: pieces of burned bone, the cold leftovers of a Folsom meal. Off went the collected and ticketed bones to the University of Chicago. There they were reduced to carbon, placed in the Geiger counter, and in due course the time since their animal possessors died was calculated. The radiocarbon date came out at 9883 years, with a possible error of less than 5 per cent.

Ten thousand years ago, then, in round numbers, Folsom people were living and hunting bison in North America. Ten thousand years ago was only a thousand years later than the time when the last big flow of glacier ice reached its outer limit at Milwaukee and Minneapolis and Yankton.

There is a good deal of evidence that the period when the Folsom people left their dart-heads and dinner scraps lying about was a period when western North America had more lakes, bigger streams, and therefore more rain than most of it has today. This is exactly what we should expect if most of Canada and part of the United States were covered with a thick ice sheet some millions of square miles in area. So the radiocarbon calendar shows that the evidence collected by geologists and archaeologists is consistent and illuminates another chapter in the ancient history of the continent.

1951

What Makes the Weather

THE SEVEN AMERICAN AIRS

WOLFGANG LANGEWIESCHE

YOU WAKE UP ONE MORNING AND YOU ARE SURPRISED: the weather, which had been gray and dreary for days and seemed as if it were going to stay that way forever, with no breaks in the clouds and no indication of a gradual clearing, is now all of a sudden clear and sunny and crisp, with a strong northwest wind blowing, and the whole world looks newly washed and newly painted.

"It" has become "fine." Why? How?

. . . A revolutionary fresh view has uncovered the rhyme and reason in the weather. Applied to your particular surprise of that morning, it has this to say:

The air which was warm, moist, and gray last night is still warm, moist, and gray this morning; but it has been pushed fifty or one hundred miles to the south and east of where you live, and has been replaced by a mass of cold, clear, dry air coming from the north or west. It is as simple as that; there is no mysterious "It" in it; just plain physical sense. It is called Air Mass Analysis.

It is based upon the researches and experiments of a physicist named Vilhelm Bjerknes, of Norway, and though in this particular case it seems almost childishly simple, it is Norway's greatest contribution to world culture since Ibsen. . . .

You might inquire next where that morning's new air came from, and just how it got to be cold, dry, and clear. And there you get close to the heart of the new weather science, where meteorology turns into honest, common-sense geography.

That air has come from Canada, where it has been quite literally air-conditioned. Not all parts of the world have the power to condition air, but Canada has. Especially in the fall and winter and early spring, the northern part of this continent becomes an almost perfectly designed mechanical refrigerator. The Rocky Mountains in the west keep currents of new air from flowing into the region. And for weeks the air lies still. The cool ground, much of it snow-covered; the ice of the frozen lakes; plus the perennial stored-up coldness of Hudson's Bay—all cool the layer of air immediately above them. . . . The result, after weeks of stagnation, is a huge mass of air that is uniformly ice-cold, dry, and clear. It stretches from the Rocky Mountains in the west to Labrador in the east, from the ice wastes of the Arctic to the prairies of Minnesota and North Dakota; and—the third dimension is the most important—it is ice-cold from the ground all the way up to the stratosphere. It is, in short, a veritable glacier of air.

That is an air mass. In the jargon of air-faring men, a mass of Polar Canadian air.

When a wave of good, fresh Polar Canadian air sweeps southward into the United States—it happens almost rhythmically every few days—you don't need a barometer to tell you so. There is nothing subtle, theoretical, or scientific about it. You can see and feel the air itself and even hear it. It comes surging out of a blue-green sky across the Dakotas, shaking the hangar doors, whistling in the grass, putting those red-checkered thick woolen jackets on the men, and lighting the stoves in the houses. It flows southward down the Mississippi Valley as a cold wave in winter, or as relief from a heat wave in summer, blowing as a northwest wind with small white hurrying clouds in it. In winter it may sweep southward as far as Tennessee and the Carolinas, bringing frosts with brilliantly clear skies, making the darkies shiver in their drafty cabins. . . .

Polar Canadian is only one of many sorts of air. To put it in the unprecise language of the layman, the great Norwegian discovery is that air must always be of some distinct type: that it is never simply air but always conditioned and flavored. What we call weather is caused by gigantic waves in the air ocean which flood whole countries and continents for days at a stretch with one sort of air or another. And there is nothing theoretical about any of these various sorts of air.

Each kind is easily seen and felt and sniffed, and is, in fact, fairly familiar even to the city dweller, although he may not realize it. Each has its own peculiar characteristics, its own warmth or coolness, dampness or dryness, milkiness or clearness. Each has its own quality of light. In each, smoke behaves differently as it pours from the chimneys: in some kinds of air it creeps lazily, in some it bubbles away, in some it floats in layers.

That is largely why the connoisseur can distinguish different types of air by smell.

Each type of air combines those qualities into an "atmosphere" of its own. Each makes an entirely different sort of day. In fact, what sort of day it is—raw, oppressive, balmy, dull, a "spring" day—depends almost entirely upon the sort of air that lies over your particular section of the country at that particular time.

And if you tried to describe the day in the old-fashioned terms—wind direction and velocity, humidity, state of the sky—you could never quite express its particular weather; but you can by naming the sort of air. An airplane pilot, once he is trained in the new weather thinking, can get quite impatient with the attempts of novelists, for instance, to describe weather. "Why don't you *say* it was Polar Canadian air and get on with your story?"

And if you are a connoisseur of airs just about the first thing you will note every morning is something like, "Ah, Caribbean air to-day"; or if you are really a judge you can make statements as detailed as, "Saskatchewan air, slightly flavored by the Great Lakes."

For just as wines do, the airs take their names and their flavors from the regions where they have matured. Of the seven airs that make up the American weather, one is quite rare and somewhat mysterious. It is known by the peculiarly wine-like name of Sec Superieur. It is believed to be of tropical origin, but it comes to this continent after spending weeks in the stratosphere somewhere above the Galápagos Islands. It is usually found only high aloft, and interests pilots more than farmers. But once in a while a tongue of it reaches the ground as hot, extremely dry, very clear weather; and wherever it licks there is a drought.

The other six airs all come from perfectly earthly places, though faraway ones. The easiest to recognize, the liveliest, is Polar Canadian. Its opposite number in the American sky is Tropical Gulf or Tropical Atlantic air—the steamy, warm air of the Eastern and Midwestern summer, the kind that comes as a southwest wind and starts people to talking about heat and humidity, the kind that is sometimes so steamy that it leaves you in doubt as to whether the sky means to be blue or overcast. This air is brewed of hot sun and warm sea water in the Caribbean region. The mechanism that does the air conditioning in this case is mostly the daily afternoon thunderstorm which carries moisture and heat high aloft in it.

Not quite so obvious is the origin of the moist, silvery, cool-in-summer, cool-in-winter air that dominates the weather of Seattle. It is called Polar Pacific, and it is a trick product. Its basic characteristics have been acquired over Siberia and it is cold and dry; but on its way across the Pacific its lower five to ten thousand feet have been warmed up and moistened. Sometimes such air comes straight across, reaching land in a couple of days. Sometimes it hangs over the water for a week, and it takes a good weatherman to predict just what sort of weather it will produce.

Its counterpart is a flavor known as Tropical Pacific. That is the air they sell to tourists in Southern California. It is really just plain South Seas air, though the story here too is not as clear-cut as it might be.

A clear-cut type is Polar Atlantic air. It sometimes blows down the New England coast as a nor'easter, cold, rainy, with low clouds. It is simply a chunk of the Grand Banks off Newfoundland gone traveling, and you can almost smell the sea.

And one air that every tourist notices in the Southwest is Tropical Continental. Its source region is the deserts of Arizona and Mexico. It is dry and hot and licks up moisture so greedily that it makes water feel on your skin as chilly as if it were gasoline. It is not an important one for America, though its European counterpart, Saharan air, is important for Europe. Oklahoma, Colorado, and Kansas are as far as it ever gets; but even so, a few extra outbreaks of it per year, and we have a dust bowl.

II

The air mass idea is simple. As great ideas often do, the air mass idea makes you feel that you have known it right along. And in a vague way, you have. Take, for example, that half-brag, half-complaint of the Texans that there is nothing between Texas and the North Pole to keep out those northers but a barbed wire fence: it contains the kernel of the whole idea— the invading air mass—but only in a fooling way. Or take the manner in which the Mediterranean people have always given definite names to certain winds (boreas, sirocco, mistral) that blow hot or cold, dry or moist, across their roofs. They are names, however, without the larger view. In creative literature such things as a cold front passage—the sudden arrival of a cold air mass—have been described several times quite accurately, but always as a local spectacle, with the key thought missing.

Actually it took genius to see it. For air is a mercurial fluid, bubbly, changeable; it is as full of hidden energies as dynamite; it can assume the most unexpected appearances. There are days, to be sure, when the air virtually advertises its origin. Offhand, you might say that on perhaps half the days of the year it does. But there are also days when its appearance is altogether misleading.

Take, for example, the amazing metamorphosis that happens to

Tropical Gulf air when it flows northward across the United States in winter. It starts out from among the Islands looking blue and sunny and like an everlasting summer afternoon. When it arrives over the northern United States that same air appears as a dark-gray shapeless, drizzling overcast, and in the office buildings of New York and Chicago the electric lights are on throughout what is considered a shivery winter day. It *is* still the same air; if we could mix a pink dye into the air, as geographers sometimes mix dyes into rivers to trace the flow of water, a cloud of pink air would have traveled from Trinidad to New York. It has hardly changed at all its actual contents of heat and water; but as far as its appearance and its feel are concerned—its "weather" value—a few days of northward traveling have reversed it almost into a photographic negative of itself.

What happens in this particular case—and it accounts for half our winter days—is simply that the cool ground of the wintry continent chills this moist, warm air mass—chills it just a little, not enough to change its fundamental character, and not all the way up into its upper levels, but in its bottommost layer and that only just enough to make it condense out some of its abundant moisture in the form of visible clouds; it is quite similar to the effect of a cold window pane on the air of a well-heated, comfortable room—there is wetness and cooling right at the window, but the bulk of the room's air is not affected.

Perhaps the oddest example of this is the trick by which Polar Pacific air, striking the United States at Seattle, cool and moist, arrives in eastern Montana and the Dakotas as a chinook, a hot, dry, snow-melting wind.

As Polar Pacific air flows up the slopes of the Sierras and the Cascades it is lifted ten thousand feet into the thinner air of higher altitude. By one law of physics the lifting should chill the air through release of pressure. If you have ever bled excess pressure out of your tires you know this cooling by release of pressure—you know how ice-cold the air comes hissing out. But in this case, by a different law of physics, Polar Pacific reacts by cooling only moderately; then it starts condensing out its moisture and thereby protecting its warmth; hence the tremendous snowfalls of the sierras, the giant redwoods, the streams that irrigate California ranches.

Once across the Cascades and the Sierras, the air flows down the eastern slopes. In descending it comes under pressure and therefore heats up, just as air heats up in a tire pump. Warmed, the air increases its capacity to hold moisture; it becomes relatively drier—thus this air sucks back its own clouds into invisible form. When it arrives over the Columbia Basin, or the country round Reno, or Owens Valley, it is regular desert air—warm, very clear, and very dry. That is why the western deserts are where they are. Flowing on eastward, it comes against another hump, the Continental Divide and the Rockies. Here the whole process repeats itself. Again the air is lifted and *should* become ice-cold; again it merely cools moderately, clouds up, and drops its remaining moisture to protect its warmth; hence the lush greenery of Coeur d'Alene, the pine forests of New Mexico. Finally, as the air flows down the eastern slope of the Rockies, compression heats it once more, as in the bicycle pump. Twice on the way up it has dropped moisture and thus failed to cool; twice on the way down it has been heated: it is now extremely dry, and twenty degrees warmer than it was at Seattle. *That* is the chinook, a wind manufactured of exactly the sort of principles that work in air-conditioning machinery, and a good example of the trickery of air masses. But it is *still* a simple thing; it is still one actual physically identical mass of air that you are following. It you had put pink smoke into it at Seattle, pink smoke would have arrived in South Dakota.

That is how the air mass concept explains all sorts of weather detail: the various kinds of rain—showery or steady; the many types of cloud—low or high, solid or broken, layered or towering; thunderstorms; fog. An air mass, thus-and-thus conditioned, will react differently as it flows over the dry plains, the freshly plowed cotton fields, the cool lakes, the hot pavements, the Rocky Mountains of the United States.

An airplane pilot's weather sense consists largely of guessing the exact manner in which a given sort of air will behave along his route. Tropical Gulf in summer over Alabama? Better not get caught in the middle afternoon with a low fuel reserve. We shall have to detour around many thunderstorms. The details are as multifarious as geography itself, but much of it has by now been put into the manuals, and the pilot memorizes such items as these:

Canadian air that passes over the Great Lakes in winter is moistened and warmed in its lower layers and becomes highly unstable. When such air hits the rolling country of western Pennsylvania and New York and the ridges of the Appalachians the hills have a sort of "trigger action" and cause snow flurries or rain squalls with very low ceilings and visibility.

In summer, Canadian air that flows into New England, dried, without passing over the Great Lakes, will be extremely clear and extremely bumpy.

Tropical Gulf over the South forms patchy ground fog just before sunrise that will persist for two or three hours.

As Polar Pacific air moves southward along the Pacific Coast it forms a layer of "high fog."

In Colorado and Nebraska fresh arriving Canadian air frequently shows as a dust storm.

Given two types of country underneath, one kind of air can produce two sorts of weather only a few miles apart. Tropical Atlantic air, for instance, appears over the hills of New England as hot and summery weather, slightly hazy, inclined toward afternoon thunderstorms. A few miles off the coast the same air appears as low banks of fog. That is because the granite and the woods are warmed all through, and actually a little warmer than Tropical Gulf air itself, at least during the day; while the ocean is much colder than the air, and cools it.

Again, one kind of country can have opposite effects on two different types of air. For example, the farms of the Middle West in the spring when the frost is just out of the ground: that sort of country feels cool to Tropical Gulf air that has flowed up the Mississippi Valley. The bottom layers of that warm moist air are chilled and thus the whole air mass is stabilized. It will stay nicely in layers; the clouds will form a flat, level overcast; smoke will spread and hover as a pall. But to a mass of freshly broken-out Canadian air that sort of country feels warm. The air in immediate contact with the ground is warmed, and the whole mass becomes bottom-light and unstable.

And that means action: a commotion much like the boiling of water on a huge scale and in slow motion. The warmed air floats away upward to the colder air aloft, forming bubbles of rising air, hundreds of feet in diameter, that are really hot-air balloons without a skin.

Those rising chunks of air are felt by fliers as bumps. When the ship flies into one it gets an upward jolt; when it flies out again it gets a downward jolt. They are what makes it possible to fly a glider, even over flat country; all you have to do is to find one of those bubbles, stay in it by circling in a tight turn, and let it carry you aloft.

The clear air, the tremendous visibility of such a day is itself the result of instability: the rising bubbles carry away the dust, the haze, the industrial smoke. The air is always roughest on one of those crisp, clear, newly washed days. If the rising air gets high enough it makes cumulus clouds, those characteristic, towering, puffy good-weather clouds. That sort of cloud is nothing but a puff of upward wind become visible. The rise has cooled the air and made its water vapor visible. Soaring pilots seek to get underneath a cumulus cloud—there is sure to be a lively upflow there. Sometimes, in really unstable air, the rising of the air reaches hurricane velocities. We call that a thunderstorm, but the lightning and thunder are only by-products of the thing. The thing itself is simply a vicious, explosive upsurging of air: the wind in thunderstorms blows sixty to one hundred miles per hour—straight up! The most daring of soaring pilots have flown into thunderstorms and have been sucked up almost to the stratosphere.

The weatherman, unlike the pilot, need not guess. He has got a slide rule; he has got the laws of gases, Charles's Law, Boyle's Law, Buys Ballot's Law at his fingertips. He has studied thermodynamics, and he has got a new device that is the biggest thing in weather science since Torricelli invented the barometer—the radio sonde with which he can take soundings of the upper air, find out just how moisture and temperature conditions are aloft, just how stable or unstable the air will be, at what level the clouds will form, and of what type they will be.

Radio sondes go up in the dead of night from a dozen airports all over the continent. The radio sonde looks like a box of candy, being a small carton wrapped in tinfoil; but it is actually a radio transmitter coupled to a thermometer and a moisture-meter. It is hung on a small parachute which is hitched to a balloon. It takes perhaps an hour for the balloon to reach the stratosphere, and all the time it signals its own readings in a strange, quacky voice, half Donald Duck, half voice from the beyond. Then it stops. You know that the balloon has burst, the parachute is letting the instrument down gently.

The next morning some farm boy finds the shiny thing in a field, with a notice attached offering a reward for mailing it back to the weather bureau.

Also the next morning a man in Los Angeles paces up and down his office, scanning the wall where last night's upper-air soundings are tacked up. Emitting heavy cigar smoke and not even looking out of the window, he dictates a weather forecast for the transcontinental airway as far east as Salt Lake City, a forecast that goes into such detail that you sometimes think he is trying to show off.

III

With the air mass idea as a key, you can make more sense out of the weather than the professional weatherman could before Bjerknes; and even if you don't understand Boyle's Law and all the intricate physics of the atmosphere, you can do a quite respectable job of forecasting.

It goes like this: suppose you are deep in Caribbean air. You will have "air mass weather": a whole series of days of the typical sort that goes with that particular type of air when it overlies your particular section of the country in that particular season. There will be all sorts of minor changes; there will be a daily cycle of weather, clouds, perhaps thunderstorms, or showers; but essentially the weather will be the same day after day. Any *real* change in weather can come only as an incursion of a new air mass—probably Polar Canadian.

And when that air mass comes you will know it. New air rarely comes gently, gradually, by imperceptible degrees; almost always the new air mass advances into the old one with a clear-cut, sharply defined forward front. Where two air masses adjoin each other you may in half an hour's driving—in five minutes' flying—change your entire weather, travel from moist, muggy, cloudy weather into clear, cool, sunny weather. That clear-cut boundary is exactly what makes an air mass a distinct entity which you can plot on a map and say, "Here it begins; here it ends"; these sharp boundaries of the air masses are called "fronts" and are a discovery as important as the air mass itself.

You are watching, then, for a "cold front," the forward edge of an advancing mass of cold air. You will get almost no advance warning. You will see the cold air mass only when it is practically upon you. But you know that sooner or later it must come, and that it will come from the northwest. Thus, an occasional long-distance call will be enough. Suppose you are in Pittsburgh, with a moist, warm southwest wind: the bare news that Chicago has a northerly wind might be enough of a clue. If you knew also that Chicago was twenty degrees cooler you would be certain that a cold air mass had swamped Chicago and was now presumably on its way to Pittsburgh, traveling presumably at something like 30 m.p.h. You could guess the time of arrival of its forward front within a few hours. That is why the most innocent weather reports are now so secret; why the British censor suppresses snow flurries in Scotland; why a submarine in the Atlantic would love to know merely the wind direction and temperature at, say, Columbus, Ohio; why the Gestapo had that weather station in Greenland.

Knowing that a cold front is coming, you know what kind of weather to expect; though some cold fronts are extremely fierce, and others quite gentle (noticeable only if you watch for them), the type is always the same. It is all in the book—Bjerknes described it and even drew pictures of it. It was the advance of such a cold front which occurred while you slept that night before you awoke to find the world fresh and newly painted.

Cold air is heavy; as polar air plows into a region occupied by tropical air it underruns; it gets underneath the warm air and lifts it up even as it pushes it back. A cold front acts physically like a cowcatcher.

Seen from the ground, the sequence of events is this: an hour or two before the cold front arrives the clouds in the sky become confused, somewhat like a herd of cattle that smells the coyotes; but you observe that by intuition rather than by measurable signs. Apart from that, there are no advance signs. The wind will be southerly to the last, and the air warm and moist.

Big cumulus clouds build up all around, some of them with dark bases, showers, and in summer thunder and lightning—that is the warm moist air going aloft. A dark bank of solid cloud appears in the northwest, and though the wind is still southerly, this bank keeps building up and coming nearer: it is the actual forward edge of the advancing cold air. When it arrives there is a cloudburst. Then the cold air comes sweeping in from the northwest with vicious gusts. This is the squall that capsizes sailboats and uproots trees, flattens forests and unroofs houses.

The whole commotion probably is over in half an hour. The wind eases up, though it is still cool and northwesterly, the rain ceases, the clouds break and new sky shows: the front has passed, the cold air mass has arrived.

The weatherman can calculate these things too. He has watched and sounded out each of the two air masses for days or even weeks, ever since it moved into his ken somewhere on the outskirts of the American world. Thus an airline weatherman may look at a temperature-moisture graph and say, "This is dynamite. This air will be stable enough as long as it isn't disturbed. But wait till some cold air gets underneath this and starts lifting it. This stuff is going to go crazy."

In making your own guess you would take the same chance that the weatherman takes every morning—that you might be right and yet get an error chalked up against you. Suppose the Chicago weatherman, seeing a cold front approach, forecasts thunderstorms. One thunderstorm passes north of the city, disturbing the 30,000 inhabitants of Waukegan. Another big one passes south of Chicago, across farms just south of Hammond, Ind., affecting another 30,000 people. None happens to hit Chicago itself, with its 3 million people. On a per capita basis, the weatherman was 98 per cent wrong! Actually he was right.

Now you are in the cold air mass, and you can reasonably expect "air mass weather" for a while rather than "frontal" weather; i.e., a whole series of whatever sort of day goes with Canadian air in your particular section of the country at that particular season.

Any real change in the weather now can again come only with an incursion of a new and different air mass—and now that will probably mean tropical maritime air of the Gulf kind. To forecast that invasion is no trick at all: you can see the forward front of the warm air mass in the sky several days before it sweeps in on the ground. Warm air is light. As Caribbean air advances into a region occupied by Canadian air it produces a pattern that is the exact opposite of the cold front. The warm front overhangs forward, overruns the cold air; the warm air mass may appear high above Boston when at ground level it is just invading Richmond, Va.

Again the sequence of events is predictable—Bjerknes drew the picture. It is the approaching warm front that makes for "bad" weather, for rain of the steady, rather than the showery kind, for low ceilings.

Consider a warm front on the morning when its foot is near Richmond and its top over Boston. Boston that morning sees streaks of cirrus in its sky—"mares' tails," the white, feathery, diaphanous cloud arranged in filaments and bands, that is so unsubstantial that the sun shines clear through it and you are hardly conscious of it as a cloud—and actually it doesn't consist of water droplets, as do most clouds, but of ice crystals. New Haven the same morning has the same kind of cloud, but slightly thicker, more nearly as a solid, milky layer. New York that same morning sees the warm air as a gray solid overcast at 8,000 feet. Philadelphia has the same sort of cloud at 5,000, with steady rain. Washington has 1,500 feet, rain. Quantico and Richmond report fog, and all airplanes are grounded. Raleigh, N.C., has clearing weather, the wind has shifted that morning to the southwest, and it is getting hot and humid there. Raleigh would be definitely behind the front, well in the warm air mass itself.

By nightfall Boston has the weather that was New Haven's in the morning. The moon, seen through a milky sheet of cirrus clouds, has a halo: "There is going to be rain." New Haven that night has New York's weather of that morning; New York has Philadelphia's; and so on down the line—the whole front has advanced one hundred miles. In forecasting the weather for Boston it is safe to guess that Boston will get in succession New Haven weather, New York weather, Philadelphia, Washington, Richmond weather—and finally Raleigh weather—in a sequence that should take two or three days: steady lowering clouds, rainy periods, some fog—followed finally by a wind shift to the southwest, and rapid breaking of clouds, and much warmer, very humid weather.

And then the cycle begins all over. You are then deep in Caribbean air again. You will have Caribbean air mass weather, and your weather eye had better be cocked northwest to watch for the first signs of polar air.

IV

There *is* a rhythm, then, in the weather, or at least a sort of rhyme, a repetitive sequence. All those folk rules that attribute weather changes to the phases of the moon, or to some other simple periodicity ("If the weather is O.K. on Friday, it is sure to rain over the week-end") are not so far from the mark after all. The rhythm does not work in terms of rain or shine; but it does work in terms of air masses; and thus, indirectly and loosely, through the tricky physics of the air, it governs also the actual weather.

What makes the air masses move, and what makes them move rhythmically—that is the crowning one of the great Norwegian discoveries. Some of it had long been known. It was understood that the motive power is the sun. By heating the tropics and leaving the polar region cold, it sets up a worldwide circulation of air, poleward at high altitude, equatorward at lower levels. It was understood that this simple circulation is complicated by many other factors such as the monsoon effect: continents heat up in summer and draw air in from over the ocean, in winter they cool and air flows out over the ocean; there was the baffling Coriolis Force that makes all moving things (on the Northern Hemisphere) curve to the right. In everyday life we don't notice it, but some geographers hold that it affects the flow of rivers, and artillerymen make allowance for it: a long-range gun is always aimed at a spot hundreds of yards to the left of the target. The monsoons and the Coriolis Force between them break up the simple pole-to-equator-to-pole flow of the air into a worldwide complicated system of interlocking "wheels"—huge eddies that show variously as tradewinds, calm belts, prevailing westerlies. Charts have been drawn of the air ocean's currents showing how air is piled up over some parts of the world, rushed away from others.

But it remained for the Norwegians to discover the polar front— perhaps the last-discovered geographical thing on this earth. Bjerknes himself first saw it—that the worldwide air circulation keeps piling up new masses of polar air in the north and pressing them southward; it keeps piling up new masses of tropical air in the south, pressing them northward; and thus forever keeps forcing tropical and polar air masses against each other along a front; that the demarcation line between tropical air masses, pressing northward, and polar air masses, pressing southward, runs clear around the world: through North America and across the Atlantic, through Europe and across Siberia, through Japan and across the Pacific. The polar front is clear-cut in some places, tends to wash out in others; but it always reëstablishes itself.

In summer, the polar front runs across North America north of the Great Lakes; in winter, it takes up a position across the United States. Wherever it is, it keeps advancing southward, retreating northward, much like a battlefront. And all the cold fronts and warm fronts are but sections of this greater front.

The rhythmical flowing of the air masses, the Norwegians discovered is simply this wave action along the polar front. . . . Except that it occurs on a scale of unhuman magnitude, wave action along the polar front is almost exactly the same thing as waves on a lake.

In a lake, a dense, heavy fluid—the water—lies underneath a thin, light fluid—the air—and the result is that rhythmical welling up and down of the lake-surface that we call waves. Along the polar front, a dense, heavy fluid, the polar air, lies to the north of a thin, lighter fluid, the tropical air; the result is a rhythmical welling southward and northward of the two kinds of air. When a water wave rolls across a lake its first manifestation is a downward bulging of the water, then an upward surging. When a wave occurs in the polar front it appears first as a northward surging of warm air, and that means all the phenomena of a warm front. Then, in the rhythmical backswing, comes the southward surging of cold air, and that means all the phenomena of a cold front. . . .

So similar are these air waves to the air-water waves of a lake that there are even whitecaps and breakers. What we call a whitecap or a breaker is a whirling together of air and water into a white foam. In the great waves along the polar front the same toppling-over can occur: warm and cold air sometimes wheel around each other, underrun and overrun each other, in a complicated, spiral pattern.

And that is where the old papery weather science of the schoolbooks merges with the realistic observations of the Norwegians. You remember about those Lows that were traveling across the weather map and brought with them bad weather. You know how a dropping barometer has always indicated the coming of bad weather—though we have never quite known why.

Now it turns out that the barometric low is nothing but one of those toppling-over waves in the polar front—or rather, it is the way in which the spiral surging of the air masses affects the barometers. Look at the Middle West when it is being swept by one of those waves, take a reading of everybody's barometer, and you get the typical low. Look at it when a low is centered, watch the kinds of air that are flowing there, the wind directions, the temperatures and humidities and you find that a low has a definite internal structure: the typical wave pattern, with a warm air mass going north and a cold air mass going south, both phases of the same wave.

Barometric pressures turn out to be not the cause of the weather, but simply a result, a rather unimportant secondary symptom of it. What weather actually is the Norwegians have made clear. It is the wave action of the air ocean.   *1942*

Newtoniana

"I do not know what 1 may appear to the world, but to myself I seem to have been only like a boy playing on the sea-shore, and diverting myself in now and then finding a smoother pebble and a prettier shell than ordinary, whilst the great ocean of truth lay all undiscovered before me."—Sir Isaac Newton

"If I have seen farther than Descartes, it is by standing on the shoulders of giants."—Sir Isaac Newton

"Newton was the greatest genius that ever existed and the most fortunate, for we cannot find more than once a system of the world to establish."—Lagrange

"There may have been minds as happily constituted as his for the cultivation of pure mathematical science; there may have been minds as happily constituted for the cultivation of science purely experimental; but in no other mind have the demonstrative faculty and the inductive faculty co-existed in such supreme excellence and perfect harmony."—Lord Macaulay

"Taking mathematics from the beginning of the world to the time when Newton lived, what he had done was much the better half."—Leibnitz

"Let Men Rejoice that so great a glory of the human race has appeared."—Inscription on Westminster Tablet

"The law of gravitation is indisputably and incomparably the greatest scientific discovery ever made, whether we look at the advance which it involved, the extent of truth disclosed, or the fundamental and satisfactory nature of this truth."—William Whewell

"Newton's greatest direct contribution to optics, appears to be the discovery and explanation of the nature of color. He certainly laid the broad foundation upon which spectrum analysis rests, and out of this has come the new science of spectroscopy which is the most delicate and powerful method for the investigation of the structure of matter.—Dayton C. Miller

"On the day of Cromwell's death, when Newton was sixteen, a great storm raged all over England. He used to say, in his old age, that on that day he made his first purely scientific experiment. To ascertain the force of the wind, he first jumped with the wind and then against it, and by comparing these distances with the extent of his own jump on a calm day, he was enabled to compute the force of the storm. When the wind blew thereafter, he used to say it was so many feet strong.—James Parton

"His carriage was very meek, sedate and humble, never seemingly angry, of profound thought, his countenance mild, pleasant and comely. I cannot say I ever saw him laugh but once, which put me in mind of the Ephesian philosopher, who laughed only once in his lifetime, to see an ass eating thistles when plenty of grass was by. He always kept close to his studies, very rarely went visiting and had few visitors. I never knew him to take any recreation or pastime either in riding out to take the air, walking, bowling, or any other exercise whatever, thinking all hours lost that were not spent in his studies, to which he kept so close that he seldom left his chamber except at term time, when he read in the schools as Lucasianus Professor, where so few went to hear him, and fewer that understood him, that ofttimes he did in a manner, for want of hearers read to the walls. Foreigners he received with a great deal of freedom, candour, and respect. When invited to a treat, which was very seldom, he used to return it very handsomely, and with much satisfaction to himself. So intent, so serious upon his studies, that he ate very sparingly, nay, ofttimes he has forgot to eat at all, so that, going into his chamber, I have found his mess untouched, of which, when I have reminded him, he would reply—'Have I?' and then making to the table would eat a bite or two standing, for I cannot say I ever saw him sit at table by himself. He very rarely went to bed till two or three of the clock, sometimes not until five or six, lying about four or five hours, especially at spring and fall of the leaf, at which times he used to employ about six weeks in his elaboratory, the fires scarcely going out either night or day; he sitting up one night and I another till he had finished his chemical experiments, in the performance of which he was the most accurate, strict, exact. What his aim might be I was not able to penetrate into, but his pains, his diligence at these set times made me think he aimed at something beyond the reach of human art and industry. I cannot say I ever saw him drink either wine, ale or beer, excepting at meals and then but very sparingly. He very rarely went to dine in the hall, except on some public days, and then if he has not been minded, would go very carelessly, with shoes down at heels, stockings untied, surplice on, and his head scarcely combed.

His elaboratory was well furnished with chemical materials, as bodies, receivers, heads, crucibles, etc. which was made very litle use of, the crucibles excepted, in which he fused his metals; he would sometimes, tho' very seldom, look into an old mouldy book which lay in his elaboratory, I think it was titled Agricola de Metallis, the transmuting of metals being his chief design, for which purpose antimony was a great ingredient. He has sometimes taken a turn or two, has made a sudden stand, turn'd himself about, run up the stairs like another Archimedes, with an Eureka fall to write on his desk standing without giving himself the leisure to draw a chair to sit down on. He would with great acuteness answer a question, but would very seldom start one. Dr. Boerhave, in some of his writings, speaking of Sir Isaac: 'That man,' says he, 'comprehends as much as all mankind besides.'—Humphrey Newton

"When we review his life, his idiosyncrasies, his periods of contrast, and his doubts and ambitions and desire for place, may we not take some pleasure in thinking of him as a man—a man like most other men save in one particular—he had genius—a greater touch of divinity than comes to the rest of us?"—David Eugene Smith

Discoveries

SIR ISAAC NEWTON

CONCERNING THE LAW OF GRAVITATION

HITHERTO WE HAVE EXPLAINED THE PHAENOMENA of the heavens and of our sea by the power of gravity, but have not yet assigned the cause of this power. This is certain, that it must proceed from a cause that penetrates to the very centres of the sun and planets, without suffering the least diminution of its force; that operates not according to the quantity of the surfaces of the particles upon which it acts (as mechanical causes used to do), but according to the quantity of the solid matter which they contain, and propagates its virtue on all sides to immense distances, decreasing always in the duplicate proportions of the distances. Gravitation towards the sun is made up out of the gravitations towards the several particles of which the body of the sun is composed; and in receding from the sun decreases accurately in the duplicate proportion of the distances as far as the orb of Saturn, as evidently appears from the quiescence of the aphelions of the planets; nay, and even to the remotest aphelions of the comets, if these aphelions are also quiescent. But hitherto I have not been able to discover the cause of those properties of gravity from phaenomena, and I frame no hypotheses; for whatever is not deduced from the phaenomena is to be called an hypothesis; and hypotheses, whether metaphysical or physical, whether of occult qualities or mechanical, have no place in experimental philosophy. In this philosophy particular propositions are inferred from the phaenomena, and afterwards rendered general by induction. Thus it was that the impenetrability, the mobility, and the impulsive force of bodies, and the laws of motion and gravitation were discovered. And to us it is enough that gravity does really exist, and act according to the laws which we have explained, and abundantly serves to account for all the motions of the celestial bodies, and of our sea.

From Newton's "Principia," edition of 1726

LAWS OF MOTION

Law I. *Every body perseveres in its state of rest, or of uniform motion in a right line, unless it is compelled to change that state by force impressed thereon.*

Projectiles persevere in their motions, so far as they are not retarded by the resistance of the air, or impelled downwards by the force of gravity. A top, whose parts by their cohesion are perpetually drawn aside from rectilinear motions, does not cease its rotation, otherwise than as it is retarded by the air. The greater bodies of the planets and comets, meeting with less resistance in more free spaces, preserve their motions both progressive and circular for a much longer time.

Law II. *The alteration of motion is ever proportional to the motive force impressed; and is made in the direction of the right line in which that force is impressed.*

If any force generates a motion, a double force will generate double the motion, a triple force triple the motion, whether that force be impressed altogether and at once, or gradually and successively. And this motion (being always directed the same way with the generating force), if the body moved before, is added to or subducted from the former motion, according as they directly conspire with or are directly contrary to each other; or obliquely joined, when they are oblique, so as to produce a new motion compounded from the determination of both.

Law III. *To every action there is always opposed an equal reaction; or the mutual actions of two bodies upon each other are always equal, and directed to contrary parts.*

Whatever draws or presses another is as much drawn or pressed by that other. If you press a stone with your finger, the finger is also pressed by the stone. If a horse draws a stone tied to a rope, the horse (if I may so say) will be equally drawn back towards the stone; for the distended rope, by the same endeavor to relax or unbend itself, will draw the horse as much towards the stone, as it does the stone towards the horse, and will obstruct the progress of the one as much as it advances that of the other. If a body impinge upon another, and by its force change the motion of the other, that body also (because of the equality of the mutual pressure) will undergo an equal change, in its own motion, towards the contrary part. The changes made by these actions are equal, not in the velocities but in the motions of bodies; that is to say, if the bodies are not hindered by any other impediments. For, because the motions are equally changed, the changes of the velocities made towards contrary parts are reciprocally proportional to the bodies.

From *Newton's "Principia," edition of 1726*

THE DISPERSION OF LIGHT

In the year 1666 (at which time I applied myself to the grinding of optick glasses of other figures than spherical) I procured me a triangular glass prism, to try therewith the celebrated phaenomena of colours. And in order thereto, having darkened my chamber, and made a small hole in my window-shuts, to let in a convenient quantity of the sun's light, I placed my prism at its entrance, that it might be thereby refracted to the opposite wall. It was at first a very pleasing divertissement, to view the vivid and intense colours produced thereby; but after a while applying myself to consider them more circumspectly, I became surprised, to see them in an oblong form; which, according to the received laws of refraction, I expected should have been circular. They were terminated at the sides with straight lines, but at the ends, the decay of light was so gradual that it was difficult to determine justly, what was their figure; yet they seemed semicircular.

Comparing the length of this colour'd Spectrum with its breadth, I found it about five times greater, a disproportion so extravagant, that it excited me to a more than ordinary curiosity to examining from whence it might proceed. I could scarce think, that the various thicknesses of the glass, or the termination with shadow or darkness, could have any influence on light to produce such an effect; yet I thought it not amiss, first to examine those circumstances, and so try'd what would happen by transmitting light through parts of the glass of divers thicknesses, or through holes in the window of divers bignesses, or by setting the prism without, so that the light might pass through it, and be refracted, before it was terminated by the hole: But I found none of these circumstances material. The fashion of the colours was in all these cases the same. . . .

The gradual removal of these suspicions led me to the Experimentum Crucis, which was this: I took two boards, and placed one of them close behind the prism at the window, so that the light might pass through a small hole, made in it for the purpose, and fall on the other board, which I placed at about 12 feet distance, having first made a small hole in it also, for some of the incident light to pass through. Then I placed another prism behind this second board, so that the light trajected through both the boards might pass through that also, and be again refracted before it arrived at the wall. This done, I took the first prism in my hand, and turned it to and fro slowly about its axis, so much as to make the several parts of the image cast, on the second board, successively pass through the hole in it, that I might observe to what places on the wall the second prism would refract them. And I saw by the variation of those places, that the light, tending to that end of the image, towards which the refraction of the first prism was made, did in the second prism suffer a refraction considerably greater than the light tending to the other end. And so the true cause of the length of that image was detected to be no other, than that light is not similar or homogenial, but consists of *Difform Rays, some of which are more Refrangible than others*; so that without any difference in their incidence on the same medium, some shall be more Refracted than others; and therefore that, according to their *particular Degrees of Refrangibility*, they were transmitted through the prism to divers parts of the opposite wall. . . .

On the Origin of Colours

The colours of all natural bodies have no other origin than this, that they are variously qualified, to reflect one sort of light in greater plenty than another. And this I have experimented in a dark room, by illuminating those bodies with uncompounded light of divers colours. For by that means any body may be made to appear of any colour. They have there no appropriate colour, but ever appear of the colour of the light cast upon them, but yet with this difference, that they are most brisk and vivid in the light of their own daylight colour. Minium appeareth there of any colour indifferently, with which it is illustrated, but yet most luminous in red, and so bise appeareth indifferently of any colour, but yet most luminous in blue. And therefore minium reflecteth rays of any colour, but most copiously those endowed with red, that is, with all sorts of rays promiscuously blended, those qualified with red shall abound most in that reflected light, and by their prevalence cause it to appear of that colour. And for the same reason bise, reflecting blue most copiously, shall appear blue by the excess of those rays in its reflected light; and the like of other bodies. And that this is the entire and adequate cause of their colours, is manifest, because they have no power to change or alter the colours of any sort of rays incident apart, but put on all colours indifferently, with which they are enlightened.

These things being so, it can be no longer disputed, whether there be colours in the dark, or whether they be the qualities of the objects we see, no nor perhaps, whether light be a body. For, since colours are the quality of light, having its rays for their entire and immediate subject, how can we think those rays qualities also, unless one quality may be the subject of, and sustain another; which in effect is to call it substance. We should not know bodies for substances; were it not for their sensible qualities, and the principle of those being now found due to something else, we have as good reason to believe that to be a substance also.

Besides, who ever thought any quality to be a heterogeneous aggregate, such as light is discovered to be? But to determine more absolutely what light is, after what manner refracted, and by what modes or actions it produceth in our minds the phantasms of colours, is not so easie; and I shall not mingle conjectures with certainties.

From Newton's "A New Theory about Light and Colours," 1672

Mathematics, the Mirror of Civilization

LANCELOT HOGBEN

From *Mathematics for the Million*

THERE IS A STORY ABOUT DIDEROT, THE Encyclopaedist and materialist, a foremost figure in the intellectual awakening which immediately preceded the French Revolution. Diderot was staying at the Russian court, where his elegant flippancy was entertaining the nobility. Fearing that the faith of her retainers was at stake, the Tsaritsa commissioned Euler, the most distinguished mathematician of the time, to debate with Diderot in public. Diderot was informed that a mathematician had established a proof of the existence of God. He was summoned to court without being told the name of his opponent. Before the assembled court, Euler accosted him with the following pronouncement, which was uttered with due gravity: "$\frac{a + b^n}{n} = x$, donc Dieu existe répondez!" Algebra was Arabic to Diderot. Unfortunately he did not realize that was the trouble. Had he realized that algebra is just a language in which we describe the *sizes* of things in contrast to the ordinary languages which we use to describe the *sorts* of things in the world, he would have asked Euler to translate the first half of the sentence into French. Translated freely into English, it may be rendered: "A number x can be got by first adding a number a to a number b multiplied by itself a certain number of times, and then dividing the whole by the number of *b*'s multiplied together. So God exists after all. What have you got to say now?" If Diderot had asked Euler to illustrate the first part of his remark for the clearer understanding of the Russian court, Euler might have replied that *x* is 3 when *a* is 1 and *b* is 2 and *n* is 3, or that *x* is 21 when *a* is 3 and *b* is 3 and *n* is 4, and so forth. Euler's troubles would have begun when the court wanted to know how the second part of the sentence follows from the first part. Like many of us, Diderot had stagefright when confronted with a sentence in size language. He left the court abruptly amid the titters of the assembly, confined himself to his chambers, demanded a safe conduct, and promptly returned to France.

Though he could not know it, Diderot had the last laugh before the court of history. The clericalism which Diderot fought was overthrown, and though it has never lacked the services of an eminent mathematician, the supernaturalism which Euler defended has been in retreat ever since. One eminent contemporary astronomer in his Gifford lectures tells us that Dirac has discovered *p* and *q* numbers. *Donc Dieu existe.* Another distinguished astronomer pauses, while he entertains us with astonishing calculations about the distance of the stars, to award M. le grand Architecte an honorary degree in mathematics. There were excellent precedents long before the times of Euler and Diderot. For the first mathematicians were the priestly calendar makers who calculated the onset of the seasons. The Egyptian temples were equipped with nilometers with which the priests made painstaking records of the rising and falling of the sacred river. With these they could predict the flooding of the Nile with great accuracy. Their papyri show that they possessed a language of measurement very different from the pretentious phraseology with which they fobbed off their prophecies on the laity. The masses could not see the connection between prophecy and reality, because the nilometers communicated with the river by underground channels, skilfully concealed from the eye of the people. The priests of Egypt used one language when they wrote in the proceedings of a learned society and another language when they gave an interview to the "sob sisters" of the Sunday press.

In the ancient world writing and reading were still a mystery and a craft. The plain man could not decipher the Rhind papyrus in which the scribe Ahmes wrote down the laws of measuring things. Civilized societies in the twentieth century have democratized the reading and writing of *sort language*. Consequently the plain man can understand scientific discoveries if they do not involve complicated measurements. He knows something about evolution. The priestly accounts of the creation have fallen into discredit. So mysticism has to take refuge in the atom. The atom is a safe place not because it is small, but because you have to do complicated measurements and use underground channels to find your way there. These underground channels are concealed from the eye of the people because the plain man has not been taught to read and write *size language*. Three centuries ago, when priests conducted their services in Latin, Protestant reformers founded grammar schools so that people could read the open bible. The time has now come for another Reformation. People must learn to read and write the language of measurement so that they can understand the open bible of modern science.

In the time of Diderot the lives and happiness of individuals might still depend on holding the correct beliefs about religion. Today the lives and happiness of people depend more than most of us realize upon the correct interpretation of public statistics which are kept by Government offices. When a committee of experts announce that the average man can live on his unemployment allowance, or the average child is getting sufficient milk, the mere mention of an average or the citation of a list of figures is enough to paralyse intelligent criticism. In reality half or more than half the population may not be getting enough to live on when the *average* man or child has enough. The majority of people living today in civilized countries cannot read and write freely in size language, just as the majority of people living in the times of Wycliff and Luther were ignorant of Latin in which religious controversy was carried on. The modern Diderot has got to learn the language of size in self-defence, because no society is safe in the hands of its clever people. . . .

The first men who dwelt in cities were *talking* animals. The man of the machine age is a *calculating* animal. We live in a welter of figures: cookery recipes, railway time-tables, unemployment aggregates, fines, taxes, war debts, overtime schedules, speed limits, bowling averages, betting odds, billiard scores, calories, babies' weights, clinical temperatures, rainfall, hours of sunshine, motoring records, power indices, gas-meter readings, bank rates, freight rates, death rates, discount, interest, lotteries, wave lengths, and tyre pressures. Every night, when he winds up his watch, the modern man adjusts a scientific instrument of a precision and delicacy unimaginable to the most cunning artificers of Alexandria in its prime. So much is commonplace. What escapes our notice is that in doing these things we have learnt to use devices which presented tremendous difficulties to the most brilliant mathematicians of antiquity. Ratios, limits, acceleration, are not remote abstractions, dimly apprehended by the solitary genius. They are photographed upon every page of our existence. We have no difficulty in answering questions which tortured the minds of very clever mathematicians in ancient times. This is not because you and I are very clever people. It is because we inherit a social culture which has suffered the impact of material forces foreign to the intellectual life of the ancient world. The most brilliant intellect is a prisoner within its own social inheritance.

An illustration will help to make this quite definite at the outset. The Eleatic philosopher Zeno set all his contemporaries guessing by propounding a series of conundrums, of which the one most often quoted is the paradox of Achilles and the tortoise. Here is the problem about which the inventors of school geometry argued till they had speaker's throat and writer's cramp. Achilles runs a race with the tortoise. He runs ten times as fast as the tortoise. The tortoise has 100 yards' start. Now, says Zeno, Achilles runs 100 yards and reaches the place where the tortoise started. Meanwhile the tortoise has gone a tenth as far as Achilles, and is therefore 10 yards ahead of Achilles. Achilles runs this 10 yards. Meanwhile the tortoise has run a tenth as far as Achilles, and is therefore 1 yard in front of him. Achilles runs this 1 yard. Meanwhile the tortoise has run a tenth of a yard and is therefore a tenth of a yard in front of Achilles. Achilles runs this tenth of a yard. Meanwhile the tortoise goes a tenth of a tenth of a yard. He is now a hundredth of a yard in front of Achilles. When Achilles has caught up this hundredth of a yard, the tortoise is a thousandth of a yard in front. So, argued Zeno, Achilles is always getting nearer the tortoise, but can never quite catch him up.

You must not imagine that Zeno and all the wise men who argued the point failed to recognize that Achilles really did get past the tortoise. What troubled them was, where is the catch? You may have been asking the same question. The important point is that you did not ask it for the same reason which prompted them. What is worrying you is why they thought up funny little riddles of that sort. Indeed, what you are really concerned with is an *historical* problem. I am going to show you in a minute that the problem is not one which presents any *mathematical* difficulty to you. You know how to translate it into size language, because you inherit a social culture which is separated from theirs by the collapse of two great civilizations and by two great social revolutions. The difficulty of the ancients was not an historical difficulty. It was a mathematical difficulty. They had not evolved a size language into which this problem could be freely translated.

The Greeks were not accustomed to speed limits and passenger-luggage allowances. They found any problem involving division very much more difficult than a problem involving multiplication. They had no way of doing division to any order of accuracy, because they relied for calculation on the mechanical aid of the counting frame or abacus. They could not do sums on paper. For all these and other reasons which we shall meet again and again, the Greek mathematician was unable to see something that we see without taking the trouble to worry about whether we see it or not. If we go on piling up bigger and bigger quantities, the pile goes on growing more rapidly without any end as long as we go on adding more. If we can go on adding larger and larger quantities indefinitely without coming to a stop, it seemed to Zeno's contemporaries that we ought to be able to go on adding smaller and still smaller quantities indefinitely without reaching a limit. They thought that in one case the pile goes on for ever, growing more rapidly, and in the other it goes on for ever, growing more slowly. There was nothing in their number language to suggest that when the engine slows beyond a certain point, it chokes off.

To see this clearly we will first put down in numbers the distance which the tortoise traverses at different stages of the race after Achilles starts. As we have described it above, the tortoise moves 10 yards in stage 1, 1 yard in stage 2, one-tenth of a yard in stage 3, one-hundredth of a yard in stage 4, etc. Suppose we had a number language like the Greeks and Romans, or the Hebrews, who used letters of the alphabet. Using the one that is familiar to us because it is still used for clocks, graveyards, and law-courts, we might write the total of all the distances the tortoise ran before Achilles caught him up like this:

$$X + I + \frac{I}{X} + \frac{I}{C} + \frac{I}{M} \text{ and so on.}$$

We have put "and so on" because the ancient peoples got into great difficulties when they had to handle numbers more than a few thousands. Apart from the fact that we have left the tail of the series to your imagination (and do not forget that the tail is most of the animal if it goes on for ever), notice another disadvantage about this script. There is absolutely nothing to suggest to you how the distances at each stage of the race are connected with one another. Today we have a number vocabulary which makes this relation perfectly evident, when we write it down as:

$$10 + 1 + \frac{1}{10} + \frac{1}{100} + \frac{1}{1,000} + \frac{1}{10,000} + \frac{1}{100,000} + \frac{1}{1,000,000} \text{ and so on.}$$

In this case we put "and so on" to save ourselves trouble, not because we have not the right number-words. These number-words were borrowed from the Hindus, who learnt to write number language after Zeno and Euclid had gone to their graves. A social revolution, the

Protestant Reformation, gave us schools which made this number language the common property of mankind. A second social upheaval, the French Revolution, taught us to use a reformed spelling. Thanks to the Education Acts of the nineteenth century, this reformed spelling is part of the common fund of knowledge shared by almost every sane individual in the English-speaking world. Let us write the last total, using this reformed spelling, which we call decimal notation. That is to say:

$$10 + 1 + 0\cdot1 + 0\cdot01 + 0\cdot001 + 0\cdot0001 + 0\cdot00001 + 0\cdot000001 \text{ and so on.}$$

We have only to use the reformed spelling to remind ourselves that this can be put in a more snappy form:

$$11\cdot111111 \text{ etc.,}$$

or still better:

$$11\cdot\dot1.$$

We recognize the fraction $0\cdot1$ as a quantity that is less than $\frac{2}{10}$ and more than $\frac{1}{10}$. If we have not forgotten the arithmetic we learned at school, we may even remember that $0\cdot1$ corresponds with the fraction $\frac{1}{9}$. This means that, the longer we make the sum, $0\cdot1 + 0\cdot01 + 0\cdot001$, etc., the nearer it gets to $\frac{1}{9}$, and it never grows bigger than $\frac{1}{9}$. The total of all the yards the tortoise moves till there is no distance between himself and Achilles makes up just $11\frac{1}{9}$ yards, and no more.

You will now begin to see what was meant by saying that the riddle presents no mathematical difficulty to you. You have a number language constructed so that it can take into account a possibility which mathematicians describe by a very impressive name. They call it the convergence of an infinite series to a limiting value. Put in plain words, this only means that, if you go on piling up smaller and smaller quantities as long as you can, you *may* get a pile of which the size is not made measurably larger by adding any more. The immense difficulty which the mathematicians of the ancient world experienced when they dealt with a process of division carried on indefinitely, or with what modern mathematicians call infinite series, limits, transcendental numbers, irrational quantities, and so forth, provides an example of a great social truth borne out by the whole history of human knowledge. Fruitful intellectual activity of the cleverest people draws its strength from the common knowledge which all of us share. Beyond a certain point clever people can never transcend the limitations of the social culture they inherit. When clever people pride themselves on their own isolation, we may well wonder whether they are very clever after all. Our studies in mathematics are going to show us that whenever the culture of a people loses contact with the common life of mankind and becomes exclusively the plaything of a leisure class, it is becoming a priestcraft. It is destined to end, as does all priestcraft, in superstition. To be proud of intellectual isolation from the common life of mankind and to be disdainful of the great social task of education is as stupid as it is wicked. It is the end of progress in knowledge. History shows that superstitions are not manufactured by the plain man. They are invented by neurotic intellectuals with too little to do. The mathematician and the plain man each need one another. Maybe the Western world is about to be plunged irrevocably into barbarism. If it escapes this fate, the men and women of the leisure state which is now within our grasp will regard the democratization of mathematics as a decisive step in the advance of civilization.

In such a time as ours the danger of retreat into barbarism is very real. We may apply to mathematics the words in which Cobbett explained the uses of grammar to the working men of his own day when there was no public system of free schools. In the first of his letters on English grammar for a working boy, Cobbett wrote these words: "But, to the acquiring of this branch of knowledge, my dear son, there is one motive, which, though it ought, at all times, to be strongly felt, ought, at the present time, to be so felt in an extraordinary degree. I mean that desire which every man, and especially every young man, should entertain to be able to assert with effect the rights and liberties of his country. When you come to read the history of those Laws of England by which the freedom of the people has been secured . . . you will find that tyranny has no enemy so formidable as the pen. And, while you will see with exultation the long-imprisoned, the heavily-fined, the banished William Prynne, returning to liberty, borne by the people from Southampton to London, over a road strewed with flowers: then accusing, bringing to trial and to the block, the tyrants from whose hands he and his country had unjustly and cruelly suffered; while your heart and the heart of every young man in the kingdom will bound with joy at the spectacle, you ought all to bear in mind, that, without a knowledge of grammar, Mr. Prynne could never have performed any of those acts by which his name has been thus preserved, and which have caused his name to be held in honour."

Today economic tyranny has no more powerful friend than the calculating prodigy. Without a knowledge of mathematics, the grammar of size and order, we cannot plan the rational society in which there will be leisure for all and poverty for none. If we are inclined to be a little afraid of the prospect, our first step towards understanding this grammar is to realize that the reasons which repel many people from studying it are not at all discreditable. As mathematics has been taught and expounded in schools no effort is made to show its social history, its significance in our own social lives, the immense dependence of civilized mankind upon it. Neither as children nor as adults are we told how the knowledge of this grammar has been used again and again throughout history to assist in the liberation of mankind from superstition. We are not shown how it may be used by us to defend the liberties of the people. Let us see why this is so.

The educational system of North-Western Europe was largely moulded by three independent factors in the period of the Reformation. One was linguistic in the ordinary sense. To weaken the power of the Church as an economic overlord it was necessary to destroy the influence of the Church on the imagination of the people. The Protestant Reformers appealed to the recognized authority of scripture to show that the priestly practices were innovations. They had to make the scriptures an open book. The invention of printing was the mechanical instrument which destroyed the intellectual power of the Pope. Instruction in Latin and Greek was a corollary of the doctrine of the open bible. This prompted the great educational innovation of John Knox and abetted the more parsimonious founding of grammar schools in England. The ideological front against popery and the wealthy monasteries strengthened its strategic position by new translations and critical inspection of the scriptural texts. That is one reason why classical scholarship occupied a place of high honour in the educational system of the middle classes.

The language of size owes its position in Western education to two different social influences. While revolt against the authority of the Church was gathering force, and before the reformed doctrine had begun to have a wide appeal for the merchants and craftsmen of the medieval boroughs, the mercantile needs of the Hansa had already led to the founding of special schools in Germany for the teaching of the new arithmetic which Europe had borrowed from the Arabs. An astonishing proportion of the books printed in the three years after the first press was set up were commercial arithmetics. Luther vindicated the four merchant gospels of addition, subtraction, multiplication, and division with astute political sagacity when he announced the outlandish doctrine that every boy should be taught to calculate. The grammar of numbers was chained down to commercial uses before people could foresee the vast variety of ways in which it was about to invade man's social life.

Geometry, already divorced from the art of calculation, did not enter into Western education by the same route. Apart from the stimulus which the study of dead languages received from the manufacture of bibles, classical pursuits were encouraged because the political theories of the Greek philosophers were congenial to the merchants who were aspiring to a limited urban democracy. The appeal of the city-state democracy to the imagination of the wealthier bourgeois lasted till after the French Revolution, when it was laid to rest in the familiar funeral urns of mural decoration. The leisure class of the Greek city-states played with geometry as people play with crossword puzzles and chess today. Plato taught that geometry was the highest exercise to which human leisure could be devoted. So geometry became included in European education as a part of classical scholarship, without any clear connection with the contemporary reality of measuring Drake's "world encompassed." Those who taught Euclid did not understand its social use, and generations of schoolboys have studied Euclid without being told how a later geometry, which grew out of Euclid's teaching in the busy life of Alexandria, made it possible to measure the size of the world. Those measurements blew up the pagan Pantheon of star gods and blazed the trail for the great navigations. The revelation of how much of the surface of our world was still unexplored was the solid ground for what we call the faith of Columbus.

Plato's exaltation of mathematics as an august and mysterious ritual had its roots in dark superstitions which troubled, and fanciful puerilities which entranced, people who were living through the childhood of civilization, when even the cleverest people could not clearly distinguish the difference between saying that 13 is a "prime" number and saying that 13 is an unlucky number. His influence on education has spread a veil of mystery over mathematics and helped to preserve the queer freemasonry of the Pythagorean brotherhoods, whose members were put to death for revealing mathematical secrets now printed in school books. It reflects no discredit on anybody if this veil of mystery makes the subject distasteful. Plato's great achievement was to invent a religion which satisfies the emotional needs of people who are out of harmony with their social environment, and just too intelligent or too individualistic to seek sanctuary in the cruder forms of animism. The curiosity of the men who first speculated about atoms, studied the properties of the lodestone, watched the result of rubbing amber, dissected animals, and catalogued plants in the three centuries before Aristotle wrote his epitaph on Greek science, had banished personalities from natural and familiar objects. Plato placed animism beyond the reach of experimental exposure by inventing a world of "universals." This world of universals was the world as God knows it, the "real" world of which our own is but the shadow. In this "real" world symbols of speech and number are invested with the magic which departed from the bodies of beasts and the trunks of trees as soon as they were dissected and described. . . .

Two views are commonly held about mathematics. One comes from Plato. This is that mathematical statements represent eternal truths. Plato's doctrine was used by the German philosopher, Kant, as a stick with which to beat the materialists of his time, when revolutionary writings like those of Diderot were challenging priestcraft. Kant thought that the principles of geometry were eternal, and that they were totally independent of our sense organs. It happened that Kant wrote just before biologists discovered that we have a sense organ, part of what is called the internal ear, sensitive to the pull of gravitation. Since that discovery, the significance of which was first fully recognized by the German physicist, Ernst Mach, the geometry which Kant knew has been brought down to earth by Einstein. It no longer dwells in the sky where Plato put it. We know that geometrical statements when applied to the real world are only approximate truths. The theory of Relativity has been very unsettling to mathematicians, and it has now become a fashion to say that mathematics is only a game. Of course, this does not tell us anything about mathematics. It only tells us something about the cultural limitations of some mathematicians. When a man says that mathematics is a game, he is making a private statement. He is telling us something about himself, his own attitude to mathematics. He is not telling us anything about the public meaning of a mathematical statement.

If mathematics is a game, there is no reason why people should play it if they do not want to. With football, it belongs to those amusements without which life would be endurable. The view which we explore is that mathematics is the language of size, and that it is an essential part of the equipment of an intelligent citizen to understand this language. If the rules of mathematics are rules of grammar, there is no stupidity involved when we fail to see that a mathematical truth is obvious. The rules of ordinary grammar are not obvious. They have to be learned. They are not eternal truths. They are conveniences without whose aid truths about the sorts of things in the world cannot be communicated from one person to another. In Cobbett's memorable words, Mr. Prynne would not have been able to impeach Archbishop Laud if his command of grammar had been insufficient to make himself understood. So it is with mathematics, the grammar of size. The rules of mathematics are rules to be learned. If they are formidable, they are formidable because they are unfamiliar when you first meet them—like gerunds or nominative absolutes. They are also formidable because in all languages there are so many rules and words to memorize before we can read newspapers or pick up radio news from foreign stations. Everybody knows that being able to chatter in several foreign languages is not a sign of great social intelligence. Neither is being able to chatter in the language of size. Real social intelligence lies in the use of a language, in applying the right words in the right context. It is important to know the language of size, because entrusting the laws of human society, social statistics, population, man's hereditary make-up, the balance of trade, to the isolated mathematician without checking his conclusions is like letting a committee of philologists manufacture the truths of human, animal, or plant anatomy from the resources of their own imaginations.

. . . The language of mathematics differs from that of everyday life, because it is essentially a rationally planned language. The languages of size have no place for private sentiment, either of the individual or of the nation. They are international languages like the binomial nomenclature of natural history. In dealing with the immense complexity of his social life man has not yet begun to apply inventiveness to the rational planning of ordinary language when describing different kinds of institutions and human behavior. The language of everyday life is clogged with sentiment, and the science of human nature has not advanced so far that we can describe individual sentiment in a clear way. So constructive thought about human society is hampered by the same conservatism as embarrassed the earlier naturalists. Nowadays people do not differ about what sort of animal is meant by Cimex or Pediculus, because these words are only used by people who use them in one way. They still can and often do mean a lot of different things when they say that a mattress is infested with bugs or lice. The study of man's social life has not yet brought forth a Linnaeus. So an argument about the "withering away of the State" may disclose a difference about the use of the dictionary when no real difference about the use of the policeman is involved. Curiously enough, people who are most sensible about the need for planning other social amenities in a reasonable way are often slow to see the need for creating a rational and international language.

The technique of measurement and counting has followed the caravans and galleys of the great trade routes. It has developed very slowly. At least four thousand years intervened between the time when men could calculate when the next eclipse would occur and the time when men could calculate how much iron is present in the sun. Between the first recorded observations of electricity produced by friction and the measurement of the attraction of an electrified body two thousand years intervened. Perhaps a longer period separates the knowledge of magnetic iron (or lodestone) and the measurement of magnetic force. Classifying things according to size has been a much harder task than recognizing the different sorts of things there are. It has been more closely related to man's social achievements than to his biological equipment. Our eyes and ears can recognize different sorts of things at a great distance. To measure things at a distance, man has had to make new sense organs for himself, like the astrolabe, the telescope, and the microphone. He has made scales which reveal differences of weight to which our hands are quite insensitive. At each stage in the evolution of the tools of measurement man has refined the tools of size language. As human inventiveness has turned from the counting of flocks and seasons to the building of temples, from the building of temples to the steering of ships into chartless seas, from seafaring plunder to machines driven by the forces of dead matter, new languages of size have sprung up in succession. Civilizations have risen and fallen. At each stage a more primitive, less sophisticated culture breaks through the barriers of custom thought, brings fresh rules to the grammar of measurement, bearing within itself the limitation of further growth and the inevitability that it will be superseded in its turn. The history of mathematics is the mirror of civilization.

The beginnings of a size language are to be found in the priestly civilizations of Egypt and Sumeria. From these ancient civilizations we see the first-fruits of secular knowledge radiated along the inland trade routes to China and pushing out into and beyond the Mediterranean, where the Semitic peoples are sending forth ships to trade in tin and dyes. The more primitive northern invaders of Greece and Asia Minor collect and absorb the secrets of the pyramid makers in cities where a priestly caste is not yet established. As the Greeks become prosperous, geometry becomes a plaything. Greek thought itself becomes corrupted with the star worship of the ancient world. At the very point when it seems almost inevitable that geometry will make way for a new language, it ceases to develop further. The scene shifts to Alexandria, the greatest centre of shipping and the mechanical arts in the ancient world. Men are thinking about how much of the world remains to be explored. Geometry is applied to the measurement of the heavens. Trigonometry takes its place. The size of the earth, the distance of the sun and moon are measured. The star gods are degraded. In the intellectual life of Alexandria, the factory of world religions, the old syncretism has lost its credibility. It may still welcome a god beyond the sky. It is losing faith in the gods within the sky.

In Alexandria, where the new language of star measurement has its beginnings, men are thinking about numbers unimaginably large compared with the numbers which the Greek intellect could grasp. Anaxagoras had shocked the court of Pericles by declaring that the sun

was as immense as the mainland of Greece. Now Greece itself had sunk
into insignificance beside the world of which Eratosthenes and Poseidonius
had measured the circumference. The world itself sank into insignificance beside the sun as Aristarchus had measured it. Ere the dark night of
monkish superstition engulfed the great cosmopolis of antiquity, men were
groping for new means of calculation. The bars of the counting frame had
become the bars of a cage in which the intellectual life of Alexandria was
imprisoned. Men like Diophantus and Theon were using geometrical
diagrams to devise crude recipes for calculation. They had almost invented
the third new language of algebra. That they did not succeed was the
nemesis of the social culture they inherited. In the East the Hindus had
started from a much lower level. Without the incubus of an old-established
vocabulary of number, they had fashioned new symbols which lent themselves to simple calculation without mechanical aids. The Moslem civilization which swept across the southern domain of the Roman Empire
brought together the technique of measurement, as it had evolved in the
hands of the Greeks and the Alexandrians, adding the new instrument
for handling numbers which was developed through the invention of the
Hindu number symbols. In the hands of Arabic mathematicians like Omar
Khayyám, the main features of a language of calculation took shape. We
still call it by the Arabic name, algebra. We owe algebra and the pattern
of modern European poetry to a non-Aryan people who would be excluded
from the vote in the Union of South Africa.

Along the trade routes this new arithmetic is brought into Europe
by Jewish scholars from the Moorish universities of Spain and by Gentile
merchants trading with the Levant, some of them patronized by nobles
whose outlook had been unintentionally broadened by the Crusades.
Europe stands on the threshold of the great navigations. Seafarers are
carrying Jewish astronomers who can use the star almanacs which Arab
scholarship had prepared. The merchants are becoming rich. More than
ever the world is thinking in large numbers. The new arithmetic or
"algorithm" sponsors an amazing device which was prompted by the need
for more accurate tables of star measurement for use in seafaring. Loga-
rithms were among the cultural first-fruits of the great navigations. Mathematicians are thinking in maps, in latitude and longitude. A new kind
of geometry (what we call graphs in everyday speech) was an inevitable
consequence. This new geometry of Descartes contains something which
Greek geometry had left out. In the leisurely world of antiquity there were
no clocks. In the bustling world of the great navigations mechanical
clocks are displacing the ancient ceremonial function of the priesthood as
timekeepers. A geometry which could represent time and a religion in

which there were no saints' days are emerging from the same social context. From this geometry of time a group of men who were studying the mechanics of the pendulum clock and making fresh discoveries about the motion of the planets devised a new size language to measure motion. Today we call it "the" calculus.

This crude outline of the history of mathematics as a mirror of civilization, interlocking with man's common culture, his inventions, his economic arrangements, his religious beliefs, may be left at the stage which had been reached when Newton died. What has happened since has been largely the filling of gaps, the sharpening of instruments already devised. Here and there are indications of a new sort of mathematics. We see a hint of it in social statistics and the study of the atom. We begin to see possibilities of new languages of size transcending those we now use, as the calculus of movement gathered into itself all that had gone before.

1937

Experiments and Ideas

BENJAMIN FRANKLIN

THE KITE

As frequent mention is made in public papers from Europe of the success of the Philadelphia experiment for drawing the electric fire from clouds by means of pointed rods of iron erected on high buildings, &, it may be agreeable to the curious to be informed, that the same experiment has succeeded in Philadelphia, though made in a different and more easy manner, which is as follows:

Make a small cross of two light strips of cedar, the arms so long as to reach to the four corners of a large thin silk handkerchief when extended; tie the corners of the handkerchief to the extremities of the cross, so you have the body of a kite; which being properly accommodated with a tail, loop, and string, will rise in the air, like those made of paper; but this being of silk, is fitter to bear the wet and wind of a thunder-gust without tearing. To the top of the upright stick of the cross is to be fixed a very sharp pointed wire, rising a foot or more above the wood. To the end of the twine, next the hand, is to be tied a silk ribbon, and where the silk and twine join, a key may be fastened. This kite is to be raised when a thunder-gust appears to be coming on, and the person who holds the string must stand within a door or window or under some cover, so that the silk ribbon may not be wet; and care must be taken that the twine does not touch the frame of the door or window. As soon as any of the thunder-clouds come over the kite, the pointed wire will draw the electric fire from them, and the kite, with all the twine, will be electrified, and the loose filaments of the twine will stand out every way, and be attracted by an approaching finger. And when the rain has wet the kite and twine, so that it can conduct the electric fire freely, you will find it stream out plentifully from the key on the approach of your knuckle. At this key the phial may charged; and from electric fire thus obtained, spirits may be kindled, and all the other electric experiments be performed, which are usually done by the help of a rubbed glass globe or tube, and thereby the sameness of the electric matter with that of lightning completely demonstrated.   *Letter to Peter Collinson, 1752*

ELECTRICAL EXPERIMENTS AND ELECTROCUTION

Your question, how I came first to think of proposing the experiment of drawing down the lightning, in order to ascertain its sameness with the electric fluid, I cannot answer better than by giving you an extract from the minutes I used to keep of the experiments I made, with memorandums of such as I purposed to make, the reasons for making them, and the observations that arose upon them, from which minutes my letters were afterwards drawn. By this extract you will see, that the thought was not so much "an out-of-the-way one," but that it might have occurred to any electrician.

"*November* 7, 1749. Electrical fluid agrees with lightning in these particulars. 1. Giving light. 2. Colour of the light. 3. Crooked direction. 4. Swift motion. 5. Being conducted by metals. 6. Crack or noise in exploding. 7. Subsisting in water or ice. 8. Rending bodies it passes through. 9. Destroying animals. 10. Melting metals. 11. Firing inflammable substances. 12. Sulphureous smell. The electric fluid is attracted by points. We do not know whether this property is in lightning. But since they agree in all particulars wherein we can already compare them, is it not probable they agree likewise in this? Let the experiment be made." . . .

The knocking down of the six men was performed with two of my large jarrs not fully charged. I laid one end of my discharging rod upon the head of the first; he laid his hand on the head of the second; the second his hand on the head of the third, and so to the last, who held, in his hand, the chain that was connected with the outside of the jarrs. When they were thus placed, I applied the other end of my rod to the prime-conductor, and they all dropt together. When they got up, they all declared they had not felt any stroke, and wondered how they came to fall; nor did any of them either hear the crack, or see the light of it. You suppose it a dangerous experiment; but I had once suffered the same myself, receiving, by accident, an equal stroke through my head, that struck me down, without hurting me: And I had seen a young woman, that was about to be electrified through the feet, (for some indisposition) receive a greater charge through the head, by inadvertently stooping forward to look at the placing of her feet, till her forhead (as she was very tall) came too near my prime-conductor: she dropt, but instantly got up again, complaining of nothing. A person so struck, sinks down doubled, or folded together as it were, the joints losing their strength and stiffness at once, so that he drops on the spot where he stood, instantly, and there is no previous staggering, nor does he ever fall lengthwise. Too great a charge might, indeed, kill a man, but I have not yet seen any hurt done by it. It would certainly, as you observe, be the easiest of all deaths. . . .

Letter to John Lining, 1755

ORIGIN OF NORTHEAST STORMS

Agreeable to your request, I send you my reasons for thinking that our northeast storms in North America begin first, in point of time, in the southwest parts: That is to say, the air in Georgia, the farthest of our colonies to the Southwest, begins to move southwesterly before the air of Carolina, which is the next colony northeastward; the air of Carolina has the same motion before the air of Virginia, which lies still more northeastward; and so on northeasterly through Pennsylvania, New-York, New-England, &c., quite to Newfoundland.

These northeast storms are generally very violent, continue sometimes two or three days, and often do considerable damage in the harbours along the coast. They are attended with thick clouds and rain.

What first gave me this idea, was the following circumstance. About twenty years ago, a few more or less, I cannot from my memory be certain, we were to have an eclipse of the moon at Philadelphia, on a Friday evening, about nine o'clock. I intended to observe it, but was prevented by a northeast storm, which came on about seven, with thick clouds as usual, that quite obscured the whole hemisphere. Yet when the post brought us the Boston newspaper, giving an account of the effects of the same storm in those parts, I found the beginning of the eclipse had been well observed there, though Boston lies N. E. of Philadelphia about 400 miles. This puzzled me because the storm began with us so soon as to prevent any observation, and being a N. E. storm, I imagined it must have begun rather sooner in places farther to the northeastward than it did at Philadelphia. I therefore mentioned it in a letter to my brother, who lived at Boston; and he informed me the storm did not begin with them till near eleven o'clock, so that they had a good observation of the eclipse: And upon comparing all the other accounts I received from the several colonies, of the time of beginning of the same storm, and, since that of other storms of the same kind, I found the beginning to be always later the farther northeastward. I have not my notes with me here in England, and cannot, from memory, say the proportion of time to distance, but I think it is about an hour to every hundred miles.

From thence I formed an idea of the cause of these storms, which I would explain by a familiar instance or two. Suppose a long canal of water stopp'd at the end by a gate. The water is quite at rest till the gate is open, then it begins to move out through the gate; the water next the gate is first in motion, and moves towards the gate; the water next to that first water moves next, and so on successively, till the water at the head of the canal is in motion, which is last of all. In this case all the water moves indeed towards the gate, but the successive times of beginning motion are the contrary way, *viz.* from the gate backwards to the head of the canal. Again, suppose the air in a chamber at rest, no current through the room till you make a fire in the chimney. Immediately the air in the chimney, being rarefied by the fire, rises; the air next the chimney flows in to supply its place, moving towards the chimney; and, in consequence, the rest of the air successively, quite back to the door. Thus to produce our northeast storms, I suppose some great heat and rarefaction of the air in or about the Gulph of Mexico; the air thence rising has its place supplied by the next more northern, cooler, and therefore denser and heavier, air; that, being in motion, is followed by the next more northern air, &c. &c., in a successive current, to which current our coast and inland ridge of mountains give the direction of northeast, as they lie N.E. and S.W. *Letter to Alexander Small, 1760*

A PROPHECY OF AERIAL INVASION

I have this day received your favor of the 2d inst. Every information in my power, respecting the balloons, I sent you just before Christmas, contained in copies of my letters to Sir Joseph Banks. There is no secret in the affair, and I make no doubt that a person coming from you would easily obtain a sight of the different balloons of Montgolfier and Charles, with all the instructions wanted; and, if you undertake to make one, I think it extremely proper and necessary to send an ingenious man here for that purpose; otherwise, for want of attention to some particular circumstance, or of not being acquainted with it, the experiment might miscarry, which, in an affair of so much public expectation, would have bad consequences, draw upon you a great deal of censure, and affect your reputation. It is a serious thing to draw out from their affairs all the inhabitants of a great city and its environs, and a disappointment makes them angry. At Bourdeaux lately a person who pretended to send up a balloon, and had received money from many people, not being able to make it rise, the populace were so exasperated that they pulled down his house and had like to have killed him.

It appears, as you observe, to be a discovery of great importance, and what may possibly give a new turn to human affairs. Convincing sovereigns of the folly of wars may perhaps be one effect of it; since it will be impracticable for the most potent of them to guard his dominions. Five thousand balloons, capable of raising two men each, could not cost more than five ships of the line; and where is the prince who can afford so to cover his country with troops for its defence, as that ten thousand men descending from the clouds might not in many places do an infinite deal of mischief, before a force could be brought together to repel them? . . .   *Letter to Jan Ingenhousz, 1784*

DAYLIGHT SAVING

You often entertain us with accounts of new discoveries. Permit me to communicate to the public, through your paper, one that has lately been made by myself, and which I conceive may be of great utility.

I was the other evening in a grand company, where the new lamp of Messrs. Quinquet and Lange was introduced, and much admired for its splendour; but a general inquiry was made, whether the oil it consumed was not in proportion to the light it afforded, in which case there would be no saving in the use of it. No one present could satisfy us in that point, which all agreed ought to be known, it being a very desirable thing to lessen, if possible, the expense of lighting our apartments, when every other article of family expense was so much augmented.

I was pleased to see this general concern for economy, for I love economy exceedingly.

I went home, and to bed, three or four hours after midnight, with my head full of the subject. An accidental sudden noise waked me about six in the morning, when I was surprised to find my room filled with light; and I imagined at first, that a number of those lamps had been brought into it; but, rubbing my eyes, I perceived the light came in at the windows. I got up and looked out to see what might be the occasion of it, when I saw the sun just rising above the horizon, from where he poured his rays plentifully into my chamber, my domestic having negligently omitted, the preceding evening, to close the shutters.

I looked at my watch, which goes very well, and found that it was but six o'clock; and still thinking it something extraordinary that the sun should rise so early, I looked into the almanac, where I found it to be the hour given for his rising on that day. I looked forward, too, and found he was to rise still earlier every day till towards the end of June; and that at no time in the year he retarded his rising so long as till eight o'clock. Your readers, who with me have never seen any signs of sunshine before noon, and seldom regard the astronomical part of the almanac, will be as much astonished as I was, when they hear of his rising so early; and especially when I assure them, *that he gives light as soon as he rises.* I am convinced of this. I am certain of my fact. One cannot be more certain of any fact. I saw it with my own eyes. And, having repeated this observation the three following mornings, I found always precisely the same result. . . .

This event has given rise in my mind to several serious and important reflections. I considered that, if I had not been awakened so early in the morning, I should have slept six hours longer by the light of the sun, and in exchange have lived six hours the following night by candle-light; and, the latter being a much more expensive light than the former, my love of economy induced me to muster up what little arithmetic I was master of, and to make some calculations, which I shall give you, after observing that utility is, in my opinion the test of value in matters of invention, and that a discovery which can be applied to no use, or is not good for something, is good for nothing.

I took for the basis of my calculation the supposition that there are one hundred thousand families in Paris, and that these families consume in the night half a pound of bougies, or candles, per hour. I think this is a moderate allowance, taking one family with another; for though, I believe some consume less, I know that many consume a great deal more. Then estimating seven hours per day as the medium quantity between the time of the sun's rising and ours, he rising during the six following months from six to eight hours before noon, and there being seven hours of course per night in which we burn candles, the account will stand thus;—

In the six months between the 20th of March and the 20th of September, there are

Nights	183
Hours of each night in which we burn candles	7
Multiplication gives for the total number of hours	1,281
These 1,281 hours multiplied by 100,000, the number of inhabitants, give	128,100,000
One hundred twenty-eight millions and one hundred thousand hours, spent at Paris by candle-light, which, at half a pound of wax and tallow per hour, gives the weight of	64,050,000

Sixty-four millions and fifty thousand of pounds, which, estimating the whole at the medium price of thirty sols the pound, makes the sum of ninety-six millions and seventy-five thousand livres tournois　　96,075,000

An immense sum! that the city of Paris might save every year, by the economy of using sunshine instead of candles. . . .

Letter to the Authors of "The Journal of Paris," 1784

BIFOCALS

By Mr. Dollond's saying, that my double spectacles can only serve particular eyes, I doubt he has not been rightly informed of their construction. I imagine it will be found pretty generally true, that the same convexity of glass, through which a man sees clearest and best at the distance proper for reading, is not the best for greater distances. I therefore had formerly two pair of spectacles, which I shifted occasionally, as in travelling I sometimes read, and often wanted to regard the prospects. Finding this change troublesome, and not always sufficiently ready, I had the glasses cut, and half of each kind associated in the same circle. . . .

By this means, as I wear my spectacles constantly, I have only to move my eyes up or down, as I want to see distinctly far or near, the proper glasses being always ready. This I find more particularly convenient since my being in France, the glasses that serve me best at table to see what I eat, not being the best to see the faces of those on the other side of the table who speak to me; and when one's ears are not well accustomed to the sounds of a language, a sight of the movements in the features of him that speaks helps to explain; so that I understand French better by the help of my spectacles.　　*Letter to George Whatley, 1785*

Exploring the Atom

SIR JAMES JEANS

From *The Universe Around Us*

AS FAR BACK AS THE FIFTH CENTURY BEFORE CHRIST, Greek philosophy was greatly exercised by the question of whether in the last resort the ultimate substance of the universe was continuous or discontinuous. We stand on the sea-shore, and all around us see stretches of sand which appear at first to be continuous in structure, but which a closer examination shews to consist of separate hard particles or grains. In front rolls the ocean, which also appears at first to be continuous in structure, and this we find we cannot divide into grains or particles, no matter how we try. We can divide it into drops, but then each drop can be subdivided into smaller drops, and there seems to be no reason, on the face of things, why this process of subdivision should not be continued for ever. The question which agitated the Greek philosophers was, in effect, whether the water of the ocean or the sand of the sea-shore gave the truest picture of the ultimate structure of the substance of the universe.

The "atomic" school, founded by Democritus, Leucippus and Lucretius, believed in the ultimate discontinuity of matter; they taught that any substance, after it had been subdivided a sufficient number of times, would be found to consist of hard discrete particles which did not admit of further subdivision. For them the sand gave a better picture of ultimate structure than the water, because they thought that sufficient subdivision would cause the water to display the granular properties of sand. And this intuitional conjecture is amply confirmed by modern science.

The question is, in effect, settled as soon as a thin layer of a substance is found to shew qualities essentially different from those of a slightly thicker layer. A layer of yellow sand swept uniformly over a red floor will make the whole floor appear yellow if there is enough sand to make a layer at least one grain thick. If, however, there is only half this much sand, the redness of the floor inevitably shews through; it is impossible to spread sand in a uniform layer only half a grain thick. This abrupt change in the properties of a layer of sand is of course a consequence of the granular structure of sand.

Similar changes are found to occur in the properties of thin layers of liquid. A teaspoonful of soup will cover the bottom of a soup plate, but a single drop of soup will only make an untidy splash. In some cases it is possible to measure the exact thickness of layer at which the properties of liquids begin to change. In 1890 Lord Rayleigh found that thin films of olive oil floating on water changed their properties entirely as soon as the thickness of the film was reduced to below a millionth of a millimetre (or a 25,000,000th part of an inch). The obvious interpretation, which is confirmed in innumerable ways, is that olive oil consists of discrete particles—analogous to the "grains" in a pile of sand—each having a diameter somewhere in the neighbourhood of a 25,000,000th part of an inch.

Every substance consists of such "grains"; they are called molecules. The familiar properties of matter are those of layers many molecules thick; the properties of layers less than a single molecule thick are known only to the physicist in his laboratory.

MOLECULES

How are we to break up a piece of substance into its ultimate grains, or molecules? It is easy for the scientist to say that, by subdividing water for long enough, we shall come to grains which cannot be subdivided any further; the plain man would like to see it done.

Fortunately the process is one of extreme simplicity. Take a glass of water, apply gentle heat underneath, and the water begins to evaporate. What does this mean? It means that the water is being broken up into its separate ultimate grains or molecules. If the glass of water could be placed on a sufficiently sensitive spring balance, we should see that the process of evaporation does not proceed continuously, layer after layer, but jerkily, molecule by molecule. We should find the weight of the water changing by jumps, each jump representing the weight of a single molecule. The glass may contain any integral number of molecules but never fractional numbers—if fractions of a molecule exist, at any rate they do not come into play in the evaporation of a glass of water.

THE GASEOUS STATE. The molecules which break loose from the surface of the water as it evaporates form a gas—water-vapour or steam. A gas consists of a vast number of molecules which fly about entirely independently of one another, except at the rare instants at which two collide, and so interfere with each other's motion. The extent to which the molecules interfere with one another must obviously depend on their sizes;

the larger they are, the more frequent their collisions will be, and the more they will interfere with one another's motion. Actually the extent of this interference provides the best means of estimating the sizes of molecules. They prove to be exceedingly small, being for the most part about a hundred-millionth of an inch in diameter, and, as a general rule, the simpler molecules have the smaller diameters, as we might perhaps have anticipated. The molecule of water has a diameter of 1.8 hundred-millionths of an inch (4.6×10^{-8} cm.), while that of the simpler hydrogen molecule is only just over a hundred-millionth of an inch (2.7×10^{-8} cm.). The fact that a number of different lines of investigation all assign the same diameters to these molecules provides an excellent proof of the reality of their existence.

As molecules are so exceedingly small, they must also be exceedingly numerous. A pint of water contains 1.89×10^{25} molecules, each weighing 1.06×10^{-24} ounce. If these molecules were placed end to end, they would form a chain capable of encircling the earth over 200 million times. If they were scattered over the whole land surface of the earth, there would be nearly 100 million molecules to every square inch of land. If we think of the molecules as tiny seeds, the total amount of seed needed to sow the whole earth at the rate of 100 million molecules to the square inch could be put into a pint pot.

These molecules move with very high speeds; the molecules which constitute the ordinary air of an ordinary room move with an average speed of about 500 yards a second. This is roughly the speed of a rifle-bullet, and is rather more than the ordinary speed of sound. As we are familiar with this latter speed from everyday experience, it is easy to form some conception of molecular speeds in a gas. It is not a mere accident that molecular speeds are comparable with the speed of sound. Sound is a disturbance which one molecule passes on to another when it collides with it, rather like relays of messengers passing a message on to one another, or Greek torch-bearers handing on their lights. Between collisions the message is carried forward at exactly the speed at which the molecules travel. If these all travelled with precisely the same speed and in precisely the same direction, the sound would of course travel with just the speed of the molecules. But many of them travel on oblique courses, so that although the average speed of individual molecules in ordinary air is about 500 yards a second, the net forward velocity of the sound is only about 370 yards a second.

At high temperatures the molecules may have even greater speeds; the molecules of steam in a boiler may move at 1000 yards a second.

It is the high speed of molecular motion that is responsible for the great pressure exerted by a gas; any surface in contact with ordinary air is exposed to a hail of molecules each moving with the speed of a rifle-bullet. With each breath we take, swarms of millions of millions of millions of molecules enter our bodies, each moving at about 500 yards a second, and nothing but their incessant hammering on the walls of our lungs keeps our chests from collapsing. To take another instance, the piston in a locomotive cylinder is bombarded by about 14×10^{28} molecules every second, each moving at about 800 yards a second. This incessant fusillade of innumerable tiny bullets urges the piston forward in the cylinder, and so propels the train. . . .

ATOMS

In the gaseous state, each separate molecule retains all the chemical properties of the solid or liquid substance from which it originated; molecules of steam, for instance, moisten salt or sugar, or combine with thirsty substances such as unslaked lime or potassium chloride, just as water does.

Is it possible to break up the molecules still further? Lucretius and his predecessors would, of course, have said: "No." A simple experiment, which, however, was quite beyond their range, will speedily shew that they were wrong.

On sliding the two wires of an ordinary electric bell circuit into a tumbler of water, down opposite sides, bubbles of gas will be found to collect on the wires, and chemical examination shews that the two lots of gas have entirely different properties. They cannot, then, both be water-vapour, and in point of fact neither of them is; one proves to be hydrogen and the other oxygen. There is found to be twice as much hydrogen as oxygen, whence we conclude that the electric current has broken up each molecule of water into two parts of hydrogen and one of oxygen. These smaller units into which a molecule is broken are called "atoms." Each molecule of water consists of two atoms of hydrogen (H) and one atom of oxygen (O); this is expressed in its chemical formula H_2O.

All the innumerable substances which occur on earth—shoes, ships, sealing-wax, cabbages, kings, carpenters, walruses, oysters, everything we can think of—can be analysed into their constituent atoms, either in this or in other ways. It might be thought that a quite incredible number of different kinds of atoms would emerge from the rich variety of substances we find on earth. Actually the number is quite small. The same atoms turn up again and again, and the great variety of substances we find on earth results, not from any great variety of atoms entering into their composition, but from the great variety of ways in which a few types of atoms can be combined—just as in a colour-print three colours can be combined so as to form almost all the colours we meet in nature, not to mention other weird hues such as never were on land or sea.

Analysis of all known terrestrial substances has, so far, revealed only 90 different kinds of atoms. Probably 92 exist, there being reasons for thinking that two, or possibly even more, still remain to be discovered. Even of the 90 already known, the majority are exceedingly rare, most common substances being formed out of the combinations of about 14 different atoms, say hydrogen (H), carbon (C), nitrogen (N), oxygen (O), sodium (Na), magnesium (Mg), aluminum (Al), silicon (Si), phosphorus (P), sulphur (S), chlorine (Cl), potassium (K), calcium (Ca), and iron (Fe).

In this way, the whole earth, with its endless diversity of substances, is found to be a building built of standard bricks—the atoms. And of these only a few types, about 14, occur at all abundantly in the structure, the others appearing but rarely.

SPECTROSCOPY. Just as a bell struck with a hammer emits a characteristic note, so every atom put in a flame or in an electric arc or discharge-tube, emits a characteristic light, which the spectroscope will resolve into its separate constituents.

The spectrum of sunlight discloses the chemical composition of the solar atmosphere, and here again we still find the same types of atoms as on earth, and no others. With a few quite unimportant exceptions, every line in the sun's spectrum can be identified as originating from some type of atom already known on earth. Of the fifteen metals which are believed to be commonest in the sun's atmosphere, seven, which account for no less than 96 per cent. of the whole, figure in our list of the fourteen elements which are commonest on earth. Actually they are precisely the seven principal constituents of terrestrial rocks, although their relative proportions are different on the sun and earth.

Thus, broadly speaking the same atoms occur in the sun's atmosphere as on earth, and the same is true of the atmospheres of the stars. It is tempting to jump to the generalisation that the whole universe is built solely of the 90 or 92 types of atoms found on earth, but at present there is no justification for this. The light we receive from the sun and stars comes only from the outermost layers of their surfaces, and so conveys no information at all as to the types of atoms to be found in the stars' interiors. Indeed we have no knowledge of the types of atoms which occur in the interior of our own earth.

THE STRUCTURE OF THE ATOM. Until quite recently, atoms were regarded as the permanent bricks of which the whole universe was built.

All the changes of the universe were supposed to amount to nothing more drastic than a re-arrangement of permanent indestructible atoms; like a child's box of bricks, these built many buildings in turn. The story of twentieth-century physics is primarily the story of the shattering of this concept.

It was towards the end of the last century that Crookes, Lenard, and above all, Sir J. J. Thomson first began to break up the atom. The structures which had been deemed the unbreakable bricks of the universe for more than 2000 years, were suddenly shown to be very susceptible to having fragments chipped off. A mile-stone was reached in 1897, when Thomson shewed that these fragments were identical no matter what type of atom they came from; they were of equal weight and they carried equal charges of negative electricity. On account of this last property they were called "electrons." The atom cannot, however, be built up of electrons and nothing else, for as each electron carries a negative charge of electricity, a structure which consisted of nothing but electrons would also carry a negative charge. Two negative charges of electricity repel one another, as also do two positive charges, while two charges, one of positive and one of negative electricity, attract one another. This makes it easy to determine whether any body or structure carries a positive or a negative charge of electricity, or no charge at all. Observation shews that a complete atom carries no charge at all, so that somewhere in the atom there must be a positive charge of electricity, of amount just sufficient to neutralise the combined negative charges of all the electrons.

In 1911 experiments by Sir Ernest Rutherford and others revealed the architecture of the atom, in its main lines at least. As we shall soon see, nature herself provides an endless supply of small particles charged with positive electricity, and moving with very high speeds, in the α-particles shot off from radio-active substances. Rutherford's method was in brief to fire these into atoms and observe the result. And the surprising result he obtained was that the vast majority of these bullets passed straight through the atom as though it simply did not exist. It was like shooting at a ghost.

Yet the atom was not all ghostly. A tiny fraction—perhaps one in 10,000—of the bullets were deflected from their courses as if they had met something very substantial indeed. A mathematical calculation shewed that these obstacles could only be the missing positive charges of the atoms.

A detailed study of the paths of these projectiles proved that the whole positive charge of an atom must be concentrated in a single very small space, having dimensions of the order of only a millionth of a millionth of an inch. In this way, Rutherford was led to propound the view of atomic structure which is generally associated with his name. He supposed the chemical properties and nature of the atom to reside in a weighty, but excessively minute, central "nucleus" carrying a positive charge of electricity, around which a number of negatively charged electrons described orbits. He had to suppose that the electrons were in motion in the atom, otherwise the attraction of positive for negative electricity would immediately draw them into the central nucleus—just as gravitational attraction would cause the earth to fall into the sun, were it not for the earth's orbital motion. In brief, Rutherford supposed the atom to be constructed like the solar system, the heavy central nucleus playing the part of the sun and the electrons acting the parts of the planets.

The modern theory of wave-mechanics casts doubt on some at least of these concepts—perhaps on all, although this is still in doubt. Thus it may prove necessary to discard many or all of them before long. Yet Rutherford's concepts provide a simple and easily visualised picture of the atom, whereas the theory of wave-mechanics has not yet been able to provide a picture at all. For this reason we shall continue to describe the atom in terms of Rutherford's picture.

According to this picture, the electrons are supposed to move round the nucleus with just the speeds necessary to save them from being drawn into it, and these speeds prove to be terrific, the average electron revolving around its nucleus several thousand million million times every second, with a speed of hundreds of miles a second. Thus the smallness of their orbits does not prevent the electrons moving with higher orbital speeds than the planets, or even the stars themselves.

By clearing a space around the central nucleus, and so preventing other atoms from coming too near to it, these electronic orbits give size to the atom. The volume of space kept clear by the electrons is enormously greater than the total volume of the electrons; roughly, the ratio of volumes is that of the battlefield to the bullets. The atom has about 100,000 times the diameter, and so about a thousand million million times the volume, of a single electron. The nucleus, although it generally weighs 3000 or 4000 times as much as all the electrons in the atom together, is at most comparable in size with, and may be even smaller than, a single electron.

We know the extreme emptiness of astronomical space. Choose a point in space at random, and the odds against its being occupied by a star are enormous. Even the solar system consists overwhelmingly of empty space; choose a spot inside the solar system at random, and there are still immense odds against its being occupied by a planet or even by a comet, meteorite or smaller body. And now we see that this emptiness extends also to the space of physics. Even inside the atom we choose a point at random, and the odds against there being anything there are immense; they are of the order of at least millions of millions to one. Six specks of dust inside Waterloo Station represent—or rather over-represent—the extent to which space is crowded with stars. In the same way a few wasps—six for the atom of carbon—flying around in Waterloo Station will represent the extent to which the atom is crowded with electrons—all the rest is emptiness. As we pass the whole structure of the universe under review, from the giant nebulae and the vast interstellar and inter-nebular spaces down to the tiny structure of the atom, little but vacant space passes before our mental gaze. We live in a gossamer universe; pattern, plan and design are there in abundance, but solid substance is rare.

ATOMIC NUMBERS. The number of elecrons which fly round in orbits in an atom is called the "atomic number" of the atom. Atoms of all atomic numbers from 1 to 92 have been found, except for two missing numbers 85 and 87. As already mentioned, it is highly probable that these also exist, and that there are 92 "elements" whose atomic numbers occupy the whole range of atomic numbers from 1 to 92 continuously.

The atom of atomic number unity is of course the simplest of all. It is the hydrogen atom, in which a solitary electron revolves around a nucleus whose charge of positive electricity is exactly equal in amount, although opposite in sign, to the charge on the negative electron.

Next comes the helium atom of atomic number 2, in which two elec-trons revolve about a nucleus which has four times the weight of the hydrogen nucleus although carrying only twice its electric charge. After this comes the lithium atom of atomic number 3, in which three electrons revolve around a nucleus having six times the weight of the hydrogen atom and three times its charge. And so it goes on, until we reach ura-nium, the heaviest of all atoms known on earth, which has 92 electrons describing orbits about a nucleus of 238 times the weight of the hydrogen nucleus.

RADIO-ACTIVITY

While physical science was still engaged in breaking up the atom into its component factors, it made the further discovery that the nuclei them-selves were neither permanent nor indestructible. In 1896 Becquerel had found that various substances containing uranium possessed the remark-able property, as it then appeared, of spontaneously affecting photographic plates in their vicinity. This observation led to the discovery of a new property of matter, namely radio-activity. All the results obtained from the study of radio-activity in the few following years were co-ordinated in the hypothesis of "spontaneous disintegration" which Rutherford and Soddy advanced in 1903. According to this hypothesis in its present form, radio-activity indicates a spontaneous break-up of the nuclei of the atoms of radio-active substances. These atoms are so far from being permanent and indestructible that their very nuclei crumble away with the mere lapse of time, so that what was once the nucleus of a uranium atom is transformed, after sufficient time, into the nucleus of a lead atom.

The process of transformation is not instantaneous; it proceeds gradually and by distinct stages. During its progress, three types of product are emitted, which are designated α-rays, β-rays, and γ-rays.

These were originally described indiscriminately as rays because all three were found to have the power of penetrating through a certain thickness of air, metal, or other substance. It was not until later that their true nature was discovered. It is well known that magnetic forces, such as, for instance, occur in the space between the poles of a magnet, cause a moving particle charged with electricity to deviate from a straight course; the particle deviates in one direction or the other according as it is charged with positive or negative electricity. On passing the various rays emitted by radio-active substances through the space between the poles of a powerful magnet, the α-rays were found to consist of particles charged with positive electricity, and the β-rays to consist of particles charged with negative electricity. But the most powerful magnetic forces which could be employed failed to cause the slightest deviation in the paths of the γ-rays, from which it was concluded that either the γ-rays were not material particles at all, or that, if they were, they carried no electric charges. The former of these alternatives was subsequently proved to be the true one.

α-PARTICLES. The positively charged particles which constitute α-rays are generally described as α-particles. In 1909 Rutherford and Royds allowed α-particles to penetrate through a thin glass wall of less than a hundredth of a millimetre in thickness into a chamber from which they could not escape—a sort of mouse-trap for α-particles. After the process had continued for a long time, the final result was not an accumulation of α-particles but an accumulation of the gas helium, the next simplest gas after hydrogen. In this way it was established that the positively charged α-particles are simply nuclei of helium atoms; the α-particles, being positively charged, had attracted negatively charged electrons to themselves out of the walls of the chamber and the result was a collection of complete helium atoms.

The α-particles move with enormous speeds, which depend upon the nature of the radio-active substance from which they have been shot out. The fastest particles of all move with a speed of 12,800 miles a second; even the slowest have a speed of 8800 miles a second, which is about 30,000 times the ordinary molecular velocity in air. Particles moving with such speeds as these knock all ordinary molecules out of their way; this explains the great penetrating power of the α-rays.

β-PARTICLES. By examining the extent to which their motion was influenced by magnetic forces, the β-rays were found to consist of negatively charged electrons, exactly similar to those which surround the nucleus in all atoms. As an α-particle carries a positive charge equal in amount to that of two electrons, an atom which has ejected an α-particle is left with a deficiency of positive charge, or what comes to the same thing, with a negative charge, equal to that of two electrons. Consequently it is natural, and indeed almost inevitable, that the ejections of α-particles should alternate with an ejection of negatively charged electrons, in the proportion of one α-particle to two electrons, so that the balance of positive and negative electricity in the atom may be maintained. The β-particles move with even greater speeds than the α-particles, many approaching to within a few per cent. of the velocity of light (186,000 miles a second). . . .

γ-RAYS. As has already been mentioned, the γ-rays are not material particles at all; they prove to be merely radiation of a very special kind.

Thus the break-up of a radio-active atom may be compared to the discharge of a gun; the α-particle is the shot fired, the β-particles are the smoke, and the γ-rays are the flash. The atom of lead which finally remains is the unloaded gun, and the original radio-active atom, of uranium or what not, was the loaded gun. And the special peculiarity of radio-active guns is that they go off spontaneously and of their own accord. All attempts to pull the trigger have so far failed, or at least have led to inconclusive results; we can only wait, and the gun will be found to fire itself in time. . . .

In 1920, Rutherford, using radio-active atoms as guns, fired α-particles at light atoms and found that direct hits broke up their nuclei. There is, however, found to be a significant difference between the spontaneous disintegration of the heavy radio-active atoms and the artificial disintegration of the light atoms; in the former case, apart from the ever-present β-rays and γ-rays, only α-particles are ejected, while in the latter case α-particles were not ejected at all, but particles of only about a quarter their weight, which proved to be identical with the nuclei of hydrogen atoms. . . .

ISOTOPES. Two atoms have the same chemical properties if the charges of positive electricity carried by their nuclei are the same. The amount of this charge fixes the number of electrons which can revolve around the nucleus, this number being of course exactly that needed to neutralise the electric field of the nucleus, and this in turn fixes the atomic number of the element. And it has for long been known that the weights of all atoms are, to a very close approximation, multiples of a single definite weight. This unit weight is approximately equal to the weight of the hydrogen atom, but is more nearly equal to a sixteenth of the weight of the oxygen atom. The weight of any type of atom, measured in terms of this unit, is called the "atomic weight" of the atom.

It used to be thought that a mass of any single chemical element, such as mercury or xenon, consisted of entirely similar atoms, every one of which had not only the same atomic number but also the same atomic weight. But Dr. Aston has shewn very convincingly that atoms of the same chemical element, say neon or chlorine, may have nuclei of a great many different weights. The various forms which the atoms of the same chemical element can assume are known as isotopes being of course distinguished by their different weights.

These weights are much nearer to whole numbers than were the old "atomic" weights of the chemists. For instance the atomic weight of chlorine used to be given as 35.5, and this was taken to mean that chlorine consisted of a mixture of atoms each 35.5 times as massive as the hydrogen atom. Aston finds that chlorine consists of a mixture of atoms of atomic weights 35 and 37 (or more accurately 34.983 and 36.980), the former being approximately three times as plentiful as the latter. In the same way a mass of mercury, of which the mean atomic weight is about 200.6, is found to be a mixture of seven kinds of atoms of atomic weights 196, 198, 199, 200, 201, 202, 204. Tin is a mixture of no fewer than eleven isotopes— 112, 114, 115, 116, 117, 118, 119, 120, 121, 122, 124.

PROTONS AND ELECTRONS. When the presence of isotopes is taken into account, the atomic weights of all atoms prove to be far nearer to integral numbers than had originally been thought. This, in conjunction with Rutherford's artificial disintegration of atomic nuclei, led to the general acceptance of the hypothesis that the whole universe is built up of only two kinds of ultimate bricks, namely, electrons and protons. Each proton carries a positive charge of electricity exactly equal in amount to the negative charge carried by an electron, but has about 1847 times the weight of the electron. Protons are supposed to be identical with the nucleus of the hydrogen atom, all other nuclei being composite structures in which both protons and electrons are closely packed together. For instance, the nucleus of the helium atom, the α-particle, consists of four protons and two electrons, these giving it approximately four times the weight of the hydrogen atom, and a resultant charge equal to twice that of the nucleus of the hydrogen atom.

NEUTRONS. Until quite recently this hypothesis was believed to give a satisfactory and complete account of the structure of matter. Then in 1931 two German physicists, Bothe and Becker, bombarding the light elements beryllium and boron with the very rapid α-particles emitted by polonium, obtained a new and very penetrating radiation which they were at first inclined to interpret as a kind of γ-radiation. Subsequently Dr. Chadwick of Cambridge shewed that it possessed properties which were inconstant with this interpretation and made it clear that the radiation consists of material objects of a type hitherto unknown to science. To the greatest accuracy of which the experiments permit these objects are found to have the same mass as the hydrogen atom, while their very high penetrating power shews that if they have any electric charge at all, it can only be a minute fraction at most of the charge of the electron.

Thus it seems likely that the radiation consists of *uncharged particles* of the same mass as the proton—something quite new in a world which until recently was believed to consist entirely of charged particles. Chadwick describes these new particles as "neutrons." Whether they are themselves fundamental constituents of matter or not remains to be seen. Chadwick has suggested that they may be composite structures, each consisting of a proton and electron in such close combination that they penetrate matter almost as freely as though they had no size at all. On the other hand Heisenberg has considered the possibility that the neutron may be fundamental, the nucleus of an atom being built up solely of positively charged protons and uncharged neutrons, while the negative electrons are confined to the regions outside the nucleus. On this view there are just as many protons in the nucleus as there are electrons outside the nucleus, the number of each being the atomic number of the element, while the excess of mass needed to make up the atomic weight is provided by the inclusion of the requisite number of neutrons in the nucleus. Isotopes of the same element differ of course merely in having different numbers of neutrons in their nuclei.

Rutherford and other physicists have considered the further possibility that other kinds of neutrons, with double the mass of the hydrogen atom, may also occur in atomic nuclei, a hypothesis for which there seems to be considerable observational support.

POSITIVE ELECTRONS. Even more revolutionary discoveries were to come. A few years ago it seemed a piece of extraordinary good luck that in the α-particles nature herself had provided projectiles of sufficient shattering power to smash up the nucleus of the atom and disclose its secrets to the observation of the physicist. More recently nature has been found to provide yet more shattering projectiles in the cosmic radiation which continually bombards the surface of the earth—probably from outer space. This radiation has such a devastating effect on the atomic nuclei that it is difficult to make much of the resulting collection of fragments. It is, however, always possible to examine any *débris*, no matter how involved, by noticing how the constituent particles move when acted on by magnetic forces.

In 1932 C. D. Anderson made observations which suggested that this *débris* contained, among other ingredients, particles having the same positive charge as the proton, but a mass only comparable with, and possibly equal to, that of the electron. The existence of such particles has been confirmed by Blackett and Occhialini at Cambridge. The new particles may well be described as positively charged electrons, and so have been named "positrons."

As these new particles are believed to emerge from atomic nuclei, it would seem plausible to suppose that they must be normal constituents of the nuclei. Yet the recent discovery of the neutron suggests other possibilities.

We have already mentioned the hypothesis, advocated by Heisenberg and others, that the nucleus consists solely of neutrons and protons. Anderson has suggested that the proton may not be a fundamental unit in the structure of matter, but may consist of a positron and a neutron in combination. Every nucleus would then contain only neutrons and positrons, and the positrons could be driven out by bombardment in the ordinary way.

The objection to this view is that the *débris* of the nuclei shattered by cosmic radiation is found to contain electrons as well as positrons, the electrons emerging, so far as can be seen, from the same atomic nuclei as the positrons. This has led Blackett and Occhialini to propound the alternative hypothesis that the electrons and positrons are born in pairs as the result of the processes of bombardment and disintegration of atomic nuclei. At first this may seem a flagrant violation of all our views as to the permanence of matter, but we shall see shortly that it is entirely in accord with the present trend of physics.

It seems fairly certain that the positron has at most but a temporary existence. For positrons do not appear to be associated with matter under normal conditions, although they ought to abound if they were being continually produced out of nuclei at anything like the rate which the observations of Blackett and Occhialini seem to indicate. They might of course rapidly disappear from view through entering into combination with negatively charged particles to form some sort of permanent stable structure, but it seems more probable, as Blackett and Occhialini themselves suggest, that they disappear from existence altogether by combining with negative electrons. Just as a pair of electrons—one positively charged and one negatively charged—can be born out of nothing but energy, so they can die in one another's arms and leave nothing but energy behind. We shall discuss the underlying physical mechanism almost immediately.

Before the existence of the positron had been observed, or even suspected experimentally, Professor Dirac of Cambridge had propounded a mathematical theory which predicted not only the existence of the positron, but also the way in which it ought to behave. Dirac's theory is too abstrusely mathematical to be explained here, but it predicts that a shower of positrons ought gradually to fade away by spontaneous combination with negative electrons, following the same law of decay as radio-active substances. And the average life of a positron is predicted to be one of only a few millionths of a second, which amply explains why the positron can live long enough to be photographed in a condensation chamber, but not long enough to shew its presence elsewhere in the universe.

RADIATION

We have so far discussed only the material constituents of matter: we have pictured the atom as being built up of some or all of the material ingredients which we have described as electrons, protons, neutrons and positrons. Yet this is not the whole story. If it were, every atom would consist of a certain number of protons and neutrons with just sufficient electrons and positrons to make the total electric charge equal to zero. Thus, apart from the insignificant weights of electrons and positrons, the weight of every atom would be an exact multiple of the weight of a hydrogen atom. Experiment shews this not to be the case.

ELECTROMAGNETIC ENERGY. To get at the whole truth, we have to recognise that, in addition to containing material electrons and protons, with possible neutrons and positrons, the atom contains yet a further ingredient which we may describe as electromagnetic energy. We may think of this, although with something short of absolute scientific accuracy, as bottled radiation.

If we disturb the surface of a pond with a stick, a series of ripples starts from the stick and travels, in a series of ever-expanding circles, over the surface of the pond. As the water resists the motion of the stick, we have to work to keep the pond in a state of agitation. The energy of this work is transformed, in part at least, into the energy of the ripples. We can see that the ripples carry energy about with them, because they cause a floating cork or a toy boat to rise up against the earth's gravitational pull. Thus the ripples provide a mechanism for distributing over the surface of the pond the energy that we put into the pond through the medium of the moving stick.

Light and all other forms of radiation are analogous to water ripples or waves, in that they distribute energy from a central source. The sun's radiation distributes through space the vast amount of energy which is generated inside the sun. We hardly know whether there is any actual wave motion in light or not, but we know that both light and all other types of radiation are propagated in such a form that they have many of the properties of a succession of waves.

The different colours of light which in combination constitute sunlight can be separated out by passing the light through a prism, thus forming a rainbow or "spectrum" of colors. The separation can also be effected by an alternative instrument, the diffraction grating, which consists merely of a metal mirror with a large number of parallel lines scratched evenly across its surface. The theory of the action of this latter instrument is well understood; it shews that actually the light is separated into waves of different wave-lengths. (The wave-length in a system of ripples is the distance from the crest of one ripple to that of the next, and the term may be applied to all phenomena of an undulatory nature.) This proves that different colours of light are produced by waves of different lengths, and at the same time enables us to measure the lengths of the waves which correspond to the different colours of light.

These prove to be very minute. The reddest light we can see, which is that of longest wave-length, has a wave-length of only $\dfrac{3}{100,000}$ inch $(7.5 \times 10^{-5}$ cm.); the most violet light we can see has a wave-length only half of this, or 0·000015 inch. Light of all colours travels with the same uniform speed of 186,000 miles, or 3×10^{10} centimetres, a second. The number of waves of red light which pass any fixed point in a second is accordingly no fewer than four hundred million million. This is called the "frequency" of the light. Violet light has the still higher frequency of eight hundred million million; when we see violet light, eight hundred million million waves of light enter our eyes each second.

The spectrum of analysed sunlight appears to the eye to stretch from red light at one end to violet light at the other, but these are not its true limits. When certain chemical salts are placed beyond the violet end of the visible spectrum, they are found to shine vividly, shewing that even out here energy is being transported, although in invisible form. And other methods make it clear that the same is true out beyond the red end of the spectrum. A thermometer, or other heat-measuring instrument, placed here will shew that energy is being received here in the form of heat.

In this way we find that regions of invisible radiation stretch indefinitely from both ends of the visible spectrum. From one end—the red— we can pass continuously to waves of the type used for wireless transmission, which have wave-lengths of the order of hundreds, or even thousands, of yards. From the violet end, we pass through waves of shorter and ever shorter wave-length—all the various forms of ultra-violet radiation. At wave-lengths of from about a hundredth to a thousandth of the wave-length of visible light, we come to the familiar X-rays, which penetrate through inches of our flesh, so that we can photograph the bones inside. Far out even beyond these, we come to the type of radiation which constitutes the γ-rays, its wave-length being of the order of $\dfrac{1}{10,000,000,000}$ inch, or only about a hundred-thousandth part of the wave-length of visible light. Thus the γ-rays may be regarded as invisible radiation of extremely short wave-length. We shall discuss the exact function they serve later. For the moment let us merely remark that in the first instance they served the extremely useful function of fogging Becquerel's photographic plates, thus leading to the detection of the radio-active property of matter.

It is a commonplace of modern electromagnetic theory that energy of every kind carries weight about with it, weight which is in every sense as real as the weight of a ton of coal. A ray of light causes an impact on any surface on which it falls, just as a jet of water does, or a blast of wind, or the fall of a ton of coal; with a sufficiently strong light one could knock a man down just as surely as with the jet of water from a fire hose. This is not a mere theoretical speculation. The pressure of light on a surface has been both detected and measured by direct experiment. The experiments are extraordinarily difficult because, judged by all ordinary standards, the weight carried by radiation is exceedingly small; all the radiation emitted from a 50 horse-power searchlight working continuously for a century weighs only about a twentieth of an ounce.

It follows that any substance which is emitting radiation must at the same time be losing weight. In particular, the disintegration of any radioactive substance must involve a decrease of weight, since it is accompanied by the emission of radiation in the form of γ-rays. The ultimate fate of an ounce of uranium may be expressed by the equation:

$$\text{1 ounce uranium} = \begin{cases} 0.8653 \text{ ounce lead,} \\ 0.1345 \quad " \quad \text{helium,} \\ 0.0002 \quad " \quad \text{radiation.} \end{cases}$$

The lead and helium together contain just as many electrons and just as many protons as did the original ounce of uranium, but their combined weight is short of the weight of the original uranium by about one part in 4000. Where 4000 ounces of matter originally existed, only 3999 now remain; the missing ounce has gone off in the form of radiation.

This makes it clear that we must not expect the weights of the various atoms to be exact multiples of the weight of the hydrogen atom; any such expectation would ignore the weight of the bottled-up electro-magnetic energy which is capable of being set free and going off into space in the form of radiation as the atom changes its make-up. The weight of this energy is relatively small, so that the weights of the atoms must be expected to be approximately, although not exactly, integral multiples of that of the hydrogen atom, and this expectation is confirmed. The exact weight of our atomic building is not simply the total weight of all its bricks; something must be added for the weight of the mortar—the electro-magnetic energy—which keeps the bricks bound together.

Thus the normal atom consists of its material constituents—protons, electrons, neutrons and positrons, or some at least of these—and also of energy, which also contributes something to its weight. When the atom re-arranges itself, either spontaneously or under bombardment, protons and electrons, or other fragments of its material structure, may be shot off in the form of α- and β-particles, and energy may also be set free in the form of radiation. This radiation may either take the form of γ-rays, or of other forms of visible and invisible radiation. The final weight of the atom will be obtained by deducting from its original weight not only the weight of all the ejected electrons and protons, but also the weight of all the energy which has been set free as radiation.

QUANTUM THEORY

The series of concepts which we now approach are difficult to grasp and still more difficult to explain, largely, no doubt, because our minds receive no assistance from our everyday experience of nature. It becomes necessary to speak mainly in terms of analogies, parables and models which can make no claim to represent ultimate reality; indeed, it is rash to hazard a guess even as to the direction in which ultimate reality lies.

The laws of electricity which were in vogue up to about the end of the nineteenth century—the famous laws of Maxwell and Faraday—required that the energy of an atom should continually decrease, through the atom scattering energy abroad in the form of radiation, and so having less and less left for itself. These same laws predicted that all energy set free in space should rapidly transform itself into radiation of almost infinitesimal wave-length. Yet these things simply did not happen, making it obvious that the then prevailing electrodynamical laws had to be given up.

CAVITY-RADIATION. A crucial case of failure was provided by what is known as "cavity-radiation." A body with a cavity in its interior is heated up to incandescence; no notice is taken of the light and heat emitted by its outer surface, but the light imprisoned in the internal cavity is let out through a small window and analysed into its constituent colours by a spectroscope or diffraction grating. This is the radiation that is known as "cavity-radiation." It represents the most complete form of radiation possible, radiation from which no colour is missing, and in which every colour figures at its full strength. No known substance ever emits quite such complete radiation from its surface, although many approximate to doing so. We speak of such bodies as "full radiators."

The nineteenth-century laws of electromagnetism predicted that the whole of the radiation emitted by a full radiator or from a cavity ought to be found at or beyond the extreme violet end of the spectrum, independently of the precise temperature to which the body had been heated. In actual fact the radiation is usually found piled up at exactly the opposite end of the spectrum, and in no case does it ever conform to the predictions of the nineteenth century laws, or even begin to think of doing so.

In the year 1900 Professor Planck of Berlin discovered experimentally the law by which cavity-radiation is distributed among the different colours of the spectrum. He further shewed how his newly-discovered law could be deduced theoretically from a system of electromagnetic laws which differed very sensationally from those then in vogue.

Planck imagined all kinds of radiation to be emitted by systems of vibrators which emitted light when excited, much as tuning forks emit sound when they are struck. The old electrodynamical laws predicted that each vibration should gradually come to rest and then stop, as the vibrations of a tuning fork do, until the vibrator was in some way excited again. Rejecting all this, Planck supposed that a vibrator could change its energy by sudden jerks, and in no other way; it might have one, two, three, four or any other integral number of units of energy, but no intermediate fractional numbers, so that gradual changes of energy were rendered impossible. The vibrator, so to speak, kept no small change, and could only pay out its energy a shilling at a time until it had none left. Not only so, but it refused to receive small change, although it was prepared to accept complete shillings. This concept, sensational, revolutionary and even ridiculous, as many thought it at the time, was found to lead exactly to the distribution of colours actually observed in cavity-radiation.

In 1917 Einstein put the concept into the more precise form which now prevails. According to a theory previously advanced by Professor Niels Bohr of Copenhagen, an atomic or molecular structure does not change its configuration, or dissipate away its energy, by gradual stages; on the contrary, the changes are so abrupt that it is almost permissible to regard them as a series of sudden jumps or jerks. Bohr supposed that an atomic structure has a number of possible states or configurations which are entirely distinct and detached one from another, just as a weight placed on a staircase has only a possible number of positions; it may be 3 stairs up, or 4 or 5, but cannot be 3¼ or 3¾ stairs up. The change from one position to another is generally effected through the medium of radiation. The system can be pushed upstairs by absorbing energy from radiation which falls on it, or may move downstairs to a state of lower energy and emit energy in the form of radiation in so doing. Only radiation of a certain definite colour, and so of a certain precise wave-length, is of any account for effecting a particular change of state. The problem of shifting an atomic system is like that of extracting a box of matches from a penny-in-the-slot machine; it can only be done by a special implement, to wit a penny, which must be of precisely the right size and weight—a coin which is either too small *or too large,* too light *or too heavy,* is doomed to fail. If we pour radiation of the wrong wave length on to an atom, we may reproduce the comedy of the millionaire whose total wealth will not procure him a box of matches because he has not a loose penny, or we may reproduce the tragedy of the child who cannot obtain a slab of chocolate because its hoarded wealth consists of farthings and half-pence, but we shall not disturb the atom. When mixed radiation is poured on to a collection of atoms, these absorb the radiation of just those wave-lengths which are needed to change their internal states, and none other; radiation of all other wave-lengths passes by unaffected.

This selective action of the atom on radiation is put in evidence in a variety of ways; it is perhaps most simply shewn in the spectra of the sun and stars. Dark lines similar to those which Fraunhofer observed in the solar spectrum are observed in the spectra of practically all stars and we can now understand why this must be. Light of every possible wave-length streams out from the hot interior of a star, and bombards the atoms which form its atmosphere. Each atom drinks up that radiation which is of precisely the right wave-length for it, but has no interaction of any kind with the rest, so that the radiation which is finally emitted from the star is deficient in just the particular wave-lengths which suit the atoms. Thus the star shews an *absorption spectrum* of fine lines. The positions of these lines in the spectrum shew what types of radiation the stellar atoms have swallowed, and so enable us to identify the atoms from our laboratory knowledge of the tastes of different kinds of atoms for radiation. But what ultimately decides which types of radiation an atom will swallow, and which it will reject?

It had been part of Planck's theory that radiation of each wave-length has associated with it a certain amount of energy, called the "quantum," which depends on the wave-length and on nothing else. The quantum is supposed to be proportional to the "frequency," or number of vibrations of the radiation per second, and so is *inversely* proportional to the wave-length of the radiation—the shorter the wave-length, the greater the energy of the quantum, and conversely. Red light has feeble quanta, violet light has energetic quanta, and so on.

Einstein now supposed that radiation of a given type could effect an atomic or molecular change, only if the energy needed for the change is precisely equal to that of a single quantum of the radiation. This is commonly known as Einstein's law; it determines the precise type of radiation needed to work any atomic or molecular penny-in-the-slot mechanism.

We notice that work which demands one powerful quantum cannot be performed by two, or indeed by any number whatever, of feeble quanta. A small amount of violet (high-frequency) light can accomplish what no amount of red (low-frequency) light can effect.

The law prohibits the killing of two birds with one stone, as well as the killing of one bird with two stones; the whole quantum is used up in effecting the change, so that no energy from this particular quantum is left over to contribute to any further change. This aspect of the matter is illustrated by Einstein's photochemical law: "in any chemical reaction which is produced by the incidence of light, the number of molecules which are affected is equal to the number of quanta of light which are absorbed." Those who manage penny-in-the-slot machines are familiar with a similar law: "the number of articles sold is exactly equal to the number of coins in the machine."

If we think of energy in terms of its capacity for doing damage, we see that radiation of short wave-length can work more destruction in atomic structures than radiation of long wave-length—a circumstance with which every photographer is painfully familiar; we can admit as much red light as we please without any damage being done, but even the tiniest gleam of violet light spoils our plates. Radiation of sufficiently short wave-length may not only rearrange molecules or atoms; it may break up any atom on which it happens to fall, by shooting out one of its electrons, giving rise to what is known as photoelectric action. Again there is a definite limit of frequency, such that light whose frequency is below this limit does not produce any effect at all, no matter how intense it may be; whereas as soon as we pass to frequencies above this limit, light of even the feeblest intensity starts photoelectric action at once. Again the absorption of one quantum breaks up only one atom, and further ejects only one electron from the atom. If the radiation has a frequency above this limit, so that its quantum has more energy than the minimum necessary to remove a single electron from the atom, the whole quantum is still absorbed, the excess energy now being used in endowing the ejected electron with motion.

ELECTRON ORBITS. These concepts are based upon Bohr's supposition that only a limited number of orbits are open to the electrons in an atom, all others being prohibited for reasons which Bohr's theory did not fully explain, and that an electron is free to move from one permitted orbit to another under the stimulus of radiation. Bohr himself investigated the way in which the various permitted orbits are arranged. Modern investigations indicate the need for a good deal of revision of his simple concepts, but we shall discuss these in some detail, partly because Bohr's picture of the atom still provides the best working mechanical model we have, and partly because an understanding of his simple theory is absolutely essential to the understanding of the far more intricate theories which are beginning to replace it.

The hydrogen atom, as we have already seen, consists of a single proton as central nucleus, with a single electron revolving around it. The nucleus, with about 1847 times the weight of the electron, stands practically at rest unagitated by the motion of the latter, just as the sun remains practically undisturbed by the motion of the earth round it. The nucleus and electron carry charges of positive and negative electricity, and therefore attract one another; this is why the electron describes an orbit instead of flying off in a straight line, again like the earth and sun. Furthermore, the attraction between electric charges of opposite sign, positive and negative, follows, as it happens, precisely the same law as gravitation, the attraction falling off as the inverse square of the distance between the two charges. Thus the nucleus-electron system is similar in all respects to a sun-planet system, and the orbits which an electron can describe around a central nucleus are precisely identical with those which a planet can describe about a central sun; they consist of a system of ellipses each having the nucleus in one focus.

Yet the general concepts of quantum-dynamics prohibit the electron from moving in all these orbits indiscriminately. Bohr's original theory supposed that the electron in the hydrogen atom could move only in certain circular orbits whose diameters were proportional to the squares of the natural numbers, and so to 1, 4, 9, 16, 25, ... Bohr subsequently modified this very simple hypothesis, and the theory of wave-mechanics has recently modified it much further.

Yet it still remains true that the hydrogen atom has always very approximately the same energy as it would have if the electron were describing one or another of these simple orbits of Bohr. Thus, when its energy changes, it changes as though the electron jumped over from one to another of these orbits. For this reason it is easy to calculate what changes of energy a hydrogen atom can experience—they are precisely those which correspond to the passage from one Bohr orbit to another. For example, the two orbits of smallest diameters in the hydrogen atom differ in energy by 16×10^{-12} erg. If we pour radiation of the appropriate wave-length on to an atom in which the electron is describing the smallest orbit of all, it crosses over to the next orbit, absorbing 16×10^{-12} erg of energy in the process, and so becoming temporarily a reservoir of energy holding 16×10^{-12} erg. If the atom is in any way disturbed from outside, it may of course discharge the energy at any time, or it may absorb still more energy and so increase its store.

If we know all the orbits which are possible for an atom of any type, it is easy to calculate the changes of energy involved in the various transitions between them. As each transition absorbs or releases exactly one quantum of energy, we can immediately deduce the frequencies of the light emitted or absorbed in these transitions. In brief, given the arrangement of atomic orbits, we can calculate the spectrum of the atom. In practice the problem of course takes the converse form: given the spectrum, to find the structure of the atom which emits it. Bohr's model of the hydrogen atom is a good model at least to this extent—that the spectrum it would emit reproduces the hydrogen spectrum almost exactly. Yet the agreement is not quite perfect, and for this reason it is now generally accepted that Bohr's scheme of orbits is inadequate to account for actual spectra. We continue to discuss Bohr's scheme, not because the atom is actually built that way, but because it provides a working model which is good enough for our present purpose.

An essential, although at first sight somewhat unexpected, feature of the whole theory is that even if the hydrogen atom charged with its

16 × 10⁻¹² erg of energy is left entirely undisturbed, the electron must, after a certain time, lapse back spontaneously to its original smaller orbit, ejecting its 16 × 10⁻¹² erg of energy in the form of radiation in so doing. Einstein shewed that, if this were not so, then Planck's well-established "cavity-radiation" law could not be true. Thus, a collection of hydrogen atoms in which the electrons describe orbits larger than the smallest possible orbit is similar to a collection of uranium or other radio-active atoms, in that the atoms spontaneously fall back to their states of lower energy as the result merely of the passage of time.

The electron orbits in more complicated atoms have much the same general arrangement as in the hydrogen atom, but are different in size. In the hydrogen atom the electron normally falls, after sufficient time, to the orbit of lowest energy and stays there. It might be thought by analogy that in more complicated atoms in which several electrons are describing orbits, all the electrons would in time fall into the orbit of lowest energy and stay there. Such does not prove to be the case. There is never room for more than one electron in the same orbit. This is a special aspect of a general principle which appears to dominate the whole of physics. It has a name—"the exclusion-principle"—but this is about all as yet; we have hardly begun to understand it. In another of its special aspects it becomes identical with the old familiar cornerstone of science which asserts that two different pieces of matter cannot occupy the same space at the same time. Without understanding the underlying principle, we can accept the fact that two electrons not only cannot occupy the same space, but cannot even occupy the same orbit. It is as though in some way the electron spread itself out so as to occupy the whole of its orbit, thus leaving room for no other. No doubt this must not be accepted as a literal picture of things, and yet the modern theory of wave-mechanics suggests that in some sense (which we cannot yet specify with much precision) the orbits of lowest energy in the hydrogen atom are possible orbits just because the electron can completely fill them, and that adjacent orbits are impossible because the electron would fill them ¾ or 1½ times over, and similarly for more complicated atoms. In this connection it is perhaps significant that no single known phenomenon of physics makes it possible to say that at a given instant an electron is at such or such a point in an orbit of lowest energy; such a statement appears to be quite meaningless and the condition of an atom is apparently specified with all possible precision by saying that at a given instant an electron is in such an orbit, as it would be, for instance, if the electron had spread itself out into a ring. We cannot say the same of other orbits. As we pass to orbits of higher energy, and so of greater diameter, the indeterminateness gradually assumes a different form, and finally becomes of but little importance. Whatever form the electron may assume while it is describing a little orbit near the nucleus, by the time it is describing a very big orbit far out it has become a plain material particle charged with electricity.

Thus, whatever the reason may be, electrons which are describing orbits in the same atom must all be in different orbits. The electrons in their orbits are like men on a ladder; just as no two men can stand on the same rung, so no two electrons can ever follow one another round in the same orbit. The neon atom, for instance, with 10 electrons is in its normal state of lowest energy when its 10 electrons each occupy one of the 10 orbits whose energy is lowest. For reasons which the quantum theory has at last succeeded in elucidating, there are, in every atom, two orbits in which the energy is equal and lower than in any other orbit. After this come eight orbits of equal but substantially higher energy, then 18 orbits of equal but still higher energy, and so on. As the electrons in each of these various groups of orbits all have equal energy, they are commonly spoken of, in a graphic but misleading phraseology, as rings of electrons. They are designated the K-ring, the L-ring, the M-ring and so on. The K-ring, which is nearest to the nucleus, has room for two electrons only. Any further electrons are pushed out into the L-ring, which has room for eight electrons, all describing orbits which are different but of equal energy. If still more electrons remain to be accommodated, they must go into the M-ring and so on.

In its normal state, the hydrogen atom has one electron in its K-ring, while the helium has two, the L, M, and higher rings being unoccupied. The atom of next higher complexity, the lithium atom, has three electrons, and as only two can be accommodated in its K-ring, one has to wander round in the outer spaces of the L-ring. In beryllium with four electrons, two are driven out into the L-ring. And so it goes on, until we reach neon with 10 electrons, by which time the L-ring as well as the inner K-ring is full up. In the next atom, sodium, one of the 11 electrons is driven out into the still more remote M-ring, and so on. Provided the electrons are not being excited by radiation or other stimulus, each atom sinks in time to a state in which its electrons are occupying its orbits of lowest energy, one in each.

So far as our experience goes, an atom, as soon as it reaches this state, becomes a true perpetual motion machine, the electrons continuing to move in their orbits (at any rate on Bohr's theory) without any of the energy of their motion being dissipated away, either in the form of radiation or otherwise. It seems astonishing and quite incomprehensible that an atom in such a state should not be able to yield up its energy still further, but, so far as our experience goes, it cannot. And this property, little though we understand it, is, in the last resort, responsible for keeping the universe in being. If no restriction of this kind intervened, the whole material energy of the universe would disappear in the form of radiation in a few thousand-millionth parts of a second. If the normal hydrogen atom were capable of emitting radiation in the way demanded by the nineteenth-century laws of physics, it would, as a direct consequence of this emission of radiation, begin to shrink at the rate of over a metre a second, the electron continually falling to orbits of lower and lower energy. After about a thousand-millionth part of a second the nucleus and the electron would run into one another, and the whole atom would probably disappear in a flash of radiation. By prohibiting any emission of radiation except by complete quanta, and by prohibiting any emission at all when there are no quanta available for dissipation, the quantum theory succeeds in keeping the universe in existence as a going concern.

It is difficult to form even the remotest conception of the realities underlying all these phenomena. The recent branch of physics known as "wave mechanics" is at present groping after an understanding, but so far progress has been in the direction of co-ordinating observed phenomena rather than in getting down to realities. Indeed, it may be doubted whether we shall ever properly understand the realities ultimately involved; they may well be so fundamental as to be beyond the grasp of the human mind.

It is just for this reason that modern theoretical physics is so difficult to explain, and so difficult to understand. It is easy to explain the motion of the earth round the sun in the solar system. We see the sun in the sky; we feel the earth under our feet, and the concept of motion is familiar to us from everyday experience. How different when we try to explain the analogous motion of the electron round the proton in the hydrogen atom! Neither you nor I have any direct experience of either electrons or protons, and no one has so far any inkling of what they are really like. So we agree to make a sort of model in which the electron and proton are represented by the simplest things known to us, tiny hard spheres. The model works well for a time and then suddenly breaks in our hands. In the new light of the wave mechanics, the hard sphere is seen to be hopelessly inadequate to represent the electron. . . . Yet as our minds have so far failed to conceive any better picture of the atom than this very imperfect model, we can only proceed by describing phenomena in terms of it.   *Edition of 1934*

The Discovery of Radium

EVE CURIE

From *Madame Curie*

AFTER ROENTGEN'S DISCOVERY OF X RAYS, HENRI
Poincaré conceived the idea of determining whether rays like the X
ray were emitted by "fluorescent" bodies under the action of light. Attracted by the same problem, Henri Becquerel examined the salts of a
"rare metal," uranium. Instead of finding the phenomenon he had expected, he observed another, altogether different and incomprehensible:
he found that uranium salts *spontaneously* emitted, without exposure to
light, some rays of unknown nature. A compound of uranium, placed on a
photographic plate surrounded by black paper, made an impression on the
plate through the paper. And, like the X ray, these astonishing "uranic"
salts discharged an electroscope by rendering the surrounding air a conductor.

Henri Becquerel made sure that these surprising properties were not
caused by a preliminary exposure to the sun and that they persisted when
the uranium compound had been maintained in darkness for several
months. For the first time, a physicist had observed the phenomenon to
which Marie Curie was later to give the name of *radioactivity*. But the
nature of the radiation and its origin remained an enigma.

Becquerel's discovery fascinated the Curies. They asked themselves
whence came the energy—tiny, to be sure—which uranium compounds
constantly disengaged in the form of radiation. And what was the nature
of this radiation? Here was an engrossing subject of research, a doctor's
thesis! The subject tempted Marie most because it was a virgin field:
Becquerel's work was very recent and so far as he knew nobody in the
laboratories of Europe had yet attempted to make a fundamental study
of uranium rays. As a point of departure, and as the only bibliography,
there existed some communications presented by Henri Becquerel at the

Academy of Science during the year 1896. It was a leap into great adventure, into an unknown realm.

There remained the question of where she was to make her experiments—and here the difficulties began. Pierre made several approaches to the director of the School of Physics with practically no results: Marie was given the free use of a little glassed-in studio on the ground floor of the school. It was a kind of storeroom, sweating with damp, where unused machines and lumber were put away. Its technical equipment was rudimentary and its comfort nil.

Deprived of an adequate electrical installation and of everything that forms material for the beginning of scientific research, she kept her patience, sought and found a means of making her apparatus work in this hole.

It was not easy. Instruments of precision have sneaking enemies: humidity, changes of temperature. Incidentally the climate of this little workroom, fatal to the sensitive electrometer, was not much better for Marie's health. But this had no importance. When she was cold, the young woman took her revenge by noting the degrees of temperature in centigrade in her notebook. On February 6, 1898, we find, among the formulas and figures: "Temperature here 6°25. [About 44° Fahrenheit.] Six degrees . . . !" Marie, to show her disapproval, added ten little exclamation points.

The candidate for the doctor's degree set her first task to be the measurement of the "power of ionization" of uranium rays—that is to say, their power to render the air a conductor of electricity and so to discharge an electroscope. The excellent method she used, which was to be the key to the success of her experiments, had been invented for the study of other phenomena by two physicists well known to her: Pierre and Jacques Curie. Her technical installation consisted of an "ionization chamber," a Curie electrometer and a piezoelectric quartz.

At the end of several weeks the first result appeared: Marie acquired the certainty that the intensity of this surprising radiation was proportional to the quantity of uranium contained in the samples under examination, and that this radiation, which could be measured with precision, was not affected either by the chemical state of combination of the uranium or by external factors such as lighting or temperature.

These observations were perhaps not very sensational to the uninitiated, but they were of passionate interest to the scientist. It often happens in physics that an inexplicable phenomenon can be subjected, after some investigation, to laws already known, and by this very fact loses its interest for the research worker. Thus, in a badly constructed detective story, if we are told in the third chapter that the woman of sinister appearance who might have committed the crime is in reality only an honest little house-wife who leads a life without secrets, we feel discouraged and cease to read.

Nothing of the kind happened here. The more Marie penetrated into intimacy with uranium rays, the more they seemed without precedent, essentially unknown. They were like nothing else. Nothing affected them. In spite of their very feeble power, they had an extraordinary individuality.

Turning this mystery over and over in her head, and pointing toward the truth, Marie felt and could soon affirm that the incomprehensible radiation was an *atomic* property. She questioned: Even though the phenomenon had only been observed with uranium, nothing proved that uranium was the only chemical element capable of emitting such radiation. Why should not other bodies possess the same power? Perhaps it was only by chance that this radiation had been observed in uranium first, and had remained attached to uranium in the minds of physicists. Now it must be sought for elsewhere. . . .

No sooner said than done. Abandoning the study of uranium, Marie undertook to examine *all known chemical bodies*, either in the pure state or in compounds. And the result was not long in appearing: compounds of another element, thorium, also emitted spontaneous rays like those of uranium and of similar intensity. The physicist had been right: the surprising phenomenon was by no means the property of uranium alone, and it became necessary to give it a distinct name. Mme Curie suggested the name of *radioactivity*. Chemical substances like uranium and thorium, endowed with this particular "radiance," were called *radio elements*.

Radioactivity so fascinated the young scientist that she never tired of examining the most diverse forms of matter, always by the same method. Curiosity, a marvelous feminine curiosity, the first virtue of a scientist, was developed in Marie to the highest degree. Instead of limiting her observation to simple compounds, salts and oxides, she had the desire to assemble samples of minerals from the collection at the School of Physics, and of making them undergo almost at hazard, for her own amusement, a kind of customs inspection which is an electrometer test. Pierre approved, and chose with her the veined fragments, hard or crumbly, oddly shaped, which she wanted to examine.

Marie's idea was simple—simple as the stroke of genius. At the crossroads where Marie now stood, hundreds of research workers might have remained, nonplussed, for months or even years. After examining all known chemical substances, and discovering—as Marie had done—the radiation of thorium, they would have continued to ask themselves in vain whence came this mysterious radioactivity. Marie, too, questioned and wondered. But her surprise was translated into fruitful acts. She had used up all evident possibilities. Now she turned toward the unplumbed and the unknown.

She knew in advance what she would learn from an examination of the minerals, or rather she thought she knew. The specimens which contained neither uranium nor thorium would be revealed as totally "inactive." The others, containing uranium or thorium, would be radioactive.

Experiment confirmed this prevision. Rejecting the inactive minerals, Marie applied herself to the others and measured their radioactivity. Then came a dramatic revelation: the radioactivity was a *great deal stronger* than could have been normally foreseen by the quantity of uranium or thorium contained in the products examined!

"It must be an error in experiment," the young woman thought; for doubt is the scientist's first response to an unexpected phenomenon.

She started her measurements over again, unmoved, using the same products. She started over again ten times, twenty times. And she was forced to yield to the evidence: the quantities of uranium found in these minerals were by no means sufficient to justify the exceptional intensity of the radiation she observed.

Where did this excessive and abnormal radiation come from? Only one explanation was possible: the minerals must contain, in small quantity, a *much more powerfully radioactive substance* than uranium and thorium.

But what substance? In her preceding experiments, Marie had already examined *all known chemical elements*.

The scientist replied to the question with the sure logic and the magnificent audaciousness of a great mind: The mineral certainly contained a radioactive substance, which was at the same time a chemical element unknown until this day: *a new element*.

A new element! It was a fascinating and alluring hypothesis—but still a hypothesis. For the moment this powerfully radioactive substance existed only in the imagination of Marie and of Pierre. But it did exist there. It existed strongly enough to make the young woman go to see Bronya one day and tell her in a restrained, ardent voice:

"You know, Bronya, the radiation that I couldn't explain comes from a new chemical element. The element is there and I've got to find it. We are sure! The physicists we have spoken to believe we have made an error in experiment and advise us to be careful. But I am convinced that I am not mistaken."

These were unique moments in her unique life. The layman forms a theatrical—and wholly false—idea of the research worker and of his discoveries. "The moment of discovery" does not always exist: the scientist's work is too tenuous, too divided, for the certainty of success to crackle out suddenly in the midst of his laborious toil like a stroke of lightning, dazzling him by its fire. Marie, standing in front of her apparatus, perhaps never experienced the sudden intoxication of triumph. This intoxication was spread over several days of decisive labor, made feverish by a magnificent hope. But it must have been an exultant moment when, convinced by the rigorous reasoning of her brain that she was on the trail of new matter, she confided the secret to her elder sister, her ally always. . . . Without exchanging one affectionate word, the two sisters must have lived again, in a dizzying breath of memory, their years of waiting, their mutual sacrifices, their bleak lives as students, full of hope and faith.

It was barely four years before that Marie had written:

Life is not easy for any of us. But what of that? We must have perseverance and above all confidence in ourselves. We must believe that we are gifted for something, and that this thing, at whatever cost, must be attained.

That "something" was to throw science upon a path hitherto unsuspected.

In a first communication to the Academy, presented by Prof. Lippmann and published in the *Proceedings* on April 12, 1898, "Marie Sklodovska Curie" announced the probable presence in pitchblende ores of a new element endowed with powerful radioactivity. This was the first stage of the discovery of radium.

By the force of her own intuition the physicist had shown to herself that the wonderful substance must exist. She decreed its existence. But its incognito still had to be broken. Now she would have to verify hypothesis by experiment, isolate this material and see it. She must be able to announce with certainty: "It is there."

Pierre Curie had followed the rapid progress of his wife's experiments with passionate interest. Without directly taking part in Marie's work, he had frequently helped her by his remarks and advice. In view of the stupefying character of her results, he did not hesitate to abandon his study of crystals for the time being in order to join his efforts to hers in the search for the new substance.

Thus, when the immensity of a pressing task suggested and exacted collaboration, a great physicist was at Marie's side—a physicist who was the companion of her life. Three years earlier, love had joined this exceptional man and woman together—love, and perhaps some mysterious fore-knowledge, some sublime instinct for the work in common.

The valuable force was now doubled. Two brains, four hands, now sought the unknown element in the damp little workroom in the Rue Lhomond. From this moment onward it is impossible to distinguish each one's part in the work of the Curies. We know that Marie, having chosen to study the radiation of uranium as the subject of her thesis, discovered that other substances were also radioactive. We know that after the examination of minerals she was able to announce the existence of a new chemical element, powerfully radioactive, and that it was the capital importance of this result which decided Pierre Curie to interrupt his very different research in order to try to isolate this element with his wife. At that time—May or June, 1898—a collaboration began which was to last for eight years, until it was destroyed by a fatal accident.

We cannot and must not attempt to find out what should be credited to Marie and what to Pierre during these eight years. It would be exactly what the husband and wife did not want. The personal genius of Pierre Curie is known to us by the original work he had accomplished before this collaboration. His wife's genius appears to us in the first intuition of discovery, the brilliant start; and it was to reappear to us again, solitary, when Marie Curie the widow unflinchingly carried the weight of a new science and conducted it, through research, step by step, to its harmonious expansion. We therefore have formal proof that in the fusion of their two efforts, in this superior alliance of man and woman, the exchange was equal.

Let this certainly suffice for our curiosity and admiration. Let us not attempt to separate these creatures full of love, whose handwriting alternates and combines in the working notebooks covered with formulae, these creatures who were to sign nearly all their scientific publications together. They were to write "We found" and "We observed"; and when they were constrained by fact to distinguish between their parts, they were to employ this moving locution:

> Certain minerals containing uranium and thorium (pitchblende, chalcolite, uranite) are very active from the point of view of the emission of Becquerel rays. In a preceding communication, *one of us* showed that their activity was even greater than that of uranium and thorium, and stated the opinion that this effect was due to some other very active substance contained in small quantity in these minerals.
>
> (Pierre and Marie Curie: *Proceedings of the Academy of Science*, July 18, 1898.)

Marie and Pierre looked for this "very active" substance in an ore of uranium called pitchblende, which in the crude state had shown itself to be four times more radioactive than the pure oxide of uranium that could be extracted from it. But the composition of this ore had been known for a long time with considerable precision. The new element must therefore be present in very small quantity or it would not have escaped the notice of scientists and their chemical analysis. . . .

They began their prospecting patiently, using a method of chemical research invented by themselves, based on radioactivity; they separated all the elements in pitchblende by ordinary chemical analysis and then measured the radioactivity of each of the bodies thus obtained. By successive eliminations they saw the "abnormal" radioactivity take refuge in certain parts of the ore. As they went on, the field of investigation was narrowed. It was exactly the technique used by the police when they search the houses of a neighborhood, one by one, to isolate and arrest a malefactor.

But there was more than one malefactor here: the radioactivity was concentrated principally in two different chemical fractions of the pitchblende. For M. and Mme Curie it indicated the existence of two new elements instead of one. By July 1898 they were able to announce the discovery of one of these substances with certainty.

"You will have to name it," Pierre said to his young wife, in the same tone as if it were a question of choosing a name for little Irène.

The one-time Mlle Sklodovska reflected in silence for a moment. Then, her heart turning toward her own country . . . answered timidly: "Could we call it 'polonium'?"

In the *Proceedings of the Academy* for July 1898 we read:

We believe the substance we have extracted from pitchblende contains a metal not yet observed, related to bismuth by its analytical properties. If the existence of this new metal is confirmed we propose to call it *polonium,* from the name of the original country of one of us.

We find another note worthy of remark.

It was drawn up by Marie and Pierre Curie and a collaborator called G. Bémont. Intended for the Academy of Science, and published in the *Proceedings* of the session of December 26, 1898, it announced the existence of a second new chemical element in pitchblende.

Some lines of this communication read as follows:

The various reasons we have just enumerated lead us to believe that the new radioactive substance contains a new element to which we propose to give the name of RADIUM.

1937

Electronics Everywhere

A. M. LOW

THE ANCIENT GREEKS AND ROMANS ACHIEVED WHAT was, at the time, a high degree of civilization by the enslavement of many thousands of human beings. Five or ten men and women worked as slaves in order that one more fortunate should, as it were, "live like a lord." With no appreciable sources of artificial power or machinery this was, in fact, the only way in which a civilization could have been built; for culture and comfort can only come with leisure. Two centuries ago, the advent of steam power reduced the need for slavery. The energy of coal began to take the place of the energy in human muscles. The harnessing of oil carried the matter further. Explosives also contributed their energy to freeing men from hard labor; a modern tunnel is bored by a few hundred men with the aid of explosives where the Romans would employ thousands for many years. Slavery has always been considered a "moral" issue, but it was largely one of science and economics. The inventor provided the political philosopher with the material means for abolishing slavery. It was the absence of any alternative which had allowed this class of labour to be so general. Slavery now lingers only in the most undeveloped countries, merely because industrial civilization has no need of human slavery; we have machines instead.

Today, another scientific discovery is further releasing human beings from toil and increasing the possibilities of leisure, health and happiness for the mass of people. A great new army of "slaves" has been recruited to do work which otherwise would require human beings. Just as no conceivable number of men could power our factories, so even the conscription of millions could not make possible the increased production resulting from the use of electronic devices. For the new slave is the electron, something so small that no one has seen it or is ever likely to see it for centuries, yet with such qualities that, under control, it can make it possible for men to talk to each other from different sides of the world, to fly aircraft without touching controls, to weld metals and cook foods, to destroy insects and disperse smoke, to control machines and make visible the invisible. These are only a few of the things that this new science and industry called electronics has given to us.

Yet the electron is one of the smallest things we know. Almost without weight, it travels at speeds measured in thousands of miles a second. The number of electrons being used in the world is quite incalculable even in astronomic figures. A single large rectifier valve in the course of a year might easily use four pounds of electrons. Only four pounds; but their number is about 2,000,000,000,000,000,000,000,000,000,000,000. When we look at a television screen we see the impact of millions of electrons a second on the screen, each impact making a little glow of light. When we turn the switch of a wireless receiver, the valves begin to move millions of electrons a minute to deal with the signals received by your aerial, generated by other electrons at the transmitter, and to manipulate them so that eventually sounds may be heard.

Just what is an electron? It is a fundamental particle of matter. Everything, from the paper on which this is printed to your own eyes which are reading it, is ultimately made up of electrons. They are called electrons after the Greek word for amber, because over 2,500 years ago the Greeks discovered that, when amber was rubbed, something happened to it that made it attract dust or small particles of other substances. What happened to the amber was that free electrons were "removed" by the rubbing, but it was not until comparatively recent years that the nature of this phenomenon was understood. Almost fifty years ago, Crookes, J. J. Thomson, Millikan and other scientists demonstrated the existence and nature of the electron.

The true discoverer of the electron was Professor J. J. Thomson, who, following the experiments of Crookes, showed that when a metallic wire was heated in a vacuum something was emitted. He weighed electrons and showed that they were negative charges of electricity carried by particles of "matter." He also demonstrated that electrons could be deflected from their path by an electrical field. Others showed that the electron was the fundamental electrical charge and that it was impossible to have less than one electron as a charge. From this came the conception of electrical charges as a particular number of particles or "specks," each exactly the same. An electrical charge was imagined as a definite number of electrons, or as a number of "grains" rather than a fluid. The new idea was that of a bucket full of grains of wheat as opposed to a bucket full of water. But electrons have wave-like qualities as well and so we have the difficult picture of "things" that sometimes appear to be particles moving like bullets and sometimes as "waves" behaving rather like the waves of sound. The conception is not easy for the imagination to grasp, but there are no difficulties in handling it mathematically. In fact, our exact knowledge of the electron is still very incomplete, but that has not prevented us from using and controlling electrons to perform hundreds of useful tasks.

All things, as most people now know, are made up of atoms and all these atoms contain, among other "parts," electrons. The number of electrons in an atom depends upon its nature. The atom of hydrogen has one electron and the number of electrons increases with each of the elements up to 92. The easiest way to think of the electrons is as small "planets" circling round a central nucleus which is made up of neutrons and protons. The electron carries a charge of negative electricity and the proton a charge of positive electricity. We can imagine electrons as planets whirling round the central sun in a solar system, although this example is not quite correct according to the latest theories. It would, perhaps, be more accurate to think in terms of a "cloud" of electrons enveloping the nucleus rather than of small bodies following well-defined orbits.

Now, what happened when the Greeks rubbed their pieces of amber was that some of the free electrons were removed to the cloth. The amber, therefore, became deficient in electron particles and so had a "definite" charge. The amber then seeks to regain its electrons and thus attracts any small pieces of dust or paper to make up for the loss it has suffered.

This is called "static" electricity. In "current" electricity, which flows more readily through the conductor as well as collecting on the surface, the atoms pass their "free" electron on to each other. The energy created at one end of the wire is sent to the other by these free electrons pushing each other onwards. Electricity will not flow in a nonconductor or insulator because these substances are composed of atoms which are without this "free" electron, anxious to pass on and leave the atom positively charged. All materials can roughly be divided into conductors and insulators, but no metal is a perfect conductor and no substance is a perfect insulator.

To produce any of the electrical effects with which we are familiar millions of electrons a second have to be "shoved on." For instance, in an electric lamp, which becomes hot because the atoms of the metal of which its filament is made cannot deal with the electrons quickly enough, we have to shove about 1,500,000,000,000,000 electrons through the wire every second. If we push a lesser number, the wire will become hot, but not sufficiently hot to glow and, of course, it will deal with a very much lesser number without becoming hot at all.

An electric lamp is an electric, rather than an electronic, device because it is designed to imprison the electrons rather than to release them after use. As described later, there is a small flow of electrons in an electric lamp, but this is accidental and to be avoided, if possible, because it would result in the lamp wearing out. In the electronic device we purposely set free from the filament as many electrons as possible, because, by the manipulation of these electrons, we can do so much useful work. The heart of an electronic device is a filament which, when heated, emits a plentiful supply of electrons. We do not now need to heat the filament to white heat to secure the desired effect. There are metals which will give out plenty of electrons at quite a moderate temperature; these have the advantage that they do not consume so much current and do not require cooling of their containers or accessories.

In every case, of course, the electrons are really moved by some sort of "generator" of electricity such as a dynamo or a battery. The electrons shove each other along the conducting wire in a kind of wave until they reach the filament when their movement heats it up so that the free electrons in the filament wire are shot out and become separated from the main body of the metal. How these electrons are afterwards dealt with will be explained later on, but it is the motion of these freed electrons that is the moving spirit of "electronics." All electronic devices incorporate purely "electrical" parts, the electricity necessary to shake the electrons out of the filament is carried to it along wires in just the same way as electricity is carried to a lamp or heater. The device probably contains condensers, mechanical switches and other purely "electrical" parts. The distinction between "electricity" and "electronics" is, in some ways, artificial, but it is convenient to distinguish this latest branch of the science of electricity which is already playing such a big part in our lives.

In England we describe the device in which free electrons are generated as "valves." The Americans call them "tubes." Both words are, perhaps, a little misleading, for acting as a "valve" is not the function of all electronic "tubes" and "tube" seems hardly the right description for hundreds of "generators" which are completely closed and look like anything but a tube. It does not matter very much what word we use to describe what is the key to almost every electronic apparatus. But the use of the word "valve" in England recalls an interesting piece of electronic history which is a good starting point for an account of how these devices generate and use electrons.

About forty-three years ago, Sir Ambrose Fleming constructed what was really the first "valve." Many years before the electron was fully dis-

covered or recognized, the great inventor Edison had observed free electrons at work without quite realizing what was happening. Edison was
experimenting with electric lamps and he noticed that sometimes there
was a glow at the base of the lamp between the two "legs" of the filament
which increasingly incandesced when heated by the passing of a growing
electric current. He studied this glow, which came to be called "The
Edison effect," and, by placing a special metal plate between the two legs
connected to a galvanometer, was able to show that a current passed
through the vacuum between the two wires. It was not until twelve years
later that Sir. J. J Thomson proved that the "current" was, in fact, a
stream of electrons. Things had literally become too hot for the electrons
in the incandescent wire and they flew out. When they hit the plate they
produced an electric current that could be measured and was directly
related to the voltage applied to the filament. Edison then found that
when this plate was connected to the negative side of the filament circuit,
no current flowed, but that if it were connected to the positive side a small
current was set up which varied in accordance with the voltage in the
lamp.

Sir Ambrose Fleming, considering this, asked whether it would not be
possible to make the stream of electrons in the lamp act as a valve allowing the electrons from a battery to flow only one way. We are all probably
familiar with many different kinds of valve. The rubber valve in your
cycle tire, for instance, allows air to be blown into the inner tube, but will
not permit it to flow the other way and escape. So this simple electronic
valve permits electrons to flow in one direction and not in the other. It is
called a "diode" valve, because it has two essential parts: the filament,
and the plate which picks up the stream of electrons generated. Naturally,
it is very different in appearance from Edison's electric lamp with a plate
at the side. To pick up the maximum number of electrons emitted by the
filament, the plate is usually made in cylindrical form to surround the hot
wire. The wire itself, instead of being chosen chiefly for its brightness
when heated, is made of a metal which readily emits electrons.

A diode valve can rectify alternating current. It can be seen that when
the current flows in one direction, the valve stops it, but that when it
flows in the other, it lets it pass. Thus, by filtering out the alternate pulses
of an alternating current it can "rectify" it, that is, turn it into direct
current flowing in one direction only. There are innumerable needs for
"rectification" in almost every branch of electronics.

The invention of the diode valve was one of the major discoveries of
wireless and, without it, we should never have had broadcasting as we
know it to-day. But an almost equally important step forward was taken

two years later when, in America, Dr. Lee De Forest added a third element to the valve and made the first "triode." This third element was called the "grid," from its appearance, and it was placed between the filament and the plate. The purpose of the grid was to regulate the flow of current of electrons between the filament and the plate. By applying a relatively small voltage to the grid, it is possible to make a great difference to the current in the plate circuit. When the grid is electrically neutral, as it were, the electrons shot out from the filament can flow to the plate only a little obstructed by the fine wires. But if you now apply a small negative charge to the grid, the electrons are repulsed, even if they do not actually strike the wire of the grid itself. Just how many are cut off from the plate will depend on the strength of the current applied to the grid. By regulating this, the flow is controlled, and a comparatively small current in the grid can make a great difference to the plate current.

This is how electrons are set to work to perform the task of amplification. The variations in a very weak current can be amplified in a triode valve and the resulting variations can be again amplified. By successive stages of amplification we obtain the necessary signal strength required to operate a loudspeaker or to set in motion any of the many mechanical actions you may require. Amplifying valves are found in almost every electronic device, and communications today would be very difficult without their help. For example, when you speak on the telephone, the electrical signals resulting become weak after they have traveled a few hundred miles. An amplifier can bring them back to their original strength without distorting them and your listener hears you clearly.

There are several other types of radio valves. One of them is also an amplifying valve which works, however, on a different principle from that of the triode. For various reasons, there are limitations to the ordinary triode and this other type of valve, called a magnetron, because it depends upon a magnetic field, has been developed especially to deal with very short wave radio signals. As will be explained later, it was of very great importance to the development of radar during the war. Magnetic control of valves was first tried about thirty years ago.

In the magnetron in its simplest form a filament runs through a metal cylinder. When the filament is heated, electrons fly off to the metal plate just as in a diode. But if powerful magnetism is applied, the paths of the electrons become curved. The more powerful the magnetic field, the greater the curve until, as will be appreciated, a point can be reached when instead of flying to the plate, the electrons make a complete circle and return to the filament. At this point, of course, the valve would be "closed" and no current would pass. It is the stage just before this that is used. Under these conditions comparatively small changes in the amount of magnetism make immense differences in the number of electrons reaching the plate; in other words, to the current that flows. So it will be clear that if the signals to be amplified act on the electromagnet producing the magnetic field, comparatively small variations can produce very great changes in the current through the magnetron. In short, high amplification is obtained.

Yet another type of electronic "tube" depends upon the fact that, when some substances are struck by light, they emit electrons. The light acts in the same stimulating way as an electric current, but no appreciable heat is generated. There are many different metals which have this property of emitting electrons when struck by light. Some only produce their electrons with particular wavelengths of light; zinc, for instance, is particularly "sensitive" to the very short waves of ultra-violet, but not to ordinary visible white light. The metal caesium, allied to sodium and potassium, is often used when visible light is the source of stimulation. The valve in which this phenomenon is used, generally called a photo-electric cell, consists of the usual glass container, the back of which is coated with a suitable metal. The metallic coating is connected to the negative side of the circuit and the positive side is connected to the "plate," which, in fact, is generally a rod or loop in the center of the glass bulb. Light enters the valve, strikes the metallic coating and electrons are emitted. These are collected by the plate and a current flows through the valve. Immediately the light is turned out, stimulation of the electrons stops and the current ceases to flow.

The amount of current produced depends upon the intensity of the light and the different metallic coatings are sensitive to different parts of the spectrum. Infra-red light, for example, however strong the beam, will produce no electrons from caesium, but shine a green light and a good stream flows. Potassium is most sensitive to blue light and, as explained, zinc does not really come into action until the limits of visible light have been passed. These properties have been turned to many useful purposes. . . .

There is yet another kind of electronic generator in which, instead of having electrons produced by light striking a metal, we have light produced by electrons striking a metal. It is a special kind of light of extremely short wavelength, very much shorter than anything that can affect the human eye, very much shorter even than ultra-violet light; but, just because of its shortness, it is able to penetrate substances which are opaque to ordinary light. These are X-rays. The electrons in an X-ray tube are generated by a filament as in the first three kinds of valve; but with this difference that a very high voltage is used to speed up the electrons in their flight. They travel many times as fast as the electrons in a wireless valve. As in the diode valve, they strike a plate, in the X-ray tube it is called the "target." A very high voltage is applied to the target which is composed of a hard metal. When the electrons strike, they produce the special kind of light we call X-rays, which pass out of the tube to be used as required.

The X-ray tube does not have a grid, for it is not a regulating "valve" but a generating tube. It has, however, a third electrode of which the purpose is to focus the stream of electrons so that the maximum number strike the target. The voltages used in the X-ray tube depend upon the "hardness" of the X-rays required, a loose term referring to the degree of vacuum and other electrical conditions. For penetrating flesh for the familiar X-ray photographs a voltage of 50,000 to 100,000 is generally sufficient, but for penetrating metals to search for flaws voltages of over 200,000 may be used.

Since X-rays are far too short, 20,000 times shorter than red light, to affect the eye, they would be of little use to us if we could not make them visible. This is done in two ways. Either they are allowed to fall on a photographic plate after passing the object to be examined, so that by development we can have a "shadow picture"; or they are made to strike a screen of special material which becomes excited and "fluoresces" under X-rays. In both cases it is a "shadow picture" that is obtained and this has limitations. It would be difficult to exaggerate the value of X-rays in medicine, atomic research and increasingly in industry for the examination of the internal structure of metallic parts to locate faults not visible on the surface, and for similar purposes.

This short account as to the exact means by which X-rays are generated in an X-ray tube when the rapidly moving electrons strike the target, may seem rather vague. Why do they produce X-rays which are "light" and not a stream of electrons? The answer is that no one really knows. But we can say that the electrons exchange some of their energy for energy of another kind, the X-rays. The process is very like that by which electric energy in a wire is converted into light, visible by the effect it has on the wire. X-rays, magnetically and otherwise, do not act like a beam of normal light.

There are a great many other kinds of electronic valves or tubes of many different shapes and sizes, each with its special purpose. All of them have in common the production of electrons in great numbers. Many vary only in size and construction from the ordinary types. To take one example, the valves used for the rectification of current, turning it from alternating current to direct current, in industry, are the same in principle as the diode, but very different in construction because of the heavy currents they have to handle.

Alternating current is efficient, easily transformed from voltage to voltage and best for many purposes, but in industry a direct current is often necessary. Some valves used for rectification have a little pool of mercury instead of the familiar wire filament. Part of the mercury is vaporized and a free emission of electrons takes place. The "plate" is generally of graphite. Banks of these rectifiers are able to deal with very heavy loads of current such as are required for the production of metallic aluminum by electrolysis.

There is another type of valve which serves as a "relay." In response to quite a feeble current, it is able to control a relatively large current. An instance of this process is given by the photoelectric cell. In most cases the current generated is very feeble, not nearly enough to open or shut a door by itself. What is required is some device that, in response to the feeble current, will control the comparatively strong one required to work the mechanism of the door. The relay does this. One special pattern is very like a triode valve, with filament, plate and grid, but instead of a vacuum in the container, a small amount of inert gas is deliberately introduced. These relays are used for such purposes as controlling stage lighting, controlling the current to a motor for rapid response to controls and controlling the switching on and off of a heavy electrical load. Relays are necessary for nearly every form of radio or other distant control. Radio robots and lighthouses employ large numbers of these special switches.

1951

Giant Brains

EDMUND CALLIS BERKELEY

From *Giant Brains*

RECENTLY THERE HAS BEEN A GOOD DEAL OF NEWS about strange giant machines that can handle information with vast speed and skill. They calculate and they reason. Some of them are cleverer than others—able to do more kinds of problems. Some are extremely fast: one of them does 5,000 additions a second for hours or days, as may be needed. Where they apply, they find answers to problems much faster and more accurately than human beings can; and so they can solve problems that a man's life is far too short to permit him to do. That is why they were built.

These machines are similar to what a brain would be if it were made of hardware and wire instead of flesh and nerves. It is therefore natural to call these machines *mechanical brains*. Also, since their powers are like those of a giant, we may call them *giant brains*.

Several giant mechanical brains are now at work finding out answers never before known. Two are in Cambridge, Massachusetts; one is at Massachusetts Institute of Technology, and one at Harvard University. Two are in Aberdeen, Maryland, at the Army's Ballistic Research Laboratories. These four machines were finished in the period 1942 to 1946. More giant brains are being constructed.

Can we say that these machines really think? What do we mean by thinking, and how does the human brain think?

HUMAN THINKING

We do not know very much about the physical process of thinking in the human brain. If you ask a scientist how flesh and blood in a human brain can think, he will talk to you a little about nerves and about electrical and chemical changes, but he will not be able to tell you very much

216

about how we add 2 and 3 and make 5. What men know about the way in which a human brain thinks can be put down in a few pages, and what men do not know would fill many libraries.

Injuries to brains have shown some things of importance; for example, they have shown that certain parts of the brain have certain duties. There is a part of the brain, for instance, where sights are recorded and compared. If an accident damages the part of the brain where certain information is stored, the human being has to relearn—haltingly and badly—the information destroyed.

We know also that thinking in the human brain is done essentially by a process of storing information and then referring to it, by a process of learning and remembering. We know that there are no little wheels in the brain so that a wheel standing at 2 can be turned 3 more steps and the result of 5 read. Instead, you and I store the information that 2 and 3 are 5, and store it in such a way that we can give the answer when questioned. But we do not know the register in our brain where this particular piece of information is stored. Nor do we know how, when we are questioned, we are able automatically to pick up the nerve channels that lead into this register, get the answer, and report it.

Since there are many nerves in the brain, about 10 billion of them, in fact, we are certain that the network of connecting nerves is a main part of the puzzle. We are therefore much interested in nerves and their properties.

A single nerve, or *nerve cell* consists of a *cell nucleus* and a *fiber*. This fiber may have a length of anything from a small fraction of an inch up to several feet. In the laboratory, successive impulses can be sent along a nerve fiber as often as 1,000 a second. Impulses can travel along a nerve fiber in either direction at a rate from 3 feet to 300 feet a second. Because the speed of the impulse is far less than 186,000 miles a second—the speed of an electric current—the impulse in the nerve is thought by some investigators to be more chemical than electrical.

We know that a nerve cell has what is called an *all-or-none response,* like the trigger of a gun. If you stimulate the nerve up to a certain point, nothing will happen; if you reach that point, or cross it—bang!—the nerve responds and sends out an impulse. The strength of the impulse, like the shot of the gun, has no relation whatever to the amount of the stimulation.

The structure between the end of one nerve and the beginning of the next is called a *synapse*. No one really knows very much about synapses, for they are extremely small and it is not easy to tell where a synapse stops and other stuff begins. Impulses travel through synapses in from ½ to 3 thousandths of a second. An impulse travels through a synapse only in one direction, from the head (or *axon*) of one nerve fiber to the foot (or *dendrite*) of another. It seems clear that the activity in a synapse is chemical. When the head of a nerve fiber brings in an impulse to a synapse, apparently a chemical called *acetylcholine* is released and may affect the foot of another fiber, thus transmitting the impulse; but the process and the conditions for it are still not well understood.

It is thought that nearly all information is handled in the brain by groups of nerves in parallel paths. For example, the eye is estimated to have about 100 million nerves sensitive to light, and the information that they gather is reported by about 1 million nerves to the part of the brain that stores sights.

Not much more is yet known, however, about the operation of handling information in a human brain. We do not yet know how the nerves are connected so that we can do what we do. Probably the greatest obstacle to knowledge is that so far we cannot observe the detailed structure of a living human brain while it performs, without hurting or killing it.

Therefore, we cannot yet tell what thinking is by observing precisely how a human brain does it. Instead, we have to define thinking by describing the kind of behavior that we call thinking. Let us consider some examples.

When you and I add 12 and 8 and make 20, we are thinking. We use our minds and our understanding to count 8 places forward from 12, for example, and finish with 20. If we could find a dog or a horse that could add numbers and tell answers, we would certainly say that the animal could think.

With no trouble a machine can do this. An ordinary 10-column adding machine can be given two numbers like 1,378,917,766 and 2,355,799,867 and the instruction to add them. The machine will then give the answer, 3,734,717,633, much faster than a man. In fact, the mechanical brain at Harvard can add a number of 23 digits to another number of 23 digits and get the right answer in ³/₁₀ of a second.

Or, suppose that you are walking along a road and come to a fork. If you stop, read the signpost, and then choose left or right, you are thinking. You know beforehand where you want to go, you compare your destination with what the signpost says, and you decide on your route. This is an operation of logical choice.

A machine can do this. The mechanical brain now at Aberdeen which was built at Bell Laboratories can examine any number that comes up in the process of a calculation and tell whether it is bigger than 3 (or any stated number) or smaller. If the number is bigger than 3, the machine will choose one process; if the number is smaller than 3, the machine will choose another process.

Now suppose that we consider the basic operation of all thinking: in the human brain it is called learning and remembering, and in a machine it is called storing information and then referring to it. For example, suppose you want to find 305 Main Street in Kalamazoo. You look up a map of Kalamazoo; the map is information kindly stored by other people for your use. When you study the map, notice the streets and the numbering, and then find where the house should be, you are thinking.

A machine can do this. In the Bell Laboratories' mechanical brain, for example, the map could be stored as a long list of the blocks of the city and the streets and numbers that apply to each block. The machine will then hunt for the city block that contains 305 Main Street and report it when found.

A machine can handle information; it can calculate, conclude, and choose; it can perform reasonable operations with information. A machine, therefore, can think.

Now when we speak of a machine that thinks, or a mechanical brain, what do we mean? Essentially, a *mechanical brain* is a machine that handles information, transfers information automatically from one part of the machine to another, and has a flexible control over the sequence of its operations. No human being is needed around such a machine to pick up a physical piece of information produced in one part of the machine, personally move it to another part of the machine, and there put it in again. Nor is any human being needed to give the machine instructions from minute to minute. Instead, we can write out the whole program to solve a problem, translate the program into machine language, and put the program into the machine. Then we press the "start" button; the machine starts whirring; and it prints out the answers as it obtains them. Machines that handle information have existed for more than 2,000 years. These two properties are new, however, and make a deep break with the past.

How should we imagine a mechanical brain? One way to think of a mechanical brain is . . . a railroad line with four stations, marked *input, storage, computer,* and *output*. These stations are joined by little gates or switches to the main railroad line. We can imagine that numbers and other information move along this railroad line, loaded in freight cars. *Input* and *output* are stations where numbers or other information go in and come out, respectively. *Storage* is a station where there are many platforms and where information can be stored. The *computer* is a special station somewhat like a factory; when two numbers are loaded on platforms 1 and 2 of this station and an order is loaded on platform 3, then another number is produced on platform 4.

We see also a tower, marked *control*. This tower runs a telegraph line to each of its little watchmen standing by the gates. The tower tells them when to open and when to shut which gates.

Now we can see that, just as soon as the right gates are shut, freight cars of information can move between stations. Actually the freight cars move at the speed of electric current, thousands of miles a second. So, by closing the right gates each fraction of a second, we can flash numbers and information through the system and perform operations of reasoning. Thus we obtain a mechanical brain.

In general, a mechanical brain is made up of:

1. A quantity of registers where information (numbers and instructions) can be stored.
2. Channels along which information can be sent.
3. Mechanisms that can carry out arithmetical and logical operations.
4. A control, which guides the machine to perform a sequence of operations.
5. Input and output devices, whereby information can go into the machine and come out of it.
6. Motors or electricity, which provide energy.

There are many kinds of thinking that mechanical brains can do. Among other things, they can:

1. Learn what you tell them.
2. Apply the instructions when needed.
3. Read and remember numbers.
4. Add, subtract, multiply, divide, and round off.
5. Look up numbers in tables.
6. Look at a result, and make a choice.
7. Do long chains of these operations one after another.
8. Write out an answer.
9. Make sure the answer is right.
10. Know that one problem is finished, and turn to another.
11. Determine *most* of their own instructions.
12. Work unattended.

They do these things much better than you or I. They are fast. The mechanical brain built at the Moore School of Electrical Engineering at the University of Pennsylvania does 5,000 additions a second. They are reliable. Even with hundreds of thousands of parts, the existing giant brains have worked successfully. They have remarkly few mechanical troubles; in fact, for one of the giant brains, a mechanical failure is of the order of once a month. They are powerful. The big machine at Harvard can remember 72 numbers each of 23 digits at one time and can do 3 operations with these numbers every second. The mechanical brains that have been finished are able to solve problems that have baffled men for many, many years, and they think in ways never open to men before. Mechanical brains have removed the limits on complexity of routine: the machine can carry out a complicated routine as easily as a simple one. Already, processes for solving problems are being worked out so that the mechanical brain will itself determine more than 99 per cent of all the routine orders that it is to carry out.

But, you may ask, can they do any kind of thinking? The answer is no. No mechanical brain so far built can: 1. Do intuitive thinking. 2. Make bright guesses, and leap to conclusions. 3. Determine *all* its own instructions. 4. Perceive complex situations outside itself and interpret them. A clever wild animal, for example, a fox, can do all these things; a mechanical brain, not yet. There is, however, good reason to believe that most, if not all, of these operations will in the future be performed not only by animals but also by machines. . . .

Most of the thinking so far done by these machines is with numbers. They have already solved problems in airplane design, astronomy, physics, mathematics, engineering, and many other sciences, that previously could not be solved. To find the solutions of these problems, mathematicians would have had to work for years and years, using the best known methods and large staffs of human computers.

These mechanical brains not only calculate, however. They also remember and reason, and thus they promise to solve some very important human problems. For example, one of these problems is the application of what mankind knows. It takes too long to find understandable information on a subject. The libraries are full of books: most of them we can never hope to read in our lifetime. The technical journals are full of condensed scientific information: they can hardly be understood by you and me. There is a big gap between somebody's knowing something and employment of that knowledge by you or me when we need it. But these new mechanical brains handle information very swiftly. In a few years machines will probably be made that will know what is in libraries and that will tell very swiftly where to find certain information. Thus we can see that mechanical brains are one of the great new tools for finding out what we do not know and applying what we do know.

Machines That Think

AND WHAT THEY MIGHT DO FOR MEN[1]

EDMUND CALLIS BERKELEY

From *Giant Brains*

THE PEN IS MIGHTIER THAN THE SWORD, IT IS OFTEN said. And if this is true, then the pen with a motor may be mightier than the sword with a motor.

In the Middle Ages, there were few kinds of weapons, and it was easy for a man to protect himself against most of them by wearing armor. As gunpowder came into use, a man could no longer carry the weight of armor that would protect him, and so armor was given up. But in 1917, armor, equipped with a motor and carrying the man and his weapons, came back into service—as the tank.

In much the same way, in the Middle Ages, there were few books, and it was easy for a man to handle nearly all the information that was in books. As the printing press came into use, man's brain could no longer handle all recorded information, and the effort to do so was given up. But in 1944, a brain to handle information, equipped with a motor and supporting the man and his reasoning, came into existence—as the sequence-controlled calculator. . . .

Now we shall discuss the future significance of machines that think, of motorized information. We shall discuss what we can foresee if we look with imagination into the future.

There are two questions we need to ask: What types of machines that think can we foresee? What types of problems to be solved by these machines can we foresee?

The machines that already exist show that some processes of thinking can already be performed very quickly:

Calculating: adding, subtracting, . . .
Reasoning: comparing, selecting, . . .
Referring: looking up information in lists, . . .

We can expect other processes of thinking to come up to high speed through the further development of thinking machines.

Nowadays when we wish to send out announcements of an event, like going to South America for a year, we may copy the addresses of our friends onto the envelopes by hand. In the future, we can see our address book as a spool of magnetic tape. When we wish to send out announcements, we put a stack of blank envelopes into the machine that will read the magnetic tape, and we press a button. Out will come the envelopes addressed.

If we wish to select only those friends of ours whose last names we put down on a list, we can write the list on another magnetic tape, place it also in the machine, and set a few switches. Then the machine will read the names on the list, find their addresses in the address-book tape, and prepare only the envelopes we want. If a friend's address changes, we can notify the machine. It will find his old address, erase it, and enter the new address.

We can foresee the development of machinery that will make it possible to consult information in a library automatically. Suppose that you go into the library of the future and wish to look up ways for making biscuits. You will be able to dial into the catalogue machine "making biscuits." There will be a flutter of movie film in the machine. Soon it will stop, and, in front of you on the screen, will be projected the part of the catalogue which shows the names of three or four books containing recipes for biscuits. If you are satisfied, you will press a button; a copy of what you saw will be made for you and come out of the machine.

After further development, all the pages of all books will be available by machine. Then, when you press the right button, you will be able to get from the machine a copy of the exact recipe for biscuits that you choose.

We are not yet at the end of foreseeable development. There will be a third stage. You will then have in your home an automatic cooking machine operated by program tapes. You will stock it with various supplies, and it will put together and cook whatever dishes you desire. Then, what you will need from the library will be a program or routine on magnetic tape to control your automatic cook. And the library, instead of producing a pictorial copy of the recipe for you to read and apply, will produce a routine on magnetic tape for controlling your cooking machine so that you will actually get excellent biscuits!

Of course, you may have other kinds of automatic producing machinery in your home or office. The furnishing of routines to control automatic machinery will become a business of importance.

Another machine that we can foresee would be used for translating from one language to any other. We can call it an *automatic translator*. Suppose that you want to say "How much?" in Swedish. You dial into the machine "How much?" and press the button "Swedish," and the machine will promptly write out "Hur mycket?" for you. It also will pronounce it, if you wish, for there would be little difficulty in recording on magnetic tape the pronunciation of the word as spoken by a good speaker of the language. The machine could be set to repeat the pronunciation several times so that the student could really learn the sound. He could learn it better, probably, by hearing it and trying to say it than he could by using any set of written symbols.

We now come to a possible machine that uses a new principle. This principle is that of being able to *recognize* signs. This machine would perceive writing on a piece of paper and recognize that all the *a*'s that appear on the paper are cases of *a*, and that all the *b*'s that appear on it are instances of *b*, and so forth. The machine could then control an electric typewriter and copy the marks that it sees. The first stage of this machine would be one in which only printed characters of a high degree of likeness could be recognized. In later stages, handwriting, even rather illegible handwriting, might be recognizable by the machine. We can call it an *automatic typist*.

The elements of the automatic typist would be the following:

1. *Phototubes* (electronic tubes sensitive to the brightness of light), which could sense the difference between black and white (these already exist).

2. A memory of the shapes of 52 letters, 10 digits, and punctuation marks. Fine distinctions would be required of this memory in some cases—like the difference between the numeral 5 and the capital letter S.

3. A control that would cause the machine to *tune* itself, so that a good matching between the marks it observed and the shapes it remembered would be reached.

4. A *triggering control* so that, when the machine had reached good enough matching between its observations and its memory, the machine would proceed to identify the marks, read them, and transfer them.

5. An electric typewriter, which would respond to the transferred instructions. (This also already exists.)

This machine is perhaps not so farfetched as it might seem. During World War II, gun-aiming equipment using the new technique *radar* reached a high stage of development. Many shots that disabled and sank enemy ships were fired in total darkness by radar-controlled guns. On the glowing screen in the control room, there were two spots, one that marked the target and one that reported the point at which the gun was aimed. These two spots could be brought almost automatically into agreement. In the same way, a report from a phototube telling the shape of an observed mark and a report from the memory of the machine telling the shape of a similar mark could be compared by the machine for likeness and, if judged enough alike, could be approved as identical.

Even the phrase "enough alike" can be applied by a machine. During World War II, tremendous advances were made in machinery for deciphering enemy messages. Machines observed various features and patterns in enemy messages, swiftly counted the frequency of these features, and carried out statistical tests. Then the machines selected those few cases in which the patterns showed meaning instead of randomness.

A machine like the automatic typist, if made flexible enough, would be, of course, extremely useful. A great load of dull office work is now being thrown on clerks whose task is to translate from writing and typing into languages that machines can read, such as punch cards. At the present time, if punch-card machines are widely used in a big company, the company must employ large numbers of girls whose sole duty is to read papers and punch up cards. A still bigger chore is the work of typists in all kinds of businesses whose main duty is to read handwriting, etc., and then copy the words on a typewriter.

Research has already begun on various features of the automatic typist because of its obvious labor-saving value. For example, many patents have been issued on schemes for dividing the area occupied by a letter or a digit into an array of spots, with a battery of phototubes each watching a spot. The reports from the phototubes together will distinguish the letter or digit. For example, if we consider A and H placed in a grill of fifteen spots, 5 long by 3 wide, then the phototubes can distinguish between A and H by sensing black or white in the spot in the middle of the top row. When we consider how easily and swiftly a human being does this, we can once more marvel at the recognizing machine we all carry around with us in our heads.

Another development that we can foresee is one that we can call the *automatic stenographer.* This is a machine that will listen to sounds and write them down in properly spelled English words. The elements of this machine can be outlined:

1. Microphones, which can sense spoken sounds (these already exist).
2. A memory storing the 40 (more or less) phonetic units or sounds that make up English, such as the 23 consonant sounds,

p	*b*	*l*	*ng*
f	*v*	*m*	*th*
t	*d*	*n*	*r*
s	*z*	*h*	*y*
k	*g*		*w*
ch	*j*		
sh	*zh* (heard in "pleasure")		

and the 17 vowel sounds,

LONG	SHORT	OTHER
A ("ate")	*a* ("cat")	*ar* ("are")
E ("eat")	*e* ("end")	*aw* ("awe")
I ("isle")	*i* ("in")	*er* ("err")
O ("owe")	*o* ("on")	*ow* ("owl")
U ("cute")	*u* ("up")	*oi* ("oil")
OO ("roof")	*oo* ("book")	

3. A collection of the rules of spelling in English, containing many statements like

The sound *b* is always spelled *b*.

The sound *sh* may be spelled *sh* (ship), *s* (sugar), *ti* (station), *ci* (physician), *ce* (ocean) or *tu* picture);

and other statements based on context, word lists, derivation, etc. These are the statements by means of which a good English speller knows how to spell even words that he hears for the first time.

4. A triggering control so that, when the machine reaches good enough matching between its observations of sounds, its memory of sounds, and its knowledge of spelling rules, the machine will identify groups of sounds as words, determine their spelling, and report the letters determined.

5. An electric typewriter, which would type the reported letters.

With this type of machine, you would dictate your letters into a machine (now existing) that would record your voice. Then the record would be placed on the automatic stenographer, and out would come your letters written and spaced as they should be.

We can foresee a recognizing machine with very general powers. Suppose that we call it an *automatic recognizer*. It will have the following elements:

1. *Input.* This element will consist of a set of observing instruments, capable of perceiving sights, sounds, etc. There will be ways of positioning or *tuning* these instruments.

2. *Memory.* This element will store knowledge. It may store the patterns of observations that we are interested in; or it may store general rules on how to find patterns of observations that we will be interested in. It will contain knowledge about acceptable groups of patterns, about actions to be performed in response to patterns, etc.

3. *Program 1.* The element "Program 1" performs a set of standard instructions. Under these instructions, the machine:

> Compares group after group of observations with the information in the memory.
>
> Compares these groups with patterns furnished, or seeks to organize the observations into patterns.
>
> Counts cases and tests frequencies.
>
> Finds out how much matching with patterns there is.
>
> Tunes the observing instruments in ways to increase matching.

4. *Program 2.* The element "Program 2" performs another set of standard instructions. Under these instructions, the machine, if it is tuned well, matches sets of observations one after another with the patterns and so reads them.

5. *Triggering Control.* This element shifts the control of the machine from Program 1 to Program 2. It does this when the machine reaches "good matching." We shall set the meaning of this into the machine in much the same way as we set "warm" into a thermostat.

6. *Output.* This element performs any action that we want, depending on recognized patterns read and any other knowledge or instructions stored in the memory.

The automatic recognizer will be capable of extraordinary tasks. With microphones and a large memory, this type of machine would be able to hear a foreign language spoken and translate it into spoken or written English. With phototubes and with an expanded filtering and decoding capacity as in deciphering machines, the automatic recognizer should be able to read a dead language, even those (such as Minoan or Etruscan) that have so far resisted efforts to read it. The machine would derive rules for the translation of the language and translate any sample.

An automatic recognizer could perhaps be equipped with many sensitive, tiny observing instruments that could be placed around or in the brain and nervous systems of animals. Then the machine might enable us to find out what activity in the nervous system corresponds with what activity in the animal.

We turn now to the second question regarding the future of machines that think: What types of problems can we foresee as solved by these machines?

Probably the foremost problem which machines that think can solve is automatic control over all sorts of other machines. This involves controlling a machine that is running so that it will do the right thing at the right time in response to information. For example, suppose that you are mowing a lawn with a mowing machine. You watch the preceding strip so as to stay next to it. You watch the ends of the strips, where you turn around. If a stick is caught in the cutting blade, you stop and take it out. Now it is entirely possible to put devices on the mowing machine so that all these things will be taken care of automatically. In fact, in the case of plowing a large field, a tractor plow can be equipped with a device that guides it next to the preceding furrow. Thus, once the first furrow around the edge has been made, riderless tractors will plow a whole field and stop in the middle.

For another example, take a gas furnace for heating steam to keep a house warm. Such a furnace has automatic controls, which respond to the following information whenever reported:

House too warm.
House not warm enough.
Too much steam pressure.
Not enough water in boiler.
Gas flame not lit.
Daytime.
Nighttime.

In fact, your own meaning of "warm" can be put into the control system: you set the dial on your thermostat at the temperature that "warm" is to be for you.

In the future many kinds of automatic control will be common. We shall have automatic pilots for flying and landing airplanes. We shall have automatic missiles for destructive purposes, such as bombing and killing, and for constructive purposes, such as delivering mail and fast freight. An article in the magazine *Fortune* for November 1946 described the automatic factory. This is a factory in which there would be automatic arms for holding stuff being manufactured, and automatic feed lines for supplying material just where it is needed. All this factory would be controlled by machines that handle information automatically and produce actions that respond to information.

This prospect fills us with concern as well as with amazement. How shall we control these automatic machines, these robots, these Frankensteins? What will there be left for us to do to earn our living?

Other problems for which we can foresee the use of machines that think are the understanding, and later the controlling, of nature. One of these problems is weather forecasting and weather control.

We can imagine the following type of machine—a *weather brain*. A thousand weather observatories all over the country observe the weather at 8 A.M. The observations are fed automatically through a countrywide network of communication lines into a central station. Here a giant machine, containing a great deal of scientific knowledge about the weather, takes in all the data reported to it. At 8:15 the weather brain starts to calculate; in half an hour it has finished, having produced an excellent forecast of the weather for the whole country. Then it proceeds to transmit its forecast all over the country. By 8:50 every weather station, newspaper, radio station, and airport in the country has the details. In October, 1945, Dr. V. K. Zworykin of the Princeton Laboratories of the Radio Corporation of America proposed solving the problem of weather forecasting in this way by a giant brain.

The weather brain will have a second stage of application. From time to time and here and there, the weather is unstable: it can be triggered to behave in one way or another. For example, recently, pellets of *frozen carbon dioxide*—often called Dry Ice—have been dropped from planes and have caused rain. In fact, a few pounds of Dry Ice have apparently caused several hundred tons of rain or snow. In similar ways, we may, for example, turn away a hailstorm so that hail will fall over a barren mountain instead of over a farming valley and thus protect crops. Or we may dispel conditions that would lead to a tornado, thus avoiding its damage. Both these examples involve local weather disturbances. However, even the greatest weather disturbances, like hurricanes and blizzards, may eventually be directed to some extent. Thus the weather may become to some degree subject to man's control, and the weather brain will be able to tell men where and when to take action.

Another scientific problem to which new machinery for handling information applies is the problem of understanding human beings and their behavior. This increased understanding may lead to much wiser dealing with human behavior.

For example, consider tests of aptitudes. If you take one of these tests, you may be asked to mark which word out of five suggested ones is nearest in meaning to a given word. Or your test may be forty simple arithmetical problems to be solved in twenty-five minutes. Or you may be given a sheet with twenty circles, and be asked to put three dots in the first, seven dots in the second, four dots in the third, eleven dots in the fourth, and so on, irregularly; you may be given a total of forty-five seconds to do this as well as you can. Now, if a vocational counselor gives you one of these tests, and if you get 84 out of 100 on it, he needs to know just what he has measured about you. Also, he needs to know whether he can reasonably forecast that, as a result of your grade of 84, you will be good at writing articles, or good at supervising the work of other people, or good at designing in a machine shop. He needs to know the records of people with scores of about 84 on this test and to have evidence supporting his forecasts.

If we wish to make the most use of the tests, we need to carry out a good deal of statistics, mathematics, and logic. For example, it will turn out that answers to some questions are much more significant than answers to others, and so we can greatly improve the quality of the tests by keeping only the more significant questions. Powerful machinery for handling calculations will be very useful in the field of aptitude testing.

But, you may ask, what if the person analyzing your answers has to use interpretations and judgments? If the judgments and interpretations can be expressed in words, and if the words can be translated into machine language, then the machine can carry out the analysis. Usually the difference between a rule and a judgment is simply this: a rule in a case in which it is hard to express all the factors being considered is called a judgment.

It is conceivable that machines that think can eventually be applied in the actual treatment of mental illness and maladjustment. Consider what a physician does. In treating a psychiatric case, such as a *neurosis*, a physician uses words almost entirely. He asks questions. He listens to the patient's answers. Each answer takes the physician nearer and nearer to a diagnosis. By and by the physician knows what most of the difficulty is. Then he must present his knowledge slowly to the patient, gradually guiding the patient to understanding. It is a psychological truth that telling a man in ten minutes what is wrong with him does not cure him. The physician seeks to free the patient from the tormenting circles of habit and worry in which he has been trapped. Often the diagnosis is short and the treatment is long; the reasons for the neurosis may soon be clear to the physician, but they may take months to become clear to the patient.

Now let us consider the following kind of machine as an aid to the physician. We might call this kind of machine a *psychological trainer*, for in many ways it is like the training machines used in World War II for training a pilot to fly an airplane. The psychological trainer would have the following properties:

1. The machine is able to show sound movies—produce pictures and utter words.
2. It is able to put before the patient: situations, problems, questions, experiences, etc.
3. It is able to take in responses from the patient.
4. It is able to receive a program of instructions from the physician.
5. Depending on the responses of the patient and on the program from the physician, the training machine can select more material to put before the patient.
6. The training machine produces a record of what it presented and of how the patient responded, so that the physician and the patient can study the record later.

What sort of films would the machine hold? The machine could be loaded with a number of films which would help in the particular type of neurosis from which the patient was suffering.

What sort of responses could the patient make? The patient might have buttons in front of him which he could press to indicate such answers as:

Yes	I don't know	Repeat
No	It depends	Go ahead

Also, the patient might hold a device—like a lie detector, perhaps—which would report his state of tenseness, etc., and so report what he really felt.

Where would the machine's questions come from? From one or more physicians very clever in the treatment of mental illness.

Suppose that the patient is inconsistent in his answers? The machine, discovering the inconsistencies, could return to the subject and ask related questions in a different way. As soon as several questions related to the same point are answered consistently, the machine could exclude groups of questions that no longer apply and could proceed to other questions that would still apply.

Patients would vary in their ability to go as fast as the machine could. So from time to time the machine would ask questions to test the effect of what it had presented; and, depending on the answers, the machine would go faster or would bring in additional material to clarify some point.

This machine might have a few advantages over ordinary treatment. For example, with the machine, treatment does not depend on the physician's making the right answer in a split second, as it may in a personal interview. Also, the patient might be franker with the machine than with the physician, for it might be arranged that the patient could review his record, and then decide whether to confess it to his physician.

Such a machine would enable physicians to treat many more patients than they now can. In fact, it is estimated that nearly 50 per cent of persons who consult physicians are suffering only from mental illness. Such a machine would therefore be a great help.

Another large group of problems for which we can foresee the use of machines that think is found in business and economics.

For example, consider production scheduling in a business or a factory. The machine takes in a description of each order received by the business and a description of its relative urgency. The machine knows (that is, has in its memory) how much of each kind of raw material is needed to fill the order and what equipment and manpower are needed to produce it. The machine makes a schedule showing what particular men and what particular equipment are to be set to work to produce the order. The machine turns out the best possible production schedule, showing who should do what when, so that all the orders will be filled in the best sequence. What is the "best" sequence? We can decide what we think is the best sequence, and we can set the machine for making that kind of selection, in the same way as we decide what is "warm" and set the thermostat to produce it!

On a much larger scale, we can use mechanical brains to study economic relations in a society. Everything produced in a society is made by consuming some materials, labor, equipment, and skill. The output produced by one man or factory or industry becomes the input for other men, factories, industries. In this way all economic units are linked together by many different kinds and degrees of dependence. The situation is, of course, complicated: it changes as time goes on and as people want different things produced. Economists have already set up simple models of economic societies and have studied them. But with machines that think, it will be possible to set up and study far more complicated models—models that are very much like the society we live in. We can then answer questions of economics by calculation instead of by arguments and counting noses. We shall be able to solve definitely such problems as: "How will a rise in the price of steel affect the farming industry?" "How much money must be paid out as wages and salaries so that consumer purchasing power will buy back what industry produces?"

1949

Some Early Pioneers in Chemistry

STEPHEN MIALL and L. M. MIALL

From Chemistry, Matter and Life

MANY OF THE FAMILIAR MATERIALS WITH WHICH WE are so well acquainted—wood, paper, bone, meat, and coal—are very complicated substances: so complicated that a hundred or fifty years ago it seemed that it was almost hopeless to understand how they were built up. The early chemists spent much of their time in studying not the familiar complicated substances, but the simpler, if rarer, ones; they investigated the elements, gold, silver, iron, lead, tin, carbon, sulfur, phosphorus, and others that had been known for a very long time. They found that the air is a mixture of oxygen and nitrogen, that water is a compound of oxygen and hydrogen; they discovered the yellowish gas, chlorine, an element that is contained in common salt. With these elements, and twenty or thirty others less familiar to most of us, they performed all kinds of experiments that have very greatly enlarged our knowledge; but most of the substances made by them are unknown outside chemical laboratories or chemical books. Their very names are unfamiliar and repellent; many of these names are long, and are meaningless except to those who possess the clues and know the chemists' language. . . .

It is convenient, because many of the simpler compounds were investigated first, to take a few instances from the early days, when chemistry began to be a science, so as to lead us on to a consideration of the more complicated structures and the singular processes that cannot easily be explained until we have grasped some of the most fundamental articles in the chemist's creed.

About a hundred and fifty years ago it was recognized that chemical elements existed, and that by the combination of these a multitude of compounds could be formed. The elements copper, silver, gold, sulfur, carbon, mercury, tin, lead, iron, arsenic, antimony, and phosphorus had long been

233

known. Platinum, zinc, cobalt, and nickel were fairly recent discoveries; during the last half of the eighteenth century the gases hydrogen, oxygen, chlorine, and nitrogen were prepared and recognized as elements, and a very few years later attempts were made to prepare other elements which had not been isolated, although compounds of them were known. Among these elements we may mention silicon, boron, aluminum, calcium, sodium, potassium, and magnesium.

These were the elementary substances available for the use of chemists a hundred and fifty years ago. Chemical experiments were then carried out in a room that more resembled an old-fashioned kitchen than a modern laboratory; most of the chemical appliances were very crude; coal-gas was not available, and the electric current did not come into use until after Volta's discovery of a primitive electric cell in 1791. There was no systematic teaching of chemistry, and the early workers had to make a good deal of their primitive apparatus; petrol and paraffin were unknown, and there were very few chemicals that you could buy at a shop, although drugs had, of course, been readily purchased for many years.

The first stage in the science of chemistry was to recognize the distinction between elements and compounds. The next stage was to recognize that one element could only combine with another in certain definite proportions. Thus hydrogen combines with oxygen, in the proportion of one part of hydrogen by weight and eight parts of oxygen, to form water, and in the proportion of one part of hydrogen by weight and sixteen parts of oxygen to form hydrogen peroxide. It will be seen that the difference in the relative weights of hydrogen and oxygen can cause great differences in the properties of the compound. It is the extra atom of oxygen that gives hydrogen peroxide its bleaching and disinfecting properties. When charcoal or coke burns in an open grate, twelve parts by weight of carbon combine with thirty-two parts by weight of oxygen to form carbon dioxide. The exhaust gases from a motorcar frequently contain a certain quantity of the poisonous carbon monoxide, in which twelve parts by weight of carbon are combined with sixteen parts of oxygen. These two are the only compounds of carbon with oxygen that have ever been prepared in a large quantity, though unusual compounds in which carbon and oxygen are combined in different proportions have been prepared in very minute quantities; in general, one element will only combine with another in one, two, or three proportions comparable with those we have already mentioned in the case of hydrogen and oxygen, and carbon and oxygen.

One of the early workers who helped to establish the science was Cavendish. Henry Cavendish was born in 1731, the elder son of Lord

Charles Cavendish, and grandson of the Duke of Devonshire; he was educated at Cambridge, and until he was about forty he lived on a very moderate allowance from his father and contracted very economical habits. He lived at Clapham Common and had a library in Soho, and his methodical nature was such that he never took a volume from his own shelves without entering it in a book. He became a Fellow of the Royal Society in 1760, and dined regularly with the club that was formed from the fellows; otherwise he shunned society and was painfully shy when strangers were introduced to him; he ordered his dinner by a note placed on his table, and his women servants were instructed to keep out of his sight; his dress was old-fashioned and often shabby, for his whole interest was in science; he hated to be bothered about business matters, and on one occasion his bankers found that he had something like £80,000 in their hands, and they sent a representative to see Mr. Cavendish; the following conversation ensued:

"We have a very large balance in hand of yours, and wish for your orders respecting it."

"If it is any trouble to you, I will take it out of your hands. Do not come here to plague me."

"Not the least trouble to us, sir, not the least; but we thought you might like some of it to be invested."

"Do so, and don't come here and trouble me, or I will remove it."

Occasionally he invited a few friends to dine at his house, and invariably gave them a leg of mutton; once he asked four scientific men to dine with him, and when the housekeeper asked what should be got for dinner Cavendish replied:

"A leg of mutton."

"Sir that will not be enough for five."

"Well, then, get two."

This anecdote illustrates not merely the oddity of the man, but also the small size of the leg of mutton in those days. Since the enclosure of pastures and the use of fertilizers the size of sheep and cattle has increased very much. One leg of mutton would now be ample for a larger party of scientific men.

Cavendish was one of the very great men of science; he was remarkably exact and painstaking, and his experiments were of great importance. He prepared hydrogen and studied its density and its power of combining with oxygen so as to form water, and was the first man to have a clear idea of the composition of water. He determined with great exactness the composition of the air, proving that it was a mixture of about one part of oxygen with four parts of nitrogen, and that, in addition to these gases, the air contained about 1 per cent of a different gas; he collected a little of this and recorded the experiment carefully; he did not know what it was, but a hundred years later Rayleigh and Ramsay discovered the gas argon, that is now often used to fill electric light bulbs, and they found that the gas that had been collected by Cavendish was argon. Cavendish also studied the production of oxides of nitrogen—compounds of oxygen and nitrogen—produced by means of electric sparks in a mixture of oxygen and nitrogen, and he worked at the composition of nitric acid. Nitric acid is a compound of nitrogen, oxygen, and hydrogen; it is a very useful liquid in chemical research and of great commercial importance, playing a part in the manufacture of explosives and fertilizers. In these ways Cavendish laid an exact foundation for the study of some of the most important elementary gases. He studied heat and electricity, and determined the density of the earth, and busied himself with geology; but these researches are rather outside our subject. He died in 1810, leaving a fortune of a million pounds and having enriched chemistry by two researches of great value, the composition of air and the composition of water.

His contemporary Joseph Priestley was as unlike Cavendish as it would be possible to be; he was born in 1733 of parents in humble circumstances, and at the age of seven was taken charge of by an aunt and educated to become a nonconformist minister. In his young days he studied electricity, and wrote a history of it which secured his election to the Royal Society in 1766. He became a Unitarian minister in Leeds, and was attracted to the study of chemistry, partly because he lived next door to a brewery where quantities of carbon dioxide were produced in the ordinary course of the fermentation of beer. He became librarian to Lord Shelburne in 1772, and remained with him for seven years investigating the different kinds of gases and making important discoveries. He was the first to prepare and publish an account of sulfur dioxide, ammonia gas, nitrous oxide (laughing gas), and oxygen. The last gas he discovered in 1774, not knowing that two years or so earlier the Swedish chemist Scheele had also discovered it, but had not published his discovery. Priestley proved that green plants are able in sunlight to absorb carbon dioxide from the air and make use of it, and to restore to the air a certain quantity of oxygen. He played a part in the discovery of the composition of the air, and invented soda water, which has nothing to do with soda, but is merely water in which a considerable quantity of carbonic acid (carbon dioxide) has been dissolved. Priestley at one time learned many foreign languages and taught them; he was a vehement theologian and a keen politician, with radical or revolutionary views; he was acrimonious in his writings, and made himself very unpopular in Birmingham, where he went to live in 1780. During the riots of 1791 the mob wrecked his house and burned his books, and he was in some danger of losing his life. Finally he emigrated to America, and died there in the year 1804.

Carl Wilhelm Scheele was another early pioneer; he was born in 1742 at Stralsund in Pomerania; when he was fourteen he was apprenticed to an apothecary at Göteborg in Sweden, and then began to experiment in chemistry. He became an apothecary at Malmö, then at Stockholm, Upsala, and Köping in Sweden, and spent all his spare time in his chemical studies. He independently discovered oxygen, ammonia, and hydrochloric acid gas (a compound of hydrogen and chlorine); he was the first to isolate the gas chlorine and to discover hydrofluoric acid, a compound of hydrogen and fluorine used for etching glass; he was also the first to prepare lactic acid, oxalic acid, citric acid, and tartaric acid; lactic acid occurs in sour milk, oxalic acid in the sorrel herb, citric acid in lemon juice, tartaric acid is made from grape juice. He was the first to isolate glycerine, and the sugar contained in milk, now called lactose, an important component of some infant foods; he prepared prussic acid (hydrocyanic acid, a compound of hydrogen, carbon, and nitrogen), and he found out the nature of prussian blue, and made many other discoveries of great interest. Cavendish, Priestley, and Scheele made so many discoveries of new elements and new compounds, and did their work so thoroughly, that chemistry was enriched by a great mass of facts that enabled later workers to deduce from them the laws of chemical combination. Had Scheele lived to be an old man the volume of his discoveries would doubtless have been much greater, but he died in 1786, in his forty-third year.

None of these three men knew much about the theory of chemistry, or the laws of chemical combination, or the nature of chemical compounds, and the little they guessed about these matters was confused and inaccurate. It was a young French chemist, Lavoisier, with that logical kind of mind that is commoner in France than elsewhere, who reduced the chaos to order, distinguished exactly between chemical elements and chemical compounds, gave names to most of the new elements, and devised a logical system of names for the numerous chemical compounds.

Antoine Laurent Lavoisier was born in Paris in 1743, and studied chemistry at the Jardin du Roi; he was the first to show that the "setting" of plaster of Paris is due to the taking up of water by the dry plaster and the combination of the two; he was soon elected a member of the French Academy. In 1768 he became a member of the *Ferme-générale*, a company to which the Government, in return for a fixed sum of money, granted the right of collecting many of the taxes. He was later made a Powder Commissioner, and effected improvements in the manufacture of saltpeter and gunpowder; he drew up reports on the cultivation of flax and potatoes and prepared a scheme for establishing experimental farms; he introduced the cultivation of the beet, and helped to improve the breed of sheep; he was secretary of the Commission of Weights and Measures that devised the metric system, and he rendered great services to his country and to chemistry. But his connection with the *Ferme-générale* and the Government was his ruin. In 1793 the Convention ordered the arrest of the twenty-eight members of the *Ferme-générale;* they were arrested and sentenced to death; a plea was made on behalf of Lavoisier, but the officer in charge declared: "La république n'a pas besoin des savants." Lavoisier was executed and his property confiscated.

Some of those who experimented in the new pastime, or science, improved the apparatus that was employed in it. Each such improvement enabled new discoveries to be made. That has remained true to some extent ever since; at any rate, it is due to the extraordinary improvements in our scientific instruments that many of our greatest modern discoveries have been made. Modern science depends upon accurate observation far more than ingenious speculation, and our knowledge of matter and its ways would be very imperfect but for our marvelous microscopes, spectroscopes, vacuum pumps, thermostats, and the other triumphs of physics and engineering. Cavendish and his contemporaries had none of these; they would have done far more if they had.

Like so much else in this world, our knowledge of the structure of matter and the nature of chemical change is very largely a case of evolution. Our alphabet is the result of three or four thousand years of gradual experiment and development, the steam engine the result of effort and improvement spread over a few hundred years. Almost every scientific discovery depends upon observations made by earlier workers. When a sufficient mass of facts has been accumulated someone comes along and finds out a law connecting them. It was necessary to have the careful work of the four great men we have mentioned, and many men of less fame, before an adequate explanation of the facts could be given; as is usual, the explanation was not due to one man alone: several of his predecessors had made guesses with some foundation of truth in them; but until all the necessary data had been collected, the theory could neither be proclaimed nor proved. The man who gave us the first great chemical theory, one that is still universally accepted, was John Dalton, not such a scientific genius as Cavendish or Lavoisier, not such a prolific discoverer as Priestley or Scheele, but a simple-minded, clear-thinking man who tried to interpret the facts simply and clearly, and succeeded in doing so. To Dalton we owe the modern theory of atoms; it was he who first believed that every element was composed of infinitely small atoms each exactly like the other, and that the atoms of any one element were different from the atoms of any other element. He pictured an atom of element A combining with one, or perhaps two, or perhaps three, atoms of another element B, and that this was the basis of all chemical combination. This is now as obvious to us all as the existence of petrol, but it was not obvious a hundred and thirty years ago. Now when we read Darwin's *Origin of Species* it seems that he devoted several hundred pages to prove what needed only to be stated in one page; his conclusions are obvious to everybody. It is hard for us to put our minds in the state that was characteristic of educated people some seventy or eighty years ago.

John Dalton, the son of a Quaker weaver, was born in Cumberland in 1776, and became a teacher in Manchester and afterwards the Secretary of the Manchester Philosophical Society. He studied meteorology, and experimented on gases, in particular some of the gaseous compounds of carbon and hydrogen, one of which is known as methane or marsh gas; he was also the first person to call attention to color blindness; he himself had this peculiarity to a marked extent. After a life free from excitement, he died in 1844.

Dalton's views did not encounter the opposition that met Darwin's views; the ancient Jewish writers had not speculated on the constitution of matter, and no question of religion or orthodoxy was involved. Dalton's Atomic Theory was published in 1807, and has never since been disputed, though modern research on the structure of the atom has led to some interesting developments. Dalton was able to calculate very roughly the relative weights of many of the various atoms. Water, he knew, consisted of one part by weight of hydrogen and eight parts by weight of oxygen. The chemists of that period did not know whether they ought to regard water as composed of two atoms of hydrogen with a relative weight of 1 each and one atom of oxygen with a relative weight of 16, or whether they ought to regard water as composed of one atom of hydrogen with a relative weight of 1 and one atom of oxygen with a relative weight of 8. Either supposition fitted in with the facts.

The chemists during the next twenty or thirty years did not spend much time in discussing such a supposition; perhaps they thought it was too metaphysical, or at any rate a waste of time, and they busied themselves in discovering new elements and new compounds, in analyzing all kinds of minerals and substances of animal or vegetable origin, in studying the shapes of crystals, and in scores of other ways. They improved very greatly their methods of analysis, and Dalton's crude list of the relative combining weights of a few elements were superseded by a far more accurate list of atomic weights—that is, relative atomic weights—of some fifty or sixty elements.

Various scientific men investigated the density of different gases and the effect of compression on them and the way in which a gas expands when it is heated, and after the publication of Dalton's Atomic Theory an Italian physicist named Avogadro published his views on the nature of the ultimate small particles of elementary or compound gases. Translating his notions into modern terms, we may say that he regarded hydrogen as a gas containing a practically infinite number of molecules, each molecule consisting of two atoms of hydrogen; chlorine gas consisted of molecules each of which was made up of two atoms of chlorine. When hydrogen combines with chlorine to form hydrogen chloride (or hydrochloric acid gas), we consider that a molecule of each gas splits up into its two atoms, and that two new molecules are formed, each containing one atom of hydrogen and one atom of chlorine. Avogadro stated in 1811 that whatever gas you considered, a cubic foot of it would contain the same number of molecules as a cubic foot of any other gas, assuming that the temperatures and the pressures were the same. This was really a considerable development, but it attracted very little attention among chemists; it was not in advance of the facts, but in advance of the ideas of scientific men.

We can mention another and more recent instance of a molecular theory being in advance of its time. We now believe that every gas consists of a number of molecules dashing about at a great speed, and when these hit the side of a vessel containing the gas, they exert a pressure on it. It is possible to calculate the number of molecules in a given volume of any gas, at a fixed temperature and pressure, to calculate the average speed of the molecules, and other such matters. This theory was developed by Waterston in 1845, by Clausius in 1857, and by Clerk Maxwell in 1859. Waterston, who anticipated the views of Clausius and Clerk Maxwell, was several years in advance of scientific opinion, and when his paper was submitted to the Royal Society, the referee said: "The paper is nothing but nonsense, unfit even for reading before the Society." But although Waterston's paper was not published at the time, it was preserved, and in 1892 Lord Rayleigh called attention to its importance, and at last arranged for its publication with a suitable explanation.

A very versatile man of science was William Hyde Wollaston, the son of a clergyman, who had fifteen children who grew up to manhood.

After studying at Cambridge, Wollaston became a country doctor, but he soon came to London to devote himself to science. He engaged in the manufacture of platinum, and made a considerable sum of money in this way; he invented an instrument, the reflecting goniometer, to enable the angles of crystals to be measured accurately, and he made slide-rules as ready appliances for making calculations.

In the year 1812 Wollaston discovered that certain compounds of similar metals crystallized in similar crystals having angles very nearly but not quite the same; thus calcium carbonate (calcite), a compound of calcium, carbon, and oxygen, crystallizes in rhombohedra with an angle of 105°5′, calcium magnesium carbonate (dolomite), a compound of calcium, magnesium, carbon, and oxygen, crystallizes in rhombohedra with an angle of 106°15′, and iron carbonate (siderite) crystallizes in rhombohedra with an angle of 107°0′. This phenomenon is called isomorphism. Wollaston discovered a new silvery-looking element called palladium, but he was an odd man and he made his discovery known in an odd and provoking way. Having prepared a small quantity of this metal, he thought he would play a practical joke on another chemist named Chenevix. He arranged in April, 1803, that a printed notice should come into the hands of Chenevix stating that a new metal called palladium was to be sold at Mrs. Forster's of Gerrard Street, Soho. Chenevix, believing that it was a fraud, bought up the whole stock, and after investigating it came to the conclusion that the substance was not a new metal, but that it was an alloy of platinum and mercury with peculiar properties. In May, 1803, Chenevix sent a paper to this effect to the Royal Society, which was read to the meeting by Wollaston, who was then one of the secretaries. Shortly afterwards an anonymous advertisement appeared in which a handsome reward was offered to anyone who should prepare any of the new substance. No one succeeded in preparing any, and in the following year Wollaston announced that he was the discoverer of palladium, and described its preparation. He intimated at the same time his discovery of another new element, rhodium, now used for the electroplating of silver. Wollaston was the first to see the dark lines in the solar spectrum that have subsequently given us a knowledge of the nature of that wonderful body the sun, and helped us to understand the structure of atoms. He was also the first to explain why it is that when we look at a portrait hanging on a wall in a room, the eyes seem to look at us, in whatever part of the room we happen to be. The explanation is really a mathematical deduction from the rules of perspective.

Chevreul, a French chemist, made a very careful examination of fats between the years 1811 and 1823; he found that the fats are mixtures of compounds of glycerine, the principal of which are the stearates, the oleates, and palmitates of glycerine. Chevreul was born in the year 1786, and died in 1889, in his hundred and third year. A writer who visited him in 1874 stated: "He is constantly at work, allowing only ten minutes for each of his meals, of which he has but two a day . . . except a small loaf at noon, which he eats standing and by the side of his alembics." He said on this occasion: "I am very old, and I have a great deal to do, so I do not wish to lose my time in eating." . . .

The advancement of scientific knowledge is the work of many men, . . . Dalton could not have discovered the broad highway of atomic theory along which we advanced so rapidly had not Cavendish, Priestley, Scheele, and Lavoisier preceded him. Lavoisier could not have reduced the infant science to a state of order had not a score of diligent workers collected a number of facts from which his genius deduced a system. After the time of Dalton we understood chemical combination far better than ever before. We think of sulfur as composed of an almost infinite number of sulfur atoms, of equal size and weight, each one weighing 32 times as much as a hydrogen atom. The atoms of sulfur are nearly indivisible, and until comparatively recent years it was thought that they could not be divided. We now know that by elaborate instruments it is possible to break up such an atom and to produce particles far too small to be seen with the help of a microscope, but these particles are not sulfur. When sulfur combines with hydrogen we picture one sulfur atom as attracting to itself two hydrogen atoms so firmly that they cannot escape. In this way is formed a molecule of hydrogen sulfide or sulfurated hydrogen, an unpleasant-smelling substance that is given off by rotten eggs, and can be made in other ways. A fragment of iron is an assembly of a number of atoms of iron each atom weighing 55.8 times as much as an atom of hydrogen. So too every other element is composed of atoms of that element. The various chemical compounds are formed of almost infinitely small molecules consisting of two, three, or four atoms of different elements in the case of the simple compounds and twenty, fifty, or a hundred, or many more atoms belonging to perhaps eight or ten elements in the case of the more complex compounds. Many of the substances found in living creatures seem to be even more complex than this. Thousands of experiments carried out day by day for more than a hundred years by a multitude of chemists in many countries have proved beyond doubt the essential truth of Dalton's theory; that in a few details it requires a little modification need cause us no surprise.   *1937*

The Foundations of Chemical Industry

ROBERT E. ROSE

PRELUDE: THE JUGGLERS

ALL OF US HAVE SEEN THE JUGGLER WHO ENTERTAINS by throwing one brightly colored ball after the other into the air, catching each in turn and throwing it up again until he has quite a number moving from hand to hand. The system which he keeps in motion has an orderly structure. He changes it by selecting balls of different colors, altering the course or the sequence of the balls, or by adding to or diminishing the number with which he plays.

With this figure in mind let us use our imaginations. Before us we have an assemblage of hundreds of thousands of jugglers varying in their degree of accomplishment; some handle only one ball, others, more proficient, keep several in motion, and there are still others of an astounding dexterity who play with an hundred or more at once. The balls they handle are of ninety different colors and sizes. The jugglers do not keep still but move about at varying rates; those handling few and light balls move more quickly than those handling many or heavier ones. These dancers bump into each other and when they do so in certain cases they exchange some of the balls which they are handling or one juggler may take all of those handled by another, but in no case are the balls allowed to drop.

THE VANISHING POINT

Now imagine the moving group to become smaller and smaller until the jugglers cease to be visible to us, even when they dance under the highest power microscope. If someone who had not seen them were to come to you and say that he proposed undertaking the problem of finding out how the balls were moving and what were the rules of the exchanges made, and further that he proposed utilizing his knowledge to control what each minute juggler was doing, you would tell him that his task was

243

hopeless. If the chemist had listened to such advice there would be no chemical industry and you would lose so much that you would not be living in the way you are.

The jugglers are the electromagnetic forces of matter, the balls are the atoms, and each group in the hands of the juggler is a molecule of a substance. In reality, of course, instead of each molecule being represented by one unit we should multiply our jugglers by trillions and trillions.

THE MASTERY OF MOLECULES

The chemist, without even seeing them, has learned to handle these least units of materials in such a way as to get the arrangements which are more useful from those less useful. This power he has acquired as the outcome of his life of research, his desire to understand, even though understanding brought him no material gain, but mere knowledge. Because of his patience and devotion he has built a number of industries; all have this in common—they serve to rearrange atoms of molecules or to collect molecules of one kind for the service of man.

THE GREAT QUEST

The study of the substances of the earth's crust, of the air over and of the waters under earth, which has led us to our present knowledge of the electron, atom, and molecule, has been more adventurous than many a great journey made when the world was young and the frontier of the unknown was not remote from the city walls. Into the unknown world of things upon the "sea that ends not till the world's end" the man of science ventured, and he came back laden with treasure greater than all the gold and precious stones ever taken from the earth. He gave these to others and he fared forth again without waving of flags, without the benediction of holy church, with no more than the courage of him who would win Nature, who had chosen a harder road than that of the great, made famous because of subduing other men. He took no arms upon his quest, scarcely enough food to keep body and soul together, but instead, fire, glass, and that most astounding of all tools, the balance. As he pushed farther and farther on his great venture and as more and more joined his little band, he brought more and more back to those who did not understand in the least what he was doing, until now the lives of all men are made easier if not happier by these strange, most useful, and most potent things of which he is the creator by reason of the understanding his journeys have given him—a power much greater than any mere black magic.

This is the story of some of the strange treasure found by him in the far lands that are about us—treasure found by learning the secret of the jugglers' dance—the dance of the least little things out of which all we know is fashioned.

SULFURIC ACID

The Great Discovery

In Sicily and other parts of the earth where there are volcanoes, lumps of a yellow crumbly "stone" are found, called brimstone (a corruption of *brennisteinn* or burning stone). This material was regarded as having curative properties; if it was burned in a house the bad odors of the sickroom of primitive times were suppressed. Also the alchemists found that it took away the metallic character of most metals and they considered it very important in their search for the philosopher's stone, the talisman that was to turn all things to gold. The alchemists found also that sulfur, when burned over water, caused the water to become acid, and one of them found further that if the burning took place in the presence of saltpeter the acid which was produced was much stronger; indeed, if concentrated it was highly corrosive. A useless find, it seemed, of interest only to the alchemist who hoped to become rich beyond the dreams of avarice, and immortal as the gods. But the chemist made this discovery of more importance to the condition of the human race than that of Columbus, because by it he gave man a kingdom different from any that could have been his by merely discovering what already existed upon earth. That is the wonder of the chemist's work; he finds that which is not upon the earth until he discovers it; just as the artist creates so does the chemist. If he did not, there would be no chemical industry to write about.

Experiment to Manufacture

Having investigated this acid, he found it a most valuable new tool with which many new and interesting things could be made, and much could be done that before had been impossible. It became necessary, then, if all men were to profit as the chemist always wishes them to do by his power, that sulfuric acid should be made easily and cheaply in large quantities. The first attempt at commercial manufacture was in 1740; before that each experimenter made what little he needed for himself. The process, that mentioned above, was carried out in large glass balloons. It was a costly method and tedious. Then in 1746 lead chambers were substituted for the glass and the industry progressed rapidly.

The whole object of this most basic of all chemical industries can be written in three simple little equations.

$$
\begin{array}{ccc}
\text{Sulfur} & \text{Oxygen} & \text{Sulfur Dioxide} \\
S & + \quad O_2 \quad = & SO_2 \\
\text{Sulfur Dioxide} & \text{Oxygen} & \text{Sulfur Trioxide} \\
SO_2 & + \quad O_2 \quad = & SO_3 \\
\text{Sulfur Trioxide} & \text{Water} & \text{Sulfuric Acid} \\
SO_3 & + \quad H_2O \quad = & H_2SO_4
\end{array}
$$

Of the three elements necessary, oxygen occurs uncombined in the air of which it forms one-fifth by volume; it is also present combined with other elements in very large quantities in water, sand, and generally throughout the earth's crust, which is nearly half oxygen in a combined condition.

The Raw Materials

The great storehouse of hydrogen on the earth is water, of which it forms one-ninth, by weight. Sulfur is not so widely distributed in large quantities but it is very prevalent, being present in all plants and animals and also in such compounds as Epsom salts, gypsum, and Glauber's salt. In the free condition, i.e., as sulfur itself, it is found in volcanic regions and also where bacteria have produced it by decomposing the products of plant decay. There is one other source of sulfur that is quite important, a compound with iron which contains so much sulfur that it will burn.

The problem then was to take these substances and from them group the elements in such order as to produce sulfuric acid.

Since sulfur burns readily, that is, unites with oxygen to form sulfur dioxide, one might expect it to take up one more atom of oxygen from the air and become sulfur trioxide. It does, but so slowly that the process would never suffice for commercial production. But there is a way of speeding up the reaction which depends on using another molecule as a go-between, thus making the oxygen more active. The principle is that of the relay. Suppose an out-fielder has to throw a ball a very long way. The chances are that the ball will not be very true and that it may fall short of reaching the base. If there is a fielder between, he can catch the ball and get it to the base with much greater energy.

The chemist uses as a go-between a catalyst (in one process), oxides of nitrogen. Molecules of this gas throw an oxygen atom directly and unfailingly into any sulfur dioxide molecule they meet, then equally certainly they seize the next oxygen atom that bumps into them and are ready for the next sulfur dioxide molecule. Since molecules in a gas mixture bump into each other roughly five billion times a second, there is a very good chance for the exchange to take place in the great lead chambers of approximately a capacity of 150,000 cubic feet into which are poured water molecules (steam), oxygen molecules (air), and sulfur dioxide, to which are added small quantities of the essential oxides of nitrogen.

The Acid Rain

A corrosive, sour drizzle falls to the floor and this is chamber acid. It is sold in a concentration of 70 to 80 per cent. The weak chamber acid is good enough for a great many industrial purposes and is very cheap. If it is to be concentrated this must be done in vessels of lead up to a certain concentration and then in platinum or gold-lined stills if stronger acid is needed. Naturally this is expensive and every effort was made to find a method of making strong sulfuric acid without the necessity of this intermediate step. Especially was this true when the dyestuffs industry began to demand very large quantities of tremendously strong sulfuric acid which was not only 100 per cent but also contained a considerable amount of sulfur trioxide dissolved in it (fuming sulfuric acid).

The difficulty was overcome by using another catalyst (platinum) in the place of the oxides of nitrogen. If sulfur dioxide and oxygen (air) are passed over the metal the two gases unite to form sulfur trioxide much more rapidly and in the absence of water. Since platinum is very expensive and its action depends on the surface exposed, it is spread on asbestos fibers and does not look at all like the shiny metal of the jeweler. This method is known as the contact process and the product is sulfur trioxide, which represents the highest possible concentration of sulfuric acid and can be led into ordinary oil of vitriol (98 per cent sulfuric acid) and then diluted with water and brought to 98 per cent acid or left as fuming acid, depending on the requirements of the case. The perfection of this process was the result of some very painstaking research because when it was tried at first it was found that the platinum soon lost its virtue as a catalyst, and it was also discovered that the reason for this was the presence of arsenic in the sulfur dioxide. To get rid of every trace of arsenic is the hardest part of the contact process.

Vitriol

Next time you visit a laboratory ask to be shown a bottle of concentrated sulfuric acid. You will see a colorless, oily liquid, much heavier than water, as you will notice if you lift the bottle. A little on your skin will raise white weals and then dissolve your body right away; paper is charred by it as by fire. When it touches water there is a hissing.

Sulfuric Acid and Civilization

A dreadful oil, but its importance to industry is astonishing. If the art of making it were to be lost tomorrow we should be without steel and all other metals and products of the metallurgical industry; railroads, airplanes, automobiles, telephones, radios, reënforced concrete, all would go because the metals are taken from the earth by using dynamite made with sulfuric acid; and for the same reason construction work of all kinds, road and bridge building, canals, tunnels, and sanitary construction work would cease.

We should have to find other ways to produce purified gasoline and lubricating oil. The textile industry would be crippled. We should find ourselves without accumulators, tin cans, galvanized iron, radio outfits, white paper, quick-acting phosphate fertilizers, celluloid, artificial leather, dyestuffs, a great many medicines, and numberless other things into the making of which this acid enters at some stage.

If at some future date, however, all of our sulfur and all of our sulfur ores are burned up the chemist will yet find ways of making sulfuric acid. Possibly he may tap the enormous deposits of gypsum which exist in all parts of the earth. This has been done to some extent already but is not a process which is cheap enough to compete with sulfuric acid made from sulfur.

NITRIC ACID

It is essential that all the heavy chemicals, that is, the most used acids, alkalies, and salts, should be made so far as possible from readily available cheap material. We use air, water, and abundant minerals on this account. Nitric acid caused the chemical industry much concern until it was found possible to make it from air, because until then its source was Chile saltpeter, or sodium nitrate, a mineral occurring in a quantity only in the arid Chilean highlands. However, this source of supply is still the most important and the process used is one of great interest.

Having made oil of vitriol, the chemist found that he could produce other acids, one of the most important of these being liberated from saltpeter by the action of sulfuric acid. When nitric acid is made in this fashion we find that the sulfuric acid is changed into sodium sulfate and remains behind in the still. One might think from this that sulfuric acid is stronger and on that account that it drives out nitric acid, but in fact this preparation depends on a very simple principle, one of great importance.

Another Dance

We may best illustrate it by returning to our former simile. Let us assume a sodium nitrate juggler moving rather slowly. He is bumped into by a sulfuric acid juggler moving at about the same rate. They exchange some of the atoms with which they are playing and in consequence one juggler holds sodium hydrogen sulfate while the other holds nitric acid.

$$NaNO_3 + H_2SO_4 \rightarrow NaHSO_4 + HNO_3$$

The nitric acid molecule does not slow down the juggler as much as the sodium hydrogen sulfate and therefore this particular dancer moves away quite fast. Suppose millions of these exchanges to be taking place; then the nitric acid molecules will continue to dance away and will not come back to exchange their atoms any more. If we keep them all in by putting a lid on, then they are forced to go back and we get no more than a sort of game of ball in which the hydrogen and sodium atoms are passed back and forth. If, on the other hand, we open the lid and put a fire under the pot, the nitric acid molecules move faster and sooner or later all of them are driven out.

Nitric acid is now made from the air in more than one way so that we are entirely independent of the beds of Chile saltpeter no matter what might happen to them. Without nitric acid we could not make gun-cotton, dynamite, TNT, picric acid, ammonium nitrate, and the other explosives which are so enormously important to our civilization. In addition, we would lose all our brilliant dyes and most of our artificial silk, from which it is easy to see that this substance is of great importance to all of us.

SALT, THE JEWEL BOX

Soda

Among the treasures to which man fell heir as the most important inhabitant of the earth was one of innumerable little cubes made of sodium and chloride, crystals of salt. These he noticed whenever seawater evaporated and he soon found, if he lived on a vegetable diet as he did in some places, that the addition of these to his food made it much more pleasant and savory. It fact, it is a necessity for the health of the human body. Hunting peoples do not use it so much because they live almost entirely on meat, which contains sufficient salt. Next it was found that salt could be employed for preserving fish and meat, and thus man was able to tide over the periods in which hunting was poor. For ages and ages it was put to no other use. Nobody but a chemist would have thought of doing anything with it. In order to understand the whole of what he did and the part which salt plays in industry owing to the chemist's activity we must go back a little.

Soap as a Hair Dye

Very early it was found that the ashes of a fire (and fires at that time were always made of wood) were useful in removing grease from the hands. They were the earliest form of soap and it is surprising how long they remained the only thing used. Our records go to show that the Romans were the first of the more civilized peoples to find out how to make real soap, and they learned it from the Gauls, who used the material which they made from wood ashes and goat's tallow for washing their hair and beards because they believed that this gave them the fiery red appearance which they thought was becoming. The Romans saw the advantage of soap over wood ashes and a very considerable trade in the making of various kinds of soaps arose, but the difficulty always was with the production of the ashes because it takes quite a lot of ashes to make even a small quantity of soap. The advantage of having something more abundant to take the place of the ashes was evident. But the real stimulus which led to the discovery of soda ash came from a different source.

Glass from Ashes and Sand

It was found that ashes heated with sand formed glass. It was also found that the ashes of marine plants, or plants occurring on the seashore, gave a much better glass than that which could be made from the ashes of land plants. In consequence of this, as the art of glass making grew, barilla, the ashes of a plant growing in the salt marshes of Spain, became an increasingly important article of commerce and upon it depended the great glass factories of France and Bohemia. Owing to the political situation which arose at the end of the eighteenth century, France found herself in danger of losing her supremacy in the art of making glass because England cut off her supply of the Spanish ashes. For some reason the French ruler at the time had vision enough to see that it might be possible to make barilla artificially from some source within the kingdom of France and he offered a prize to any one who would make his country independent of Spain. We have seen that the chemist's business is the transmutation of one kind of material into another, and naturally it was the chemist who came forward with a solution of the problem. Since this process is now supplanted by a more economical one, we will merely outline it here.

Limestone to Washing Soda

Remember that it is essential to start from some abundant common material. Le Blanc, the chemist who solved the problem, knew that the Spanish ashes contained sodium carbonate, the formula of which we write as Na_2CO_3; that is, it is a combination of sodium, carbon, and oxygen. There are a great many carbonates in nature and among these is that of calcium which we know as chalk, limestone, or marble, depending on the way in which it crystallizes. In this we have a substance of the formula $CaCO_3$. Suppose, then, we write the two compounds side by side: Na_2CO_3, $CaCO_3$. Evidently the only difference is that in one we have two atoms of sodium (Na_2) in place of one of calcium (Ca) in the other. Salt contains sodium and is very common. If, then, we can get the sodium radical from the sodium chloride and the carbonate radical from the limestone and join the two pieces we will get sodium carbonate, which is what we want. What Le Blanc did was to treat sodium chloride with sulfuric acid. This gave him sodium sulphate and hydrochloric acid. Then he heated the sodium sulfate with coke or charcoal and limestone, after which he extracted the mass with water and found that he had sodium carbonate in solution.

The steps do not sound difficult but it was really a great feat to make them commercially possible. In the first stage when sulfuric acid acted on the salt, hydrochloric acid was given off and this was a great nuisance. The amount of it produced exceeded any use that could be found for it and it was poured away; being highly acid it undermined the houses in the neighborhood and caused a great deal of trouble. Later, it became the most valuable product of the process because it was converted into bleaching powder by a method that we will take up subsequently.

Industry a Result of Chemical Discovery

It is interesting to learn that this process which France invented in her extremity became one of the largest industrial developments in England. It caused the flourishing there of the sulfuric acid industry because this acid was necessary for the process and, as we have seen, sulfuric acid is tremendously valuable in a great variety of directions. It also made possible the development of an enormous textile industry because the making of cloth needs soap and bleach, both of which were first supplied in abundance as a consequence of Le Blanc's discovery.

To return to the story of the chemist's transformations of salt, the present process for the conversion of this compound into sodium carbonate is by the action of ammonia and carbon dioxide upon a saturated solution of it, the carbon dioxide being obtained from limestone. When these three substances are brought together a change takes place which can best be described by the following equation:

$$\underset{NH_3}{\underset{\text{Ammonia}}{}} + \underset{H_2O}{\underset{\text{Water}}{}} + \underset{CO_2}{\underset{\substack{\text{Carbon}\\\text{Dioxide}}}{}} = \underset{NH_4HCO_3}{\underset{\substack{\text{Ammonium}\\\text{Bicarbonate}}}{}}$$

$$\underset{NaCl}{\underset{\text{Salt}}{}} + \underset{NH_4HCO_3}{\underset{\substack{\text{Ammonium}\\\text{Bicarbonate}}}{}} = \underset{NaHCO_3}{\underset{\substack{\text{Sodium}\\\text{Bicarbonate}}}{}} + \underset{NH_4Cl}{\underset{\substack{\text{Ammonium}\\\text{Chloride}}}{}}$$

The change that takes place depends on the fact that sodium bicarbonate is comparatively insoluble and separates out. It is collected and then heated, the heat causing it to turn into sodium carbonate, carbon dioxide, and water.

$$2\,NaHCO_3 = Na_2CO_3 + CO_2 + H_2O$$

In this process the essential thing is to keep the ammonia in the system, because it is used over and over again and, if it escapes, an expense arises out of all proportion to the value of the carbonate which must be sold at a price of about two cents per pound. The ammonia goes out of the reaction, as indicated in the equation, in the form of ammonium chloride and this is returned to the process by allowing quicklime, made by heating limestone in kilns, to decompose the chloride. The other part of the limestone (the carbon dioxide) is also used in the process, as shown in the first equation. We start then with salt, water, and limestone, and we finish with calcium chloride and sodium carbonate.

Caustic Soda

This is not all that the chemist was able to do with salt. In soap making much better results are obtained if, instead of using wood ashes which give us nothing but an impure soft potash soap, we use sodium hydroxide or caustic soda. Now, caustic soda is something which does not occur in nature because it always combines with the carbon dioxide of the air or with some acid material and disappears. The old method of making it was to take the soda of the Le Blanc process and to treat it with slaked lime. In this way we can make about a 14 per cent solution of caustic soda which is then evaporated if it is required in a more concentrated form. This method of making caustic soda was sufficiently economical to give us all that we needed at very reasonable prices, but eventually a better method was discovered.

Caustic soda is NaOH, that is to say, it is water (H_2O) in which one of the hydrogens has been replaced by sodium. If in any way we could make this reaction take place, $NaCl + HOH = NaOH + HCl$, we would get directly two products which we want. Unfortunately, it is impossible to get salt to exchange atoms in this way with water. However, a study of salt solutions showed that the atoms of sodium and chlorine were actually separated when in solution and that they also acquired a property which would allow of their segregation. They became electrically charged and it is always possible to attract an electrically charged body by using a charged body of opposite sign. If, then, we put the positive and the negative pole of a battery or another source of electricity in a solution of salt the chlorine will wander away to the positive and the sodium will wander to the negative pole.

Electrons

What takes place can best be described by a rough analogy. Suppose two automobiles of different makes are running side by side, keeping together because of the friendship which exists between the two parties. Now suppose these two machines have an accident in which, by a freak, one wheel is torn off one car and added to the other. Assume that the occupants of the car are not damaged and that the cars can still run; also that the fifth wheel is a distinct nuisance. If there were two garages at considerable distances, one of which specialized in taking off extra wheels and the other did nothing but put on missing wheels, and the accident were a common one involving thousands of machines, then it would be natural for the cars to move in opposite directions to these two garages and if we assume that all the wheels are interchangeable, then there might be a traffic between the garages, by another road perhaps, the wheels being sent from one to the other.

This very rough picture is intended to describe the fact that when the sodium and chlorine atoms of salt are separated by water the electrons of which they are composed are distributed in such a way that there is an extra one in the chlorine which (an electron being negative) makes the chlorine particle negative, while the sodium lacks one electron and therefore becomes positive since it was neutral before. The result, then, of this electrolysis or use of the electric current in separating the charged atoms of sodium chloride (the ions as they are called) is that sodium and chlorine are given off at the two poles. Now, chlorine is not very soluble in water and can be collected as a gas. The sodium, on the other hand, as each little particle is liberated, reacts with the water about it to give hydrogen and sodium hydroxide. Therefore, we have accomplished what we set out to do, only instead of getting sodium hydroxide and hydrogen chloride we get sodium hydroxide, chlorine, and hydrogen.

Electricity

The success of this method is due to discoveries in another field of science. Only when Michael Faraday's researches on the nature of the electric current made available another source of energy different from heat, was it possible for the chemist to carry out what has just been described; at first only in a very small way but, as the production of electricity became more and more economical, ever on a larger scale until now the industry is a most important one.

Chlorine

So far we have directed our attention almost entirely to the sodium atom of salt; the other part of the molecule, the chlorine, is also extremely valuable to us. It used to be set free by oxidizing hydrochloric acid of the Le Blanc process with manganese dioxide. Now, as we have just seen, we get it directly from a solution of salt by electrolysis.

Uses of Caustic Soda

The two servants which the chemist has conjured out of salt by using electricity are extremely valuable, though if they are not handled rightly they are equally as dangerous as they are useful when put to work. Caustic soda is a white, waxy-looking solid which is extremely soluble in water and attracts moisture from the air. It is highly corrosive, destroying the skin and attacking a great many substances. When it is allowed to act on cellulose in the form of cotton the fiber undergoes a change which results in its acquiring greater luster so that the process of mercerizing, as it is called, is valuable industrially. The manufacture of artificial silk made by the viscose method depends on the fact that caustic soda forms a compound with cellulose. Practically all the soap manufactured at the present time is produced by the action of caustic soda on fat. The by-product of this industry is glycerol which is used in making dynamite. In fact, soda is just as important among alkalies as sulfuric acid is among acids.

Uses of Chlorine

Chlorine, the partner of sodium, is a frightfully destructive material. It attacks organic substances of all kinds, destroying them completely, and it also attacks all metals, even platinum and gold, though fortunately, if it is quite dry, it does not react with iron, and on that account it can be stored under pressure in iron cylinders. Although it is such a deadly gas if allowed to run wild, yet it is extremely useful and its discovery has been very greatly to the advantage of the human race. First of all, it is employed in the manufacture of bleaching powder, a product which enables the cotton industry to work far more intensively than it otherwise could. Formerly cotton was bleached by laying it on the grass, but that is much too slow for our present mode of life. In fact, we have no room for it because it has been calculated that the cotton output of Manchester, England, would require the whole county as a bleaching field and this is obviously impossible. Then came the discovery that this same compound could be used in purifying our water supplies of dangerous disease-breeding bacteria and this has reduced the typhoid death rate from that of a very dangerous epidemic disease to a negligible figure. Now, whenever the water supply of a city is questionable, chlorine is pumped right into the mains or else a solution made from bleaching powder is used. Twenty parts of bleaching powder per million is sufficient to kill 90 to 95 per cent of all the bacteria in the water. For medical use, a solution of hypochlorous acid, which is the active principle of bleaching powder, has been developed into a marvelous treatment for deep-seated wounds, and recoveries which formerly would have been out of the question are now possible. Chlorine is also used in very large amounts in making organic chemicals which the public enjoys as dyestuffs or sometimes does not enjoy as pharmaceuticals or medicines.

All in all, the products obtained from the little salt cube are of extreme necessity and importance to every one of us and their utilization shows what can be done when men of genius devote themselves to the acquisition of real knowledge and then translate their discoveries into commercial enterprises for the benefit of humanity.

CHEMISTRY AND UNDERSTANDING

The brief story for which we have space indicates but very dimly the real interest and fascination the chemist has in handling matter. His knowledge has increased to such a point that he can build you a molecule almost to order to meet any specifications. To be without any knowledge of chemistry is to go through life ignorant of some of the most interesting aspects of one's surroundings; and yet the acquisition of some knowledge of this subject is by no means hard. There are any number of books which tell the story in simple language if you do not wish to study the science intensively. On the other hand, all that you need is a real interest and a willingness to think as you read.

1924

Man's Synthetic Future

ROGER ADAMS

THE PRESENT UNCERTAINTIES FACING THE PEOPLES of the world, and the startling discoveries in science during the past few decades, have stimulated many to prognosticate about the future. Numerous and various forecasts have been made as to national groupings, forms of government, celestial transportation, sources of food, new building materials, and modes of living. Some predict communization of the world, others that there will be internal revolutions against communism and fascism, bringing about the return of freedom of speech and action to all people....

My remarks will be based on projecting the chemical discoveries of the past to logical achievements in the future. One hundred years ago all materials used by man were derived directly from natural sources—plants, animals, and minerals. The chemist has, through the past six decades, so perfected his knowledge of the intricacies of molecules through physical and chemical methods that he is now able to determine the patterns in which the atoms are combined in nature's substances. Indeed he is able to assemble atoms according to his own design and thus produce many of these same substances by synthesis. Moreover, he has discovered how to create new, better, and cheaper compounds based on a knowledge of natural products.

One of the first industries transformed by chemistry was dye manufacturing, an industry that is now 99 per cent synthetic. In a second field, drugs and medicinals are over 75 per cent of synthetic origin. Natural gums and resins at present account for only 5 per cent of the 2.3 million pounds of plastics produced in the United States last year. More than half the 500 million gallons of paint used annually are based on synthetic products. Over 50 per cent of today's rubber is synthetic, and over 20 per cent of the textiles. The field of synthetic detergents has had a phenomenal growth, until more than one billion pounds are produced annually. This figure is still well below the amount of soap consumed.

During World War I we became conscious of shortages of raw and finished materials, especially chemicals; of shortages of certain foods and of the necessity for substitutes. During World War II, and now during the rearmament period, the shortages are primarily in raw materials. We normally consider that the United States has abundant resources, yet the Government lists 167 strategic items that must be imported. Stockpiling by the Government of materials essential to both war and peace, but not indigenous to the United States or found here in less than the required quantities, has resulted in artificial price increases.

Let us consider for a moment our mineral supplies. The most widely distributed metals are iron, aluminum, magnesium, and titanium. They are available in amounts sufficient to supply the world's needs for hundreds of years. Aluminum and its alloys will continue to replace steel and other metals in even larger measure than in recent years. Magnesium, a very light metal, has found many uses, especially in alloys, but certain of its properties would appear to limit its extensive industrial application. Titanium, about which much has been heard in recent months, is fourth in abundance of all metals, and its ores are widespread over the world. It is truly the metal with an attractive future. Only half as heavy as steel, it is, in a pure state, ductile, very significantly heat- and chemical-resistant, and readily forms valuable alloys. It does not corrode even in sea water. For jet engines it is ideal. Its applications would be exceedingly numerous were it not for the cost. Titanium dioxide, a common derivative, which can be obtained readily from the native ore, is familiar as a superior white pigment for outdoor house paints and in finely divided form as a delustrant for rayon and nylon. The cheap production of pure titanium metal, however, has baffled the efforts of chemists and metallurgists for years. The annual supply of the metal has been only a few hundred tons, and it has sold at a price of $10 to $20 or more per pound, thus restricting its use to items where properties are all important and cost is a small factor. But now the Government is supporting the construction of plants that will provide an annual production of several thousand tons to be used primarily for military purposes. The cost of production, even on the larger scale contemplated, is likely to bring the price down to not less than $5 a pound, a figure much too high for general industrial application. One of the liveliest chemical problems today is the attempt to discover a cheaper way of obtaining pure titanium metal from its ores. When solved, several of the metals now considered so essential for certain steels and alloys will be in less demand.

Proved mineral deposits of all ores of less common metals, such as copper, lead, zinc, manganese, chromium, tungsten, tin, and others, would appear to have a limited life. There is, however, still much territory on earth that has not been prospected, and there still exists the possibility of mineral deposits being found deep in the earth or under lakes and seas. It has been reported that under the lakes in central Finland rich bodies of ore have recently been discovered. Perhaps the future supplies are under water or in the frozen regions of the Poles.

There is a fantastically large source of chemicals hardly touched at present in sea water. The amounts of chemicals in sea water have from time to time been published, but I venture to repeat them. A cubic mile of sea water contains 143,000,000 tons of sodium chloride, more than 300,000 tons of bromide, and over 5,000,000 tons of magnesium. A host of other metals are present in lesser amounts. When it is considered that there are over 300,000,000 cubic miles of sea water, the potential supply of metals and salts is staggering. At present, sea water is a source of salt in some countries and an economic source of magnesium and bromine in the United States. The future chemist and engineer will discover a practical method of recovering many of the other minerals for commercial use. Paraphrasing Longfellow—

> Would'st thou, so the chemist questioned,
> Learn the secret of the seas?
> Only those who're trained in science
> Divine the possibilities.

The use of petroleum and natural gas for fuels, and more recently as raw materials for strategic organic chemicals, has been stupendous. During the past 25 years, the consumption of petroleum has increased, on the average, 4 per cent a year, and of natural gas 10 per cent a year. The present demand for petroleum has reached a level of 2 billion barrels a year. The demand for natural gas is 7 billion cubic feet annually, 10 per cent of which is consumed in the chemical industry.

As of January 1951, proved reserves of petroleum had been established which, on the basis of present annual consumption, would last for 15 years and those of natural gas 26 to 27 years. More significant, however, is the fact that in spite of the continuous increased consumption of these products the 1951 reserves substantially exceeded those of 1950. Exhaustion of supplies has been predicted periodically for three decades, but still new reserves continue to be discovered, although with greater difficulty and at increased expense. Even if the supply in the United States decreases more rapidly than elsewhere, the reserves in foreign lands will be adequate for a long time. From 1859 to 1951, almost a century, about 41 billion barrels of oil have been produced. All this would not fill a space

1.6 cubic miles in volume. This is insignificant in relation to the total volume of oil likely still to be found in the world.

But even when the petroleum is exhausted, huge reserves of coal, oil shale, and lignite are available. By appropriate processing, the study of which is well advanced if not yet perfected, these may be converted into gasoline and related products. On the basis of present consumption, coal, oil shale, and lignite reserves would last 700 or 800 years, but allowing for difficulties of recovery and for increased demand it would appear conservative to estimate they will last for at least 200 to 300 years. I am willing to prophesy that when the time of exhaustion arrives scientists will have found substitutes.

Petroleum, originally a source merely of kerosene, then of gasoline and lubricating oil, has become, along with natural gas, the raw material for a host of aliphatic and aromatic chemicals upon which many of our chemical industries are founded. The magnitude can be realized best by citing that 1.25 billion pounds of butadiene, obtained by an appropriate cracking process from petroleum, are used annually for 825,000 tons of synthetic rubber. From 3½ billion pounds of ethylene, propylene, butylene, and isobutylene, 16 billion pounds of derivatives are made each year. Just a decade or two ago the chemical industry relied upon coal tar, the volatile liquids obtained when coal is coked, for many of its raw materials. But with increased use of petroleum for power, and of natural gas for heating, less coal is being coked and the supply of chemicals from the coal tar is much smaller than the demand. Industry has now turned to petroleum for a substantial proportion of its chemicals for the synthesis of dyes, drugs, plastics, and fibers.

Rapid mechanization has made search for substances to produce energy as well as heat one of our prime objectives. A hundred years ago, it was wood, and now fossil fuels have the attention of a multitude of technologists. It is difficult to conceive of modern life without power and heat. In spite of the discovery from year to year of more reserves of energy-containing materials, the time before these are exhausted is at most a matter of a few hundred years and then a new source of energy must be available.

A perpetual supply of energy comes from the sun. How vast it is compared to the energy-supplying materials on earth may be realized by a comparison presented in an article by Eugene Ayres. Suppose that all the coal, lignite, peat, tar sands, crude petroleum, natural gas, and oil shale that we are likely to produce in the future on the basis of the most optimistic estimates were collected. Suppose that all the timber of the world were cut into cordwood. Moreover, suppose that all the uranium and thorium that are likely ever to be discovered were purified and made ready for nuclear fission. Suppose now that this fuel were distributed over the face of the earth, that the sun were suddenly extinguished, and that the fuel were ignited to give energy at the rate at which we are accustomed to receive it from the sun—the combustible fuel would be gone in three days. Nuclear reactions would last a few hours. The energy that actually reaches the earth from the sun is over 30,000 times that of all the fuel and water power now used. There is absolutely nothing that can be a competitor of the sun. It is fortunate that we shall continue to have plenty of solar energy, which, directly or indirectly, serves to keep the world an attractive place in which to live.

Of the annual land vegetation, only 14 per cent is consumed as food, fuel, lumber, paper, and chemicals. The balance of 86 per cent is returned to the earth to maintain essential biological balance. With our ever-increasing population, it is doubtful whether the fuel use of vegetation can be increased to any very great extent.

Sooner or later the inexhaustible supply of energy from the sun will be used to supplement, or in large measure to replace, energy-containing materials on earth. Only limited progress has so far been made. Of the scientists' approaches for collecting the sun's energy several have shown some promise. A popular study has been that of the single-celled alga *Chlorella pyrenoidosa*. This plant multiplies at a rate that appears to be limited only by the carbon dioxide content of the water. Carbon dioxide in the air amounts to 0.03 per cent. It has been found that algae in pans of water 6 inches deep are capable of absorbing up to 2 per cent of the total solar energy falling on a given area as compared with less than 0.1 per cent for average agriculture. A yield of 15 dry tons per acre has been realized, which is nearly five times that of the best land growth, and scientists believe that this yield can be trebled. The Carnegie Institution has recently reported what is claimed to be the first large-scale experiments with *Chlorella*. Whether these algae may be used directly for cattle or human food, or whether they may be converted more profitably into chemicals or fuel is a problem for the future. To provide 1 billion barrels of motor fuel from algae would require an area of 35,000 square miles, assuming 35 dry tons of algae per acre could be obtained.

Photosynthesis, the process by which all vegetation is created, is not well understood. In essence, the plant converts the low-energy compounds, carbon dioxide and water, to carbohydrates and oxygen in the presence of chlorophyll. Attempts have been made to replace chlorophyll by synthetic dyes and inorganic chemicals. It has been reported that from certain experiments an amount of energy is absorbed equivalent to that absorbed in the presence of chlorophyll.

The use of glass, sometimes with reflectors, to collect the heat from the sun shows promise of becoming practical. Energy absorption seven times as efficient as the most optimistic agricultural proposals has been claimed. Apparatus is now in use for the heating of water by the sun.

Phosphors are chemicals that absorb radiant energy and radiate it after a certain length of time. Such chemicals might be employed to absorb energy from the sun during the day and for illuminating purposes at night. Even though inefficient in this process of absorption and emission, the amount of the sun's available energy is so great that this procedure is not beyond the realm of practical possibility.

New sources of energy, however important they may be, are not an immediate problem but one for future generations of chemists and engineers. With our present adequate raw materials, let us explore what discoveries may be expected. "Synthetic polymers" is a term used by the chemist for the giant molecules he has learned how to manufacture from very simple ones. Such polymers possess very different physical properties and relatively inert chemical properties compared to the substances from which they are derived. Synthetic rubber, plastics, resins, and fibers fall into this category.

Today's synthetic rubber is the equivalent of natural rubber when fabricated into tires for passenger automobiles. Many improvements in the processing of synthetic rubber for tires have been made in the past decade, the most interesting of which has been recent—the incorporation of a substantial amount of petroleum in the mix. The resulting tires are claimed to have no inferior qualities, and some superior ones, to those that are oil-free. Moreover, they can be made more cheaply, and a substantial amount of raw rubber is conserved. A synthetic rubber suitable for heavy-duty tires on trucks, busses, and other large vehicles has yet to be found. Present synthetic rubber tires when used for this purpose are susceptible to a heat buildup that leads to excessive degradation. The eventual discovery of a synthetic rubber for this purpose is merely a matter of time. Moreover, special rubbers, capable of withstanding the cold of the Arctic and the heat of the equatorial desert regions without losing the required elasticity, and those which are oil-resistant and suited for low-temperature utilization, will be added to the list.

Dozens of various kinds of plastics are now sold commercially. These vary from the clear and transparent, especially suitable for ornamental purposes or for airplane windshields, to very tough, chemical- and heat-resistant plastics for use as gaskets in chemical operations involving corrosive materials. There are resins and plastics for parts of chemical equipment; for coatings of wire to be used in the construction of small motors operating at high temperatures to produce the power of an ordinary larger motor; for the waterproofing of fabrics; for finishes of wood, metals, and even stoneware. Plastics are available for all types of bristles, and others are suitable for replacement of metals even where strength is a primary factor. The future will see transparent plastics that will not discolor and with surfaces that will not craze or scratch readily; finishes for wood and metals that will remain durable for long periods of time in the presence of sunlight and salt air; and flexible, waterproof and moistureproof film of any desired strength.

Cotton, silk, and wool have been the fibers used almost exclusively for fabrics until a few decades ago. Rayon and acetate silk were then introduced. These are both chemical modifications of cellulose, derived usually from cotton or wood. In spite of the fact that they lack many of the desirable properties of the natural fibers, particularly wet-strength and recoverability of the original shape upon drying, these fibers have been widely accepted and have supplemented or in part replaced cotton and silk. Acetate fabric possesses a luxurious "feel" and drapes in soft, lustrous folds. Acetate blends remarkably well with other fibers. Just recently it has been announced that a rayon has been made in which the basic structure has been so modified that the resulting product has the wet-strength exhibited by natural fibers. If this is authentic, one of the greatest steps forward in rayon manufacture since its inception will have been achieved.

About 15 years ago nylon, a strictly synthetic fiber, made by combining very simple molecules into a complex one similar to those nature furnishes us, made its appearance. Chiefly because of its rapid-drying properties, its durability, and its resistance to fungi and insects, it has found many applications for which natural fibers are not suitable. Natural silk, for which nylon is a substitute, has never recovered its prewar status. The brilliant researches in Japan extending over a period of 40 years, when the silkworm was nurtured and pampered until he produced an egg-shaped instead of peanut-shaped cocoon with a filament twice as long as formerly and of double strength, will be of no avail by the time the synthetic chemist has had a decade or more of additional experience. The uses for nylon have become so numerous that the demand cannot be met by present production facilities. Newer synthetic fibers have appeared on the market—for example, Orlon, Acrilan, Dynel, which resemble one another somewhat in properties and are all based on the same simple chemical, acrylonitrile. These fabrics are utilized particularly for seat covers, curtains, and filter cloths in industry. They are also suitable in the apparel field because of their smart appearance, long wear, and easy laundering. Still another synthetic fiber is Dacron, which resists wrinkling, water, and moths as does no other fiber. Suits made of Dacron go through rainstorms without losing their crease and can be cleaned with soap and water without losing the original shape after drying.

Rapid drying is effected because the threads do not absorb water and drying consists merely in the evaporation of surface moisture. But this nonabsorption of moisture leads to a certain amount of discomfort, particularly in hot weather. Consequently, closely woven fabrics for shirts and undergarments have in large measure been replaced by those with a sheer or open weave. To find a fiber that will dry rapidly and at the same time permit moisture to penetrate is asking more than the chemist is likely to discover, since they are two incompatible properties. But these synthetic fibers must be improved in other ways, or new fibers found which have the desired properties, before natural fibers will be extensively replaced. The present synthetic fibers do not take dyes as effectively as natural fibers, and up to the present it has been impossible to manufacture fabrics with the attractive colors so frequently found in silk and wool. Synthetic fibers also have the annoying property of melting or changing color if the pressing iron is too hot. The "feel" of synthetic textiles has been improved, but the resiliency of wool or the warm, soft "feel" of silk has not yet been duplicated in the synthetics. When, however, synthetic fibers are blended with wool or rayon in various proportions, fabrics with many of the desirable properties of each of the components have been obtained.

Certain representatives of the petroleum industry, when called upon to make speeches in foreign lands on the progress of petroleum chemistry, have demonstrated the achievements by clothing themselves completely—suit, necktie, shirt, underclothing, and socks—with synthetic fibers, the primary chemicals for which are all derived from petroleum. For any traveler in foreign lands, the convenience of synthetic-fiber wearing apparel is superlative.

I predict the discovery of synthetic fibers which the public will prefer for most purposes to the natural fibers. An official of the wool industry made a statement recently that the demand for wool as a fabric will never be replaced. These words were spoken by one completely unfamiliar with the potentialities of chemical research. Just as the automobile replaced the wagon, synthetic fibers will replace the natural fibers. Half the wool now consumed in the United States will be replaced by synthetic fibers within 10 to 20 years, the time being dependent primarily on the restrictions which industry encounters in materials and money for plant construction. Synthetic fibers to replace cotton will also be discovered; these will be strong, durable, and moisture-absorbing, thus making them suitable and comfortable for wearing apparel. They will not, however, be rapid-drying.

The plastics to replace cotton will also serve to replace natural leather for shoe uppers. For years excellent leather substitutes, especially for seat coverings and bookbinding, have been available but not for shoes. Natural leather permits moisture to penetrate, and the feet remain dry except when it is unusually hot. The present artificial leathers do not have this property. As a consequence, when shoes of this material are worn the feet become moist and uncomfortable. With durable, moisture-absorbing plastics, the problem of synthetic shoe uppers will be solved.

Plant life is essential to human existence, and the chemist will contribute much in this field. By well-known processes of selection and plant breeding, the agriculturist has succeeded, during the 40 years that soybeans have been grown in this country, in increasing the oil content from 16 or 17 per cent to 21 or 22 per cent. Hybrid seed corn, which is now widely used by farmers, results in an increase in crop yield sometimes as high as 50 per cent, essentially without any additional requirements in the soil. The inference from these achievements is that proper chemical treatment of plants could result in fundamental modification of their metabolism. By standard agricultural development methods the future will see food crops in which the size of the plant is dwarfed and the fruit, kernels, or ears of corn are of greater size. In this way, more plants can be grown in a given area and the subsequent crop will be larger.

Another means of providing a greater crop from a given acreage is by plant-growth stimulants—chemicals that accelerate the growth and maturation of plants. Several are known, and chemists will discover new and better ones, with the eventual result that two crops of the same or different plants may be grown during the normal season where now only one crop is possible. Perhaps during these experiments we may find substances that will not merely speed up the growth of a plant but cause its fruit to be larger—for example, pears, apples, or oranges the size of grapefruit. If this seems fantastic, just consider the coconut-milk factor recently discovered in academic experiments. On its addition to a basal nutrient agar medium, mature plant cells are caused to subdivide; for example, cylindrical slices of carrot will grow rapidly.

Plant physiology is still in its infancy, and it must be better understood before rapid advancement in the cultivation and control of plants can reach a maximum. Experiments performed in Germany during the past

10 years permit one to envisage remarkable achievements in the future. In the flowers of the forsythia, those early yellow blooms which decorate gardens in many parts of the country in the early spring, it has been observed that the pollen of one flower never fertilizes the stigma of the same flower, nor does it fertilize a flower of the same type whether the flower is on the same or another bush. Formation of seed occurs in flowers where the pollen comes from long stamens and is accepted by flowers with long stigmas. Similarly, pollen from flowers with short stamens fertilizes flowers with short stigmas. Other combinations result in nonfertilization. A chemical study of pollen from long and short stamens has revealed that, although closely related chemicals are in each, they are actually different. With this discovery, a procedure was developed whereby fertilization of these flowers could be made to occur by chemical treatment where it would not have occurred naturally.

Not too remote from these experiments is that of spraying the blossoms of tomato plants with 2,4-D a chemical commonly used for killing broad-leaved plants. This not only causes many more of the earlier blooms to mature into fruit, but the tomatoes formed are seedless. With this start, let us look forward to seedless raspberries, blackberries, cranberries, and perhaps many other kinds of fruits, such as watermelons, pears, and apples.

One of the banes of the farmer or the florist is the insect pests that either destroy or greatly reduce his crops. The varieties of insects and mites are many, and consequently different kinds of chemicals have been sought to eliminate them. DDT is effective in the killing of flies, mosquitoes, and many insects that attack plants, but it is not universally good. Several other insecticides are available, each with its special properties for use on a certain type of insect. Periodic spraying of crops, however, is not only expensive but inefficient, since it is impossible to reach all parts of the plant. The chemist must search for a more ideal insecticide. The ultimate will be a chemical, repellent to all insects and mites and innocuous to plants and to higher animals, a substance which when sprayed on the leaves will be absorbed and completely translocated by means of the plant juices. Why not seek also a combination of minerals and fertilizer required as plant food that can be absorbed through the leaves rather than to follow the traditional custom of fertilizing the soil with chemicals, a large proportion of which is washed away by the rain before plant absorption has occurred?

The farmer also requires chemicals to control weeds and to simplify his cultivation problems. Rapid advances have been made in this area, and many chemicals are known that are toxic to certain kinds of vegetation. Chemicals will sometime be available to sterilize the soil completely toward grasses and weeds but not toward the desired crop. Because of the similarity of many plants to each other, it may be necessary to provide a series of chemicals, each of which will effectively kill just one kind of several closely related plants. The layman will welcome the day when he can effectively kill the crabgrass in his bluegrass lawn.

Far more important information will eventually result from the study of plants. Each plant, with the aid of the sun's energy, converts carbon dioxide and water in presence of mineral salts into a wide variety of chemicals, such as starch, cellulose, protein, vegetable oils, chlorophyll, and many other complex organic molecules in smaller amounts. These reactions take place at ordinary temperatures under very mild conditions, commonly known as "biological conditions." In comparison, the chemist is a clumsy operator. He requires massive equipment, often high temperatures and pressures, skillful engineering, and a number of operations to achieve what the plant does with a little sunlight and the simplest of chemicals. The chemist has discovered a few reactions that take place under very mild conditions and result in the formation of complex molecules from several simple ones. But he is a long way from understanding how nature operates. When, a few centuries hence, such reactions can be duplicated in the laboratory our present production methods for many organic chemicals, ingenious and skillful as they now appear, will look archaic.

Characteristic of each plant is its ability always to build up the same chemicals year after year. It has been observed, however, that if a plant is moved to a different climate the relative amounts of the chemicals present may often be modified. The day will come when a plant, after treatment with a certain chemical, will be inhibited from synthesizing one or more of the substances normally found within its structure or, on the other hand, the plant may be stimulated to create one or more of its chemicals in much larger amounts. Thus fodder crops might result from plants which now contain some toxic constituent, or plants which contain physiologically active medicinal substances may be induced to produce them in larger quantities.

The present food supply of the world, if properly distributed, would be adequate. With the steady increase in population, sooner or later all the arable land will be utilized, and even intensive farming of the soil through improved agricultural methods, plant stimulants, weed-controlling agents, pesticides, and other developments will not meet the world's food requirements. The resources of the sea will then be more intensively exploited than at present. Fish is a valuable food of high protein and rich vitamin content. It can be expanded to supplement meat supply. I envisage a more systematic fishing industry than at present—certain types of fish ranches—large fenced-off water areas in which fish are grown, fed, and annually harvested—analogous to cattle ranches. Sea farming will be a term comparable to land farming. Marine plants for food, fuel, or chemical use will be grown and harvested like land crops instead of the present system of collecting what happens to be washed ashore. When, with these extensions, the food supplies reach the limit the chemist will provide antifertility compounds which upon addition to the diet will assure a means of controlling the birth rate.

The diets of humans have been improved until now many ailments resulting from diet deficiencies are well understood and have largely been overcome either by balancing or supplementing the food intake. Concentrated or synthetic foods containing just the necessary constituents for human growth and development are feasible, but they will never be accepted by persons in good health as long as eating attractive food is the most general and universally liked human activity. In spite of properly adjusted diets, the human race is susceptible to a long list of bacterial, virus, fungus, and degenerative diseases, some of which have thus far resisted the efforts of science.

Until half a century ago medicinal products for treatment of disease were confined chiefly to plant or animal extracts or principles discovered originally through the cut-and-try methods of the physicians of earlier ages. The chemist has now synthesized many of these principles and on the basis of this knowledge has been able to produce other products superior to the natural. Drugs that have not been derived from the basic information provided by nature have been fortuitous or have been discovered usually by serendipity, a combination of skillful observation and chance that leads so often during scientific research to unexpected achievements of basic or applied importance.

Even though a marvelous array of drugs is now available, and a vast storehouse of information has been collected, the laws of chemotherapy are still unrevealed and decades will pass before a rational chemical basis will be provided for discovery of new therapeutic agents. The knowledge of the living cell in which the chemical reactions are constantly occurring to provide the life process is still very meager. However, the elaborate series and combinations of reactions in the cell are gradually being untangled. The cell functions in health and disease will sooner or later be clarified.

While these more basic explorations are progressing, search for more effective drugs by present procedures will be intensified. New and better drugs for combatting bacterial diseases may be expected. I envisage the gradual replacement of the drugs which must be administered intravenously or intramuscularly by others of equal or greater potency which may be taken orally. Many of the most stubborn diseases of mankind are those caused by viruses, such as the common cold, poliomyelitis, spinal meningitis, influenza, virus pneumonia, mumps, and measles. Satisfactory drugs for their treatment are lacking. The retarded progress in this field in contrast to that made in the study of bacterial diseases is the result of the absence of suitable laboratory or animal assay methods for determining the effectiveness of any chemical agent upon a particular virus. Bacteria can be grown in the laboratory, but viruses propagate only within living bacteria or living cells. Research in the next decades will solve the vexing problem of finding viricides, and thus open a new chapter in medical therapy.

For the degenerative diseases, such as cancer, heart disease, or arteriosclerosis, it is unlikely that complete cures can be found, but the organic chemist will succeed in providing products that will eliminate susceptibility toward these diseases.

As the physiology of the cell becomes better known, and the relation of chemical structure to cell and tissue is revealed, chemically induced mutation of cells may become possible. Certain hormones and other drugs are now known which affect the physical being as well as the mental attitude of an individual. The future may bring to us a series of drugs that will permit deliberate molding of a person, mentally and physically. When this day arrives the problems of control of such chemicals will be of concern to all. They would present dire potentialities in the hands of an unscrupulous dictator.

What may we expect from atomic energy and radioactive substances? The ores of uranium and thorium are found in only limited quantities on this earth. The industrial applications of atomic energy are, therefore, likely to be limited to special situations, such as submarine propulsion or power units to be used in isolated spots, inaccessible to the ordinary energy-bearing materials. Radioactive substances will continue to find more and more utilization in elucidation of organic and physiological reactions, particularly metabolic degradations and transformations. Whereas biochemical studies will probably lead to compounds which may go far toward the prevention of cancer, the newer α-, β-, and γ-radiations from radioisotopes are likely to be found more effective for reducing or arresting growth of certain types of tumors than the older radium radiation. Promising results have been obtained by introducing such a substance as radioactive gold directly by mechanical means into certain tumors. In the diagnostic field many applications of radioactive substances may be anticipated. Thus it is now possible to demonstrate the presence of a tumor in the brain, and even to localize it accurately from outside the skull by means of certain radioactive iodine-tagged chemicals.

In 1780, Benjamin Franklin, in a letter to Joseph Priestley, wrote as follows:

The rapid progress true science now makes, occasions my regretting sometimes that I was born so soon. It is impossible to imagine the height to which may be carried, in a thousand years, the power of man over matter. We may perhaps learn to deprive large masses of their gravity, and give them absolute levity, for the sake of easy transport. Agriculture may diminish its labor and double its produce; all diseases may be by sure means prevented or cured, not excepting even that of age, and our lives lengthened at pleasure even beyond the antediluvian standard. O that moral science were in a fair way of improvement, that men would cease to be wolves to one another, and that human beings would at length learn what they now improperly call humanity.

Let us see what has happened during the 170 years since this was written. We do not know yet how to eliminate gravity so as to facilitate transport. In agriculture, however, Franklin's predictions have already come true. When this country was founded, it took nine people on the farm to feed themselves plus one city dweller. Today, in contrast, one man on the farm feeds himself, four city people, and one person overseas.

There can be no complaint about the achievements in treatment of many diseases by use of various serums, vaccines, hormones, vitamins, antibiotics, antihistamines, and a host of others. The life expectancy of a child has increased from 50 years in 1900 to 68 years at the present time. With these results already recorded, Franklin's predictions, which relate to 830 years hence, will in large measure be correct.

Pictures of the past show log cabins, sailing frigates, oil lamps, caravans, and prairie schooners, crude utensils, hand weaving, and the man with the hoe cultivating the fields. Today life is mechanized, electrified, abundant, easy, because of the push-button era. In the future citizens will more effectively farm the land and the seas; obtain necessary minerals from the oceans; clothe themselves from coal and oil; keep themselves warm by using the stored energy of the sun; be cured of any ailments by a variety of drugs and medicinals; be happy, healthy, and kittenish at 100 years of age; and perhaps attend interplanetary football matches in the Rose Bowl.

1952

Space, Time and Einstein*

PAUL R. HEYL

WHETHER WE UNDERSTAND IT OR NOT, WE HAVE all heard of the Einstein theory, and failure to understand it does not seem incompatible with the holding of opinions on the subject, sometimes of a militant and antagonistic character.

Twenty-four years have elapsed since Einstein published his first paper on relativity, dealing principally with certain relations between mechanics and optics. Since that time a new generation has grown up to whom pre-Einstein science is a matter of history, not of experience. Eleven years after his first paper Einstein published a second, in which he broadened and extended the theory laid down in the first so as to include gravitation. And now again, thirteen years later, in a third paper, Einstein has broadened his theory still farther so as to include the phenomena of electricity and magnetism.

In view of the rekindling of interest in Einstein because of the appearance of his latest paper it may be worth while to re-examine and restate the primary foundations upon which his theory rests.

The general interest taken in this subject is frequently a matter of wonder to those of us who must give it attention professionally, for there are in modern physical science other doctrines which run closely second to that of Einstein in strangeness and novelty, yet none of these seems to have taken any particular hold on popular imagination.

Perhaps the reason for this is that these theories deal with ideas which are remote from ordinary life, while Einstein lays iconoclastic hands on two concepts about which every intelligent person believes that he really knows something—space and time.

Space and time have been regarded "always, everywhere and by all," as independent concepts, sharply distinguishable from one another, with no correlation between them. Space is fixed, though we may move about

* Publication approved by the Director of the Bureau of Standards of the U. S. Department of Commerce.

270

in it at will, forward or backward, up or down; and wherever we go our experience is that the properties of space are everywhere the same, and are unaltered whether we are moving or stationary. Time, on the other hand, is essentially a moving proposition, and we must perforce move with it. Except in memory, we can not go back in time; we must go forward, and at the rate at which time chooses to travel. We are on a moving platform, the mechanism of which is beyond our control.

There is a difference also in our measures of space and time. Space may be measured in feet, square feet or cubic feet, as the case may be, but time is essentially one-dimensional. Square hours or cubic seconds are meaningless terms. Moreover, no connection has ever been recognized between space and time measures. How many feet make one hour? A meaningless question, you say, yet something that sounds very much like it has (since Minkowski) received the serious attention of many otherwise reputable scientific men. And now comes Einstein, rudely disturbing these old-established concepts and asking us to recast our ideas of space and time in a way that seems to us fantastic and bizarre.

What has Einstein done to these fundamental concepts?

He has introduced a correlation or connecting link between what have always been supposed to be separate and distinct ideas. In the first place, he asserts that as we move about, the geometrical properties of space, as evidenced by figures drawn in it, will alter by an amount depending on the speed of the observer's motion, thus (through the concept of velocity) linking space with time. He also asserts in the second place that the flow of time, always regarded as invariable, will likewise alter with the motion of the observer, again linking time with space.

For example, suppose that we, with our instruments for measuring space and time, are located on a platform which we believe to be stationary. We can not be altogether certain of this, for there is no other visible object in the universe save another similar platform carrying an observer likewise equipped: but when we observe relative motion between our platform and the other it pleases our intuition to suppose our platform at rest and to ascribe all the motion to the other.

Einstein asserts that if this relative velocity were great enough we might notice some strange happenings on the other platform. True, a rather high velocity would be necessary, something comparable with the speed of light, say 100,000 miles a second; and it is tacitly assumed that we would be able to get a glimpse of the moving system as it flashed by. Granting this, what would we see?

Einstein asserts that if there were a circle painted on the moving platform it would appear to us as an ellipse with its short diameter in the direction of its motion. The amount of this shortening would depend upon the speed with which the system is moving, being quite imperceptible at ordinary speeds. In the limit, as the speed approached that of light, the circle would flatten completely into a straight line—its diameter perpendicular to the direction of motion.

Of this shortening, says Einstein, the moving observer will be unconscious, for not only is the circle flattened in the direction of motion, but the platform itself and all it carries (including the observer) share in this shortening. Even the observer's measuring rod is not exempt. Laid along the diameter of the circle which is perpendicular to the line of motion it would indicate, say, ten centimeters; placed along the shortened diameter, the rod, being itself now shortened in the same ratio, would apparently indicate the same length as before, and the moving observer would have no suspicion of what we might be seeing. In fact, he might with equal right suppose himself stationary and lay all the motion to the account of our platform. And if we had a circle painted on our floor it would appear flattened to him, though not to us.

Again, the clock on the other observer's platform would exhibit to us, though not to him, an equally eccentric behavior. Suppose that other platform stopped opposite us long enough for a comparison of clocks, and then, backing off to get a start, flashed by us at a high speed. As it passed we would see that the other clock was apparently slow as compared with ours, but of this the moving observer would be unconscious.

But could he not observe our clock?

Certainly, just as easily as we could see his.

And would he not see that our clock was now faster than his? "No," says Einstein. "On the contrary, he would take it to be slower."

Here is a paradox indeed! *A*'s clock appears slow to *B* while at the same time *B*'s clock appears slow to *A*! Which is right?

To this question Einstein answers indifferently:

"Either. It all depends on the point of view."

In asserting that the rate of a moving clock is altered by its motion Einstein has not in mind anything so materialistic as the motion interfering with the proper functioning of the pendulum or balance wheel. It is something deeper and more abstruse than that. He means that the flow of time itself is changed by the motion of the system, and that the clock is but fulfilling its natural function in keeping pace with the altered rate of time.

A rather imperfect illustration may help at this point. If I were traveling by train from the Atlantic to the Pacific Coast it would be necessary for me to set my watch back an hour occasionally. A less practical but mathematically more elegant plan would be to alter the rate of my watch before starting so that it would indicate the correct local time during the whole journey. Of course, on a slow train less alteration would be required. The point is this: that a timepiece keeping local time on the train will of necessity run at a rate depending on the speed of the train.

Einstein applies a somewhat similar concept to all moving systems, and asserts that the local time on such systems runs the more slowly the more rapidly the system moves.

It is no wonder that assertions so revolutionary should encounter general incredulity. Skepticism is nature's armor against foolishness. But there are two reactions possible to assertions such as these. One may say: "The man is crazy" or one may ask: "What is the evidence?"

The latter, of course, is the correct scientific attitude. To such a question Einstein might answer laconically: "Desperate diseases require desperate remedies."

"But," we reply, "we are not conscious of any disease so desperate as to require such drastic treatment."

"If you are not," says Einstein, "you should be. Does your memory run back thirty years? Or have you not read, at least, of the serious contradiction in which theoretical physics found itself involved at the opening of the present century?"

Einstein's reference is to the difficulty which arose as a consequence of the negative results of the famous Michelson-Morley experiment and other experiments of a similar nature. The situation that then arose is perhaps best explained by an analogy.

If we were in a boat, stationary in still water, with trains of water-waves passing us, it would be possible to determine the speed of the waves by timing their passage over, say, the length of the boat. If the boat were then set in motion in the same direction in which the waves were traveling, the apparent speed of the waves with respect to the boat would be decreased, reaching zero when the boat attained the speed of the waves; and if the boat were set in motion in the opposite direction the apparent speed of the waves would be increased.

If the boat were moving with uniform speed in a circular path, the apparent speed of the waves would fluctuate periodically, and from the magnitude of this fluctuation it would be possible to determine the speed of the boat.

Now the earth is moving around the sun in a nearly circular orbit with a speed of about eighteen miles per second, and at all points in this orbit light waves from the stars are constantly streaming by. The analogy of the boat and the water-waves suggested to several physicists, toward the close of the nineteenth century, the possibility of verifying the earth's motion by experiments on the speed of light.

True, the speed of the earth in its orbit is only one ten-thousandth of the speed of light, but methods were available of more than sufficient precision to pick up an effect of this order of magnitude. It was, therefore, with the greatest surprise, not to say consternation, that the results of all such experiments were found to be negative; that analogy, for some unexplained reason, appeared to have broken down somewhere between mechanics and optics; that while the speed of water-waves varied as it should with the speed of the observer, the velocity of light seemed completely unaffected by such motion.

Nor could any fault be found with method or technique. At least three independent lines of experiment, two optical and one electrical, led to the same negative conclusion.

This breakdown of analogy between mechanics and optics introduced a sharp line of division into physical science. Now since the days of Newton the general trend of scientific thought has been in the direction of removing or effacing such sharp lines indicating differences in kind and replacing them by differences in degree. In other words, scientific thought is monistic, seeking one ultimate explanation for all phenomena.

Kepler, by his study of the planets, had discovered the three well-known laws which their motion obeys. To him these laws were purely empirical, separate and distinct results of observation. It remained for Newton to show that these three laws were mathematical consequences of a single broader law—that of gravitation. In this, Newton was a monistic philosopher.

The whole of the scientific development of the nineteenth century was monistic. Faraday and Oersted showed that electricity and magnetism were closely allied. Joule, Mayer and others pointed out the equivalence of heat and work. Maxwell correlated light with electricity and magnetism. By the close of the century physical phenomena of all kinds were regarded as forming one vast, interrelated web, governed by some broad and far-reaching law as yet unknown, but whose discovery was confidently expected, perhaps in the near future. Gravitation alone obstinately resisted all attempts to coordinate it with other phenomena.

The consequent reintroduction of a sharp line between mechanics and optics was therefore most disturbing. It was to remove this difficulty that Einstein found it necessary to alter our fundamental ideas regarding space and time. It is obvious that a varying velocity can be made to appear constant if our space and time units vary also in a proper manner, but in introducing such changes we must be careful not to cover up the changes in velocity readily observable in water-waves or sound waves.

The determination of such changes in length and time units is a purely mathematical problem. The solution found by Einstein is what is known as the Lorentz transformation, so named because it was first found (in a simpler form) by Lorentz. Einstein arrived at a more general formula and, in addition, was not aware of Lorentz's work at the time of writing his own paper.

The evidence submitted so far for Einstein's theory is purely retrospective; the theory explains known facts and removes difficulties. But it must be remembered that this is just what the theory was built to do. It is a different matter when we apply it to facts unknown at the time the theory was constructed, and the supreme test is the ability of a theory to predict such new phenomena.

This crucial test had been successfully met by the theory of relativity. In 1916 Einstein broadened his theory to include gravitation, which since the days of Newton had successfully resisted all attempts to bring it into line with other phenomena. From this extended theory Einstein predicted two previously unsuspected phenomena, a bending of light rays passing close by the sun and a shift of the Fraunhofer lines in the solar spectrum. Both these predictions have now been experimentally verified.

Mathematically, Einstein's solution of our theoretical difficulties is perfect. Even the paradox of the two clocks, each appearing slower than the other, becomes a logical consequence of the Lorentz transformation. Einstein's explanation is sufficient, and up to the present time no one has been able to show that it is not necessary.

Einstein himself is under no delusion on this point. He is reported to have said, "No amount of experimentation can ever prove me right; a single experiment may at any time prove me wrong."

Early in the present year Einstein again broadened his theory to include the phenomena of electricity and magnetism. This does not mean that he has given an electromagnetic explanation of gravitation; many attempts of this kind have been made, and all have failed in the same respect —to recognize that there is no screen for gravitation. What Einstein has done is something deeper and broader than that. He has succeeded in finding a formula which may assume two special forms according as a constant which it contains is or is not zero. In the latter case the formula gives us Maxwell's equations for an electromagnetic field; in the former, Einstein's equations for a gravitative field.

1929

PART FOUR

THE WORLD OF LIFE

Synopsis

A. THE RIDDLE OF LIFE

WE HAVE SCANNED THE SKIES, WANDERED OVER THE earth, penetrated the atom. As yet we have not touched the World of Life.

What is this Life? In what shadowy spot, as yet only beginning to be understood, does the transition from the dead to the quick take place? We know many of the processes involved in living. We still do not know what life really is. And yet, it is possible to see how living things exist in nature—their chemical properties, actions and reactions, adaptation to environment, development and multiplication. That is the theme of The Characteristics of Organisms by Sir J. Arthur Thomson and Patrick Geddes.

We can also trace the course of man's belief in the spontaneous origin of life, especially as it relates to the study of the smallest living creatures under the microscope. The study begins with Leeuwenhoek, Paul de Kruif's account of the testy Dutchman who, looking through his homemade microscopes, was the first to see those tiny "animalcules" which we call microbes. The more he looked, the more he found—in the tissues of a whale, the scales of his own skin, the head of a fly, the sting of a flea. He watched them attack mussels and so realized that life lives on life. It is doubtful whether he knew that life, under conditions as they now exist normally on earth, must always come from life or that microbes play a dominant role in disease.

Those were discoveries that were to take centuries and test the abilities of men like Spallanzani, Redi, Pasteur, Tyndall, Koch. We no longer think that eels develop spontaneously in stagnant pools, that kittens (without parents) spring from piles of dirty clothes. The idea is so foreign to us that we hardly believe men could have thought it possible. Yet the classic experiments which disproved once and for all the doctrine of spontaneous generation were performed no earlier than the last century by Pasteur and Tyndall. Pasteur showed that water boiled in flasks to which the dust-filled air was not admitted would never generate life. He showed that flasks opened in Paris contained numerous microbes, while those opened in the Jura mountains contained few or none. "There is no condition known today," he wrote, "in which you can affirm that microscopic beings came into the world without germs, without parents like themselves."

Yet somewhere along the road, if we may believe the latest researches, life and nonlife seem to merge. One attack on the problem has been made by experimenters like Wendell Stanley. Working with filterable viruses, composed of molecules which may be made up of millions of atoms yet which are far smaller than anything observed by Leeuwenhoek, they seem to have reached a point on the scale bridging the gap between the living and the dead. Are these viruses alive? It depends on our definition of life. By some standards they are, by others they are not.

There is still another and even more recent approach to the problem, an approach which gives aid and comfort to the spontaneous generationists, but in a way never dreamed of by them. Workers like Oparin in Russia (the originator of the theory), and Harold Urey, George Wald and S. L. Miller in the United States have suggested, with experiments to back their theories, that under conditions as they probably existed when our planet was young and with the assistance of electrical discharges such as lightning, spontaneous generation did occur during the long stretches of early geologic time. It is this attempt to "bring the origin of life within the realm of natural phenomena" which Professor Wald of Harvard discusses in The Origin of Life.

B. THE SPECTACLE OF LIFE

Plants and animals differ from one another in myriad ways and the most obvious is that of size. We do not often stop to analyze this difference, as Haldane does so amusingly in On Being the Right Size. Haldane is a famous geneticist, but he is also a writer of charm and wit. As there are differences, so are there similarities at every level of the plant and animal kingdom. One of the most striking is described in Parasitism and Degeneration by Jordan and Kellogg. From single-celled plants and animals to vertebrates, in amazing environments and through amazing metamorphoses, the parasites live on others; unable to find a host, they die.

Next we turn to the spectacle of life in individual species. Flowering Earth is a long, full history of the plant kingdom. Donald Culross Peattie traces the steps from the first single-celled life which appeared on earth, to the algae, the Age of Seaweeds, the first plants which grew on land, the fern forests, the conifers and cycads, and finally to the modern floras. He tells us

about the function of chlorophyll, the breathing of plants. He shows how
even the iron deposits of Minnesota were formed by microscopic plants.

T. H. Huxley's Lobster helps us "to see how the application of common
sense and common logic to the obvious facts it presents, inevitably leads us
into all the branches of zoological science." He shows us the unity of plan
and diversity of execution which characterize all animals, whether they swim,
crawl, fly, swing from trees or walk the ground.

We travel from the simplest to the highest in animal life, beginning with
The Life of the Simplest Animals in which Jordan and Kellogg show how
single-celled animals eat, react, reproduce. Secrets of the Ocean, at high
and low tide, and under the waves, are disclosed for us by William Beebe,
with sea worms, shrimps and fishes playing roles. In The Warrior Ants by
Haskins we see many resemblances to man's own wars, much that we can
learn about the human race. Ditmars, known for his work on snakes, and
his assistant Greenhall introduce us to one of the most exciting of all naturalist adventures in The Vampire Bat. (Eckstein shows us the intelligence
of Ancestors, in apes that pull ropes and stack boxes, that react emotionally
like men.)

C. THE EVOLUTION OF LIFE

With the great apes we have reached a stage of development which
approaches that of man, and thinking about apes leads us inevitably to a
consideration of Evolution. Here again is a theory that has changed our
entire way of thinking and in Darwinisms we obtain a brief insight into the
character of the man who originated it. Darwin and "The Origin of Species"
by Sir Arthur Keith, points out that Darwin's masterpiece is still as fresh
as when it was first written. Darwin recognized that variation in nature is
the means by which natural selection can operate. How variation occurred
he did not know. It remained for others to analyze the problem further: de
Vries and Bateson discovered that plants and animals are subject not only to
small variations but also to large and sudden "mutations." And as a result
of these inherited mutations, new varieties are swiftly bred.

It was then that biologists rediscovered the work of a forgotten Austrian
monk. Hugo Iltis, one of his compatriots now in this country, describes
Gregor Mendel and His Work with clarity and charm. These are the basic
laws of modern genetics. With the discovery of the genes and the chromosomes, further advances have been made. Their function is explained in
Part Five, in You and Heredity by Amram Scheinfeld, a selection that might
well have been included here, had its emphasis not been so strongly on man
himself.

So much for the main evolutionary thread. But there are important by-
ways. Julian Huxley, grandson of the great T. H. Huxley and himself a well-
known biologist, explores one of them in The Courtship of Animals, tracing
the influence of the theory of sexual selection on our interpretation of ani-

mals' development and variation. In Magic Acres, Alfred Toombs describes amusingly the effects of the laws of heredity on plant and animal breeding. Use of our knowledge has made possible such experimental stations as that at Beltsville, Maryland, "where the hens lay colored eggs, where the tomatoes sprout whiskers, and the apples defy the law of gravity."

A. THE RIDDLE OF LIFE

The Characteristics of Organisms

SIR J. ARTHUR THOMSON and PATRICK GEDDES

From Life: Outlines of General Biology

FROM A COMMON-SENSE POINT OF VIEW THE apartness of living creatures from non-living things seems conspicuous. It appears almost self-evident that an organism is something more than a mechanism. But when we inquire into the basis of this common conviction we usually find that the plain man is thinking of the highest animals, such as horses and dogs, in which he recognises incipient personalities, in a world quite different, he says, from that of machines, or from that of the stars or stones. His conviction rests on his recognition of them as kindred in spirit; but he hesitates when we ask him to consider the lower animals, down to corals and sponges, and still more when we ask what he thinks about plants. In such relatively simple organisms as corals and seaweeds, he detects no mental aspect; and apart from this, they show him but little of that bustling activity which is part of his picture of what "being alive" means. Thus, while he was sure that dog and wheelbarrow were separated by a great gulf, he is not so convinced about the difference between a coral and a stone. It is, therefore, for the biologist to explain as clearly as he can the fundamental characteristics of all living creatures. . . .

PERSISTENCE IN SPITE OF CEASELESS CHANGE

The symbol of the organism is the burning bush of old; it is all afire, but it is not consumed. The peculiarity is not that the organism is in continual flux, for chemical change is the rule of the world; the characteristic feature is that the changes in the organism are so regulated that the integrity of the system is sustained for a longer or shorter period. That excellent physiologist, Sir Michael Foster, used to say that "a living body is a vortex of chemical and molecular change"; and the

280

image of a vortex expresses the fundamental fact of persistence, in spite of continual flux.

Here it is fitting to quote one of the classic passages in modern biological literature, what Huxley said of the vital vortex in his *Crayfish* (1880, p. 84):

"The parallel between a whirlpool in a stream and a living being, which has often been drawn, is as just as it is striking. The whirlpool is permanent, but the particles of water which constitute it are incessantly changing. Those which enter it, on the one side, are whirled around and temporarily constitute a part of its individuality; and as they leave it on the other side, their places are made good by new-comers. . . .

"Now, with all our appliances, we cannot get within a good many miles, so to speak, of the crayfish. If we could, we should see that it was nothing but the constant form of a similar turmoil of material molecules which are constantly flowing into the animal on the one side, and streaming out on the other."

The comparison has great force and utility; it vivifies the fundamental fact that streams of matter and energy, such as food and light, are continually passing into the organism, and that other streams are continually passing out, for instance in the form of carbon dioxide and heat. On the other hand, the comparison has its weakness and possible fallaciousness; for it is too simple. It does not do justice to the characteristic way in which the organism-whirlpool acts on the stream which is its environment; it does not do justice to the characteristic way in which the organism-whirlpool gives rise to others like itself. No one who believes that higher animals (at least) have a mental aspect that counts, can agree that the organism is exhaustively described as "nothing but the constant form of a turmoil of material molecules." And even if the mental aspect be ignored, there remains as a fundamental characteristic that the "constant form" is secured by organic regulation from within. Life is nothing if not *regulative*.

Biology has come nearer the crayfish since Huxley's day, and it is profitable to linger over the fact that the living creature persists in spite of its ceaseless change. As a matter of fact it persists because of the self-repairing nature of its ceaseless change. Hence we give prominence to this material flux.

METABOLISM OF PROTEINS.—Proteins are nitrogenous carbon-compounds that are present in all organisms, and, apart from water, of which there is seldom less than 70 per cent., they constitute the chief mass of the living substance. They are intricate compounds, with large molecules, which are built up of groups of amino-acids, i. e. fatty acids in which one of the hydrogen atoms is replaced by the *amino*-group NH_2. Proteins, such as white of egg, or the casein of cheese, or the gluten of wheat, do not readily diffuse through membranes; they occur, as will be afterwards explained, in a colloid state, and although some, e. g. hæmoglobin, the red pigment of the blood, are crystallisable, they are not known in a crystalloid state in the living body. Though relatively stable bodies, proteins are continually breaking down and being built up again within the cells of the body, partly under the direct influence of ferments or enzymes.

There are constructive, synthetic, upbuilding, or winding-up chemical processes always going on in the living organism, which are conveniently summed up in the word *anabolism*, applicable, of course, to the synthesis of other carbon-compounds besides proteins, notably to the formation of carbohydrates in the sunned green leaf. There are also disruptive, analytic, down-breaking, running-down chemical processes always going on in the living organism, which are conveniently summed up in the word *katabolism*—applicable, of course, to other carbon-compounds besides proteins, as, for example, to the breaking down of amino-acids into fatty acids and ammonia. To include the two sets of processes, anabolism and katabolism, the general term metabolism is used. It is convenient to use this term in a broad way, as the equivalent of the German word "Stoffwechsel" (change of stuff), to include all the chemical routine of the living body. The present point is that living always involves the metabolism of proteins; and that this is so regulated that the living creature lives on from day to day, or from year to year, even from century to century.

There is intense activity of a simple kind when the fragment of potassium rushes about on the surface of the basin of water, but it differs markedly from the activity of the Whirligig Beetle (Gyrinus) that swims swiftly to and fro, up and down in the pool. The difference is not merely that the chemical reactions in the beetle are much more intricate than is the case with the potassium, and that they involve eventually the down-breaking and up-building of protein molecules. The big difference is that the potassium fragment soon flares all its activity away and changes into something else, whereas the beetle retains its integrity and lasts. It may be said, indeed, that it is only a difference in time, for the beetle eventually dies. But this is to miss the point. The peculiarity we are emphasising is that for certain variable periods the processes of winding-up in organisms more than compensate for the processes of running down. A primitive living creature was not worthy of the name until it could balance its accounts for some little time, until it could in some measure counter its katabolism by its anabolism. Perhaps it was only a creature of a day, which died in the chill of its first night, probably after reproducing its kind; but the point is that during its short life it was not like a glorified potassium fragment or a clock running down. It was to some extent winding itself up as well as letting itself run down. It was making ends meet physiologically.

In the immense furnaces of the stars, with unthinkably high temperatures, it may be that hydrogen is being lifted up into more complex forms of matter, but on the earth all the chemico-physical clocks are running down. . . .

In the little corner of the universe where we move, we are living in a time of the running down of chemico-physical clocks. But the characteristic of living organisms is that they wind themselves up. . . .

COLLOIDAL PROTOPLASM.—The accumulation of energy in organisms is mainly effected by storing complex chemical substances, not merely as reserves in the ordinary sense, like the plant's starch and the animal's fat, but in the living substance itself in the form of increased protein material. The chemical formula of egg-albumin, to take a familiar protein, is often given as $C_{1428}H_{2244}N_{364}O_{462}S_{14}$; and this hints at the complexity of these substances. In the strict sense, protein material does not form definite stores in animals, though it is a common reserve in the seeds of plants, but it accumulates as the amount of living matter increases. The potential chemical energy of the complex carbon-compounds found in living cells is particularly valuable because the living matter occurs in a colloidal state. Of this it is enough to say that a watery "solution" holds in suspension innumerable complex particles, too small to be seen, even with the microscope, but large enough to have an appreciable surface. The particles do not clump together or sink because each carries an electric charge, and like charges repel one another. . . .

SPECIFICITY.—Each kind of organism has its chemical individuality, implying a specific molecular structure in some of the important constituents, and a corresponding routine of reactions. This is particularly true of the proteins, and there are probably special proteins for each genus at least. There is chemical specificity in the milk of nearly related mammals, such as sheep and goats; and, as Gautier showed in detail, in the grape-juices of nearly related vines. A stain due to the blood of a rabbit can be readily distinguished from a stain due to the blood of a fowl or of a man. More than that, as Reichert and Brown have demonstrated conclusively (1909), the blood of a horse can be distinguished from that of an ass. The crystals of the hæmoglobin or red blood pigment of a dog differ from those of a wolf, from which the dog evolved, and even from those of the Australian dingo, which seems to be the result of domesticated dogs going wild and feral. Even the sexes may be distinguished by their blood, and there are two or three cases among insects where the colour of the male's blood is different from the female's. The familiar fact that some men cannot eat particular kinds of food, such as eggs, without more or less serious symptoms, is a vivid illustration of specificity. It looks as if a man was individual not merely in his finger-prints, but as to his chemical molecules. Every man is his own laboratory. Modern investigation brings us back to the old saying: "All flesh is not the same flesh; but there is one kind of flesh of men, another flesh of beasts, another of fishes and another of birds." . . .

To some who have not looked into the matter it may seem almost preposterous to speak of a particular protein for every genus at least. But the work of Emil Fischer and others has shown that there is inconceivable variety in the groupings and proportional representations of the twenty-odd amino-acids and diamino-acids which constitute in varied linkages the complex protein molecules. There must be a million million possibilities and more. As there are about 25,000 named and known species of Vertebrates and about 250,000 (some would say 500,000) named and known species of Invertebrates, there may readily be particular proteins for every species of animal, leaving plenty to spare for all the plants.

GROWTH, MULTIPLICATION, AND DEVELOPMENT

The organism's power of absorbing energy acceleratively, and of accumulating it beyond its immediate needs, suggests another triad of qualities—growing, reproducing, and developing, which may be profitably considered together. . . .

GROWTH.—The power of growth must be taken as a fundamental characteristic of organisms, for it cannot as yet be re-described in chemical and physical terms. The word is a convenient label for a variety of processes which lead to an increase in the amount of living matter, and while there are chemical and physical factors involved in these processes, we are bound in the present state of science to admit that growth depends on the veiled tactics of life. Its results are extraordinary achievements, which would be astounding if they were not so familiar. From a microscopic egg-cell there develops an embryo-plant which may grow, say, into a Californian "Big Tree"—perhaps three hundred feet in height and over three thousand years old. A frog is about three or four inches in length, its egg-cell is under a tenth of an inch in diameter; "the mass of the human adult is fifteen billion times that of the human ovum." In the strict sense growth means an increase in the amount of the organism's living matter or protoplasm, but it is often associated, as in a cucumber, with great accumulation of water; or, as in the case of bone, with the formation of much in the way of non-living walls around the living cells. . . .

The indispensable condition of growth is that income be greater than expenditure. A variable amount of the food-income is used to meet the everyday expenses of living; the surplus is available for growth; and this must be understood as including, besides increase in size, that imperceptible growth which brings about the replacement of worn-out cells by fresh ones. Green plants are great growers when compared with animals—the Giant Bamboo may grow a foot in a day—and that is mainly because they get food-materials at a low chemical level, that is to say from the air and the soil-water. Helped by its chlorophyll, the green plant is able to use part of the energy of the sunlight that bathes its leaves to build up sugars, starch, and proteins, first of course for its own maintenance and for its growth, thereafter for "reserves," variously stored for its own future, or that of its offspring. On this highly profitable synthesis and storage in the plant, the growth of all animals depends—directly in the case of the sheep and other herbivores, indirectly in the case of the tiger and other carnivores.

Food is thus obviously an indispensable condition of growth; but there are some puzzling cases, e. g. the striking growth behaviour of a single fragment of Planarian worm, without food-canal, and thus incapable of ingesting food; yet soon growing a new head and posterior end, fashioning itself anew into a perfect miniature worm. Here, as in a germinating seed, there must have been absorption of water and utilisation of the previous material in a less condensed form.

Another curious form of growth is expressed in the replacement of lost parts, such as the claw of a crab, or the arm of a starfish; and here again the body yields supplies. One of the most extraordinary instances of such replacement-growth is that seen annually when the stag, having dropped his antlers, rapidly grows a new set, which, in the monarch, may weigh seventy pounds!

The great majority of animals have a definite limit of growth, an optimum size, which is normally attained by the adult and rarely exceeded; so there must be some method of growth-regulation. On the other hand, some fishes and reptiles continue growing as long as they live, just like many trees; and this shows that a limit of size is not fundamentally insisted on by nature.

When we think of giants and dwarfs, and of the rarity of their occurrence, the idea of regulation is again suggested. So also when we observe the occurrence—yet rare occurrence—of monstrous growths among animals, we see that growth is essentially a *regulated* increase in the amount of adjustment of living matter. By what means is such regulation affected? The modern answer to this question is twofold. Regulation is partly due to certain hormones (chemical "messengers") which are produced in "ductless glands" and distributed by the blood. Thus the hormones of the thyroid gland, and those of the pituitary body, have, among other functions, that of growth-control. Again, it has been shown that parts where metabolism is most intense, e. g. the growing point of a stem, exert a sway or dominance over the growth of other parts, as we shall see more fully later.

Another feature of growth is its periodicity. All are familiar with the rings of growth on the cut stem of a tree, which mark its years, through the well-marked seasonal alternation of spring and summer wood, which are different in texture. This instance is no exceptional case, but a vivid illustration of the rhythmic periodicity of life. The same is seen in the zoning of fish-scales and the barring of birds' feathers, and in the familiar growth-lines on the shells of the seashore.

Familiarity is apt to dull our eyes to the marvel of growth—the annual covering of the brown earth with verdure; the desert blossoming as the rose; the spreading of the green veil over the miles of woodland; the bamboo rising so quickly that one can see it grow; the Sequoia or Big Tree continuing to increase in bulk for three thousand years; the coral-polyps adding chalice to chalice till they form a breakwater a thousand miles long; the Arctic jellyfish becoming bigger and bigger till the disc is over seven feet in diameter and the tentacles trail in the waves for over a hundred feet. Again, many an animal egg-cell develops into a body that weighs billions of times as much as its beginning; and this is far exceeded in the growing up of giants--like a Blue Whale, eighty-five feet in length, or an Atlantosaurus with a thigh-bone as high as a tall man.

MULTIPLICATION.—The corollary of growth is multiplication, a term that we are using here in preference to the more general word reproduction, which includes the whole series of functions concerned with giving rise to other organisms. Multiplication essentially means separating off portions or buds, spores or germ-cells, which start a new generation. In the asexual method of separating off large pieces, the connection with growth is obvious; multiplication occurs as a consequence of instabilities which follow overgrowth. As Haeckel said long ago, reproduction is discontinuous growth. Its externally simplest form is seen in the division of an overgrown unicellular organism, yet in the everyday division of most of the cells of plants and animals, this has been elaborated into an intricate process, which secures that each of the two daughter-cells gets a meticulously precise half of everything that is in the parent-cell.

The connection between growth and cell-division is not far to seek. Spencer, Leuckart, and James pointed out independently that as a cell of regular shape increases in volume, it does not proportionately increase in surface. If it be a sphere, the volume of cell-substance or cytoplasm to be kept alive increases as the cube of the radius, while the surface, through which the keeping alive is effected, by various processes of diffusion, increases only as the square. Thus there tends to set in a hazardous disproportion between volume and surface, and this may set up instability. The disturbed balance is normally restored by the cell dividing into two cells. . . .

In cases of sexual reproduction, where germ-cells are separated off to start a new generation, the relation between growth and multiplication is not, of course, so direct as in cases of asexual reproduction by fission or fragmentation. It may be pointed out that reproduction often occurs at the limit of growth, and that there is a familiar seesaw between feeding and breeding periods, between leafing and flowering, between nutrition and reproduction.

The division of a cell is one of the wonders of the world. Bateson wrote: "I know nothing which to a man well trained in scientific knowledge and method brings so vivid a realisation of our ignorance of the nature of life as the mystery of cell-division. . . . It is this power of spontaneous division which most sharply distinguishes the living from the non-living. . . . The greatest advance I can conceive in biology would be the discovery of the instability which leads to the continued division of the cell. When I look at a dividing cell I feel as an astronomer might do if he beheld the formation of a double star: that an original act of creation is taking place before me."

In the present youthful condition of biology it is wise to return at frequent intervals to concrete illustrations. We need the warmth of actual facts to help us to appreciate the quality of reproductivity which we are only beginning to understand. In one day the multiplication of a microbe may result in a number with thirty figures. Were there an annual plant with only two seeds, it could be represented by over a million in the twenty-first year. But a common British weed (*Sisymbrium officinale*) has often three-quarters of a million of seeds, so that in three years it could theoretically cover the whole earth. Huxley calculated that if the descendants of a single green-fly all survived and multiplied, they would, at the end of the first summer, weigh down the population of China. A codfish is said to produce two million eggs, a conger eel ten millions, an oyster twenty-millions. The starfish Luidia, according to Mortensen, produces two hundred million eggs every year of its life.

DEVELOPMENT.—In active tissues, like muscle or gland, wear and tear is inevitable, especially in the less labile parts of the cells—the furnishings of life's laboratories, such as the for the most part ultra-microscopic films that partition the cyptoplasm into areas. When the results of the wear and tear over-accumulate, they tend to depress activity and in time to inhibit it; and this means ageing, towards death. But this decline of vitality may be counteracted by rejuvenescence-processes in the ageing cells, or by the replacement of worn-out cells by new ones. In some cases the hard-worked cells go fatally out of gear, as in the brain of the busy summer-bee, which does not usually survive for more than six or eight weeks. In other cases, as in ordinary muscle, the recuperation afforded by food and rest is very perfect, and the same cell may continue active for many years. Such cells are comparable to the relatively simple unicellular animals, like the amœbæ, which recuperate so thoroughly that they evade natural death altogether. In another set of cases, e. g. the lining cells of the stomach, or the epithelium covering the lips, the senescent cells die and drop off, but are replaced by others. The outer epidermic layer of the skin (the stratum corneum) is continually wearing away, and as continually being replaced by contributions from the more intensely living and growing deeper stratum (the stratum Malpighii). Similarly at the tip of a rootlet there is a cap of cells which are always dying away and being replaced from the delicate growing point which they protect. From such replacement of cells there is an easy transition to the re-growth of lost parts. The starfish re-grows its lost arm, the crab its claw, the snail its horn, the earthworm its head. From cells below the plane of separation there is in each case a regulated growth, which replaces what has been lost. We have already mentioned a very striking instance, in which regrowth is normal, and in organic and seasonal rhythm independent of any violence from without—namely, the re-growth which gives the stag new antlers to replace those of the previous year. . . . The needful renewal of embryonic tissue is rarely seen, unless there be some recurrent need for it. Most lizards can re-grow their long tail if that has been snapped off by a bird or surrendered in fear or in battle, but the chameleon which keeps its tail coiled round the branch, has not unnaturally lost this power. Long-limbed animals like crabs, and starfishes with their lank arms, have great regenerative capacity, in striking contrast to the compact and swiftly moving fishes, which cannot even replace a lost scale! The recurrence of non-fatal injuries is not common among the higher animals, so their power of regenerating important parts has waned. Enough of this, however; our present point is that the regeneration of lost parts illustrates a renewal of that regulated growth of complicated structure which is characteristic of embryonic development. Out of apparently simple cells at the stump of a snail's horn, the whole can be regrown, including the eye at the tip; and this may occur not once only, but forty times. From the broken portion of a Begonia leaf there buds a complete plant—to root and shoot and flower. From such reconstruction there is but a step to the asexual multiplication of many plants and animals—whether by the bulbils of the lily, the budding of the hydra in the pond, or the halving of the Planarian worm. When the tail-half of the dividing Planarian worm proceeds to differentiate a new head, with brain-ganglia, eyes, and mouth complete, there is an obvious *development*—the formation of new and complex structures out of the undifferentiated and apparently simple. . . .

In his discussions of the characteristics of living creatures, Huxley was wont to lay emphasis on what he called "cyclical development." Within the embryo-sac, within the ovule, within the ovary of the flower, a miniature plant is formed by the division and re-division of the fertilised egg-cell. The ovule becomes a seed; and this, when sown, a seedling. By insensible steps there is fashioned a large and varied fabric, of root and shoot, of leaves and flowers. But sooner or later, after this development is complete, the grass begins to wither and the flower thereof to fade. In the case of an annual plant, there is soon nothing left but the seeds, which begin the cycle anew. . . .

Among animals the egg-cell, in many cases microscopic, divides and redivides, and an embryo is built up. Division of labour sets in among its units. . . . Some cells become nervous, others muscular, others glandular, others skeletal; and so the differentiating process continues. Hereditary contributions from parents and ancestors find expression, some of fundamental importance and others relatively trivial; the past lives on in the present; often the individual shows, in varying degree, evidence that it is "climbing up its own genealogical tree." Sometimes the embryo develops steadily and directly into the likeness of its kind, as in birds and mammals, with only traces of circuitousness, such as notochord and gill-clefts disclose—tell-tale evidence of the lien the past continues to hold on the present. . . .

BEHAVIOUR, ENREGISTRATION, AND EVOLUTION

A third triad of qualities which are distinctive of the living organisms may be summed up in the words behaviour, registration, and evolution, in which as in previous triads an underlying unity may perhaps be discerned.

BEHAVIOUR.—Herbert Spencer spoke of life as "effective response," and from the amœba upwards we recognize among animals the power of linking actions in a chain so that the result is behaviour—always purposive and in the higher reaches purposeful. Responses are common in the inorganic world—from gentle weathering to volcanic explosion— but non-living things do not show the living creature's power of reacting in a self-preservative way. Among plants, for various reasons, such as the fixed habit of the great majority and the enclosing of the cells in cellulose, there is relatively little exhibition of that purposive "doing of things" which we call behaviour, but we must not forget the insurgent activities of climbing plants or the carnivorous adventures of Venus's Fly-trap and the Sundew.

ENREGISTRATION.—A bar of iron is never quite the same after it has been severely jarred; the "fatigue of metals" is one of the serious risks of engineering; the violin suffers from mishandling. But these are hardly more than vague analogies of the distinctive power that living creatures have of enregistering the results of their experience, of establishing internal rhythms, of forming habits, and of remembering. As W. K. Clifford put it: "It is the peculiarity of living things not merely that they change under the influence of surrounding circumstances, but that any change which takes place in them is not lost, but retained, and, as it were, built into the organism, to serve as the foundation for future action." . . . In various forms this is a distinctive feature of the living creature.

EVOLUTION.—In the attempt to understand organisms we must envisage them as a whole, we must see them in the light of evolution. Thus it must be recognized as characteristic of organisms that they give origin to what is new; they have evolved and evolution is going on. There is variability in the crystalline forms which the same substance may assume; the modern physicist tells us of "isotopes" like the different kinds of "lead," which have the same chemical properties, yet differ in the structure of the nucleus of their atoms; the modern chemist even assures us of the transmutation of elements, thus not a little justifying the medieval alchemist's dream and quest. . . . Yet these are only suggestive analogies; for the living organism is the supreme, though unconscious, creative chemist.

No doubt there are species that show nowadays little or no variation; there are conservative living types that seem to have remained the same since their remains were first buried in the mud millions of years ago, but the larger fact is variability. In multitudes of cases the offspring show something new.

What impressions of variability we get at a "show"—whether of dogs or pigeons, roses or pansies! Here we have, as it were, the fountain of life rising high in the air—blown into strange forms by the breeze, yet modulated, to its own ceaseless waxings and wanings, by varying pressures from its source. Two hundred different "forms" or varieties are described by Jordan in one of the commonest of small Crucifers, the whitlow-grass or *Draba verna*; and these are no longer fluctuating but breeding true. Again, Lotsy speaks of the bewildering diversity exhibited by a series of about two hundred specimens of the Common Buzzard (*Buteo buteo!*) in the Leyden Museum, "hardly two of which are alike." . . .

GLIMPSES OF LIFE

Our discussions of living creatures are apt to be too abstract and cold; we lose the feeling of the mysterious which all life should suggest. In our inhibiting conventionality we run the risk of false simplification. Therefore, at the risk of a little repetition, we devote the rest of this discussion to what might be called "glimpses of life"—the contrast between the living creature and a crystal, the quality of vital insurgence, the fact of organic beauty.

CRYSTALS AND ORGANISMS.—When Linnæus wrote his famous, yet now partly outworn, aphorism, "Stones grow; Plants grow and live; Animals grow and live and feel," he must have been thinking of crystals. For ordinary stones do not grow—except smaller; whereas crystals afford beautiful illustrations of increase in size. Suppose, says Sir William Bragg in his luminous lectures "Concerning the Nature of Things" (1925), the crystallographer wishes to get a fine big crystal of common salt, he suspends a minute, well-formed crystal in a solution of brine at a concentration just ready to form a salt precipitate. That is step one. He also makes sure of a certain temperature, which he knows from previous experience to be suitable to tempt the atoms of sodium and chlorine to give up their freedom "when they meet an assemblage of atoms already in perfect array—that is to say when they come across a suspended crystal." Sometimes the solution is kept in gentle movement so that various parts of it get a chance of meeting the nucleus, which, so to speak, tempts them to settle down—freezing into architecture. Into the physics of this we need not here enter; our point is simply that in a suitable environment, with time and quiet, a crystal-unit "grows." By accretion it becomes a handsome large crystal. Onto its faces other crystal-units are added, and on the new faces more again, until there is formed—an edifice. . . .

The crystal increases in size in an orderly way; how does this differ from the growth of an animal or a plant? Is there a real resemblance, or is it a misleading analogy? The first answer is that a crystal increases in size at the expense of material, usually a solution, that is chemically the same as itself; whereas animals and plants feed on substances different from their own living matter—often very different. This is sound commonsense, and yet the edge is taken off it a little by two facts, first that it is possible to feed an amœba on amœbæ, or a tadpole on tadpoles, or a rat on rats; and, secondly, it is possible to increase the size of a crystal when it is placed in a solution of a chemically different substance, which has, however, the same form of crystallisation.

Then one might lay emphasis on the fact that the increase in the size and weight of a crystal is by accretion from without, whereas organisms grow by taking in raw materials, altering these, and building from within. . . .

But there is another, more general, way of looking at the difference between crystal increase and organic growth: the one is passive and the other is active. It is not so much that the crystal grows, as that it is added to by other crystal units—usually, moreover, in saturated solution. But an organism actively takes in its food, actively changes and distributes it, and actively builds with it.

But some authorities who press the analogy between crystals and creatures bring forward another supposed resemblance. If a crystal is broken there is a neat mending, provided there is the proper environment. There is more rapid accretion at the broken surface than elsewhere; the repair is often in proportion. This is very suggestive of the way in which an animal or a plant replaces a lost part or repairs an injury. If a crystal be broken into two, each half may form a perfect whole. If a Planarian worm or a Hydra be cut across, each half usually "regenerates" an entire animal. But the crystal's "regeneration" is passive, from without, and homogeneous; that of the organism is active, from within, and heterogeneous.

Another supposed resemblance that has been emphasised is the power of lying latent that may be seen in crystal and creature alike. The seed of a plant may remain dry for a decennium, but sow it and it will germinate. The egg or the half-developed embryo of an animal may lie unchanged for many years, but give it the appropriate environment and it will resume its activity. Entire animals like "vinegar-eels" may remain without hint of life for many years; but it is only necessary to put them in their proper surroundings to see them revive and multiply. Everyone knows how the spores of microbes may lie low for a long time and be blown about by the wind, but let one light on a suitable medium and it reasserts its power—perhaps its virulence to our undoing.

Now it is a similar power of lying latent that enthusiasts claim for crystals. Thus Dr. A. E. H. Tutton, one of the leading authorities, says: The virility of a crystal is unchanged and permanent. He pictures very vividly what may happen to a crystal of quartz detached by the weathering of a piece of granite thousands of years ago. It may be "subsequently knocked about the world as a rounded sand grain, blown over deserts by the wind, its corners rounded off by rude contact with its fellows and subjected to every variety of rough treatment." But if it happen in our own day to "find itself in water containing in solution a small amount of the material of which quartz is composed, silicon-dioxide, it will begin to sprout and grow again." From a grain of sand in such conditions several typical crystals of quartz may grow out in different directions. "This marvellously everlasting power possessed by a crystal, of silent imperceptible growth, is one of the strangest functions of solid matter, and one of the fundamental facts of science which is rarely realised, compared with many of the more obvious phenomena of nature."

But Dr. Tutton chose a very resistant crystal; what he says of the crystal of quartz would not be so true of a crystal of common salt, just as what we said of the vinegar thread worm would not hold for the earthworm. When atoms are very firmly locked together in an intricate space-lattice system we do not expect them to be changeful. It is not easy to induce a diamond to change its state. But the persistence of some organisms through years of latent life is much more remarkable, for they often become dry and brittle, and thus pass out of the colloidal state which is characteristic of living matter. Yet they do not die. As for the prolonged persistence of some organisms when they are not in a latent state, the marvel there is that they retain their intact integrity in spite of the ceaseless internal bustle of metabolism. *Plus ça change, plus c'est la même chose.*

It is certainly a noteworthy fact that many kinds of crystals, not larger than bacteria, float about in the air as microbes do. And just as a microbe may set up a far-reaching change when it lights on a suitable medium, so a microscopic crystal landing in a solution which is in a properly receptive condition may set up crystallisation. But the differences seem to us to be greater than the resemblances; for the minute crystal is but a passive peg to which molecules attach themselves, while the microbe is an active agent that attacks the medium and fills it with its progeny.

No one wishes to think of living creatures as if they had not antecedents in the non-living world. Science is not partial to Melchizedeks. On the other hand, we hold to the apartness and uniqueness of life. Dr. A. E. H. Tutton begins his fine book on *The Natural History of Crystals* (London, 1924), by saying that no definition of life has yet been advanced that will not apply equally well to crystals, but we have given reasons for not accepting this statement. The living creature's growth, repair, and reproduction are very different from those of crystals; life is an enduring activity, persisting in spite of its metabolism; the organism enregisters its experience and acts on its environment; it is a masterful, even creative, agency. The crystal, especially the gem, is a new synthesis, compared with the disarray of the dust; the organism is another and on a different line.

THE INSURGENCE OF LIFE.—It is difficult to find the fit word to denote the quality of irrepressibility and unconquerability which is characteristic of many living creatures. There are some, no doubt, that drift along, but it is much more characteristic to go against the stream. Life sometimes strikes one as a tender plant, a flickering flame; and who can forget that one of the Ephemerides or mayflies has an aërial life of but a single hour! At other times, the impression we get is just the opposite, for the living creature often shows itself tenacious, tough, and dogged. In his admirable *Introduction to the Study of Trees* (Home Univ. Library, 1927), Dr. Macgregor Skene of Bristol University mentions that three carefully measured stumps of the "big tree," *Sequoia gigantea*, of California showed rings going back to 1,087, 1,122, and 1,305 years B.C. The actual record for the second tree was 2,996 years and for the third 3,197, without allowing for some rings that have been lost in the centre. A specimen of the dragon-tree on Teneriffe is supposed to be 6,000 years old, and a bald cypress near Oaxaca in Mexico, 110 feet high with a circumference of 107 feet at breast height, is credited with over 6,000 years. As these giants are still standing, their longevity is *inferred*, whereas that of the felled Sequoias is proved by the ring counts. But, in any case, there is astounding tenacity of life, and, without going out of Britain, we may find other impressive illustrations. For, as Dr. Skene says, "it is quite certain that we have many oaks which have passed their thousand years, and some which may be much older." Another way of looking at the insurgence of life is to think of some of the extraordinary haunts which many living creatures have sought out. Colonel Meinertzhagen, speaking recently of the lofty Tibetan plateau, directed attention to the herds of antelopes and kiangs (wild ponies) that seem to be able to thrive on next to nothing! The explorer marked out with his field-glass an area where he saw a small herd of kiangs feeding, and then visited the spot. Measuring a space one hundred yards by ten, he gathered up every scrap of vegetation, and the result was a quaint collection—seventeen withered blades of coarse grass and seven small alpines—not enough to feed a guinea-pig! Of course, the kiangs had been there before him, but there was little but very frugal fare all around. Meinertzhagen, to whom we owe much information on the altitude of bird flight, saw a flock of swifts at 18,800 feet. At 19,950 feet he shot a raven which showed undue inquisitiveness as to his movements; at 21,059 feet, the highest point reached, he found a family of wall-creepers—dainty little refugees of the mountains. Facts like these must be taken into consideration in our total conception of life, for they are surely as essential to the picture as the semi-permeability of the cell-membrane, or any other fundamental fact of life-structure. No doubt hunger is a sharp spur; the impelling power of the struggle for existence cannot be gainsaid; but we cannot get away from the impression that we must also allow for something analogous to the spirit of adventure. At all events, the facts show that while the environment selects organisms, often winnowing very roughly, there are other cases where organisms select their environment, and often adventurously. There is a quality of tentativeness in many organisms, that look out not merely for niches of opportunity into which to slink, but for new kingdoms to conquer.

THE FACT OF BEAUTY.—No one who studies Animate Nature can get past the fact of Beauty. It is as real in its own way as the force of gravity. It used to be spoken of as though it were a quality of the exotic —of the Orchid and the Bird of Paradise—now we feel it most at our doors. St. Peter's lesson has been learned, and we find naught common on the earth. As one of our own poets has said: Beauty crowds us all our life. We maintain that all living things are beautiful; save those which do not live a free life, those that are diseased or parasitised, those that are half-made, and those which bear the the marks of man's meddling fingers—monstrosities, for instance, which are naturally non-viable, but live a charmed life under human protection. With these exceptions all living creatures are beautiful, especially when we see them in their natural surroundings. To those who maintain that Animate Nature is spotted with ugliness, we would reply that they are allowing themselves to be preoccupied with the quite exceptional cases to which we have referred, or that they are unable to attain the detachment required in order to appreciate the esthetic points of, say, a snake or any other creature against which there is a strong racial or personal prejudice.

To call a jellyfish anything but beautiful is either a confusion of thought
or a submission to some unpleasant association, such as being severely
stung when bathing. That there are many quaint, whimsical, grotesque
creatures must be granted, to which conventionally minded zoologists
who should have known better have given names like *Moloch horridus*,
but we have never found any dubiety in the enthusiasm with which artists
have greeted these delightfully grotesque animals; and the makers of
beauty surely form the court of appeal for all such cases.

When we say that all free-living, fully formed, healthy living creatures
are beautiful, we mean that they excite in the spectator the characteristic
kind of emotion which is called esthetic. The thing of beauty is a joy for
ever. The esthetic emotion is distinctive; it brings no satiety; it is annexed
to particular qualities of shape, colour, and movement; it grows as we
share it with others; it grips us as organisms, body and soul, and remains
with us incarnate. Why should the quality of exciting this distinctive emotion be pervasive throughout the world of organisms, as compelling in new
creatures which the human eye never saw before as in the familiar
favourites with which our race has grown up? It is possible that some
light is thrown on this question when we analyse the esthetic delight which
every normally constituted man feels when he watches the Shetland ponies
racing in the field, the kingfisher darting up the stream like an arrow made
of a piece of rainbow, the mayflies rising in a living cloud from a quiet
stretch of the river, or the sea-anemones nestling like flowers in the niches
of the seashore rocks. The forms, the colours, the movements, set up
agreeable rhythmic processes in our eyes, agreeable rhythmic messages
pass to our brain, and the good news—the pleasedness—is echoed throughout the body, in the pulse, for instance, and in the beating of the heart, as
Wordsworth so well knew. The esthetic emotion is certainly associated
with a pleasing bodily resonance; in other words, it has its physiological
side. The second factor in our esthetic delight is perceptual. The "form"
of what we contemplate is significant for us and satisfies our feeling. The
more meaning is suffused into the material, the more our sense of beauty
is enhanced. The lines and patterns and colours of living creatures go to
make up a "form" which almost never disappoints. . . . We suggest for
consideration the general conclusion that all free-living, full-grown,
wholesome organisms have the emotion-exciting quality of beauty. And
is not our humanly sympathetic appreciation of this protean beauty of
the world inherent and persistent in us as also part of the same world of
life, and evolved far enough to realise it more fully, communicate it to
each other more clearly?

1931

Leeuwenhoek

FIRST OF THE MICROBE HUNTERS

PAUL DE KRUIF

From *Microbe Hunters*

I

TWO HUNDRED AND FIFTY YEARS AGO AN OBSCURE man named Leeuwenhoek looked for the first time into a mysterious new world peopled with a thousand different kinds of tiny beings, some ferocious and deadly, others friendly and useful, many of them more important to mankind than any continent or archipelago.

Leeuwenhoek, unsung and scarce remembered, is now almost as unknown as his strange little animals and plants were at the time he discovered them. This is the story of Leeuwenhoek, the first of the microbe hunters. . . . Take yourself back to Leeuwenhoek's day, two hundred and fifty years ago, and imagine yourself just through high school, getting ready to choose a career, wanting to know—

You have lately recovered from an attack of mumps, you ask your father what is the cause of mumps, and he tells you a mumpish evil spirit has got into you. His theory may not impress you much, but you decide to make believe you believe him and not to wonder any more about what is mumps —because if you publicly don't believe him you are in for a beating and may even be turned out of the house. Your father is Authority.

That was the world about three hundred years ago, when Leeuwenhoek was born. It had hardly begun to shake itself free from superstitions, it was barely beginning to blush for its ignorance. It was a world where science (which only means trying to find truth by careful observation and clear thinking) was just learning to toddle on vague and wobbly legs. It was a world where Servetus was burned to death for daring to cut up and examine the body of a dead man, where Galileo was shut up for life for daring to prove that the earth moved around the sun.

Antony Leeuwenhoek was born in 1632 amid the blue windmills and low streets and high canals of Delft, in Holland. His family were burghers of an intensely respectable kind and I say intensely respectable because they were basket-makers and brewers, and brewers are respectable and highly honored in Holland. Leeuwenhoek's father died early and his mother sent him to school to learn to be a government official, but he left school at sixteen to be an apprentice in a dry-goods store in Amsterdam. That was his university. . . .

At the age of twenty-one he left the dry-goods store, went back to Delft, married, set up a dry-goods store of his own there. For twenty years after that very little is known about him, except that he had two wives (in succession) and several children most of whom died, but there is no doubt that during this time he was appointed janitor of the city hall of Delft, and that he developed a most idiotic love for grinding lenses. He had heard that if you very carefully ground very little lenses out of clear glass, you would see things look much bigger than they appeared to the naked eye. . . .

It would be great fun to look through a lens and see things bigger than your naked eye showed them to you! But *buy* lenses? Not Leeuwenhoek! There never was a more suspicious man. Buy lenses? He would make them himself! During these twenty years of his obscurity he went to spectacle-makers and got the rudiments of lens-grinding. He visited alchemists and apothecaries and put his nose into their secret ways of getting metals from ores, he began fumblingly to learn the craft of the gold- and silversmiths. He was a most pernickety man and was not satisfied with grinding lenses as good as those of the best lens-grinder in Holland, they had to be better than the best, and then he still fussed over them for long hours. Next he mounted these lenses in little oblongs of copper or silver or gold, which he had extracted himself, over hot fires, among strange smells and fumes. . . .

Of course his neighbors thought he was a bit cracked but Leeuwenhoek went on burning and blistering his hands. Working forgetful of his family and regardless of his friends, he bent solitary to subtle tasks in still nights. The good neighbors sniggered, while that man found a way to make a tiny lens, less than one-eighth of an inch across, so symmetrical, so perfect, that it showed little things to him with a fantastic clear enormousness. . . .

Now this self-satisfied dry-goods dealer began to turn his lenses onto everything he could get hold of. He looked through them at the muscle fibers of a whale and the scales of his own skin. He went to the butcher shop and begged or bought ox-eyes and was amazed at how prettily the crystalline lens of the eye of the ox is put together. He peered for hours at the build of the hairs of a sheep, of a beaver, of an elk, that were transformed from their fineness into great rough logs under his bit of glass. He delicately dissected the head of a fly; he stuck its brain on the fine needle of his microscope—how he admired the clear details of the marvelous big brain of that fly! He examined the cross-sections of the wood of a dozen different trees and squinted at the seeds of plants. He grunted "Impossible!" when he first spied the outlandish large perfection of the sting of a flea and the legs of a louse. That man Leeuwenhoek was like a puppy who sniffs—with a totally impolite disregard of discrimination—at every object of the world around him!

II

But at this time, in the middle of the seventeenth century, great things were astir in the world. Here and there in France and England and Italy rare men were thumbing their noses at almost everything that passed for knowledge. "We will no longer take Aristotle's say-so, nor the Pope's say-so," said these rebels. "We will trust only the perpetually repeated observations of our own eyes and the careful weighings of our scales; we will listen to the answers experiments give us and no other answers!" So in England a few of these revolutionists started a society called The Invisible College, it had to be invisible because that man Cromwell might have hung them for plotters and heretics if he had heard of the strange questions they were trying to settle.

... Remember that one of the members of this college was Robert Boyle, founder of the science of chemistry, and another was Isaac Newton. Such was the Invisible College, and presently, when Charles II came to the throne, it rose from its depths as a sort of blind-pig scientific society to the dignity of the name of the Royal Society of England. And they were Antony Leeuwenhoek's first audience! There was one man in Delft who did not laugh at Antony Leeuwenhoek, and that was Regnier de Graaf, whom the Lords and Gentlemen of the Royal Society had made a corresponding member because he had written them of interesting things he had found in the human ovary. Already Leeuwenhoek was rather surly and suspected everybody, but he let de Graaf peep through those magic eyes of his, those little lenses whose equal did not exist in Europe or England or the whole world for that matter. What de Graaf saw through those microscopes made him ashamed of his own fame and he hurried to write to the Royal Society:

"Get Antony Leeuwenhoek to write you telling of his discoveries."

And Leeuwenhoek answered the request of the Royal Society with all the confidence of an ignorant man who fails to realize the profound wisdom of the philosophers he addresses. It was a long letter, it rambled over every subject under the sun, it was written with a comical artlessness in the conversational Dutch that was the only language he knew. The title of that letter was: "A Specimen of some Observations made by a Microscope contrived by Mr. Leeuwenhoek, concerning Mould upon the Skin, Flesh, etc.; the Sting of a Bee, etc." The Royal Society was amazed, the sophisticated and learned gentlemen were amused—but principally the Royal Society was astounded by the marvelous things Leeuwenhoek told them he could see through his new lenses. The Secretary of the Royal Society thanked Leeuwenhoek and told him he hoped his first communication would be followed by others. It was, by hundreds of others over a period of fifty years. They were talkative letters full of salty remarks about his ignorant neighbors, of exposures of charlatans and of skilled explodings of superstitions, of chatter about his personal health—but sandwiched between paragraphs and pages of this homely stuff, in almost every letter, those Lords and Gentlemen of the Royal Society had the honor of reading immortal and gloriously accurate descriptions of the discoveries made by the magic eye of that janitor and shopkeeper. What discoveries!

. . . When Leeuwenhoek was born there were no microscopes but only crude hand-lenses that would hardly make a ten-cent piece look as large as a quarter. Through these—without his incessant grinding of his own marvelous lenses—that Dutchman might have looked till he grew old without discovering any creature smaller than a cheese-mite. You have read that he made better and better lenses with the fanatical persistence of a lunatic; that he examined everything, the most intimate things and the most shocking things, with the silly curiosity of a puppy. Yes, and all this squinting at bee-stings and mustache hairs and what-not were needful to prepare him for that sudden day when he looked through his toy of a gold-mounted lens at a fraction of a small drop of clear rain water to discover—

What he saw that day starts this history. Leeuwenhoek was a maniac observer, and who but such a strange man would have thought to turn his lens on clear, pure water, just come down from the sky? What could there be in water but just—water? You can imagine his daughter Maria—she was nineteen and she took such care of her slightly insane father!—watching him take a little tube of glass, heat it red-hot in a flame, draw it out to the thinnest of a hair. . . .

He squints through his lens. He mutters guttural words under his breath. . . .

Then suddenly the excited voice of Leeuwenhoek: "Come here! Hurry! There are little animals in this rain water. . . . They swim! They play around! They are a thousand times smaller than any creatures we can see with our eyes alone. . . . Look! See what I have discovered!"

Leeuwenhoek's day of days had come. . . . This janitor of Delft had stolen upon and peeped into a fantastic sub-visible world of little things, creatures that had lived, had bred, had battled, had died, completely hidden from and unknown to all men from the beginning of time. Beasts these were of a kind that ravaged and annihilated whole races of men ten millions times larger than they were themselves. Beings these were, more terrible than fire-spitting dragons or hydra-headed monsters. They were silent assassins that murdered babes in warm cradles and kings in sheltered places. It was this invisible, insignificant, but implacable—and sometimes friendly—world that Leeuwenhoek had looked into for the first time of all men of all countries.

This was Leeuwenhoek's day of days. . . .

III

. . . How marvelous it would be to step into that simple Dutchman's shoes, to be inside his brain and body, to feel his excitement—it is almost nausea!—at his first peep at those cavorting "wretched beasties."

That was what he called them, and this Leeuwenhoek was an unsure man. Those animals were too tremendously small to be true, they were too strange to be true. So he looked again, till his hands were cramped with holding his microscope and his eyes full of that smarting water that comes from too-long looking. But he was right! Here they were again, not one kind of little creature, but here was another, larger than the first, "moving about very nimbly because they were furnished with divers incredibly thin feet." Wait! Here is a third kind—and a fourth, so tiny I can't make out his shape. But he is alive! He goes about, dashing over great distances in this world of his water-drop in the little tube. . . . What nimble creatures!

"They stop, they stand still as 'twere upon a point, and then turn themselves round with that swiftness, as we see a top turn round, the circumference they make being no bigger than that of a fine grain of sand." So wrote Leeuwenhoek. . . .

But where did these outlandish little inhabitants of the rainwater come from? Had they come down from the sky? Had they crawled invisibly over the side of the pot from the ground? Or had they been created out of nothing by a God full of whims? Well, there was only one way to find out where they came from. "I will experiment!" he muttered.

. . . Then he took a big porcelain dish, "glazed blue within," he washed it clean, out into the rain he went with it and put it on top of a big box so that the falling raindrops would splash no mud into the dish. The first water he threw out to clean it still more thoroughly. Then intently he collected the next bit in one of his slender pipes, into his study he went with it. . . .

"I have proved it! This water has not a single little creature in it! They do not come down from the sky!"

But he kept that water; hour after hour, day after day he squinted at it —and on the fourth day he saw those wee beasts beginning to appear in the water along with bits of dust and little flecks of thread and lint. That was a man from Missouri! Imagine a world of men who would submit all of their cocksure judgments to the ordeal of the common-sense experiments of a Leeuwenhoek!

Did he write to the Royal Society to tell them of this entirely unsuspected world of life he had discovered? Not yet! He was a slow man. He turned his lens onto all kinds of water, water kept in the close air of his study, water in a pot kept on the high roof of his house, water from the not-too-clean canals of Delft and water from the deep cold well in his garden. Everywhere he found those beasts. He gaped at their enormous littleness, he found many thousands of them did not equal a grain of sand in bigness, he compared them to a cheese-mite and they were to this filthy little creature as a bee is to a horse. He was never tired with watching them "swim about among one another gently with a swarm of mosquitoes in the air. . . ."

Of course this man was a groper. He was a groper and a stumbler as all men are gropers, devoid of prescience, and stumblers, finding what they never set out to find. His new beasties were marvelous but they were not enough for him, he was always poking into everything, trying to see more closely, trying to find reasons. Why is the sharp taste of pepper? That was what he asked himself one day, and he guessed: "There must be little points on the particles of pepper and these points jab the tongue when you eat pepper. . . ."

But are there such little points?

He fussed with dry pepper. He sneezed. He sweat, but he couldn't get the grains of pepper small enough to put under his lens. So, to soften it, he put it to soak for several weeks in water. Then with fine needles he pried the almost invisible specks of the pepper apart, and sucked them up in a little drop of water into one of his hair-fine glass tubes. He looked—

Here was something to make even this determined man scatter-brained. He forgot about possible small sharp points on the pepper. With the interest of an intent little boy he watched the antics of "an incredible number of little animals, of various sorts, which move very prettily, which tumble about and sidewise, this way and that!"

So it was Leeuwenhoek stumbled on a magnificent way to grow his new little animals.

And now to write all this to the great men off there in London! Artlessly he described his own astonishment to them. Long page after page in a superbly neat handwriting with little common words he told them that you could put a million of these little animals into a coarse grain of sand and that one drop of his pepper-water, where they grew and multiplied so well, held more than two-million seven-hundred-thousand of them. . . .

This letter was translated into English. It was read before the learned skeptics . . . and it bowled the learned body over! What! The Dutchman said he had discovered beasts so small that you could put as many of them into one little drop of water as there were people in his native country? Nonsense! The cheese mite was absolutely and without doubt the smallest creature God had created.

But a few of the members did not scoff. This Leeuwenhoek was a confoundedly accurate man: everything he had ever written to them they had found to be true. . . . So a letter went back to the scientific janitor, begging him to write them in detail the way he had made his microscope, and his method of observing.

. . . He replied to them in a long letter assuring them he never told anything too big. He explained his calculations (and modern microbe hunters with all of their apparatus make only slightly more accurate ones!); he wrote these calculations out, divisions, multiplications, additions, until his letter looked like a child's exercise in arithmetic. He finished by saying that many people of Delft had seen—with applause!—these strange new animals under his lens. He would send them affidavits from prominent citizens of Delft—two men of God, one notary public, and eight other persons worthy to be believed. But he wouldn't tell them how he made his microscopes.

That was a suspicious man! He held his little machines up for people to look through, but let them so much as touch the microscope to help themselves to see better and he might order them out of his house. . . . He was like a child anxious and proud to show a large red apple to his playmates but loath to let them touch it for fear they might take a bite out of it.

So the Royal Society commissioned Robert Hooke and Nehemiah Grew to build the very best microscopes, and brew pepper water from the finest quality of black pepper. And, on the 15th of November, 1677, Hooke came carrying his microscope to the meeting—agog—for Antony Leeuwenhoek had not lied. Here they were, those enchanted beasts! The members rose from their seats and crowded round the microscope. They peered, they exclaimed: this man must be a wizard observer! That was a proud day for Leeuwenhoek. And a little later the Royal Society made him a Fellow, sending him a gorgeous diploma of membership in a silver case with the coat of arms of the society on the cover. "I will serve you faithfully during the rest of my life," he wrote them. And he was as good as his word, for he mailed them those conversational mixtures of gossip and science till he died at the age of ninety. But send them a microscope? Very sorry, but that was impossible to do, while he lived.

IV

Those little animals were everywhere! He told the Royal Society of finding swarms of those sub-visible beings in his mouth—of all places: "Although I am now fifty years old," he wrote, "I have uncommonly well-preserved teeth, because it is my custom every morning to rub my teeth very hard with salt, and after cleaning my large teeth with a quill, to rub them vigorously with a cloth. . . ." But there still were little bits of white stuff between his teeth, when he looked at them with a magnifying mirror. . . .

What was this white stuff made of?

From his teeth he scraped a bit of this stuff, mixed it with pure rain water, stuck it in a little tube on to the needle of his microscope, closed the door of his study—

What was this that rose from the gray dimness of his lens into clear distinctness as he brought the tube into the focus? Here was an unbelievably tiny creature, leaping about in the water of the tube "like the fish called a pike." There was a second kind that swam forward a little way, then whirled about suddenly, then tumbled over itself in pretty somersaults. There were some beings that moved sluggishly and looked like wee bent sticks, nothing more, but that Dutchman squinted at them till his eyes were red-rimmed—and they moved, they were alive, no doubt of it! There was a menagerie in his mouth! There were creatures shaped like flexible rods that went to and fro with the stately carriage of bishops in procession, there were spirals that whirled through the water like violently animated corkscrews. . . .

You may wonder that Leeuwenhoek nowhere in any of those hundreds of letters makes any mention of the harm these mysterious new little animals might do to men. He had come upon them in drinking water, spied upon them in the mouth; as the years went by he discovered them in the intestines of frogs and horses, and even in his own discharges; in swarms he found them on those rare occasions when, as he says, "he was troubled with a looseness." But not for a moment did he guess that his trouble was caused by those little beasts, and from his unimaginativeness and his carefulness not to jump to conclusions modern microbe hunters— if they only had time to study his writings—could learn a great deal. . . .

The years went by. He tended his little dry-goods store, he saw to it the city hall of Delft was properly swept out, he grew more and more crusty and suspicious, he looked longer and longer hours through his hundreds of microscopes, he made a hundred amazing discoveries. In the tail of a little fish stuck head first into a glass tube he saw for the first time of all men the capillary blood vessels through which blood goes from the arteries to the veins—so he completed the Englishman Harvey's discovery of the circulation of the blood. The most sacred and improper and romantic things in life were only material for the probing, tireless eyes of his lenses. Leeuwenhoek discovered the human sperm, and the cold-blooded science of his searching would have been shocking, if he had not been such a completely innocent man! The years went by and all Europe knew about him. Peter the Great of Russia came to pay his respects to him, and the Queen of England journeyed to Delft only to look at the wonders to be seen through the lenses of his microscopes. He exploded countless superstitions for the Royal Society, and aside from Isaac Newton and Robert Boyle he was the most famous of their members. But did these honors turn his head? They couldn't turn his head because he had from the first a sufficiently high opinion of himself! His arrogance was limitless—but it was equaled by his humility when he thought of that misty unknown that he knew surrounded himself and all men. . . .

He was an amazingly healthy man, and at the age of eighty his hand hardly trembled as he held up his microscope for visitors to peep at his little animals or to exclaim at the unborn oysters. . . . Years after his discovery of the microbes in his mouth one morning in the midst of his coffee drinkings he looked once more at the stuff between his teeth—

What was this? There was not a single little animal to be found. Or there were no living animals rather, for he thought he could make out the bodies of myriads of dead ones—and maybe one or two that moved feebly, as if they were sick. "Blessed Saints!" he growled: "I hope some great Lord of the Royal Society doesn't try to find those creatures in his mouth, and fail, and then deny my observations. . . ."

But look here! He had been drinking coffee, so hot it had blistered his lips, almost. He had looked for the little animals in the white stuff from between his front teeth. It was just after the coffee he had looked there— Well?

With the help of a magnifying mirror he went at his back teeth. Presto!

"With great surprise I saw an incredibly large number of little animals, and in such an unbelievable quantity of the aforementioned stuff, that it is not to be conceived of by those who have not seen it with their own eyes." Then he made delicate experiments in tubes, heating the water with its tiny population to a temperature a little warmer than that of a hot bath. In a moment the creatures stopped their agile runnings to and fro. He cooled the water. They did not come back to life—so! It was that hot coffee that had killed the beasties in his front teeth! ...

If Antony Leeuwenhoek failed to see the germs that cause human disease, if he had too little imagination to predict the rôle of assassin for his wretched creatures, he did show that sub-visible beasts could devour and kill living beings much larger than they were themselves. He was fussing with mussels, shellfish that he dredged up out of the canals of Delft. He found thousands of them unborn inside their mothers. He tried to make these young ones develop outside their mothers in a glass of canal water. "I wonder," he muttered, "why our canals are not choked with mussels, when the mothers have each one so many young ones inside them!" Day after day he poked about in his glass of water with its slimy mass of embryos, he turned his lens on to them to see if they were growing—but what was this? Astounded he watched the fishy stuff disappear from between their shells—it was being gobbled up by thousands of tiny microbes that were attacking the mussels greedily. ...

"Life lives on life—it is cruel, but it is God's will," he pondered. "And it is for our good, of course, because if there weren't little animals to eat up the young mussels, our canals would be choked by those shellfish, for each mother has more than a thousand young ones at a time!" So Antony Leeuwenhoek accepted everything and praised everything, and in this he was a child of his time, for in his century searchers had not yet, like Pasteur who came after them, begun to challenge God, to shake their fists at the meaningless cruelties of nature toward mankind, her children. ...

He passed eighty, and his teeth came loose as they had to even in his strong body; he didn't complain at the inexorable arrival of the winter of his life, but he jerked out that old tooth and turned his lens onto the little creatures he found within that hollow root—why shouldn't he study them once more? There might be some little detail he had missed those hundred other times! Friends came to him at eighty-five and told him to take it easy and leave his studies. He wrinkled his brow and opened wide his still bright eyes: "The fruits that ripen in autumn last the longest!" he told them—he called eighty-five the autumn of his life! ...

That was the first of the microbe hunters. In 1723, when he was ninety-one years old and on his deathbed, he sent for his friend Hoogvliet. He could not lift his hand. His once glowing eyes were rheumy and their lids were beginning to stick fast with the cement of death. He mumbled:

"Hoogvliet, my friend, be so good as to have those two letters on the table translated into Latin. . . . Send them to London to the Royal Society. . . ."

So he kept his promise made fifty years before, and Hoogvliet wrote, along with those last letters: "I send you, learned sirs, this last gift of my dying friend, hoping that his final word will be agreeable to you."

1926

The Origin of Life

GEORGE WALD

ABOUT A CENTURY AGO THE QUESTION, HOW DID LIFE begin? which has interested men throughout their history, reached an impasse. Up to that time two answers had been offered: one that life had been created supernaturally, the other that it arises continually from the nonliving. The first explanation lay outside science; the second was now shown to be untenable. For a time scientists felt some discomfort in having no answer at all. Then they stopped asking the question.

Recently ways have been found again to consider the origin of life as a scientific problem—as an event within the order of nature. In part this is the result of new information. But a theory never rises of itself, however rich and secure the facts. It is an act of creation. Our present ideas in this realm were first brought together in a clear and defensible argument by the Russian biochemist A. I. Oparin in a book called *The Origin of Life*, published in 1936. Much can be added now to Oparin's discussion, yet it provides the foundation upon which all of us who are interested in this subject have built.

The attempt to understand how life originated raises a wide variety of scientific questions, which lead in many and diverse directions and should

end by casting light into many obscure corners. At the center of the enterprise lies the hope not only of explaining a great past event—important as
that should be—but of showing that the explanation is workable. If we
can indeed come to understand how a living organism arises from the non-
living, we should be able to construct one—only of the simplest description, to be sure, but still recognizably alive. This is so remote a possibility
now that one scarcely dares to acknowledge it; but it is there nevertheless.

One answer to the problem of how life originated is that it was created.
This is an understandable confusion of nature with technology. Men are
used to making things; it is a ready thought that those things not made by
men were made by a superhuman being. Most of the cultures we know
contain mythical accounts of a supernatural creation of life. Our own
tradition provides such an account in the opening chapters of Genesis.
There we are told that beginning on the third day of the Creation, God
brought forth living creatures—first plants, then fishes and birds, then
land animals and finally man.

The more rational elements of society, however, tended to take a more
naturalistic view of the matter. One had only to accept the evidence of
one's senses to know that life arises regularly from the nonliving: worms
from mud, maggots from decaying meat, mice from refuse of various
kinds. This is the view that came to be called spontaneous generation.
Few scientists doubted it. Aristotle, Newton, William Harvey, Descartes,
van Helmont, all accepted spontaneous generation without serious question. Indeed, even the theologians—witness the English Jesuit John Turber-
ville Needham—could subscribe to the view, for Genesis tells us, not that
God created plants and most animals directly, but that He bade the earth
and waters to bring them forth; since this directive was never rescinded,
there is nothing heretical in believing that the process has continued.

But step by step, in a great controversy that spread over two centuries,
this belief was whittled away until nothing remained of it. First the
Italian Francesco Redi showed in the seventeenth century that meat placed
under a screen, so that flies cannot lay their eggs on it, never develops
maggots. Then in the following century the Italian abbé Lazzaro Spallanzani showed that a nutritive broth, sealed off from the air while boiling,
never develops microorganisms, and hence never rots. Needham objected
that by too much boiling Spallanzani had rendered the broth, and still
more the air above it, incompatible with life. Spallanzani could defend his
broth; when he broke the seal of his flasks, allowing new air to rush in,
the broth promptly began to rot. He could find no way, however, to show
that the air in the sealed flask had not been vitiated. This problem finally
was solved by Louis Pasteur in 1860, with a simple modification of Spal-

lanzani's experiment. Pasteur too used a flask containing boiling broth, but instead of sealing off the neck he drew it out in a long, S-shaped curve with its end open to the air. While molecules of air could pass back and forth freely, the heavier particles of dust, bacteria and molds in the atmosphere were trapped on the walls of the curved neck and only rarely reached the broth. In such a flask the broth seldom was contaminated; usually it remained clear and sterile indefinitely.

This was only one of Pasteur's experiments. It is no easy matter to deal with so deeply ingrained and common-sense a belief as that in spontaneous generation. One can ask for nothing better in such a pass than a noisy and stubborn opponent, and this Pasteur had in the naturalist Félix Pouchet, whose arguments before the French Academy of Sciences drove Pasteur to more and more rigorous experiments. When he had finished, nothing remained of the belief in spontaneous generation.

We tell this story to beginning students of biology as though it represents a triumph of reason over mysticism. In fact it is very nearly the opposite. The reasonable view was to believe in spontaneous generation; the only alternative, to believe in a single, primary act of supernatural creation. There is no third position. For this reason many scientists a century ago chose to regard the belief in spontaneous generation as a "philosophical necessity." It is a symptom of the philosophical poverty of our time that this necessity is no longer appreciated. Most modern biologists, having reviewed with satisfaction the downfall of the spontaneous generation hypothesis, yet unwilling to accept the alternative belief in special creation, are left with nothing.

I think a scientist has no choice but to approach the origin of life through a hypothesis of spontaneous generation. What the controversy reviewed above showed to be untenable is only the belief that living organisms arise spontaneously under present conditions. We have now to face a somewhat different problem: how organisms may have arisen spontaneously under different conditions in some former period, granted that they do so no longer.

To make an organism demands the right substances in the right proportions and in the right arrangement. We do not think that anything more is needed—but that is problem enough.

The substances are water, certain salts—as it happens, those found in the ocean—and carbon compounds. The latter are called *organic* compounds because they scarcely occur except as products of living organisms.

Organic compounds consist for the most part of four types of atoms: carbon, oxygen, nitrogen and hydrogen. These four atoms together constitute about 99 per cent of living material, for hydrogen and oxygen also form water. The organic compounds found in organisms fall mainly into four great classes: carbohydrates, fats, proteins and nucleic acids. The fats are simplest, each consisting of three fatty acids joined to glycerol. The starches and glycogens are made of sugar units strung together to form long straight and branched chains. In general only one type of sugar appears in a single starch or glycogen; these molecules are large, but still relatively simple. The principal function of carbohydrates and fats in the organism is to serve as fuel—as a source of energy.

The nucleic acids introduce a further level of complexity. They are very large structures, composed of aggregates of at least four types of unit —the nucleotides—brought together in a great variety of proportions and sequences. An almost endless variety of different nucleic acids is possible, and specific differences among them are believed to be of the highest importance. Indeed, these structures are thought by many to be the main constituents of the genes, the bearers of hereditary constitution.

Variety and specificity, however, are most characteristic of the proteins, which include the largest and most complex molecules known. The units of which their structure is built are about 25 different amino acids. These are strung together in chains hundreds to thousands of units long, in different proportions, in all types of sequence, and with the greatest variety of branching and folding. A virtually infinite number of different proteins is possible. Organisms seem to exploit this potentiality, for no two species of living organism, animal plant, possess the same proteins.

Organic molecules therefore form a large and formidable array, endless in variety and of the most bewildering complexity. One cannot think of having organisms without them. This is precisely the trouble, for to understand how organisms originated we must first of all explain how such complicated molecules could come into being. And that is only the beginning. To make an organism requires not only a tremendous variety of these substances, in adequate amounts and proper proportions, but also just the right arrangement of them. Structure here is as important as composition—and what a complication of structure! The most complex machine man has devised—say an electronic brain—is child's play compared with the simplest of living organisms. The especially trying thing is that complexity here involves such small dimensions. It is on the molecular level; it consists of a detailed fitting of molecule to molecule such as no chemist can attempt.

One has only to contemplate the magnitude of this task to concede that the spontaneous generation of a living organism is impossible. Yet here we are—as a result, I believe, of spontaneous generation. It will help to digress for a moment to ask what one means by "impossible."

With every event one can associate a probability—the chance that it will occur. This is always a fraction, the proportion of times the event occurs in a large number of trials. Sometimes the probability is apparent even without trial. A coin has two faces; the probability of tossing a head is therefore 1/2. A die has six faces; the probability of throwing a deuce is 1/6. When one has no means of estimating the probability beforehand, it must be determined by counting the fraction of successes in a large number of trials. . . .

In such a problem as the spontaneous origin of life we have no way of assessing probabilities beforehand, or even of deciding what we mean by a trial. The origin of a living organism is undoubtedly a stepwise phenomenon, each step with its own probability and its own conditions of trial. Of one thing we can be sure, however: whatever constitutes a trial, more such trials occur the longer the interval of time.

The important point is that since the origin of life belongs in the category of at-least-once phenomena, time is on its side. However improbable we regard this event, or any of the steps which it involves, given enough time it will almost certainly happen at least once. And for life as we know it, with its capacity for growth and reproduction, once may be enough.

Time is in fact the hero of the plot. The time with which we have to deal is of the order of two billion years. What we regard as impossible on the basis of human experience is meaningless here. Given so much time, the "impossible" becomes possible, the possible probable, and the probable virtually certain. One has only to wait: time itself performs the miracles.

This brings the argument back to its first stage: the origin of organic compounds. Until a century and a quarter ago the only known source of these substances was the stuff of living organisms. Students of chemistry are usually told that when, in 1828, Friedrich Wöhler synthesized the first organic compound, urea, he proved that organic compounds do not require living organisms to make them. Of course it showed nothing of the kind. Organic chemists are alive; Wöhler merely showed that they can make organic compounds externally as well as internally. It is still true that with almost negligible exceptions all the organic matter we know is the product of living organisms.

The almost negligible exceptions, however, are very important for our argument. It is now recognized that a constant, slow production of organic molecules occurs without the agency of living things. Certain geological phenomena yield simple organic compounds. So, for example, volcanic eruptions bring metal carbides to the surface of the earth, where they react with water vapor to yield simple compounds of carbon and hydrogen. The familiar type of such a reaction is the process used in old-style bicycle lamps in which acetylene is made by mixing iron carbide with water.

Recently Harold Urey, Nobel laureate in chemistry, has become interested in the degree to which electrical discharges in the upper atmosphere may promote the formation of organic compounds. One of his students, S. L. Miller, performed the simple experiment of circulating a mixture of water vapor, methane (CH_4), ammonia (NH_3) and hydrogen —all gases believed to have been present in the early atmosphere of the earth—continuously for a week over an electric spark. The circulation was maintained by boiling the water in one limb of the apparatus and condensing it in the other. At the end of the week the water was analyzed by the delicate method of paper chromatography. It was found to have acquired a mixture of amino acids! Glycine and alanine, the simplest amino acids and the most prevalent in proteins, were definitely identified in the solution, and there were indications it contained aspartic acid and two others. The yield was surprisingly high. This amazing result changes at a stroke our ideas of the probability of the spontaneous formation of amino acids.[1]

A final consideration, however, seems to me more important than all the special processes to which one might appeal for organic syntheses in inanimate nature.

It has already been said that to have organic molecules one ordinarily needs organisms. The synthesis of organic substances, like almost everything else that happens in organisms, is governed by the special class of proteins called enzymes—the organic catalysts which greatly accelerate chemical reactions in the body. Since an enzyme is not used up but is returned at the end of the process, a small amount of enzyme can promote an enormous transformation of material.

Enzymes play such a dominant role in the chemistry of life that it is exceedingly difficult to imagine the synthesis of living material without their help. This poses a dilemma, for enzymes themselves are proteins, and hence among the most complex organic components of the cell. One is asking, in effect, for an apparatus which is the unique property of cells in order to form the first cell.

This is not, however, an insuperable difficulty. An enzyme, after all, is only a catalyst; it can do no more than change the *rate* of a chemical reaction. It cannot make anything happen that would not have happened,

---

[1] [Miller's epochal experiment has been promptly and successfully repeated in laboratories at Oak Ridge, Yale, and the Carnegie Institution of Washington's Geophysical Laboratory. More than 20 of the amino acids have been thus naturally synthesized. Other atmospheric mixtures, always excluding free oxygen, have been used successfully. Eds.]

though more slowly, in its absence. Every process that is catalyzed by an enzyme, and every product of such a process, would occur without the enzyme. The only difference is one of rate.

Once again the essence of the argument is time. What takes only a few moments in the presence of an enzyme or other catalyst may take days, months or years in its absence; but given time, the end result is the same.

Indeed, this great difficulty in conceiving of the spontaneous generation of organic compounds has its positive side. In a sense, organisms demonstrate to us what organic reactions and products are *possible*. We can be certain that, given time, all these things must occur. Every substance that has ever been found in an organism displays thereby the finite probability of its occurrence. Hence, given time, it should arise spontaneously. One has only to wait.

It will be objected at once that this is just what one cannot do. Everyone knows that these substances are highly perishable. Granted that, within long spaces of time, now a sugar molecule, now a fat, now even a protein might form spontaneously, each of these molecules should have only a transitory existence. How are they ever to accumulate; and, unless they do so, how form an organism?

We must turn the question around. What, in our experience, is known to destroy organic compounds? Primarily two agencies: decay and the attack of oxygen. But decay is the work of living organisms, and we are talking of a time before life existed. As for oxygen, this introduces a further and fundamental section of our argument.

It is generally conceded at present that the early atmosphere of our planet contained virtually no free oxygen. Almost all the earth's oxygen was bound in the form of water and metal oxides. If this were not so, it would be very difficult to imagine how organic matter could accumulate over the long stretches of time that alone might make possible the spontaneous origin of life. This is a crucial point, therefore, and the statement that the early atmosphere of the planet was virtually oxygen-free comes forward so opportunely as to raise a suspicion of special pleading. I have for this reason taken care to consult a number of geologists and astronomers on this point, and am relieved to find that it is well defended. I gather that there is a widespread though not universal consensus that this condition did exist. Apparently something similar was true also for another common component of our atmosphere—carbon dioxide. It is believed that most of the carbon on the earth during its early geological history existed as the element or in metal carbides and hydrocarbons; very little was combined with oxygen.

This situation is not without its irony. We tend usually to think that the environment plays the tune to which the organism must dance. The environment is given; the organism's problem is to adapt to it or die. It has become apparent lately, however, that some of the most important features of the physical environment are themselves the work of living organisms. Two such features have just been named. The atmosphere of our planet seems to have contained no oxygen until organisms placed it there by the process of plant photosynthesis. It is estimated that at present all the oxygen of our atmosphere is renewed by photosynthesis once in every 2,000 years, and that all the carbon dioxide passes through the process of photosynthesis once in every 300 years. In the scale of geological time, these intervals are very small indeed. We are left with the realization that all the oxygen and carbon dioxide of our planet are the products of living organisms, and have passed through living organisms over and over again.

In the early history of our planet, when there were no organisms or any free oxygen, organic compounds should have been stable over very long periods. This is the crucial difference between the period before life existed and our own. If one were to specify a single reason why the spontaneous generation of living organisms was possible once and is so no longer, this is the reason.

We must still reckon, however, with another destructive force which is disposed of less easily. This can be called spontaneous dissolution—the counterpart of spontaneous generation. We have noted that any process catalyzed by an enzyme can occur in time without the enzyme. The trouble is that the processes which synthesize an organic substance are reversible: any chemical reaction which an enzyme may catalyze will go backward as well as forward. We have spoken as though one has only to wait to achieve syntheses of all kinds; it is truer to say that what one achieves by waiting is *equilibria* of all kinds—equilibria in which the synthesis and dissolution of substances come into balance.

In the vast majority of the processes in which we are interested the point of equilibrium lies far over toward the side of dissolution. That is to say, spontaneous dissolution is much more probable, and hence proceeds much more rapidly, than spontaneous synthesis. For example, the spontaneous union, step by step, of amino acid units to form a protein has a certain small probability, and hence might occur over a long stretch of time. But the dissolution of the protein or of an intermediate product into its component amino acids is much more probable, and hence will go ever so much more rapidly. The situation we must face is that of patient Penelope waiting for Odysseus, yet much worse: each night she undid the weaving of the preceding day, but here a night could readily undo the work of a year or a century.

How do present-day organisms manage to synthesize organic compounds against the forces of dissolution? They do so by a continuous expenditure of energy. Indeed, living organisms commonly do better than oppose the forces of dissolution; they grow in spite of them. They do so, however, only at enormous expense to their surroundings. They need a constant supply of material and energy merely to maintain themselves, and much more of both to grow and reproduce. A living organism is an intricate machine for performing exactly this function. When, for want of fuel or through some internal failure in its mechanism, an organism stops actively synthesizing itself in opposition to the processes which continuously decompose it, it dies and rapidly disintegrates.

What we ask here is to synthesize organic molecules without such a machine. I believe this to be the most stubborn problem that confronts us—the weakest link at present in our argument. I do not think it by any means disastrous, but it calls for phenomena and forces some of which are as yet only partly understood and some probably still to be discovered.

At present we can make only a beginning with this problem. We know that it is possible on occasion to protect molecules from dissolution by precipitation or by attachment to other molecules. A wide variety of such precipitation and "trapping" reactions is used in modern chemistry and biochemistry to promote syntheses. Some molecules appear to acquire a degree of resistance to disintegration simply through their size. So, for example, the larger molecules composed of amino acids—polypeptides and proteins—seem to display much less tendency to disintegrate into their units than do smaller compounds of two or three amino acids. . . .

Such molecular aggregates, of various degrees of material and architectural complexity, are indispensable intermediates between molecules and organisms. We have no need to try to imagine the spontaneous formation of an organism by one grand collision of its component molecules. The whole process must be gradual. The molecules form aggregates, small and large. The aggregates add further molecules, thus growing in size and complexity. Aggregates of various kinds interact with one another to form still larger and more complex structures. In this way we imagine the ascent, not by jumps or master strokes, but gradually, piecemeal, to the first living organisms.

Where may this have happened? It is easiest to suppose that life first arose in the sea. Here were the necessary salts and the water. The latter is not only the principal component of organisms, but prior to their formation provided a medium which could dissolve molecules of the widest variety and ceaselessly mix and circulate them. It is this constant mixture and collision of organic molecules of every sort that constituted in large part the "trials" of our earlier discussion of probabilities.

The sea in fact gradually turned into a dilute broth, sterile and oxygen-free. In this broth molecules came together in increasing number and variety, sometimes merely to collide and separate, sometimes to react with one another to produce new combinations, sometimes to aggregate into multimolecular formations of increasing size and complexity.

What brought order into such complexes? For order is as essential here as composition. To form an organism, molecules must enter into intricate designs and connections; they must eventually form a self-repairing, self-constructing dynamic machine. For a time this problem of molecular arrangement seemed to present an almost insuperable obstacle in the way of imagining a spontaneous origin of life, or indeed the laboratory synthesis of a living organism. It is still a large and mysterious problem, but it no longer seems insuperable. The change in view has come about because we now realize that it is not altogether necessary to *bring* order into this situation; a great deal of order is implicit in the molecules themselves.

The epitome of molecular order is a crystal. In a perfect crystal the molecules display complete regularity of position and orientation in all planes of space. At the other extreme are fluids—liquids or gases—in which the molecules are in ceaseless motion and in wholly random orientations and positions.

Lately it has become clear that very little of a living cell is truly fluid. Most of it consists of molecules which have taken up various degrees of orientation with regard to one another. That is, most of the cell represents various degrees of approach to crystallinity—often, however, with very important differences from the crystals most familiar to us. Much of the cell's crystallinity involves molecules which are still in solution—so-called liquid crystals—and much of the dynamic, plastic quality of cellular structure, the capacity for constant change of shape and interchange of material, derives from this condition. Our familiar crystals, furthermore, involve only one or a very few types of molecule, while in the cell a great variety of different molecules come together in some degree of regular spacing and orientation—i.e., some degree of crystallinity. We are dealing in the cell with highly mixed crystals and near-crystals, solid and liquid. The laboratory study of this type of formation has scarcely begun. Its further exploration is of the highest importance for our problem.

In a fluid such as water the molecules are in very rapid motion. Any molecules dissolved in such a medium are under a constant barrage of collisions with water molecules. This keeps small and moderately sized molecules in a constant turmoil; they are knocked about at random, colliding again and again, never holding any position or orientation for more than an instant. The larger a molecule is relative to water, the less it is disturbed by such collisions. Many protein and nucleic acid molecules are so large that even in solution their motions are very sluggish, and since they carry large numbers of electric charges distributed about their surfaces, they tend even in solution to align with respect to one another. It is so that they tend to form liquid crystals. . . .

Recently several particularly striking examples have been reported of the spontaneous production of familiar types of biological structure by protein molecules. Cartilage and muscle offer some of the most intricate and regular patterns of structure to be found in organisms. A fiber from either type of tissue presents under the electron microscope a beautiful pattern of cross striations of various widths and densities, very regularly spaced. The proteins that form these structures can be coaxed into free solution and stirred into completely random orientation. Yet on precipitating, under proper conditions, the molecules realign with regard to one another to regenerate with extraordinary fidelity the original patterns of the tissues.

We have therefore a genuine basis for the view that the molecules of our oceanic broth will not only come together spontaneously to form aggregates but in doing so will spontaneously achieve various types and degrees of order. This greatly simplifies our problem. What it means is that, given the right molecules, one does not have to do everything for them; they do a great deal for themselves.

Oparin has made the ingenious suggestion that natural selection, which Darwin proposed to be the driving force of organic evolution, begins to operate at this level. He suggests that as the molecules come together to form colloidal aggregates, the latter begin to compete with one another for material. Some aggregates, by virtue of especially favorable composition or internal arrangement, acquire new molecules more rapidly than others. They eventually emerge as the dominant types. Oparin suggests further that considerations of optimal size enter at this level. A growing colloidal particle may reach a point at which it becomes unstable and breaks down into smaller particles, each of which grows and redivides. All these phenomena lie within the bounds of known processes in non-living systems.

We suppose that all these forces and factors, and others perhaps yet to be revealed, together give us eventually the first living organism. That achieved, how does the organism continue to live?

We have already noted that a living organism is a dynamic structure. It is the site of a continuous influx and outflow of matter and energy. This is the very sign of life, its cessation the best evidence of death. What is the primal organism to use as food, and how derive the energy it needs to maintain itself and grow?

For the primal organism, generated under the conditions we have described, only one answer is possible. Having arisen in an oceanic broth of organic molecules, its only recourse is to live upon them. There is only one way of doing that in the absence of oxygen. It is called fermentation: the process by which organisms derive energy by breaking organic molecules and rearranging their parts. The most familiar example of such a process is the fermentation of sugar by yeast, which yields alcohol as one of the products. Animal cells also ferment sugar, not to alcohol but to lactic acid. These are two examples from a host of known fermentations.

The yeast fermentation has the following over-all equation: $C_6H_{12}O_6 \rightarrow 2 CO_2 + 2 C_2H_5OH + energy$. The result of fragmenting 180 grams of sugar into 88 grams of carbon dioxide and 92 grams of alcohol is to make available about 20,000 calories of energy for the use of the cell. The energy is all that the cell derives by this transaction; the carbon dioxide and alcohol are waste products which must be got rid of somehow if the cell is to survive.

The cell, having arisen in a broth of organic compounds accumulated over the ages, must consume these molecules by fermentation in order to acquire the energy it needs to live, grow and reproduce. In doing so, it and its descendants are living on borrowed time. They are consuming their heritage, just as we in our time have nearly consumed our heritage of coal and oil. Eventually such a process must come to an end, and with that life also should have ended. It would have been necessary to start the entire development again.

Fortunately, however, the waste product carbon dioxide saved this situation. This gas entered the ocean and the atmosphere in ever-increasing quantity. Some time before the cell exhausted the supply of organic molecules, it succeeded in inventing the process of photosynthesis. This enabled it, with the energy of sunlight, to make its own organic molecules: first sugar from carbon dioxide and water, then, with ammonia and nitrates as sources of nitrogen, the entire array of organic compounds which it requires. The sugar synthesis equation is: $6 CO_2 + 6 H_2O + sunlight \rightarrow C_6H_{12}O_6 + 6 O_2$. Here 264 grams of carbon dioxide plus 108 grams of water plus about 700,000 calories of sunlight yield 180 grams of sugar and 192 grams of oxygen.

This is an enormous step forward. Living organisms no longer needed to depend upon the accumulation of organic matter from past ages; they could make their own. With the energy of sunlight they could accomplish the fundamental organic syntheses that provide their substance, and by fermentation they could produce what energy they needed.

Fermentation, however, is an extraordinarily inefficient source of energy. It leaves most of the energy potential of organic compounds unexploited;

consequently huge amounts of organic material must be fermented to provide a modicum of energy. It produces also various poisonous waste products—alcohol, lactic acid, acetic acid, formic acid and so on. In the sea such products are readily washed away, but if organisms were ever to penetrate to the air and land, these products must prove a serious embarrassment.

One of the by-products of photosynthesis, however, is oxygen. Once this was available, organisms could invent a new way to acquire energy, many times as efficient as fermentation. This is the process of cold combustion called respiration: $C_6H_{12}O_6 + 6\,O_2 \rightarrow 6\,CO_2 + 6\,H_2O + energy$. The burning of 180 grams of sugar in cellular respiration yields about 700,000 calories, as compared with the approximately 20,000 calories produced by fermentation of the same quantity of sugar. This process of combustion extracts all the energy that can possibly be derived from the molecules which it consumes. With this process at its disposal, the cell can meet its energy requirements with a minimum expenditure of substance. It is a further advantage that the products of respiration—water and carbon dioxide—are innocuous and easily disposed of in any environment.

It is difficult to overestimate the degree to which the invention of cellular respiration released the forces of living organisms. No organism that relies wholly upon fermentation has ever amounted to much. Even after the advent of photosynthesis, organisms could have led only a marginal existence. They could indeed produce their own organic materials, but only in quantities sufficient to survive. Fermentation is so profligate a way of life that photosynthesis could do little more than keep up with it. Respiration used the material of organisms with such enormously greater efficiency as for the first time to leave something over. Coupled with fermentation, photosynthesis made organisms self-sustaining; coupled with respiration, it provided a surplus. . . .

The entry of oxygen into the atmosphere also liberated organisms in another sense. The sun's radiation contains ultraviolet components which no living cell can tolerate. We are sometimes told that if this radiation were to reach the earth's surface, life must cease. That is not quite true. Water absorbs ultraviolet radiation very effectively, and one must conclude that as long as these rays penetrated in quantity to the surface of the earth, life had to remain under water. With the appearance of oxygen, however, a layer of ozone formed high in the atmosphere and absorbed this radiation. Now organisms could for the first time emerge from the water and begin to populate the earth and air. Oxygen provided not only the means of obtaining adequate energy for evolution but the protective blanket of ozone which alone made possible terrestrial life.

This is really the end of our story. Yet not quite the end. Our entire concern in this argument has been to bring the origin of life within the compass of natural phenomena. It is of the essence of such phenomena to be repetitive, and hence, given time, to be inevitable.

This is by far our most significant conclusion—that life, as an orderly natural event on such a planet as ours, was inevitable. The same can be said of the whole of organic evolution. All of it lies within the order of nature, and apart from details all of it was inevitable.

Astronomers have reason to believe that a planet such as ours—of about the earth's size and temperature, and about as well lighted—is a rare event in the universe. Indeed, filled as our story is with improbable phenomena, one of the least probable is to have had such a body as the earth to begin with. Yet though this probability is small, the universe is so large that it is conservatively estimated at least 100,000 planets like the earth exist in our galaxy alone. Some 100 million galaxies lie within the range of our most powerful telescopes, so that throughout observable space we can count apparently on the existence of at least 10 million million planets like our own.

What it means to bring the origin of life within the realm of natural phenomena is to imply that in all these places life probably exists—life as we know it. Indeed, I am convinced that there can be no way of composing and constructing living organisms which is fundamentally different from the one we know—though this is another argument, and must await another occasion. Wherever life is possible, given time, it should arise. It should then ramify into a wide array of forms, differing in detail from those we now observe (as did earlier organisms on the earth) yet including many which should look familiar to us—perhaps even men.

We are not alone in the universe, and do not bear alone the whole burden of life and what comes of it. Life is a cosmic event—so far as we know the most complex state of organization that matter has achieved in our cosmos. It has come many times, in many places—places closed off from us by impenetrable distances, probably never to be crossed even with a signal. As men we can attempt to understand it, and even somewhat to control and guide its local manifestations. On this planet that is our home, we have every reason to wish it well. Yet should we fail, all is not lost. Our kind will try again elsewhere.

1954

On Being the Right Size

J. B. S. HALDANE

From *Possible Worlds*

THE MOST OBVIOUS DIFFERENCES BETWEEN different animals are differences of size, but for some reason the zoologists have paid singularly little attention to them. In a large textbook of zoology before me I find no indication that the eagle is larger than the sparrow, or the hippopotamus bigger than the hare, though some grudging admissions are made in the case of the mouse and the whale. But yet it is easy to show that a hare could not be as large as a hippopotamus, or a whale as small as a herring. For every type of animal there is a most convenient size, and a large change in size inevitably carries with it a change of form.

Let us take the most obvious of possible cases, and consider a giant man sixty feet high—about the height of Giant Pope and Giant Pagan in the illustrated *Pilgrim's Progress* of my childhood. These monsters were not only ten times as high as Christian, but ten times as wide and ten times as thick, so that their total weight was a thousand times his, or about eighty to ninety tons. Unfortunately the cross sections of their bones were only a hundred times those of Christian, so that every square inch of giant bone had to support ten times the weight borne by a square inch of human bone. As the human thigh-bone breaks under about ten times the human weight, Pope and Pagan would have broken their thighs every time they took a step. This was doubtless why they were sitting down in the picture I remember. But it lessens one's respect for Christian and Jack the Giant Killer.

To turn to zoology, suppose that a gazelle, a graceful little creature with long thin legs, is to become large, it will break its bones unless it does one of two things. It may make its legs short and thick, like the rhinoceros, so that every pound of weight has still about the same area

321

of bone to support it. Or it can compress its body and stretch out its legs obliquely to gain stability, like the giraffe. I mention these two beasts because they happen to belong to the same order as the gazelle, and both are quite successful mechanically, being remarkably fast runners.

Gravity, a mere nuisance to Christian, was a terror to Pope, Pagan, and Despair. To the mouse and any smaller animal it presents practically no dangers. You can drop a mouse down a thousand-yard mine shaft; and, on arriving at the bottom, it gets a slight shock and walks away, provided that the ground is fairly soft. A rat is killed, a man is broken, a horse splashes. For the resistance presented to movement by the air is proportional to the surface of the moving object. Divide an animal's length, breadth, and height each by ten; its weight is reduced to a thousandth, but its surface only to a hundredth. So the resistance to falling in the case of the small animal is relatively ten times greater than the driving force.

An insect, therefore, is not afraid of gravity; it can fall without danger, and can cling to the ceiling with remarkably little trouble. It can go in for elegant and fantastic forms of support like that of the daddy-longlegs. But there is a force which is as formidable to an insect as gravitation to a mammal. This is surface tension. A man coming out of a bath carries with him a film of water of about one-fiftieth of an inch in thickness. This weighs roughly a pound. A wet mouse has to carry about its own weight of water. A wet fly has to lift many times its own weight and, as everyone knows, a fly once wetted by water or any other liquid is in a very serious position indeed. An insect going for a drink is in as great danger as a man leaning out over a precipice in search of food. If it once falls into the grip of the surface tension of the water—that is to say, gets wet—it is likely to remain so until it drowns. A few insects, such as water-beetles, contrive to be unwettable; the majority keep well away from their drink by means of a long proboscis.

Of course tall land animals have other difficulties. They have to pump their blood to greater heights than a man, and therefore, require a larger blood pressure and tougher blood-vessels. A great many men die from burst arteries, especially in the brain, and this danger is presumably still greater for an elephant or a giraffe. But animals of all kinds find difficulties in size for the following reason. A typical small animal, say a microscopic worm or rotifer, has a smooth skin through which all the oxygen it requires can soak in, a straight gut with sufficient surface to absorb its food, and a single kidney. Increase its dimensions tenfold in every direction, and its weight is increased a thousand times, so that if it is to use its muscles as efficiently as its miniature counterpart, it will need a thousand times as much food and oxygen per day and will excrete a thousand times as much of waste products.

Now if its shape is unaltered its surface will be increased only a hundredfold, and ten times as much oxygen must enter per minute through each square millimetre of skin, ten times as much food through each square millimetre of intestine. When a limit is reached to their absorptive powers their surface has to be increased by some special device. For example, a part of the skin may be drawn out into tufts to make gills or pushed in to make lungs, thus increasing the oxygen-absorbing surface in proportion to the animal's bulk. A man, for example, has a hundred square yards of lung. Similarly, the gut, instead of being smooth and straight, becomes coiled and develops a velvety surface, and other organs increase in complication. The higher animals are not larger than the lower because they are more complicated. They are more complicated because they are larger. Just the same is true of plants. The simplest plants, such as the green algae growing in stagnant water or on the bark of trees, are mere round cells. The higher plants increase their surface by putting out leaves and roots. Comparative anatomy is largely the story of the struggle to increase surface in proportion to volume.

Some of the methods of increasing the surface are useful up to a point, but not capable of a very wide adaptation. For example, while vertebrates carry the oxygen from the gills or lungs all over the body in the blood, insects take air directly to every part of their body by tiny blind tubes called tracheae which open to the surface at many different points. Now, although by their breathing movements they can renew the air in the outer part of the tracheal system, the oxygen has to penetrate the finer branches by means of diffusion. Gases can diffuse easily through very small distances, not many times larger than the average length travelled by a gas molecule between collisions with other molecules. But when such vast journeys—from the point of view of a molecule—as a quarter of an inch have to be made, the process becomes slow. So the portions of an insect's body more than a quarter of an inch from the air would always be short of oxygen. In consequence hardly any insects are much more than half an inch thick. Land crabs are built on the same general plan as insects, but are much clumsier. Yet like ourselves they carry oxygen around in their blood, and are therefore able to grow far larger than any insects. If the insects had hit on a plan for driving air through their tissues instead of letting it soak in, they might well have become as large as lobsters, though other considerations would have prevented them from becoming as large as man.

Exactly the same difficulties attach to flying. It is an elementary principle of aeronautics that the minimum speed needed to keep an aeroplane of a given shape in the air varies as the square root of its length. If its linear dimensions are increased four times, it must fly twice as fast. Now the power needed for the minimum speed increases more rapidly than the weight of the machine. So the larger aeroplane, which weighs sixty-four times as much as the smaller, needs one hundred and twenty-eight times its horsepower to keep up. Applying the same principles to the birds, we find that the limit to their size is soon reached. An angel whose muscles developed no more power weight for weight than those of an eagle or a pigeon would require a breast projecting for about four feet to house the muscles engaged in working its wings, while to economize in weight, its legs would have to be reduced to mere stilts. Actually a large bird such as an eagle or kite does not keep in the air mainly by moving its wings. It is generally to be seen soaring, that is to say balanced on a rising column of air. And even soaring becomes more and more difficult with increasing size. Were this not the case eagles might be as large as tigers and as formidable to man as hostile aeroplanes.

But it is time that we pass to some of the advantages of size. One of the most obvious is that it enables one to keep warm. All warm-blooded animals at rest lose the same amount of heat from a unit area of skin, for which purpose they need a food-supply proportional to their surface and not to their weight. Five thousand mice weigh as much as a man. Their combined surface and food or oxygen consumption are about seventeen times a man's. In fact a mouse eats about one quarter its own weight of food every day, which is mainly used in keeping it warm. For the same reason small animals cannot live in cold countries. In the arctic regions there are no reptiles or amphibians, and no small mammals. The smallest mammal in Spitzbergen is the fox. The small birds fly away in winter, while the insects die, though their eggs can survive six months or more of frost. The most successful mammals are bears, seals, and walruses.

Similarly, the eye is a rather inefficient organ until it reaches a large size. The back of the human eye on which an image of the outside world is thrown, and which corresponds to the film of a camera, is composed of a mosaic of 'rods and cones' whose diameter is little more than a length of an average light wave. Each eye has about a half a million, and for two objects to be distinguishable their images must fall on separate rods or cones. It is obvious that with fewer but larger rods and cones we should see less distinctly. If they were twice as broad two points would have to be twice as far apart before we could distinguish them at a given distance. But if their size were diminished and their number increased we should see no better. For it is impossible to form a definite image smaller than a wave-length of light. Hence a mouse's eye is not a small-scale model of a human eye. Its rods and cones are not much smaller than ours, and therefore there are far fewer of them. A mouse could not distinguish one human face from another six feet away. In order that they should be of any use at all the eyes of small animals have to be much larger in proportion to their bodies than our own. Large animals on the other hand only require relatively small eyes, and those of the whale and elephant are little larger than our own.

For rather more recondite reasons the same general principle holds true of the brain. If we compare the brain-weights of a set of very similar animals such as the cat, cheetah, leopard, and tiger, we find that as we quadruple the body-weight the brain-weight is only doubled. The larger animal with proportionately larger bones can economize on brain, eyes, and certain other organs.

Such are a very few of the considerations which show that for every type of animal there is an optimum size. Yet although Galileo demonstrated the contrary more than three hundred years ago, people still believe that if a flea were as large as a man it could jump a thousand feet into the air. As a matter of fact the height to which an animal can jump is more nearly independent of its size than proportional to it. A flea can jump about two feet, a man about five. To jump a given height, if we neglect the resistance of the air, requires an expenditure of energy proportional to the jumper's weight. But if the jumping muscles form a constant fraction of the animal's body, the energy developed per ounce of muscle is independent of the size, provided it can be developed quickly enough in the small animal. As a matter of fact an insect's muscles, although they can contract more quickly than our own, appear to be less efficient; as otherwise a flea or grasshopper could rise six feet into the air.

1928

Parasitism and Degeneration

DAVID STARR JORDAN AND
VERNON LYMAN KELLOGG

From Evolution and Animal Life

T HE TERM PARASITISM, AS WELL AS THE TERM degeneration, cannot be very rigidly defined. To prey upon the bodies of other animals is the common habit of many creatures. If the animals which live in this way are free, chasing or lying in wait for or snaring their prey, we speak of them in general as predatory animals. But if they attach themselves to the body of their prey or burrow into it, and are carried about by it, live on or in it, then we call them parasites. And the difference in habit between a lion and an intestinal worm is large enough and marked enough to make very clear to us what is meant when we speak of one as predatory and the other as a parasite. But how shall we class the lamprey, that swims about until it finds a fish to which it clings, while sucking away its blood? It lives mostly free, hunting its prey, clinging to it for a while, and is carried about by it. Closely related to the lampreys are the hag fishes, marine eel-like fishes that attach themselves by a sucker-like mouth to living fishes and gradually scrape and eat their way into the abdominal cavity of the host. These "hags" or "borers" approach more nearly to the condition of an internal parasite than any other vertebrate. And what about the flea? In its immature life it lives as a white grub or larva in the dust of cracks and crevices, of floors and cellars and heaps of débris; here it pupates, and finally changes into the active leaping blood-sucking adult which finds its way to the body of some mammal and clings there sucking blood. But it can jump off and hunt other prey; it leaves the host body entirely to lay its eggs, and yet it feeds as a parasite, at least it conforms to the definition of parasite in the essential fact of being carried about on or in the host body, while feeding at the host's expense. . . .

The bird lice which infest the bodies of all kinds of birds and are found especially abundant on domestic fowls, live upon the outside of the bodies of their hosts, feeding upon the feathers and dermal scales. They are examples of *external parasites*. Other examples are fleas and ticks, and the crustaceans called fish lice and whale lice, which are attached to marine animals. On the other hand, almost all animals are infested by certain parasitic worms which live in the alimentary canal, like the tapeworm, or imbedded in the muscles, like the trichina. These are examples of *internal parasites*. Such parasites belong mostly to the class of worms, and some of them are very injurious, sucking the blood from the tissues of the host, while others feed solely on the partly digested food. There are also parasites that live partly within and partly on the outside of the body, like the *Sacculina*, which lives on various kinds of crabs. The body of the *Sacculina* consists of a soft sac which lies on the outside of the crab's body, and of a number of long, slender rootlike processes which penetrate deeply into the crab's body, and take up nourishment from within. The *Sacculina* is itself a crustacean or crablike creature. The classification of parasites as external and internal is purely arbitrary, but it is often a matter of convenience.

Some parasites live for their whole lifetime on or in the body of the host, as is the case with the bird lice. Their eggs are laid on the feathers of the bird host; the young when hatched remain on the bird during growth and development, and the adults only rarely leave the body, usually never. These may be called *permanent parasites*. On the other hand, fleas leap off or on a dog apparently as caprice dictates; or, as in other cases, the parasite may pass some definite part of its life as a free nonparasitic organism, attaching itself, after development, to some animal, and remaining there for the rest of its life. These parasites may be called *temporary parasites*. But this grouping or classification, like that of the external and internal parasites, is simply a matter of convenience, and does not indicate at all any blood relationship among the members of any one group.

Some parasites are so specialized in habit and structure that they are wholly unable to go through their life history, or to maintain themselves, except in a single fixed way. They are dependent wholly on one particular kind of host, or on a particular series of hosts, part of their life being passed in one and another part in one or more other so-called intermediate hosts. These parasitic species are called *obligate parasites*, while others with less definite, more flexible requirements in regard to their mode of development and life are called *facultative parasites*. These latter may indeed be able to go through life as free-living, nonparasitic animals, although, with opportunity, they live parasitically.

In nearly all cases the body of a parasite is simpler in structure than the body of other animals which are closely related to the parasite—that is, animals that live parasitically have simpler bodies than animals that live free active lives, competing for food with the other animals about them. This simplicity is not primitive, but results from the loss or atrophy of the structures which the mode of life renders useless. Many parasites are attached firmly to their host, and do not move about. They have no need of the power of locomotion. They are carried by their host. Such parasites are usually without wings, legs, or other locomotory organs. Because they have given up locomotion they have no need of organs of orientation, those special sense organs like eyes and ears and feelers which serve to guide and direct the moving animal; and most nonlocomotory parasites will be found to have no eyes, nor any of the organs of special sense which are accessory to locomotion and which serve for the detection of food or of enemies. Because these important organs, which depend for their successful activity on a highly organized nervous system, are lacking, the nervous system of parasites is usually very simple and undeveloped. Again, because the parasite usually has for its sustenance the already digested highly nutritious food elaborated by its host, most parasites have a very simple alimentary canal, or even no alimentary canal at all. Finally, as the fixed parasite leads a wholly sedentary and inactive life, the breaking down and rebuilding of tissue in its body go on very slowly and in minimum degree, and there is no need of highly developed respiratory and circulatory organs, so that most fixed parasites have these systems of organs in simple condition. Altogether the body of a fixed, permanent parasite is so simplified and so wanting in all those special structures which characterize the higher, active, complex animals, that it often presents a very different appearance from those animals with which we know it to be nearly related.

The simplicity of parasites does not indicate that they belong to the groups of primitive simple animals. Parasitism is found in the whole range of animal life, from primitive to highest, although the vertebrate animals include very few parasites and these of little specialization of habit. But their simplicity is something that has resulted from their mode of life. It is the result of a change in the body structure which we can often trace in the development of the individual parasite. Many parasites in their young stages are free, active animals with a better or more complex body than they possess in their fully developed or adult stage. The simplicity of parasites is the result of degeneration—a degeneration that has been brought about by their adoption of a sedentary, non-competitive parasitic life. And this simplicity of degeneration, and the simplicity of primitiveness should be sharply distinguished. Animals that are primitively simple have had only simple ancestors; animals that are simple by degeneration often have had highly organized, complex ancestors. And while in the life history or development of a primitively simple animal all the young stages are simpler than the adult, in a degenerate animal the young stages may be, and usually are, more complex and more highly organized than the adult stage.

In the few examples of parasitism (selected from various animal groups) that are described in the following pages all these general statements are illustrated.

In the intestines of crayfishes, centipedes, and several kinds of insects may often be found certain one-celled animals (Protozoa) which are living as parasites. Their food, which they take into their minute body by absorption, is the intestinal fluid in which they lie. These parasitic Protozoa belong to the genus *Gregarina*. . . . There are, besides *Gregarina*, many other parasitic one-celled animals, several kinds living inside the cells of their host's body. Several kinds of these have been proved to be the causal agents of serious human diseases. Conspicuous among these are the minute parasitic Sporozoa which are the actual cause of the malarial and similar fevers that rack the human body in nearly all parts of the world. . . .

When a mosquito (at least of a certain kind) sucks blood from a malarial patient the blood parasites are of course taken in also and deposited in the stomach where digestion of the blood begins. Now when the zygotes [resting egg cells] are formed in the mosquito's stomach they do not remain lying in the stomach cavity but move to the wall of the stomach and partially penetrate it. As many as five hundred zygotes have been found in the stomach walls of a single mosquito. The zygote now increases rapidly in size, becoming a perceptible nodule on the outer side of the stomach wall, but soon its nucleus and protoplasm begin to break up by repeated division (the parts all being held together, however, in the wall of the zygote), and by the end of the twelfth or fourteenth day the zygote's protoplasm may have become divided into ten thousand minute sporozoites. The zygote wall now breaks down, thus releasing the thousands of active little sporozoites into the general body cavity of the mosquito. This cavity is filled with flowing blood plasm—insects do not have a closed but an almost completely open circulatory system—and swimming about in this plasm the sporozoites soon make their way forward and into the salivary glands of the mosquito. Now when the insect pierces a human being to suck blood, it injects a certain amount of salivary fluid into the wound (presumably to keep the blood from clotting at the puncture) and with this fluid go many of the sporozoites. Thus a new infection of malaria is made. The sporozoites may lie in the salivary glands for several weeks, and so for the whole time from twelve to fourteen days after the mosquito has become infected with the malarial parasite by sucking blood from a malarial patient until the sporozoites in the salivary glands finally die, it is a means of the dissemination of the disease. There can be no malaria without mosquitoes to propagate and disseminate it, and yet no mosquitoes can propagate and disseminate malaria without having access to malarial patients. . . .

In the great branch or phylum of flatworms, that group of animals which of all the principal animal groups is widest in its distribution, perhaps a majority of the species are parasites. Instead of being the exception, the parasitic life is the rule among these worms. Of the three classes into which the flatworms are divided, almost all of the members of two of the classes are parasites. The common tapeworm, which lives parasitically in the intestine of man, is a good example of one of these classes. It has the form of a narrow ribbon, which may attain the length of several yards, attached at one end to the wall of the intestine, the remainder hanging freely in the interior. Its body is composed of segments or serially arranged parts, of which there are about eight hundred and fifty altogether. It has no mouth nor alimentary canal. It feeds simply by absorbing into its body, through the surface, the nutritious, already digested liquid food in the intestine. There are no eyes nor other special sense organs, nor any organs of locomotion. The body is very degenerate. The life history of the tapeworm is interesting, because of the necessity of two hosts for its completion. The eggs of the tapeworm pass from the intestine with the excreta, and must be taken into the body of some other animal in order to develop. In the case of one of the several species of tapeworms that infest man, this other host must be the pig. In the alimentary canal of the pig the young tapeworm develops and later bores its way through the walls of the canal and becomes imbedded in the muscles. There it lies, until it finds its way into the alimentary canal of man by his eating the flesh of the pig. In the intestine of man the tapeworm continues to develop until it becomes full grown. . . .

Another group of animals, many of whose members are parasites, are the roundworms or threadworms. The free-living roundworms are active, well-organized animals, but the parasitic kinds all show a greater or less degree of degeneration. One of the most terrible parasites of man is a roundworm called *Trichina spiralis*. It is a minute worm, from one to three millimeters long, which in its adult condition lives in the intestine of man or of the pig or other mammals. The young are born alive and bore through the walls of the intestine. They migrate to the voluntary muscles of the hosts, especially those of the limbs and back, and here each worm coils itself up in a muscle fiber and becomes inclosed in a spindle-shaped cyst or cell. A single muscle may be infested by hundreds of thousands of these minute worms. It has been estimated that fully one hundred million encysted worms may exist in the muscles of a "trichinized" human body. The muscles undergo more or less degeneration, and the death of the host may occur. It is necessary, for the further development of the worms, that the flesh of the host be eaten by another mammal, as the flesh of the pig by man, or the flesh of man by a pig or rat. The *Trichinæ* in the alimentary canal of the new host develop into active adult worms and produce new young.

In the Yellowstone Lake the trout are infested by the larvæ or young of a roundworm which reach a length of twenty inches, and which are often found stitched, as it were, through the viscera and the muscles of the fish. The infested trout become feeble and die, or are eaten by the pelicans which fish in this lake. In the alimentary canal of the pelican the worms become adult, and parts of the worms containing eggs escape from the alimentary canal with the excreta. These portions of worms are eaten by the trout, and the eggs give birth to new worms which develop in the bodies of the fish with disastrous effects. It is estimated that for each pelican in Yellowstone Lake over five million eggs of the parasitic worms are discharged into the lake.

The young of various carnivorous animals are often infested by one of the species of roundworms called "pup worms." Recent investigations show that thousands of the young or pup fur seals are destroyed each year by these parasites. The eggs of the worm lie through the winter in the sands of the breeding grounds of the fur seal. The young receive them from the fur of the mother and the worm develops in the upper intestine. It feeds on the blood of the young seal, which finally dies from anæmia. On the sand beaches of the seal islands in Bering Sea there are every year thousands of dead seal pups which have been killed by this parasite. On the rocky rookeries, the young seals are not affected by this parasite.

Among the more highly organized animals the results of a parasitic life, in degree of structural degeneration, can be more readily seen. A well-known parasite, belonging to the Crustacea—the class of shrimps, crabs, lobsters, and crayfishes—is *Sacculina*. The young *Sacculina* is an active, free-swimming larva much like a young prawn or young crab. But the adult bears absolutely no resemblance to such a typical crustacean as a crayfish or crab. The *Sacculina* after a short period of independent existence attaches itself to the abdomen of a crab, and there completes its development while living as a parasite. In its adult condition it is simply a great tumorlike sac, bearing many delicate rootlike suckers which penetrate the body of the crab host and absorb nutriment. The *Sacculina* has no eyes, no mouth parts, no legs, or other appendages, and hardly any of the usual organs except reproductive organs.

Other parasitic crustacea, as the numerous kinds of fish lice which live attached to the gills or to other parts of fish, and derive all their nutriment from the body of the fish, show various degrees of degeneration. With some of these fish lice the female, which looks like a puffed-out worm, is attached to the fish or other aquatic animal, while the male, which is perhaps only a tenth of the size of the female, is permanently attached to the female, living parasitically on her.

Among the insects there are many kinds that live parasitically for part of their lives, and not a few that live as parasites for their whole lives. The true sucking lice and the bird lice live for their whole lives as external parasites on the bodies of their host, but they are not fixed— that is, they retain their legs and power of locomotion, although they have lost their wings through degeneration. The eggs of the lice are deposited on the hair of the mammal or bird that serves as host; the young hatch and immediately begin to live as parasites, either sucking the blood or feeding on the hair or feathers of the host. . . . The ichneumon flies are parasites of other insects, especially of the larvæ of beetles and moths and butterflies. In fact, the ichneumon flies do more to keep in check the increase of injurious and destructive caterpillars than do all our artificial remedies for these insect pests. . . .

One of the most remarkable ichneumon flies is *Thalessa*, which has a very long, slender, flexible ovipositor, or egg-laying organ. An insect known as the pigeon horntail deposits its eggs, by means of a strong, piercing ovipositor, half an inch deep in the trunk wood of growing tree. The young or larval pigeon horntail is a soft-bodied white grub, which bores deeply into the trunk of the tree, filling up the burrow behind it with small chips. The *Thalessa* is a parasite of the pigeon horntail, and "when a female *Thalessa* finds a tree infested by the pigeon horntail, she selects a place which she judges is opposite a pigeon horntail burrow, and, elevating her long ovipositor in a loop over her back, with its tip on the bark of the tree, she makes a derrick out of her body and proceeds with great skill and precision to drill a hole into the tree. When the pigeon horntail burrow is reached she deposits an egg in it. The larva that hatches from this egg creeps along this burrow until it reaches its victim, and then fastens itself to the horntail larva, which it destroys by sucking its blood. The larva of *Thalessa*, when full grown, changes to a pupa within the burrow of its host, and the adult gnaws a hole out through the bark if it does not find the hole already made by the pigeon horntail."

. . . Almost all of the mites and ticks, animals allied to the spiders, live parasitically. Most of them live as external parasites, sucking the blood of their host, but some live underneath the skin like the itch mites, which cause, in man, the disease known as the itch.

Among the vertebrate animals there are not many examples of true parasitism. The hagfishes or borers have been already mentioned. These are long and cylindrical, eel-like creatures, very slimy and very low in structure. The mouth is without jaws, but forms a sucking disk, by which the hagfish attaches itself to the body of some other fish. By means of the rasping teeth on its tongue, it makes a round hole through the skin, usually at the throat. It then devours all the muscular substance of the fish, leaving the viscera untouched. When the fish finally dies it is a mere hulk of skin, scales, bones, and viscera, nearly all the muscle being gone. Then the hagfish slips out and attacks another individual.

The lamprey, another low fish, in similar fashion feeds leechlike on the blood of other fishes, which it obtains by lacerating the flesh with its rasp-like teeth, remaining attached by the round sucking disk of its mouth.

Certain birds, as the cowbird and the European cuckoo, have a parasitic habit, laying their eggs in the nests of other birds, leaving their young to be hatched and reared by their unwilling hosts.

We may also note that parasitism and consequent structural degeneration are not at all confined to animals. Many plants are parasites and show marked degenerative characteristics. The dodder is a familiar example, clinging to living green plants and thrusting its haustoria or rootlike suckers into their tissue to draw from them already elaborated nutritive sap. Many fungi like the rusts of cereals, the mildew of roses, etc., are parasitic. Numerous plants, too, are parasites, not on other plants, but on animals. Among these are the hosts of bacteria (simplest of the one-celled plants) that swarm in the tissues of all animals, some of which are causal agents of some of the worst of human and animal diseases (as typhoid fever, diphtheria, and cholera in man, anthrax in cattle). There are also many more highly organized fungi that live in and on the bodies of insects, often killing them by myriads. One of the great checks to the ravages of the corn- and wheat-infesting chinch bug of the Mississippi Valley is a parasitic fungus. In the autumn, house flies may often be seen dead against a windowpane surrounded by a delicate ring or halo of white. This ring is composed of spores of a fungus which has grown through all the tissues of the fly while alive, finally resulting in its death. The spores serve to inoculate other flies that may come near.

Just as in animals, so in plants; parasitic kinds, especially among the higher groups as the flowering plants, often show marked degeneration. Leaves may be reduced to mere scales, roots are lost, and the water-conducting tissues greatly reduced. This degeneration in plants naturally affects primarily those parts which in the normal plant are devoted to the gathering and elaboration of inorganic food materials, namely, the leaves and stems and roots. The flowers or reproductive organs usually retain, in parasites, all of their high development.

While parasitism is the principal cause of degeneration of animals, other causes may be also concerned. Fixed animals or animals leading inactive or sedentary lives, also become degenerate, even when no parasitism is concerned. . . .

A barnacle is an example of degeneration through quiescence. The barnacles are crustaceans related most nearly to the crabs and shrimps. The young barnacle just from the egg is six-legged, free-swimming, much like a young prawn or crab, with single eye. In its next larval stage it has six pairs of swimming feet, two compound eyes, and two large antennæ or feelers, and still lives an independent, free-swimming life. When it makes its final change to the adult condition, it attaches itself to some stone or shell, or pile or ship's bottom, loses its compound eyes and feelers, develops a protecting shell, and gives up all power of locomotion. Its swimming feet become changed into grasping organs, and it loses most of its outward resemblances to the other members of its class.

Certain insects live sedentary or fixed lives. All the members of the family of scale insects, in one sex at least, show degeneration that has been caused by quiescence. One of these, called the red orange scale, is very abundant in Florida and California and in other orange-growing regions. The male is a beautiful, tiny, two-winged midge, but the female is a wingless, footless little sac without eyes or other organs of special sense, and lies motionless under a flat, thin, circular, reddish scale composed of wax and two or three cast skins of the insect itself. The insect has a long, slender, flexible, sucking beak, which is thrust into the leaf or stem or fruit of the orange on which the "scale bug" lives and through which the insect sucks the orange sap, which is its only food. It lays eggs or gives birth to young under its body, under the protecting wax scale, and dies. From the eggs hatch active little larval scale bugs with eyes and feelers and six legs. They crawl from under the wax scale and roam about over the orange tree. Finally, they settle down, thrust their sucking beak into the plant tissues, and cast their skin. The females lose at this molt their legs and eyes and feelers. Each becomes a mere motion-less sac capable only of sucking up sap and of laying eggs. The young males, however, lose their sucking beak and can no longer take food, but they gain a pair of wings and an additional pair of eyes. They fly about and fertilize the saclike females, which then molt again and secrete the thin wax scale over them.

. . . Loss of certain organs may occur through other causes than para-sitism and a fixed life. Many insects live but a short time in their adult stage. May flies live for but a few hours or, at most, a few days. They do not need to take food to sustain life for so short a time, and so their mouth parts have become rudimentary and functionless or are entirely lost. This is true of some moths and numerous other specially short-lived insects. Among the social insects the workers of the termites and of the true ants are wingless, although they are born of winged parents, and are descendants of winged ancestors. The modification of structure de-pendent upon the division of labor among the individuals of the com-munity has taken the form, in the case of the workers, of a degeneration in the loss of the wings. Insects that live in caves are mostly blind; they have lost the eyes, whose function could not be exercised in the darkness of the cave. Certain island-inhabiting insects have lost their wings, flight being attended with too much danger. The strong sea breezes may at any time carry a flying insect off the small island to sea. Probably only those which do not fly much survive, and so by natural selection wingless breeds or species are produced. Finally, the body may be modified in color and shape so as to resemble some part of the environment, and thus the animal may be unperceived by its enemies.

When we say that a parasitic or quiescent mode of life leads to or causes degeneration, we have explained the stimulus or the ultimate rea-son for the degenerative changes, but we have not shown just how parasitism or quiescence actually produces these changes. Degeneration or the atrophy and disappearance of organs or parts of a body is often said to be due to disuse. That is, the disuse of a part is believed by many naturalists to be the sufficient cause for its gradual dwindling and final loss. That disuse can so affect parts of a body during the lifetime of an individual is true. A muscle unused becomes soft and flabby and small. Whether the effects of such disuse can be inherited, however, is open to serious doubt. . . . If not, some other immediate cause, or some other cause along with disuse, must be found.

We are accustomed, perhaps, to think of degeneration as necessarily implying a disadvantage in life. A degenerate animal is considered to be not the equal of a nondegenerate animal, and this would be true if both kinds of animals had to face the same conditions of life. The blind, foot-less, simple, degenerate animal could not cope with the active, keen-sighted, highly organized nondegenerate in free competition. But free competition is exactly what the degenerate animal has nothing to do with. Certainly the *Sacculina* lives successfully; it is well adapted for its own peculiar kind of life. For the life of a scale insect, no better type of structure could be devised. A parasite enjoys certain obvious advantages in life, and even extreme degeneration is no drawback, but rather favors it in the advantageousness of its sheltered and easy life. As long as the host is successful in eluding its enemies and avoiding accident and injury, the parasite is safe. It needs to exercise no activity or vigilance of its own; its life is easy as long as its host lives. But the disadvantages of parasitism and degeneration are apparent also. The fate of the parasite is usually bound up with the fate of the host. When the enemy of the host crab prevails, the *Sacculina* goes down without a chance to struggle in its own defense. But far more important than the disadvantage in such particular or individual cases is the disadvantage of the fact that the parasite cannot adapt itself in any considerable degree to new conditions. It has become so specialized, so greatly modified and changed to adapt itself to the one set of conditions under which it now lives, it has gone so far in its giving up of organs and body parts, that if present conditions should change and new ones come to exist, the parasite could not adapt itself to them. The independent, active animal with all its organs and all its functions intact, holds itself, one may say, ready and able to adapt itself to any new conditions of life which may gradually come into exist-ence. The parasite has risked everything for the sake of a sure and easy life under the presently existing conditions. Change of conditions means its extinction.

1908

Flowering Earth

DONALD CULROSS PEATTIE

From *Flowering Earth*

CHLOROPHYLL: THE SUN TRAP

WHAT WE LOVE, WHEN ON A SUMMER DAY WE STEP into the coolness of a wood, is that its boughs close up behind us. We are escaped, into another room of life. The wood does not live as we live, restless and running, panting after flesh, and even in sleep tossing with fears. It is aloof from thoughts and instincts; it responds, but only to the sun and wind, the rock and the stream—never, though you shout yourself hoarse, to propaganda, temptation, reproach, or promises. You cannot mount a rock and preach to a tree how it shall attain the kingdom of heaven. It is already closer to it, up there, than you will grow to be. And you cannot make it see the light, since in the tree's sense you are blind. You have nothing to bring it, for all the forest is self-sufficient; if you burn it, cut, hack through it with a blade, it angrily repairs the swathe with thorns and weeds and fierce suckers. Later there are good green leaves again, toiling, adjusting, breathing—forgetting you.

For this green living is the world's primal industry; yet it makes no roar. Waving its banners, it marches across the earth and the ages, without dust around its columns. I do not hold that all of that life is pretty; it is not, in purpose, sprung for us, and moves under no compulsion to please. If ever you fought with thistles, or tried to pull up a cattail's matted rootstocks, you will know how plants cling to their own lives and defy you. The pond-scums gather in the cistern, frothing and buoyed with their own gases; the storm waves fling at your feet upon the beach the limp sea-lettuce wrenched from its submarine hold—reminder that there too, where the light is filtered and refracted, there is life still to intercept and net and by it proliferate. Inland from the shore I look and see the coastal ranges clothed in chaparral—dense shrubbery and scrubbery, close-fisted, intricately branched, suffocating the rash rambler in the noon heat with

337

its pungency. Beyond, on the deserts, under a fierce sky, between the harsh lunar ranges of unweathered rock, life still, somehow, fights its way through the year, with thorn and succulent cell and indomitable root.

Between such embattled life and the Forest of Arden, with its ancient beeches and enchanter's nightshade, there is no great biologic difference. Each lives by the cool and cleanly and most commendable virtue of being green. And though that is not biological language, it is the whole story in two words. So that we ought not speak of getting at the root of a matter, but of going back to the leaf of things. The orator who knows the way to the country's salvation and does not know that the breath of life he draws was blown into his nostrils by green leaves, had better spare his breath. And before anyone builds a new state upon the industrial prole-tariat, he will be wisely cautioned to discover that the source of all wealth is the peasantry of grass.

The reason for these assertions—which I do not make for metaphorical effect but maintain quite literally—is that the green leaf pigment, called chlorophyll, is the one link between the sun and life; it is the conduit of perpetual energy to our own frail organisms.

For inert and inorganic elements—water and carbon dioxide of the air, the same that we breathe out as a waste—chlorophyll can synthesize with the energy of sunlight. Every day, every hour of all the ages, as each continent and, equally important, each ocean rolls into sunlight, chlorophyll ceaselessly creates. Not figuratively, but literally, in the grand First Chapter Genesis style. One instant there are a gas and water, as lifeless as the core of earth or the chill of space; and the next they are become living tissue—mortal yet genitive, progenitive, resilient with all the dewy adaptability of flesh, ever changing in order to stabilize some unchanging ideal of form. Life, in short, synthesized, plant-synthesized, light-synthesized. Botanists say photosynthesized. So that the post-Biblical synthesis of life is already a fact. Only when man has done as much, may he call himself the equal of a weed.

Plant life sustains the living world; more precisely, chlorophyll does so, and where, in the vegetable kingdom, there is not chlorophyll or some-thing closely like it, then that plant or cell is a parasite—no better, in vital economy, than a mere animal or man. Blood, bone and sinew, all flesh is grass. Grass to mutton, mutton to wool, wool to the coat on my back— it runs like one of those cumulative nursery rhymes, the wealth and diversity of our material life accumulating from the primal fact of chloro-phyll's activity. The roof of my house, the snapping logs upon the hearth, the desk where I write, are my imports from the plant kingdom.

But the whole of modern civilization is based upon a whirlwind spending of the plant wealth long ago and very slowly accumulated. For, fundamentally, and away back, coal and oil, gasoline and illuminating gas had green origins too. With the exception of a small amount of water power, a still smaller of wind and tidal mills, the vast machinery of our complex living is driven only by these stores of plant energy.

We, then, the animals, consume those stores in our restless living. Serenely the plants amass them. They turn light's active energy to food, which is potential energy stored for their own benefit. Only if the daisy is browsed by the cow, the maple leaf sucked of its juices by an insect, will that green leaf become of our kind. So we get the song of a bird at dawn, the speed in the hoofs of the fleeing deer, the noble thought in the philosopher's mind. So Plato's Republic was builded on leeks and cabbages.

Animal life lives always in the red; the favorable balance is written on the other side of life's page, and it is written in chlorophyll. All else obeys the thermodynamic law that energy forever runs down hill, is lost and degraded. In economic language, this is the law of diminishing returns, and it is obeyed by the cooling stars as by man and all the animals. They float down its Lethe stream. Only chlorophyll fights up against the current. It is the stuff in life that rebels at death, that has never surrendered to entropy, final icy stagnation. It is the mere cobweb on which we are all suspended over the abyss.

And what then is this substance which is not itself alive but is made by life and makes life, and is never found apart from life?

I remember the first time I ever held it, in the historic dimness of the old Agassiz laboratories, pure, in my hands. My teacher was an owl-eyed master, with a chuckling sense of humor, who had been trained in the greatest laboratory in Germany, and he believed in doing the great things first. So on the first day of his course he set us to extracting chlorophyll, and I remember that his eyes blinked amusement behind his glasses, because when he told us all to go and collect green leaves and most went all the way to the Yard for grass, I opened the window and stole from a vine upon the wall a handful of Harvard's sacred ivy.

We worked in pairs, and my fellow student was a great-grand-nephew or something of the sort, of Elias Fries, the founder of the study of fungi. Together we boiled the ivy leaves, then thrust them in alcohol. After a while it was the leaves which were colorless while the alcohol had become green. We had to dilute this extract with water, and then we added benzol, because this will take the chlorophyll away from the alcohol which, for its part, very conveniently retains the yellow pigments also found in leaves. This left us with a now yellowish alcohol and, floating on top of it, a thick green benzol; you could simply decant the latter carefully off into a test tube, and there you had chlorophyll extract, opaque, trembling, heavy, a little viscous and oily, and smelling, but much too rankly, like a lawn-mower's blades after a battle with rainy grass.

Then, in a darkened room where beams from a spectroscope escaped in painful darts of light as from the cracks in an old-fashioned magic lantern, we peered at our extracted chlorophyll through prisms. Just as in a crystal chandelier the sunlight is shattered to a rainbow, so in the spectroscope light is spread out in colored bands—a long narrow ribbon, sorting the white light by wave lengths into its elemental parts. And the widths, the presence or the absence, of each cross-band on the ribbon, tell the tale of a chemical element present in the spectrum, much as the bands on a soldier's insignial ribbon show service in Asia, in the tropics, on the border, in what wars. When the astronomer has fixed spectroscope instead of telescope upon a distant star, he reads off the color bands as easily as one soldier reads another's, and will tell you whether sodium or oxygen, helium or iron is present.

Just so our chlorophyll revealed its secrets. The violet and blue end of the spectrum was almost completely blacked out. And that meant that chlorophyll absorbed and used these high-frequency waves. So, too, the red and orange were largely obliterated, over at the right hand side of our tell-tale bar. It was the green that came through clearly. So we call plants green because they use that color least. It is what they reject as fast as it smites the upper cells; it is what they turn back, reflect, flash into our grateful retinas.

It was only routine in a young botanist's training to make an extraction and spectrum analysis of chlorophyll. My student friends over in the chemistry laboratories were more excited than I about it. They were working under Conant, before he became president of Harvard and had to sneak into his old laboratory at night with a key he still keeps. For chlorophyll was Conant's own problem. His diagram of its structure, displayed to me by his students, was closely worked over with symbols and signs, unfolded to something like the dimensions of a blue print of Boulder Dam, and made clear—to anyone who could understand it!— how the atoms are arranged and deployed and linked in such a tremendous molecule as $MgN_4C_{55}H_{72}O_5$.

To Otto and Alfred and Mort every jot and joint in the vast Rube Goldberg machinery of that structural formula had meaning, and more than meaning—the geometrical beauty of the one right, inevitable position for every atom. To me, a botanist's apprentice, a future naturalist, there was just one fact to quicken the pulse. That fact is the close similarity between chlorophyll and hemoglobin, the essence of our blood.

So that you may lay your hand upon the smooth flank of a beech and say, "We be of one blood, brother, thou and I."

The one significant difference in the two structural formulas is this: that the hub of every hemoglobin molecule is one atom of iron, while in chlorophyll it is one atom of magnesium.

Iron is strong and heavy, clamorous when struck, avid of oxygen and capable of corruption. It does not surprise us by its presence in our blood stream. Magnesium is a light, silvery, unresonant metal; its density is only one seventh that of iron, it has half of iron's molecular weight, and melts at half the temperature. It is rustless, ductile and pliant; it burns with a brilliant white light rich in actinic rays, and is widely distributed through the upper soil, but only, save at mineral springs, in dainty quantities. Yet the plant succeeds always in finding that mere trace that it needs, even when a chemist might fail to detect it.

How does the chlorophyll, green old alchemist that it is, transmute the dross of earth into living tissue? its hand is swifter than the chemist's most sensitive analyses. In theory, the step from water and carbon dioxide to the formation of sugar (the first result readily discerned) must involve several syntheses; yet it goes on in a split hundredth of a second. One sunlight particle or photon strikes the chlorophyll, and instantaneously the terribly tenacious molecule of water, which we break down into its units of hydrogen and oxygen only with difficulty and expense, is torn apart; so too is the carbon dioxide molecule. Building blocks of the three elements, carbon, hydrogen and oxygen, are then whipped at lightning speed into carbonic acid; this is instantly changed over into formic acid— the same that smarts so in our nerve endings when an ant stings us. No sooner formed than formic acid becomes formaldehyde and hydrogen peroxide. This last is poisonous, but a ready enzyme in the plant probably splits it as fast as it is born into harmless water and oxygen, while the formaldehyde is knocked at top speed into a new pattern—and is grape sugar, glucose. And all before you can say Albert Einstein. Indeed, by the time you have said Theophrastus Bombastus Aureolus Paracelsus von Hohenheim, the sugar may have lost a modicum of water—and turned into starch, the first product of photosynthesis that could be detected by the methods of fifty years ago.

At this very instant, with the sun delivering to its child the earth, in the bludgeoning language of mathematics, 215×10^{15} calories per second, photosynthesis is racing along wherever the leaf can reach the light. (All else goes to waste.) True, its efficiency is very low—averaging no better than one per cent, while our machines are delivering up to twenty-five per cent of the fuel they combust. But that which they burn—coal and gas, oils and wood—was made, once, by leaves in ancient geologic times. The store of such energy is strictly finite. Chlorophyll alone is hitched to what is, for earthly purposes, the infinite.

Light, in the latest theory, is not waves in a sea of ether, or a jet from a nozzle; it could be compared rather to machine gun fire, every photo-electric bullet of energy traveling in regular rhythm, at a speed that bridges the astronomical gap in eight minutes. As each bullet hits an electron of chlorophyll it sets it to vibrating, at its own rate, just as one tuning fork, when struck, will cause another to hum in the same pitch. A bullet strikes—and one electron is knocked galley west into a dervish dance like the madness of the atoms in the sun. The energy splits open chlorophyll molecules, recombines their atoms, and lies there, dormant, in foods.

The process seems miraculously adjusted. And yet, like most living processes, it is not perfect. The reaction time of chlorophyll is not geared as high as the arrival of the light-bullets. Light comes too fast; plants, which are the very children of light, can get too much of it. Exposure to the sunlight on the Mojave desert is something that not a plant in my garden, no, nor even the wiry brush in the chaparral, could endure. Lids against the light plants do not have; but by torsions of the stalk some leaves may turn their blades edge-on to dazzling radiation, and present them again broadside in failing light. Within others the chlorophyll granules too, bun or pellet-shaped as they are, can roll for a side or frontal exposure toward the light. In others they can crowd to the top of a cell and catch faint rays, or sink or flee to the sides to escape a searing blast . . . .

When I began to write these pages, before breakfast, the little fig tree outside my window was rejoicing in the early morning light. It is a special familiar of my work, a young tree that has never yet borne fruit. It is but a little taller than I, has only two main branches and forty-three twigs, and the brave if not impressive sum of two hundred and sixteen leaves—I have touched every one with a counting finger. Though sparse, they are large, mitten-shaped, richly green with chlorophyll. I compute, by measuring the leaf and counting both sides, that my little tree has a leaf surface of about eighty-four square feet. This sun-trap was at work today long before I.

Those uplifted hand-like leaves caught the first sky light. It was poor for the fig's purpose, but plant work begins from a nocturnal zero. When I came to my desk the sun was full upon those leaves—and it is a wondrous thing how they are disposed so that they do not shade each other. By the blazing California noon, labor in the leaves must have faltered from very excess of light; all the still golden afternoon it went on; now as the sun sets behind a sea fog the little fig slackens peacefully at its task.

Yet in the course of a day it has made sugar for immediate burning and energy release, put by a store of starch for future use; with the addition of nitrogen and other salts brought up in water from the roots it has built proteins too—the very bricks and mortar of the living protoplasm, and the perdurable stuff of permanent tissue. The annual growth ring in the wood of stem and twigs has widened an infinitesimal but a real degree. The fig is one day nearer to its coming of age, to flowering and fruiting. Then, still leafing out each spring, still toiling in the sunlight that I shall not be here to see, it may go on a century and more, growing eccentric, solidifying whimsies, becoming a friend to generations. It will be "the old fig" then. And at last it may give up the very exertion of bearing. It will lean tough elbows in the garden walks, and gardeners yet unborn will scold it and put up with it. But still it will leaf out till it dies.

Dusk is here now. So I switch on the lamp beside my desk. The power-house burns its hoarded tons of coal a week, and gives us this instant and most marvelous current. But that light is not new. It was hurled out of the sun two hundred million years ago, and was captured by the leaves of the Carboniferous tree-fern forests, fell with the falling plant, was buried, fossilized, dug up and resurrected. It is the same light. And, in my little fig tree as in the ancient ferns, it is the same unchanging green stuff from age to age, passed without perceptible improvement from evolving plant to plant. What it is and does, so complex upon examination, lies about us tranquil and simple, with the simplicity of a miracle.

THE SEEDS OF LIFE

This earth, this third planet from the sun, was lifeless once. The rocks tell that much. There is one place in the world where the complete record is written on a single stone tablet. The Grand Canyon of the Colorado River is a cross section of geologic time. Cut by a master hand, the testimony appears to our eyes marvelously magnified. The strata burn with their intense elemental colors; they are defined as sharply as chapters, and the book is flung wide open. A silver thread of river underscores the bottom-most line, the dark Vishnu schist where no life ever was.

Mother-rock, these lowest strata are aboriginal stuff. They are without a fossil, without a trace of the great detritus of living, the shells and shards, the chalky or metallic excreta of harsh, primitive existence. These pre-life eras have been past for a long time—two billion years, perhaps. Perhaps a little more. Astronomical sums of time are so great that they bankrupt the imagination. We listen to the geologists and physicists wrangling over their accounts and compounding vast historical debts with the relish of usurers, but it is all one to us after the first million years.

No matter here how they arrived at their calculations. As plantsmen we are interested in the moment when the first plant began. For there was raised the flag of life.

The first life on earth—I have no doubt of it—was plant life. Any organism that could exist upon a naked planet would have to be completely self-supporting. It would have to be such a being as could absorb raw, elemental materials and, using inorganic sources of energy, make living protoplasm of them. Such describes no animal. But it perfectly describes an autotrophic plant. An autotroph is a self-sustaining vital mechanism.

The geologist's picture of the younger stages of this our agreeable planet home resembles the Apocalyptic doom for the world that I once heard predicted to innocents in a Presbyterian Sunday School. For the geologist sees flaming jets of incandescent gas, bolts and flashes that, condensing as they cooled, became a swarm of planetesimals, fragments comparable to great meteoric masses of stone and metal. These, by all the rules of orthodox astronomy, must rush together whenever their orbits came too close. So, by shocking impacts, the world was slapped together at random. It grew snowball fashion. It probably grew hotter, rather than cooler, from the friction and energy of the collisions, and the increasing pressure on the core must have generated a heat to melt the heart of a stone. So, in a molten state, the heaviest elements sank to the gravitational center, and formed the lithosphere—terra firma itself—while the lightest rose to become the atmosphere.

That atmosphere, it is presumed, was far, far thicker than it is today. It was perhaps hundreds of miles high, and may have had an abundance of now rare gases, like helium and hydrogen, neon and argon, and possibly even very poisonous gases, sulphur-drenched vapors, deadly combinations of carbon with oxygen, of oxygen with nitrogen. Almost certainly there was much less free oxygen and free nitrogen and carbon dioxide, than now, and correspondingly little scope for life as we know it.

But dense mists of water vapor, of steam clouds forever moiling and trailing about the stony little sphere, there must have been. For the oceans were, presumably, all up in the air. Only with cooling they began to condense, to fail in century-long cloudbursts, filling the deeps and hollows. At first, perhaps, striking hot rock, they were immediately turned to hissing steam again. The stabilization of the oceans alone must have been an awesomely long affair. It is doubtful if any sunlight at all got through that veil of primordial cloud, and the earth, viewed from Mars, would have been as unsatisfactory as Venus seen from the earth today, for the clouds of Venus never lift. Darkness then, darkness over the peaks clawed by the fingers of the deluge and dragged into the oceans; darkness over the forming seas that were not salty and full of an abundant and massive life, but fresh water, like that of the present Great Lakes. Fresh, and empty of life, warm, and dark. Darkness, and warmth, and water. Dark and warm as the womb, and awash with an amniotic fluid.

And into this uterine sea fell the seeds of life.

The oldest fossils in the oldest of all fossil-bearing rocks, the Archaeozoic, tell six unmistakable things:

The first organisms of which there is any record on the stone tablets of time were cellular, just like all modern organisms.

They were aquatic, like all the most primitive organisms.

They were plants, unmistakably.

They were microscopic.

And they were bacteria.

Of course these were bacteria of a very special sort. Not in the least like the germs that cause diseases of man or those useful scavengers, saprophytes, that break up dead plant and animal remains and excreta. For these dread parasites and vulturine saprophytes are finicking and highly specialized. The parasites are hothouse species, most of them unable to endure more than a few hours outside very modern and complex bodies; even the saprophytes imply the presence of higher organisms to feed on. Not one is an autotroph. Not one sustains itself.

No, the kind of bacteria that left their marks upon the ineradicable record is a sort never studied by medicine. They are autotrophs, sufficient unto themselves. They invade no living bodies; they are probably not related at all to those which do, and if one kind is bacteria, the other ought really to have a clear name of its own. But there is no other common English name for them; botanists call everything "bacteria" which is so small that very little structure can be discerned.

One at least of these autotrophic bacteria that lived in the dark, hot, fresh-water ocean, was the selfsame plant that is found today in mineral springs heavily charged with iron, in old wells driven through hardpan, in those rusty or tannic-looking brooks that seep away from stagnant bogs, where bog iron ore is gathering. Its name is Leptothrix. The Archaeozoic rocks are about one billion years old. In all that time the ochre Leptothrix has not changed one atom. As it reproduces simply by fission—the splitting of one bacterial cell into two—it has never died. It is, in body, immortal, and may outlive all other races.

The place to look for Leptothrix is around a mineral spring. On the rocks, in little nubbly reefs, in the brooks running from the springs, there waves a yellowish-rusty slime. This has a greasy feeling to the fingers; it rubs away instantly to nothing. But when you tease a little out in a drop of water, and shove the drop, on its clean glass slide, under the lens, the slime comes to life. For besides a great deal of shapeless rusty blobs and cobwebs, there are imbedded in this mass long unpartitioned filaments or tubes. They look a bit like root hairs under low magnification, and are surrounded by a nimbus of slime.

But the walls of the filament are absolutely definite; they proclaim organization, clear-cut form, something with the shape that only the living take on. And those walls of the filaments are of iron, deposited around the living bacterial cells by accretion.

As for the bacterial cells themselves, they are elliptical bodies, but remarkable for having "tails." So, placed end to end, they look like pollywogs packed into a boy's pea shooter. When overcrowded, some of the bacteria escape. Then by their lashing polar tails they swim free, just like a sperm cell of a seaweed or a mammal. Soon a fresh deposit of iron settles around them. As it lengthens, daughter cells come to fill it, by fission of the mother-cell.

Actual living Leptothrix colonies fully charged with active bacteria are not especially easy to find. Often one hunts for hours on bacterial slides, encountering only empty sheaths. But their fossil imprint is particularly sharp and unmistakable. And the sheaths, being iron, and not living matter subject to decay, have long lasting powers. Thus in the iron-charged waters that overlay some of the most ancient of rocks, Leptothrix flourished for countless dark ages, slowly, slowly dropping the detritus of its outworn shards, building up an ooze that, under the terrific pressure of the water above, became iron ore.

But how, it is right to ask, was Leptothrix able to live without photosynthesis? How was it nurtured in a water that contained few or none of sea water's rich salts of today, but only a bitter diet of iron compounds?

Leptothrix lived then, as it does today, by oxidizing iron. When we oxidize carbon (burn coal) we release enough energy to turn all the mills of the world. When oxygen rushes into the lungs of an asphyxiated man, his anemic blood is refreshed; his eyelids flutter, he comes to life. Life is one vast oxidation, one breathing and burning. Man and his beasts are fueled by the plants; the plants consume the earth stuff they built up by their green sun-power; but Leptothrix, aboriginal, microscopic Leptothrix, taps atomic energy. It literally eats iron.

Such is chemosynthesis, contrasted with photosynthesis. In a darkened world of water, chemosynthesis was then the only possible synthesis—or assembling of materials into life—and how effective it was for how long can be judged from the work of Leptothrix in the waters that once rolled above the Mesabi range, north of Lake Superior. This iron seam, believed to be largely the work of iron bacteria depositing a subterranean reef, is called by engineers simply "The Range," for beside it there is no other comparable. It is the range of all iron ranges, and so great and so heavy is the ore yearly moved out of it, that the locks of the Sault canal, though open only six or seven months of the year, and having a traffic deeply loaded only on the out voyage, transmit more tonnage than any other canal in the world, excepting none. . . .

Others of these element-consuming bacteria oxidize carbon or hydrogen or nitrogen or ammonia or marsh gas. When they combust this last, then the will-o'-the-wisp dances over the bogs. Still another has manganese for its staff of life. Manganese, by the way, is an alloy of the steel used to burglar-proof safes. But it is no proof against the microscopic, hard-headed Cladothrix. Variously we are being used or served by these masters of a fundamental and simple way of life, the autotrophic bacteria. Some of them have holdfasts, like a kelp or rooted waterweed, so that instead of floating at random, they can grow forest-wise in the waters they inhabit. These enter water pipes and vegetate there, like some flaccid but indomitable eel-grass in a stream, till the pipes are wholly stopped.

Of the bacterial autotrophs one you may smell on the air, and the odor is very like that of rotten eggs. For this one (and its name, if you like, is Beggiatoa) battens upon brimstone. It lives in the mud of curative baths, and grows in sulphur springs, and by building up a slimy reef it makes a bowl about some geysers, enduring and even luxuriating in a zone of their waters that is hot but just not too hot for it. To look at, this sulfur bacterium is colorless. Under the lens, you may see its strands slither, slipping over each other in a perpetual undulant motion with the indifference of a knot of bored snakes.

Now, this ill-smelling Medusa is important to all of us alive here. Not so much because it is sometimes implanted by engineers in septic tanks as a valuable destroyer, as because of its greed for the sulfur on which it lives. It is after sulfur everywhere, anywhere, that it can get it in Nature.

Abbreviating the chemistry of it, the result of Beggiatoa's use of sulfur is sulfuric acid. This is combined with the limes of the soil, creating a compound of calcium and sulfur that is exactly the fertilizer for which all roots are hungering. They do not use, they can not absorb, the sulfur and sulfurous compounds around them until Beggiatoa has produced this particular form of it.

And living protoplasm must have sulfur, especially for its nucleus. Just a pinch of this mustard among the elements—but that pinch is indispensable to the cuisine. So Beggiatoa unlocks for all the rest of life this invaluable yellow ingredient.

All these autotrophs, with their strange diets and their labor in the dark, are without color. But there is one more autotrophic group which catch the attention because they are pigmented. And the pigments, although not usually green, are photosynthetic.

The red or purple bacteria must, then, have light for their work. Equally, they must *not* have free oxygen, for it is fatal to them. When we cultured them in the old Agassiz laboratory, we filled the flask to the brim with water, stoppered it against air, and put it in the sunshine at the window. There photosynthesis began.

How, since here was no chlorophyll? The answer refers the imagination to antiquity. The pigment of the reds or purples is called bacterio-purpurin, and I don't think anyone knows very much about it, but this much is plain to any mind: bacterio-purpurin (the red) is the complementary color of chlorophyll (the green). So these two utilize just the opposite parts of the spectrum. Imagine, then, that murky and chaotic age of the world, when sunlight was probably of quite another quality than this upon my desk today, and filtered many of the rays that make so gay the little patio garden beyond the window. What used that strange sunlight, what toiled even then at the beginning of the industry that is the world's greatest, may have been—must have been—the purple bacteria.

Early as these purple laborers were at the mighty business, those pallid brother autotrophs, the iron and sulfur bacteria were, I think, earlier still. For they required not even the tool of light. They were already active in the day of darkness, in the beginning of things. It is difficult to picture any earlier form of life. . . .

THE FIRST ALGAS

So in the beginning of things life here on earth must have been, after all, Adamite—a single, simple kind of organism.

Whether that first-life was bacterial, or algal, or some sort of spontaneous colloidal protein system that began to live, this planet in Archaeozoic times (estimated at one to two billion years ago) was so impoverished as to variety that a full account of its flora—and fauna, if any—would make a paper so concise, so lacking in disputatious matter and naked of footnotes that a right-thinking college faculty would scarcely accept it as a doctoral thesis. . . .

Precisely because life is pliant and fluid, it is also, like water, most difficult to maintain in any shape it does not wish to take. And very hard it is to turn life from the channels that it has itself grooved deep. The resilience of life is probably the strongest thing in the universe. For though the mineral kingdom is vast and mighty, with the abrupt flinty hardness of all reality, it is for that very reason rigid. And because it is rigid, the mountains can do no other than stand still and let the lichens leach them, the delicate mosses pry them open with exquisite fingers, the invisible bacteria riddle them, and the rain and wind reduce them to dust.

But you can batter a seaweed on the reefs for twice ten million years, without changing its inner convictions. All that the surf has been able to accomplish in these eons is to knock the spores out of the slippery fronds—and so set them adrift to colonize some other reef.

Yet there have been changes in the Green Kingdom, sweeping changes, far-reaching in their consequences to all of us animals, to the very crust of the planet we inhabit and, literally, to the air we breathe. Were it not for these changes, which we call evolution, no lily would rise from the muck, no alder shake pollen from its curls in the March wind.

The significant fact is that all the really great changes have come from the inside out. They are born of the inner nature of the organism itself. They must have lain there, inherent as a possibility (more, as an irrepressible necessity) in the first Adamite organism, just as a tall pine is potential in a soft pinyon seed no larger than a child's tooth.

These changes are the history of the Green Kingdom. It is a history with as many dynasties and disasters as the history of China, though I find it much easier to remember than the long singsong of the wars and rulers of Cathay. But, like the history of a very ancient people, the story of plants on earth shows the antiquity of things called modern. As China invented tools of civilization and forgot them again, as it piled up annals and archives for hundreds of years, and lost them in a dark age or through the whim of a bibliophobe ruler, so in the plant kingdom almost every scheme has been tried once, or many times.

In every part of the sea and on every continent, life has set up one green stage set after another, taken it down, shipped it elsewhere, put up a new one. Giant seaweeds were rolled into beach wrack, fossilized sometimes into great stone dumplings, where now the corn of Illinois stands high, the chaff of threshing blows in the hot sun, and the soul longs for the sea. Sixteen times the sea came and went there, alternating with lofty fern forests. A resinous grove of pine-like trees thrust deep, reached high, where now the Papago Indian cuts a cactus to cup in his dark hands one luke-warm drink against the Arizona sun. And the petrified slab of a vanished tree that lies on my desk shows its every smallest cell exactly replaced by a crystalline mineral, as if the Medusa had looked upon that classic wood.

This tale of the rise and fall of the dynasties of growth must be pieced out of the rocks and fitted together with a strong and cementing likelihood. Fossil records make up our fragmentary evidence. It is all held together by the assumption that life began as something simple and adapted to easy conditions, and progressed toward fitness for the conquest of more hostile environments. The inferences from this assumption are borne out by the fossil record, such as it is.

What that record is, and is not, Darwin expressed when he said that the story of life is written in a book whose language or code changes with every chapter, and of which all but a few pages have been lost, the little that remains being scattered to the ends of the earth and senselessly jumbled.

So every fossil on a museum shelf is a three-fold miracle. First, the plant had to die under the most exceptional conditions remote from the normal course of events, which is swift decay, dissolution, and reworking of the mold into new forms of life. Then, by a wildly fortuitous set of circumstances, the fossilized evidence must not be washed into the sea, or buried several miles under sedimentary rocks, but had to come to light, be bared by erosion, or deprived of its Stygian privacy in the course of mining or excavating. And then, as the most unlikely chance of all, a paleobotanist (a very rare fellow even in a densely packed congress of botanists) had to pass by and collect the specimen before it was burned for coal, ground up for cement, washed away or otherwise hopelessly obliterated.

The longer the time elapsed, the less the likelihood that some tangible record will have survived. For that reason, and because the very earliest life was so sparse, so minute and fragile, the first rocks that could have borne life have almost nothing to tell us. They are nearly blank. But not quite. They speak, from their staggering thickness, of a measure of time that lasted longer than all the time that has gone by since—perhaps twice as long. But they speak of life.

To judge from the bacterial traces in them, life was tediously slow in gathering momentum. The little earth flew around the sun in its annual course millions and millions of times, and the sun on its unguessable track had plunged unthinkable distances into space, before much change had come about in those first vital experiments. We were in some other quarter of the universe; our sun appeared, from the viewpoint of other stars, to belong to some constellation from which it has now fallen, while the bacteria were leisurely taking the calcium carbonate out of the sea water and depositing it in the oceanic oozes, as the minute and brief lives perpetually and vastly died. And, as they laid down the great limestone beds, over the acid and sterile granites, so on land they were, surely, delving into the rocks. Bacteria have been brought up from borings five hundred and even fifteen hundred feet below the surface. So they have riddled and mollified the rocks and prepared the loams.

And as surely as they were altering their environment, the bacteria were themselves changing. Not that they were, as a race, departing, for their seed is still upon earth, the most numerous, important, and likely to outlast the ages. But they were giving rise—there seems little doubt of it—to the blue-green pond silks you see today still in stagnant waters.

These Blue-Green algas, just visible to the naked eye as shaky strands in a ditch, or the merest cast of jade across a lily pond, are the second chapter in plant history. It can be read only with a microscope, and it happens that I opened at its pages, in those primer days when I was given my first fine lens. This microscope was not new nor particularly convenient, but it was originally the best from a good factory of lens makers. It was given me, in those young plant hunting days in the Carolinas, by a woman naturalist who had used it to study bees and pollen. I remember how she put it in my hands with a silent blessing on my enthusiasm and a dry smile at its scope.

As soon as I got it home, I gently opened that case so like a traveling shrine, and drew forth the stately and intricate image, itself the god that sees what is hidden. Then I went out to the ditch across the road and scooped up a saucer full of pond silks. With pipette I snuffled up a long drop of water and green tress, lowered a little on a slide, and sealed it with a cover-glass. I was very serious about my technique, and I knew enough, at least, to realize that the Algae are a great and a right beginning.

My eye to the shaft, I lowered the lens by the big wheel almost to the slide, peered in, rolled it slowly up, and saw the algal jungle come clear but distant. Then I snapped in the high power and began, with the fine wheel, to hunt for the focus again.

First there was a green blur; then, as a falling aviator must, I saw the green tops of the forest rush upward, come clearer, nearer, till I was in it and plunging through the top storey into lower tiers. I held my hand—and suddenly there was life—the first living microscopic forms I had ever seen, and green with the good green of the great kingdom. No bacteria here, no unearthly and devious modes of living, but chlorophyll, and clear cellular form. As it was a water forest, a sargassum, it was horizontal, the jetsam of a micro-sea. I began to revolve the stage itself, and felt like a Magellan. . . .

The Algae love the damp, the stagnant ponds, the rolling ocean. They are, historically speaking, children of the sea, ancients of the first watery world, so much older than the Rockies that when those mountains were buckled up in a continental camp, their limestones carried up with them fossilized seaweeds two miles into the air. Even today, whether they go down into the earth or up to the glacial snows, the Algae are still —wherever you find them—aquatics. Somehow they divine a thread of water or a mere film of it. So from that primal fresh-water sea in which they were born, they have invaded the modern brine and the drying continents. They are found in snow and on flower pots, in the coruscating soda of shrinking desert lakes, whether in Tartary or Utah, in hot springs of New Zealand and Iceland, in sponges and the toe hairs of tree sloths and on the legs of a Russian tick. They are collected on Antarctic ice and from the roots of cycads in tropical rain forests. I have seen them where they form an unholy fluffy felt in the muck of slum yards, and I have looked down from the top of a skyscraper, in a wilderness of steel and stone, and seen their flagrant green in the lily pond of a penthouse terrace.

Once you begin to think about algas, and to look for them, you see them everywhere. The Blue-Green Algae look, and are, slimier than the Green. Many are poisonous; most are associated with polluted water; their presence indicates something unhealthy—for us. They are the sort of organisms that Aristotle, peering into his "primordial slime," conceived as originating from the mud itself. But all these qualities only serve to show from how far they have come—from a fabulous age and an earth that would have been uninhabitable for us, when the seas were not salt and the continents were brimstone, and the very sun looked down with a different light in its eye.

For the blue pigment of the Blue-Greens, adapted no doubt to capture solar energy also in a different part of the spectrum, masks the raw green chlorophyll. True that the Blue-Greens flourish in modern sunlight—but only in their gelatine sheath. Deprived of that, they are killed by direct light, just as bacteria are. Indeed, these Blue-Green Algae are next in seniority to the autotrophic bacteria, and resemble various of them significantly. In their filamentous or spherical shape, for instance, their slimy sheaths, their slow creep or oscillation. Too, they are devoid of starch, that stored wealth for man and beast, which pervades most of the rest of the plant kingdom. And the Blue-Greens, be it noted, are, like the bacteria, devoid of any sexual type of reproduction.

But they have chlorophyll, they have set up in the great photosynthetic business, and like all green water plants, they give off bubbles of oxygen. As presumably the Blue-Greens throve in the warm, fresh seas of ancient time, so some to this day live only in hot springs, whether at Rotorua geyser in New Zealand, or our own Yellowstone. Endlessly rising and dying, they deposit the weird sinter that makes the basins of the geysers so picturesque, and they build up a sort of rubble or tufa, or become solidified to an onyx-like travertine rock.

Or some Blue-Greens cause the "water-bloom" on pools, sometimes identified by botanists as Aphanizomenon but known as "Fanny" by the engineers who try to get rid of it, for it is fatal to cattle, with an unknown poison. Some Blue-Greens are more red than green, and one of them, prodigiously multiplying in the water between two deserts, has given the Red Sea its ancient name.

It is like crossing the frontier into a friendly country, to leave the Blue-Greens for the true Greens. As they form part of the grazing for so many aquatic small fry that feed the big ones, they are indirectly useful to us; they are the pasturage—biologists call it the plankton—of all the waters that can sustain them. And the Greens are, as they leave the reaches in which they resemble the bacteria-like Blue-Greens, honest plants such as we can better understand. They do their work by clear chlorophyll, and store starch and fats as higher plants do, and are built up of cellulose and pecten just as are the most aristocratic trees. And, save for the most primitive, the Greens have sex. They may be said, indeed, to have originated it.

That plants share sex with the animal kingdom is one more proof of the oneness of life. Yet mankind was a long time in perceiving the obvious. The ancients grew figs and olives, apples, peaches and chestnuts, as well as daughters, and saw that in youth their trees were barren, that they came to flower at a certain age, and fulfilled their purpose when they bore their fruit. And still men did not draw the simple parallel. The idea of sex in plants was scarcely proposed until the seventeenth century and accepted in the eighteenth only after furious opposition even from scientists.

And its purpose appears (since there are many, and very effective, non-sexual ways in which plants can reproduce themselves) to be the renewed vigor that comes with the conjunction of individual strains of protoplasm. Along with that refreshment of vital energy, there is implied the commingling of separate hereditary strains. Non-sexual reproduction endlessly multiplies the old individual, with all its virtues or weaknesses. But in a world of beings sexually divided, sexually united, enrichment is infinite, permutation endless. So evolution, slow to gather momentum, discovering the device of sex in the Green Algae swept forward upon its indomitable and unpredictable flood tide.

THE SEAWEEDS

Over my study mantelpiece, where the barometer and the great triton shells repose, is stretched the big sailing chart of this California coast on which I live. Worked intricately as a thumb-print with soundings and fathom lines, it shows the edge of the continent cutting across the upper right-hand corner, and off shore, in the currents, the islands of the Santa Barbara Channel. On clear days from my veranda, through an arch of live-oaks I can see them rise, abrupt and purple-shadowed. For they are the tops of an old mountain chain, and so upon the map they lie singularly alike in shape, very much like a flight of cormorants migrating parallel to the mainland. My eyes, so often lifting from my desk to seek them, find them there stretching out long goosy necks that bear small heads, or, as if foreshortened, they appear to sail upon wings edge-on. They hold the Channel in a light embrace; outposts of terra firma in the wilderness of sea, they temper it to inhabiting life.

On a fair day the Channel glitters azure, emerald-streaked where the sea is so thick with the life it bears that it refracts the sunlight, red with the moiling kelp beds, purpled by a passing cloud. Shallow, as biological fathoms are reckoned, deep as the angler thinks of depth, dark with the Kuro Shiwo stream that has crept here in a mighty arc from Japan.

Here off the tawny continental flank, in the lee of Santa Rosa, Santa Cruz, San Miguel, sleeps the Pacific from May until December. The broad ruddy band of the kelp beds, well off shore, never changes place. These giant kelps of the California coast are the largest in the world. Elk kelp and sea-otter's cabbage and the iodine kelp have dimensions of forest trees. Forty and sixty feet deep they are rooted by suckering holdfasts; their stems, flaccid but tough, may attain two hundred, three hundred feet in length. Their foliage is ample and heavy as the leaves of a rubber tree; they are buoyed up by double rows of bladders, or sometimes by a single float the size of a grapefruit. Some, like the trees of earth, are permanent perennials; in others which are annuals this leviathan growth is the work of a single season. Upon these towering, wavering Algae—the Browns— perch countless others, as the lianas and orchids cling upon the boughs of the over-earth tropical forests. For the most, these clinging frailties are Reds, and there are others of them, membranous and filigreed, that tremble on the ocean floor beneath the shelter of the lofty Browns, like moss and ferns that hug the ground between great roots. Such is the ocean jungle. It hangs such leathery curtains of foliage in the water and is flung abroad like an undulant carpet so wide upon the surface, that the fall and swell of the ocean's breathing is stilled by it. Within this breakwater, the seas lie harbor calm.

Beneath, in the depths of the great kelp forest, the small fry dash for shelter, in terror of swordfish and albacore and tuna. Here the crabs nibble the algal pasturage, and the sea slugs, which mimic the colors of the vegetation, crawl and mouth, and the kelp fish builds her nest of woven weed. Above these beds, all summer, in a leisure that gives thieves time to fall out, the gulls quarrel and rise, to settle again with a twinkling of sunlit wings. Brown pelicans plunge there; black cormorants from the wild Farallones fish these banks; loons dive with an oily ease, and sometimes a heron stands upon the buoyed kelp tops, gazing morosely into the water. Day after day—only calm and sunshine, kelp and fish and birds. Boats give the beds a wide berth, for fear of the weed in their propellers; fishermen hate it in their nets. No swimmer who loves his life would dive in that sargasso of the great Browns, nor could he endure the pressure of the deeps where the most fragile of all the Reds delight to live. The Browns, with their special pigments masking the chlorophyll, go down in the seawater till the orange and the yellow light have been filtered out. But the Reds can carry on their photosynthesis four hundred feet below the surface, where even the green and blue light fails, and only the violet rays still reach the delicate mechanism. In such secrecy dwell fragile perennials and summer annuals that live and die and are not seen by men, it may be, for years.

But halcyon weather, even here, cannot always endure. The winter rains come finally, and some night, after a day of grey brooding, they begin as a scamper of drops across the roof, a wind-blown hail of acorns, then a dance of rain, that becomes a ceaseless march. It rains till the dry arroyos run again; it rains till the rocks roll down the brooks; it rains till the hills begin to slide, and yet it has only begun to rain.

In January the first storm approaches. It gathers on the north Pacific, and sweeps down even into the Channel's shelter. It troubles the seaweed forest, then twists it and tortures it, and pulls it by the roots and breaks it. The annuals come up, then the permanent growth. The living break-water is broken with the waters; it is dragged up to the top, rolled in the green jaws of the combers, and flung, fighting and slithering back in vain, on the rocks, and pounded there. The rising tide carries it, a helpless wrack, to the high beach where it must bleach and rot.

After such a storm I lately came to the shore. The sea was mild in a warm sun; sails languished on the fishing banks; gulls were back on the kelp, and the kelp was back in its place, off shore, all but the loot flung up, not yet reclaimed by an incoming tide.

High up under the rocks, the giant kelps and tangs were thrust into an untouchable mound of decay that was waist high. Lower on the strand lay the lighter jetsam, the small Browns and the many Reds, in windrows tangled with eel grass and surf grass. Already these frail lives of the deep were passing swiftly, blanching or blackening. For them, this sunny air was a world too harshly illuminated, too arid for life.

But in the tide pools where they had been flung with sea urchins and starfish, they still lived, floating out with a vitality like the moving hair of the drowned. There I lifted wavering membranes of the edible Porphyras and the scarlet tousle of Plocamiums, filigree and point lace, fluted ribbons and lappets, sea-mosses as dark as the branching stains in agate, filmy ferns that lay upon my palm as insubstantial as the impress of a fossil growth. They were so unbelievably thin that when I had mounted them on stiff white paper they passed, with those who saw them, for the stroke of a water colorist's brush.

For I carried home a vasculum full of seaweeds, and with my fingers under water coaxed them all apart. When I had disengaged every filament and swept it clean of grit and parasites with a fine brush, my ocean algas emerged as lovely as are flowers. Botanically it was possible to assort and classify them among the major types, called roughly the Greens and Reds and Browns. But the colors were subtler than that. They were seashell pink and sunset rose, saffron and Tyrian and smoke-velvet, tannic wood-red, lake, carmine, verdigris, Spanish green, olive, maroon, garnet and emerald. Only cathedral windows have such soft and glowing stains. . . .

Of all algal morasses—and there are great ones on the north coast of Norway, in the fjords of Alaska, around New Zealand and the Great Barrier reef, off Good Hope and Cape Horn—the most fabulous is the Sargasso Sea. Sargassum, the Gulf weed, is not, individually, a conspicuous plant. It looks rather like a sprig of holly, with crinkly leaves and gas-filled bladders that might be mistaken for berries. Rather, the sheer mass has given rise to the legend that ships, from the time of Columbus, have become entangled in its gigantic eddy of stagnation and are still wedged there, rotting at Lethe's wharf. It is certainly so dense at times that a row boat is unable to make progress and has sometimes to be hauled back to the mother ship.

It harbors untold billions of microscopic animals and plants, hydroids that look like feathers, colonial creatures that resemble moss, and molluscs, crabs, shrimps, seahorses, pipe-fish and other small fry without end. Above all the Sargasso has been discovered to be the long unknown resort of the eels, who migrate here, mate, and die, and here their young mature to the elver stage before they begin their incredible journey to their parent rivers and ponds in the interior of Europe and America.

The sheer weight of the Gulf weed in the Sargasso Sea has been computed at ten millions tons. It is a free-floating raft of plants, torn by storms perhaps, from its mooring somewhere in the Gulf of Mexico and the Caribbean and caught in the eddy of the Gulf Stream and Equatorial counter-current. Yet one looks in vain for gigantic gardens that could supply such an assemblage of weed. More, this vast plant drift sometimes utterly disappears. So that several scientists, sailing by at such a time, have "disproved" the Sargasso Sea as a myth. Others who have seen it say that it sinks below the surface, to rise again at certain seasons. But no man knows. The Sargasso remains one of the ancient secrets of ocean, and it gives us some suggestion of what the seas were like in that period of geologic time that has been named the Age of Seaweeds.

Not that then there were necessarily more, or more variety than we know today. But there was, except for bacteria, presumably nothing else. There may even have been no land above the waters for a long time, but only a world sea or Panthalassa. In this shallow all-ocean the algas could have rooted far more extensively than now. And when the continents arose, the seaweeds in that eon that was theirs, a time longer than that which has gone by since the first land plants appeared, were slowly evolving toward the mastery of their environment. They were adapting themselves to the increasing brininess of the ocean, to the conquest of the deeps and of the tidal shores. Perhaps it was they who first set green foot on shore, but of that we know nothing.

What we do know from the book of fossils is that the seaweeds in their Age were developing most of the traits of plants. Starting with the slimy Blue-Greens and the mere hair-like Greens the algas progressed through branching, through the welding of filament to filament into a ribbon tissue, through the layer of one tissue on another so that real body and substance were established, till they had reached a complex structure differentiated into definite organs like roots, leaves, stems, spore-cases and complex sex organs. The life history of some of the highest of the Reds is as complex as that of an orchid or a pine. In beauty and color some Algae are, indeed, flowers of the sea; others, in bulk and height and foliage, are the trees.

And some of these early comers have even built the land we walk on. Their surfaces encrusted with lime, they have, by their endless living and dying, created reefs and atolls, isles and peninsulas, and even great limestone blankets of the continents. Animal corals get all the credit for such architecture; the coralline Algae and others of the stony little sea-weeds have probably done full half the work. Taking on the forms of flat, crusty lichens, of stony feathers, of brittle jointed pink lobster feelers, of minute mermaids' fans and mermen's shaving brushes, glove fingers and tremulous green toadstools, these calcareous masons are growing today beneath the clear waters of the Bay of Naples, the Great Sound of Bermuda, the reef of Funafuti, the stagnation of the old moat around the fortress at Key West. But they are only the living generation that exists delicately upon the bones of their ancestors of Proterozoic times, when layer by layer, in little swirls and knolls and bosses, they lifted the land above the sea, and left their fossil imprint in the rocks.

For the most part, other kinds of Algae, alas, make wretched fossils. A seaweed alive is little more than an evanescent pellicle of life surrounding impounded seawater; ordinarily it dies and vanishes without trace, except for the rare exquisite impress of some Red of a vanished age, and, occasionally, a great brown kelp like Nematophycus, one of the giants that lolled in the seas that stood then over interior Canada. Its fossil stem was a thing so stoutly dimensioned that it was taken, first, to be some ancestral sort of yew bole.

But such as they are, the fossils of the Age of Seaweeds proclaim a tremendous story of conquest, the domination of an element by life. The sea teemed then. Yet in all that time, between half a billion and a billion years, the face of the rock was bare. Without land plants to give them browse, animals too were imprisoned in the sea, for it is a trap as well as a world. The Age of Seaweeds was the age of Invertebrates. Every order of spineless animal we know today, and many that are extinct like the scorpion-like trilobites, flourished in those submarine gardens or ranged the deeps and the open spaces. Jelly-fish and sea anemones, octopi and squids, hydroids and bryozoöns, sea slugs and sea snails and great conchs, tritons, nautili, and abalones populated the algal jungles. The lampreys, writhing and suckering, evolved, and finally even fishes. And still life was wholly aquatic. On land was a harsher world, with drying winds, without the old maternal medium to buoy plants, to bring them all salts, all minerals, in its perpetual convection. But it was a much more stimulating environment, destined to call forth great things of life and lead it to triumph. Yet still on all the earth there was no flower and no voice; the continents were coursed by winds that blew no one any good and carved by rains for which there was no root or throat to be grateful.

THE FERN FORESTS

Three hundred and fifty million years ago is as far away as a star. To describe a plant that was growing then would seem the attempt of a madman or a magician, so lost in time is it now. In the eons since it was green, whole populations of plants have arisen and conquered the world and fallen again, leaving here and there a few survivors to persist, altering with the ages, vague reminders of what the world was like in their day.

Their day was yesterday or the day before. Three hundred and fifty million years ago is forgotten time. It is no more than the day after the Age of Seaweeds. No sensible every-day botanist would look about him for evidence of what then was green, not in the growing world that is his field. But there is another kind of botanist, extremely rare, extremely learned, who has added to a mastery of common plant knowledge a quarter of a century or even half a lifetime, of very special training. He is the paleobotanist, and his task is to unriddle the rocks. He has to work backward from the known to the obscure, by almost metaphysical detective work. His clues are appallingly few, all but hopelessly incomplete. He is lucky if he finds any fossil showing two organs from the same plant attached, and though he may find all the parts in separate fossils, he has no scientific right to put them together. Rather he must fit each faint evidence into its one right place in the whole enormous picture—the vast evolutionary system of plant history, the vanished floras of any one of a billion years of life on earth.

Even to examine this evidence would appear a task of crushing tedium. After your paleobotanist has climbed cliffs, or descended into coal mines, or lowered himself into quarries, after he has come staggering home from some ledgy glen with his knapsack bulging with heavy specimens, he sorts out the clattering haul in a rough fashion. Very commonly he has to slice his rocks into thin sections for microscopic examination. A rotary saw covered with diamond dust is used for this, and the art of it consists in cutting in the right plane. Then the fragile slice is secured to glass, the surface is polished down with carborundum until it is so thin that it is transparent; this film of rock is mounted under Canada balsam, and the paleobotanist has his specimen ready for examination. From it, referring to the colossal amount of information on plant structure on file in his brain, concerning seeds, pollen grains, spores, cones, leaves, cross-section patterns of twigs or stems, he may be able to supply his fragment with an idea of the rest of its parts.

Among these detectives of the vanished, these pioneers into the remote past, a great name is that of Sir John William Dawson. Eighty years ago Sir John was cracking rocks and pawing over the fragments on thè Gaspé peninsula of Canada, when he came on a fossil fragment in a stratum of early Devonian age, that gave him a start. He was a God-fearing, Bible-swearing gentleman who did not, in that year of grace 1859, take any stock in M Darwin's blasphemy about the descent of man. But he was a good paleobotanist, for all of that, and when he found a land plant square in the middle of the Age of Seaweeds, he knew he had made a discovery.

He took his stony fragment home to Nova Scotia, where he was born, and went to work on it. Neither mad nor a magician, he dared to look back three hundred and fifty million years, and see what must have been growing then. He was so sure of what he saw that he could take up a pencil and draw it. I have that picture before me. It is a picture of the earliest known plant upon the earth. Sir John called it Psilophyton, which means "naked plant." Very naked it looks, very new for all it is so old— a skinny, wiry, straggling thing, no more than the dim beginning of an idea for a plant. Which is just about what it was.

The shoot seems to have been scarcely a foot in height; it had a bit of underground stem without roots; it had branches, but without leaves, and at the tips of them it bore spore cases (for it was to be ages before seeds fell upon the ready earth). This thing, this meagre, venturesome, growing and certainly green thing, lost in the interminable darknesses of time gone by, came alive again in the mind of Sir John William Dawson.

Too lively, his imagination! said his colleagues to one another. Psilophyton, it was smilingly decided, never grew anywhere outside of his head. For more than fifty years the drawing was thought of as a curiosity, a scribbling without scientific value.

One day, in the terrible year of 1915, when the English and Germans were dying at Ypres and the French and Germans at Artois, two British paleobotanists, over-age for service, were plying their peaceable if unappreciated trade in the mountains of Aberdeenshire, when they unearthed a Devonian marsh, turned by time into a dark chippy sort of flint called chert, and full of fossils. This bog, when it was a bog, must have been close to the ocean, although the village of Rhynie, hard by, is now thirty miles from the North Sea and well up in the hills. So Robert Kidston and William Lang called the first of their plants to be described, Rhynia.

They saw that Rhynia must have grown very thickly in the bog, in a green swale like rushes in a marsh today; they saw that it stood about eight inches high, that it had neither leaves nor roots but only underground stems and rootlets, that it bore spore cases—that it was, indeed, so like Sir John William Dawson's drawing of the imaginary Psilophyton that Psilophyton must have been very real indeed.

And in the years since, it has turned up in fossil at points so far scattered as Connecticut, Maine, Scotland, Wales, Germany, and Victoria in Australia. No doubt any more of Dawson's bold guess, no doubt of the importance of Psilophyton, the "naked plant," the first known plant citizen in the land. Spores like a fern's give hint, in this bleak tentative little ancestor, of great things to come.

They came with the centuries, the hundreds of centuries, the measures of time that we can deal with only as we riffle the leaves of a book. Through the flicker of those eons we get a glimpse of landscape, tundra-like, bog-like, clothed in a harsh and stunted flora all a dead level of green. Pattern of leaf or color of flower there was none. But green, with its attendant bronze and grey of decay to lower the key, green creeping over the land, irresistible as today's ivy that splits the stones, ultimate as the grass on our graves.

And time, time flowing serenely by, in the millions of tranquil years of the Middle Devonian. There were no great mountains then arising; the continents seem even to have subsided, around their edges, letting in the shallow seas where the fierce Devonian fishes swam and the coral reefs grew higher and the great brown seaweed rolled. Where Pennsylvania is tossed up today into limestone folds, the country was flat and marshy as lowland South Carolina, and there the oils and natural gas were gathering under the subterranean domes of rock. Seams of coal were forming in the plant-choked lakes of Germany and China. Everywhere there was an immense and ever increasing growth, a constant forward surge of the Green Kingdom. Gone are rootless, naked, stunted, rushy Psilophyton and all its cretin kind. Little trees take their place. And larger trees. Woody tissue increases, strengthens, solves the momentous task of all land plants, of lifting water dead against gravity. A seaweed can loll in the water, buoyed by it and even saturate with it. A tree must hold aloft its crown of leaves and top-heavy branches; it must defy the storms, and supply its ultimate bud and leaf with water. Already the new environment is calling forth from resourceful life a magnificent effort in response.

And always, you must remember, there were spores, sowing the wind, and falling in the water. Spores fine as pollen, fine as ash; spores big and heavy as seeds. Some spores that actually were seeds. Spores by the million from a single spore case, spores by the billion from a single plant. Spores in astronomical figures, in numbers carried to a power to stagger mathematicians, sowing the wind and the wave and the earth, recklessly wasted, yet indomitably fertile. They alighted without sound, yet it was, for all that, a mighty footfall.

By the Late or Upper Devonian times, some seventy-five million years after naked Psilophyton put in its shy appearance, green life is no longer uncertain of itself on land, in the new trying element of air. Already the descendants of Psilophyton have diverged along widely different lines.

Like the builders of the tower of Babel, they started out with much in common, but time parts them; they are no longer near of kin; they speak different tongues, turn backs, move to the four quarters of plant destiny— true fern, club-moss, conifer and seed-fern. All four are found in Late Devonian fossils. And each in turn is destined to its day. Three will rise and fall. One, the last, the dark horse among them, whose very existence was unrecognized until a few years ago because its fossils were grouped among the true ferns, will emerge triumphant as the ancestor of our living flora.

But in this antiquity, eternal slow and all but fathomless, the first golden age of the plants rose with the ferns and the club-mosses—rose into the stately swampy forests of the great Carboniferous Age. This was the classic period. From this our own industrial modernity actually stems. Yet there was not then so much as a groping scheme for the man-like in anything living. Only a vast lush growing, over the earth. The climate of what is now the United States was tropical; delicate tree ferns flourished within a few degrees of the poles, long as must, even then, have been the polar nights. The very air was not the clear American atmosphere we breathe; it must have been more heavily blanketed with moisture and carbon dioxide that kept the earth's heat close under an almost permanent cloud.

Those paleobotanists, chipping and peering, have discovered in the rocks as many as a thousand species of Carboniferous plants. They are all gone today; only a few dwindled descendants show the power of continuity. In the horsetails by the marsh, little and harsh like stemfuls of soft pine needles, persist all the traits of forest-tall, ancestral Calamites of the Coal Age. Calamites had a trunk like a tall pine, then, and leaves in tufts; it left a long reflection in the stagnant water. But when today a muskrat drops into a pond bordered with horsetails they tremble at the ripple. Peasants use them for scraping the grease of pots and pans, call them scouring rushes, fling them, ignominious with the bacon fat, into the fire. So low have the descendants of great Calamites fallen.

If you walk in our northern pine woods, if you have an eye to subtle beauty, you know Lycopodium, that trails its stems like a cedar garland along the ground; they call it club-moss or ground pine. Nevertheless it is neither moss nor pine but a fugitive and prostrated collateral descendant of a tree that in the Coal Age grew to a hundred feet and more, straight up. Four feet thick it grew, rough-scaled like an alligator's skin, and it clutched the still queasy earth with a mighty root system. There were plants whose branches drifted in the water, and climbing ferns, and broad lowlier fronds to make an undergrowth beneath the soaring boles of these great lycopods. Light shafted between them misty with the ever-lasting vapor; the silence must have hung as heavy as a pall. For there was not a bird in all that forest to lift the voice of hope; there was not a fur-bearer, with a drop of the milk of mother-kindness. Between earth and water lived amphibian things, newt-like, eel-like, dragging their elon-gated shapes, as much as eight feet long, upon the new experiment of legs. The hot damp air was stirred by insect life, primitive but already boldly ambitious. There were roaches to the hundreds of species, some of them gigantic, and crawling forms foreshadowing bugs and termites, and through those steamy forest depths there darted a dragon fly with a wing-spread of thirty inches. Never in the ages since have the insects equalled that for size.

That world that was seems less believable than a nightmare on waking. Yet not only are the rocks written with witness to it, but it was the very source, the immediate prompting, of today's civilization. When it was discovered that coal could smelt iron, human history turned its course, following the vein laid down in the Carboniferous era. The ships of England began carrying coal from Newcastle. Manchester rose from its sleepy peace to become one of the greatest and grimiest cities in the world. Mauch Chunk, in Pennsylvania, where Audubon hunted bears, turned in his lifetime into a labor-troubled colliery. Settlers ripped the virgin prairie sod from Illinois and laid bare its soft bituminous beds. German steel mills blackened the skies under which Goethe had dreamed Roman-tic Natural philosophy. Women stevedores of Nagasaki ran panting with black diamonds on their backs, unloading the dirty British collier. Cot-tage industry gave way before the factory. Coal-poor nations paid yellow earth metal for this dirty black mineral that made the wheels of the world go around.

Long the geologists had no clear notion what coal was made of. Or-ganic its origin certainly was. But who could see details in a lump of mineralized midnight? It was one of my old teachers who literally made coal transparent. He worked for fifteen years before he learned the secret of softening and bleaching coal.

His method is to soak his specimen for two years in chlorate of soda dissolved in concentrated hydrofluoric acid. At the end of that time this patient man has it washed all one night in slowly running water, then in strong alcohol and after that in carbolic acid. Then again it is cleansed with water, and the now merely clouded and much mollified lump of antiquity is imbedded in nitrocellulose and sliced one twelve-thousandth of an inch thin.

In the high-ceiled dinginess of his cluttered little north room, this professorial collier let us look into his microscope at such coal shavings magnified five hundred times. He had specimens from all over the world —Pocahontas anthracite, Kentucky cannel or "coal of the long flame," as the French call it, soft bituminous carbon from the man-killing mines of Illinois, paper coals from Russia. And we were botanists enough to see at a glance into the truth of them. Charred cellulose; club-moss spores with their unmistakable three furrows; tree fern wood crushed by the terrible pressure of the centuries piled upon it. All the forests of the Carboniferous era, jumbled and charred and tortured, but legible still as plant life.

The circumstances that conspired to lock up such treasure are several. Water was its first keeper; under water the bacteria and fungi do not comparably attack dead wood. The wooden piles under the city of Venice have been found to be intact after a thousand years; cypress wood —wood still, not fossil—is dug out of Maryland swamps where cypress no longer grows, and it is still uninjured after an estimated ten thousand years.

The second keeper of the treasure was fire. Lightning or spontaneous combustion seem forever to have started great conflagrations among the inflammable lycopods, and by charring the outside tissue, the fire saved the surface from decay and so saved all.

Lastly, time and the weight of earth went to the making of coal. Upon the accumulating beds of plant detritus poured endlessly the silt and mud of the rivers. The oceans came and went, over the fallen forests, and the terrific weight of their waters caused a very heat of pressure that carbonized the sinking wealth which once was life.

But why did they fall, those forests? Why did a dynasty mighty enough to conquer earth vanish utterly from it?

They grew too great, perhaps; it may be that they brought their own downfall. Times change, we say; the very climate of the world changed then. A cold breath of disaster blew down upon the tropical plant kings; the first winter of the world was coming, and their time was done. . . .

From the South Pole the glaciers moved inexorably forward; they drove much further toward the equator than the northern hemisphere glacier that came in the time of man, for they were much bigger and more aggressive. Before their icy breath the sultry jungles of the Carboniferous withered. They were gripped by the bitter death of freezing and by the slow death of drought. For the waters of which they had so prodigal a need were locked in the ever increasing ice fields. The very level of the oceans must have fallen; the marshes must have shrunken, the air have lost its steamy richness upon which had floated the olden spores.

This the fern forests could not survive; here was revealed the fatal weakness of the very elaboration of their development. For the life history of a fern (and of a horsetail and a club-moss) has two separate phases, called the alternation of generations. The first is the plant we see, non-sexual, simply bearing spores. But the spores, when they germinate, do not give rise to more ferns, but to the second phase, the sexual. In this, the fern appears as insignificant as a lichen, but its tiny flat body bears the male and female sex organs; from these spring the fern form again.

The male cells, with their lashing tails, can only reach the egg cells if they can swim to them. They cannot cross dry land; they are not adapted to air travel, like spores. Even a rainy day, even a film of dew, may suffice to make possible the fertilization of the dainty little ferns of today. But the gigantic ferns and fern-allies of the Carboniferous, to keep alive and to complete their life cycle, required water and more water, a world that was a sodden plenty of it. And it failed them; the carbon dioxide failed them; the glaciers advanced, and cold dry winds blew them no luck from any quarter. Over-specialized, over-tender, spendthrift of their grandeur, the Carboniferous plants went down like a civilization that has itself created the Nemesis by which it is destroyed.

But life is never really routed. After the glaciers had withdrawn, a new flora spread everywhere, with the swiftness of a foot-loose horde. It was wrought out of the passing ferns, but it was hardy, fecund and aggressive. It was a low and weedy growth fit to face the bluster of the bleak day; there is evidence of it even on fossils from Antarctica, found in the collections of Captain Scott's tragic expedition.

Nor was this coarse and sturdy rabble all that grew. The race of conifers was pushing up; the seed-ferns had given rise, before they perished, to a new line, more gloriously destined than any other though still only groping its way toward flowers and fruit. But the first golden age—some unwintered confidence, some unchecked and monstrous extravagance—was over.

CONIFERS AND CYCADS

At the end of May, when I haunted the Lompoc ranges, the best of the season was already over. It is a curious countryside, unlike any other in America that I know, salt but dry, sunny with a wash of fog over the sunshine. On the grassy polished hills and across the open heath-like scrub the bird life is especially easy to see and hear. The lupine had been glorious in flower, a month before, sweeping the land in patches the purple-blue color of shadow, the poppies running beside them like molten metal. Then uprose those foreign invaders, the wild oats and mustard.

Now they too were bronzing in the march of the summer days. The brooks dwindled to a whisper; the cattle lazed in the deep shade of the live oaks that cluster in the folds of the hills and climb toward the top with their peculiar grace of following the land's contour in harmonious slopes of their own. In the pines there was no shade, only the desultory sizzling of some little bird that eluded me. I was in that first dazed spell of an oncoming southern summer, when the air is full of the dusty incense of hay and the insect thunder of bees who can find no more opening flowers. It is time to go, then, but you have already lost your will to go, consenting with indolence to stay and be withered.

But anywhere in this state you are likely to remember some other place in it as beautiful as the spot where you are standing, and utterly different. So there came down to me from the high places something less sensible than a wind, but as strong and sudden, urging and reviving me. Once your mind quits one place for another, you stifle if you lag behind it. When I had no liberty but a fortnight doled out annually, when I had no car and all the children were little, I had to stay behind, wherever my thoughts went. I lived through the attacks, then, *in situ*, but now I like to think that there is no cure for me but to go. . . .

So we made a prompt start that morning, with little ceremony about it but with some reverence preparing in us, for we went to visit giants in the earth. Of all that has survived from the Mesozoic, which began two hundred million years ago and ended about 55,000,000 B.C., Sequoia is the king. It is so much a king that, deposed today from all but two corners of its empire, superseded, outmoded, exiled and all but exterminated, it still stands without rival. And from all over the world, those who can make the pilgrimage come sooner or later to its feet, and do it homage.

Of Sequoia there are two species left, though once they were as various and abundant as are today the pines, their lesser brothers. One is the coastal redwood of California, which is the tallest tree in the world, and the other is the Big Tree of the Sierra Nevada, which is the mightiest in bulk. These two surviving species were here before the last glacial period. But as a genus or clan of species Sequoia has its roots in a day of fabulous eld. This noble line knew the tyrant lizards; through its branches swept the pterodactyls on great batty wings. As they saw the coming of the first birds, crawling up out of lizard shapes, so the forebears of our Sequoia witnessed the evolution of the first mammals when these still laid eggs, when they were low-skulled opossum-like things, when they became scuttling rodents that perhaps, gnawing and sucking at dinosaur eggs, brought down that giant dynasty from its very base.

Sequoia as a tribe saw the rise of all the most clever and lovely types of modern insects—the butterflies and moths, the beetles and bees and ants. Yet since there were then none of the intricate inter-relationships that have developed between modern flower and modern bee, Sequoia sowed the wind. It had flowers of an antique sort, flowers by technical definition, at least; petals and scent they had none. But their pollen must have been golden upon that ancient sunlight, and the communicable spark of futurity was in it. For Sequoia towers still upon its mountain top, and I was going there. . . .

It is a long climb still through the foothills of the Sierra. But now I sit up, with a lifted face. Beyond, higher in the east, portent is gathering. It takes shape, cloud-colored, gleaming with a stern reality where the sun smites a rocky forehead. Then appears that eternally moving miracle—snow in the summer sky. Sierra Nevada. . . .

The forests march upon the car; the ruddy soaring trunks of the sugar pines close around in escort. One hundred and two hundred feet overhead, their foliage is not even visible, screened by the lower canopy spread by western yellow pines which are giants in themselves. Groves of white fir, smelling like Christmas morning, troop between the yellow pines. Aisles of incense cedar with gracious down-sweeping boughs and flat sprays of gleaming foliage invite the eye down colonnaded avenues, fragrance drifting from their censers that appear to smoke with the long afternoon light. It grows darker with every mile, darker and deeper in moss and lichen, dim with the dimness of a vanished era. We have got back into earliest spring, at this altitude, and the blossoming dogwood troops along, illuminating the dusky places with a white laughter.

. . . Now, as the land of sunny levels has fallen remotely out of sight, there is a prescience in the cold air, of grandeur. We have climbed into the shadows; the drifts of snow are thicker between great roots, and richer grows the livid green mantle of staghorn lichen that clothes all Sierra wood in green old age. The boles of the sugar pines, which are kings, give place before the coming of an emperor. The sea sound of the forest deepens a tone in pitch. The road is twisting to find some way between columns so vast they block the view. They are not in the scale of living things, but geologic in structure, fluted and buttressed like colossal stone work, weathered to the color of old sandstone. They are not the pillars that hold up the mountains. They are Sequoia. The car has stopped, and I am standing in the presence.

Centuries of fallen needles make silence of my step, and the command upon the air, very soft, eternal, is to be still. I am at the knees of gods. I believe because I see, and to believe in these unimaginable titans strengthens the heart. Five thousand years of living, twelve million pounds of growth out of a tiny seed. Three hundred vertical feet of growth, up which the water travels every day dead against gravity from deep in the great root system. Every ounce, every inch, was built upward from the earth by the thin invisible stream of protoplasm that has been handed down by the touch of pollen from generation to generation, for a hundred million years. Ancestral Sequoias grew here before the Sierra was uplifted. Today they look down upon the plains of men. No one has ever known a Sequoia to die a natural death. Neither insects nor fungi can corrupt them. Lightning may smite them at the crown and break it; no fire gets to the heart of them. They simply have no old age, and the only down trees are felled trees.

In their uplifted hands they permit the little modern birds, the passerine song birds, vireos and warblers, tanagers and thrushes, to nest and call. I heard, very high above me in the luminous glooms, voices of such as these. I saw, between the huge roots that kept a winter drift, the snow-plant thrust through earth its crimson fist. A doe—so long had I stood still—stepped from behind the enormous bole and, after a long dark liquid look, ventured with inquiring muzzle to touch my outheld hand. Bright passing things, these nestle for an hour in the sanctuary of the strong and dark, the vast and incalculably old.

That day I stood upon a height in time that let me glimpse the Mesozoic. It followed the Coal Age, the age of the fern forests, and it was itself the age of Gymnosperms. Sequoias are Gymnosperms. So are the pines, the larches, spruces, fir, yew, cypress, cedar—all that we call conifers, though there are other Gymnosperms that do not bear cones.

The Gymnosperms are, literally translating, "the naked-seeded" plants. For their seed is not completely enclosed in any fruit or husk, as it is in the higher modern plants that truly fruit and flower. Neither is the Gymnosperm egg or ovule completely enclosed in an ovary, as in the true flowers. To make an analogy, you could say that the Gymnosperms are plants without wombs, while the Angiosperms, the true flowering plants with genuine fruits, are endowed with that engendering sanctuary.

But though the seeds of the Gymnosperms are naked, they are seeds, and the seed is mightier than the spore. For the seed contains an embryo. Spores are very many and very small; they blow lightly about the world and find a lodging easily. But the seed is weighted with a great thing. Within even the tiniest lies the germ of a fetal plantlet, its fat cotyledons or first baby leaves till crumpled in darkness, its primary rootlet ready to thrust and suckle at the breast of earth.

This vital secret was inherited from the seed-ferns, back in misty days when the ferns were paramount. The conifers bore it forward; the true flowering plants were to carry it on and spread it in blossoming glory. Of that there was no sign in the Mesozoic forests. They must have been dark with an evergreen darkness, upright with a stern colonnaded strength. For they developed the power of building wood out of earth, not the punky wood of the tree ferns, but timber as we know it.

And we know no timber like the conifers'. No other trees are cut on such a scale. Where they grow, wooden cities swiftly rise, railroads are bent to them, mushroom fortunes arise from them, great fleets are built to export them. Scandinavia is one vast lumber camp, supplying western Europe; Port Oxford cedar of Oregon crosses the ocean in a perpetual stream of logs, supplying Japan and China; Kauri pines of New Zealand feed the wood hunger of barren Australia. The world's books and newspapers are printed on coniferous pulp; it is driving silk and cotton to the wall, as sources of cellulose and textile fibre. For beautiful grains, for capacity to take stains, the evergreen woods are incomparable. The living conifers are to us what the dead coal forests are.

But they can be replenished. They can be grown and cut as crops, and they yield a profit on poor sandy and rocky soil, or in swampy lands where no other crop could be hopefully tilled. Thrifty, fertile, tough, industrial, they are of all trees the most practical. Ancient in lineage beyond all others, they rise tall and straight in the pride of their aristocracy. Sea-voiced, solemn, penciled against the sky, their groves are poetic as no leafier places. Conifers stand in the sacred temple yards of Japan, where, with venerating care, their old limbs are supported by pillars. They line the solemn approaches to the tombs of the Chinese emperors at Jehol. Solomon sought them in the peaks of Lebanon for his temple. But in all the world there are none like those in our western states.

And it was in the Black Hills of Wyoming that a fragment of the Mesozoic lay hidden till the days when the West came to be called new country. Miners on their way to Deadwood, cowboys riding herd, found strange stone shapes, and broke off fragments. What lay in those calloused brown fingers, turned over curiously, ignorantly, was once sprung in the Gothic glooms of the Mesozoic forests. These were cycads, a kind of Gymnosperm which must have formed the undergrowth of those prehistoric coniferous woods, hundreds and hundreds of species of them. A few linger today, scattered thinly over the tropics of the world. Some call them sago-palms; they have an antique look, stiff, sparse and heavy; crossed in pairs upon a coffin, they impart a funebrial dignity. Cretin of stature, for the most part, growing sometimes only six feet in a thousand years, they are beloved in the Japanese dwarf horticulture, cherished in family pride there, since a cycad of even moderate size may represent a long domestic continuity.

What pride, then, and what a ring of age was there in the first set of fossil cycads from the Black Hills rim to reach the men of science at the National Museum in 1893! Professor Lester Ward hastened to the field, and what he found there, besides the bones of a great dinosaur and the petrified logs of old conifers, were not imprints but complete petrifactions. Atom by atom the living tissue had been replaced by stone. Here were hundreds of fruits, all the leaves a gloating paleobotanist could desire, perfect trunks, every detail of wood structure preserved, and dozens of species, some dwarf, some colossal.

Ward took back with him what he could. Other students hurried to the find; Yale and the Universities of Iowa and Wyoming have great collections from Deadwood, and the government museums too. Tourists carted away entire specimens, and what remained might have been utterly scattered and destroyed, had not Professor G. R. Wieland saved the last rich tract in the Black Hills. Close to the mountain where Borglum carved his heroic profiles, the scientist filed on the area under the homestead laws, and then presented his claim to his country. It has since been made Cycad National Monument.

These cycads, when the world was young and they were flourishing, must have brought into the dark monotony of the evergreen forests the first bright splashes of color. For the seeds of cycads are gorgeous scarlet or yellow or orange, borne on the edge of the leaf or commonly in great cones. They are sweet and starchy to the taste, and perhaps Archaeopteryx, that first feathered bird in all time, crunched them in the teeth that he still kept, reminder of his lizard ancestry. So, it may be, the earliest animals came to aid in the dissemination of plants, as squirrels do today, and birds. Somehow, at least, the cycads over-ran the world. Their reign had grandeur, but its limits narrowed. There is evidence that some of the Mesozoic cycads flowered only at the end of their immensely long lives— a thousand years, perhaps. Then, after one huge cone of fruit was set, the plant died to the very root. A hero's death, but a plan ill fit to breed a race of heroes. In the cupped hand of the future lay other seeds, with a fairer promise.

THE RISE OF THE MODERN FLORAS

For every man there is some spot on earth, I think, which he has pledged himself to return to, some day, because he was so happy there once. Even to long for it is holiday of a sort. These visits of revery may be all that he can pay it, for years, perhaps until his shade is free to haunt where it pleases. But some are lucky; some get back, and find it, to every trembling leaf and stanch old tree trunk, untouched by any alteration but the seasons'.

My place, my chosen bailiwick in the hereafter, is in the Appalachian country, field of my earliest forays when I turned plantsman at twenty. Those mountains, the oldest on the face of the continent, are the kindest. They are blue with the haze of southern warmth, covered with a rustling mantle of shade, abloom in spring, full of falls and brooks where the white quartz gleams, as good as diamonds to any child. And I was a child there. So when I go back, it seems like home, all over again each time.

But the home core of it lies under no roof but the Carolina sky. It has walls, yes, high rocky ones that pocket fern and orchis, saxifrage and trillium, and it is inhabited, not only by the cardinal and thrush, but by a minor deity of its own. She is a waterfall, white, radiant, immortal if not living, and she is always there for me when I go back.

I was away from her for many years, but I had the place by heart. During that long absence there came to me a request for a report of my Carolina glen, and there on the other side of the ocean, amid the hot dust of Mediterranean hills, I was able to compose from memory a list—a florula, as botanists call it—of all that grew beside the falls. Verifying it years later, on an exile's return, I found I had omitted only two species.

For there is a particularity about the flora of that ancient mountain chain. It has no parallel, as I have said, save in high places in China and Japan. But it is esoteric in more than range; it is the last stand of what I have called the Renaissance of plant life. After the pillared glooms of the Mesozoic forests, after the day of conifer might and cycad ascendancy, the first great flowering of the world began. Through the Tertiary, the last age of antiquity, the eon before modernity dawned, this experiment of blossoming went on. And what grew then, all over a world that was warmer than ours and spared our harsh extremes, was very much the same flora that nods and glistens in the spray of my laughing falls.

Never in time before had the forests bloomed or spread broad, filmy and deciduous leaves. And neither in all storied Europe nor in our own magnificent West is there today a living grace like that of the Appalachian woods in spring. My glen is a temple of it, the waterfall niched in the far heart. To reach it, I used to take the nine o'clock local from the Piedmont village; with the help of two engines to drag us up the steepest grade east of the Rockies, the train would attain the water tank in fifteen minutes, and stop there, panting, to drop the extra engine. I dropped off there, too. And when the train, wagging its dragon tail, had vanished, I was alone with April. In the morning freshness there was no sound but the music of leaves, and the rushing of many confluent brooks. Cross a meadow, and there was the entrance to the glen, screened in sunny greenery. At once the smell of lichen and loam and fern blew out to me, sharpened with the honeyed odor of azaleas, and I always stopped a minute just to listen with closed eyes, and to draw a deep breath of happiness.

Then the glen once more received me.

Hours like those make no saga. Eventless in their perfection, they cannot be communicated like a tale. There is nothing to tell but how the sunlight is green-filtered and cool with the breath of falling water, how the trail follows the stream up and up, over fallen logs, with the summons of the hidden cascade rushing ever louder in your ears, and the sense of green, light-hearted sacrosanct deepening as the rock walls rise. How when you thirst there, you drink from cupped hands at that spring that gushes from the brow of a rock to drum in a perpetual shower upon the Euclidian beauty of trillium. The trilliums there have different odors that are in my nostrils now as I remember—one smelled of roses, one of honey, one of bay rum, one of crushed strawberries, one had no scent, and the last perfume I can neither describe nor forget, for it was loveliest of all.

This is not science; this is trifling with the great plant story I have set out to tell. But, I tell you, just to remember that place is holiday for me. There was no time there, except, far and lonely through the leaves, the whistle of the noon train coming down, when I would know I could let myself eat lunch at last, on the broad rock table at the foot of the falls. After all, there was not much science then for me in the glen, in those boyhood visits that I remember best. But I carried into it, along with my vasculum for collecting, just enough knowledge to set all I saw alight with realization. I knew I stood amid the purest example of the plant life of another age left in the world today. I was learning to name everything I touched or smelled or saw abloom high overhead, like the white fragrant bells of the sourwood swinging seventy-five feet above me, loud with the eagerness of bees. I knew the redbud by its rose-magenta flowers like small butterflies, the buckeye lifting its turrets of pale yellow blossoms, the silver-bell tree hanging drooping clusters. Dogwood of course I knew, and azalea, rhododendron, mountain laurel; some species of all these are tall as trees in my glen. Taller trees stand protector, soft magnolias and hard maples with scarlet flowers, black gums and sweet gums, tulip trees, hickories, and butternuts of the indelible dye, that stains the fingers still as once it dyed the shirts of Jackson's fighting hosts.

The glen was my book, that April I was twenty. I idled over it, watching the rhododendron snow its petals on the dark pools that spun them round in a swirl of brown foam and beached them on a tiny coast glittering with mica and fool's gold. But I got it by heart, the dripping rocks, the ferny grottos, the eternal freshness, the sense of loam, of deep sweet decay, of a chain of life continuous and rich with the ages. The walking fern I gathered there, that walks across its little forest world by striking root with its long tips, tip to root and root to tip walking away from the localities that knew it once, has its oriental counterpart; of that I was aware. And I knew that Shortia, the flower that was lost for a century after Michaux found it "dans les hautes montagnes de Carolinie," has its next of kin upon the mountains of Japan. Sometimes I met mountain people hunting ginseng for the Chinese market; long ago the Chinese all but exterminated that herbalistic panacea of theirs, and now they turn for it to the only other source, the Appalachians.

Later I came to understand what mighty upheavals of the earth, what changes in the world's weather had scattered this once wide-spread flora and locked it away in mountains an ocean and a continent apart. Once the Appalachian-Oriental forests overspread the whole of the north temperate world. Witness of that has been found in amber cast up from the Baltic, blossoms of the Tertiary lying imprisoned there in a waxen perfection. Again at the village of Florissant, in Colorado, a fossil flora rich in Appalachian and tropical types tells how different then was the lie of the land and the very air that blew over it.

For in that pre-Adamite day the earth was a more equable sort of place, and the pattern of its lands was more solid and more even. Tropic and arctic both were tempered. It was a genial and cosmopolitan world; tree fern and laurel reached to Greenland, and the elephant and the camel and the tiger lived in the United States. For millions of years a lush and sprightly plant life labored untroubled in the sun, laying down the soft Tertiary coals that today are found so widely in western America.

But it was a young world still, and not a settled one. One by one the land bridges of the continents began to break, isolating Madagascar from India, cutting off Australia from Asia. The Antarctic bridges sank beneath the sea, and the great North Atlantic bridge went too.

And as the land sank, elsewhere it rose, in impassable mountain barriers. The Rockies rose, tilting up the trans-Mississippi plains with them, giving us the prairies and Pike's Peak. In time, in many millennia, the Sierra Nevada was in its turn thrust up; it caught the Great Basin between its snows and the Rockies, and turned it into a desert. In South America the Andes shouldered high through the old tropical rain forest.

The Himalayas were lifted from the hot Gangetic jungles. In Europe the Alps came into being.

All over the world the temperature must have begun to go down, as the glaciers gathered. Winters lasted longer, frost came earlier. The banner of autumn colors, perhaps, was hung for the first time in those earliest deciduous woods. And now, when England was covered with mountains of ice, and woolly mammoths and mastodons, bison and reindeer and the fierce dire wolves were roaming France, a creature called *Pithecanthropus erectus* made his low-browed appearance.

In that uneasy world, the glaciers came and went perhaps four times. Tundras and bogs full of peat moss and reindeer lichen bordered those ice fields. Dust bowls of wind-blown loess filled central Europe and our West and Middle West. Rockies and Alps and Sierra wore immense ice caps almost to their bases. All that was soft and fair and genial in the old Tertiary flora was killed, or driven into refuges like far China or my Blue Ridge hills. And man, who is always at his best in hard times, lighted his first camp fires against the great winter of the Pleistocene glacial period.

Fire, the fire of life, leaps to its every chance. Quench it here, its seed springs there, and races in conquering flame on every lucky wind. None more indomitable than the green fire of plant life. Adjusting to drought and cold, to sopping bog and bleak desert, it caught hold, seized its chances, and evolved into that triumphant conflagration we may call the Great Northern Flora.

It covers Europe today, Iceland and what little of Greenland is not still wrapped in its particular ice age; it ranges across Siberia, Alaska and Canada, and has found its way deep into the United States; it is, in the temperate zone, the modern flora. Like much else in modern life, it is strong, dominant, aggressive, not built to last but to catch as catch can. It is for a short life and a flowery one; it runs to annuals and low soft perennials, to high fertility and modest living standards. At its best it is beautiful, with the brave beauty of Canterbury bells of Transylvania, lupines of California, foxgloves of England, golden daisies of the prairies. It can be ugly, with the pushing coarseness of pigweed and tumbleweed and burdock. It can overrun the territory it claims by mob rule, a rabble of dandelions crowding in the lawn, blue devil deviling the farmer, arrogant thistles of Europe taking the pampas over, mile by mile, and gorse, thorn-armed and bannered with showy blossoms, driving the almost Mesozoic timid flora of New Zealand back into a last stand in the mountains.

When the glaciers caught the Tertiary vegetation between their ice and the impassable barriers represented by Alps, Mediterranean and Sahara, they crushed out its delicate life. Let the patricians fall, and the plebeians rise up, vigorous with those hardier virtues that are bred in a long cruel competition. They must have lain potential in the older, more primitive Tertiary families, but suppressed, throughout the days of its pride, like the fertile lowly in some ancient oligarchic civilization.

The plants that repopulated Europe came out of the Russian steppes, out of the Caucasus, that cradle of races, out of what are today the many-peopled, many-tongued Balkans, and the Siberian forests and high Asiatic plateaux. They filled Europe with a colorful polyarchy of innumerable tribes, each forced to excel the others in fertility and armament, defense and aggression. They invaded all environments, called to aid ancient wind and modern insects, even birds to pollinate them. Some are so vital that they will do without pollination and yet set seed. There is no end to the cunning of their devices of penetration: winged seeds and barbed seeds, and creeping roots throwing up endless suckers. With thorny stems and poisonous alkaloids they defend themselves. They store their strength in corms, taproots, bulbs. In blazing desert reaches their leaves grow narrow as needles, as if squinting against the glare; in forests, they lay out their broad leaves with an intricate care to catch every ray of the light. They are life as we know it today, ingenious, indomitable, all a struggle for a place in the sun.

Now plants had entered into intense competition with *Homo sapiens*, a creature determined to clear his lands for a few species like wheat and barley, rice and maize. Those plants that did not enter his good graces fought him as weeds, or betook themselves to bogs and moors, strands and alpine meadows where he would not molest them. So we have not only nettles and cockles and tares, but the flora of the herbalists, of Grimm's fairy-tales, of the Scotch heather and the Irish bogs, of the plain of Marathon, with poet's narcissus blooming from the blood of heroes. This is the rich plant civilization that gives us scarlet anemones of Provence, the alpine blossoms that the poet-botanist Haller gathered, and wide-eyed arctic wildflowers named by Linnaeus upon his Lapland faring.

It has inherited the earth, this Great Northern Flora, like man himself. And it has followed him wherever he has gone, wherever, with his plough and axe, his petted cereals and his close-cropping cattle, he comes to lord it over native peoples and native vegetations unequipped to repel him. English sheep brought English burs in their wool to New Zealand. At man's heels Russian thistle invaded North America like a Tartar host, spreading from west to east on the wind of conquest; man settled our western cactus in Australia, and there it has become a bristling horde harrying all that grows in its way.

So a sinless world altered, and with gardens came the weeds in them. What is a weed? I have heard it said that there are sixty definitions. For me, a weed is a plant out of place. Or, less tolerantly, call it a foreign aggressor, which is a thing not so mild as a mere escape from cultivation, a visitor that sows itself innocently in a garden bed where you would not choose to plant it. Most weeds have natal countries, whence they have sortied. So Japanese honeysuckle, English plantain, Russian thistle came from lands we recognize, but others, like gypsies, have lost all record of their geographic origin. Some of them turn up in all countries, and are listed in no flora as natives. Some knock about the seaports of the world, springing up wherever ballast used to be dumped from the old sailing ships. Others prefer cities; they have lost contact with sweet soil, and lead a guttersnipe existence. A little group occurs only where wool waste is dumped, others are dooryard and pavement weeds, seeming to thrive the more as they are trod by the feet of man's generations. Some prized in an age of simpler tastes have become garden *declassés* and street urchins; thus it comes about that the pleasant but plebeian scent of Bouncing Bet, that somewhat blowsy pink of old English gardens, is now one of the characteristic odors of American sidewalk ends, where the pavement peters out and the shacks and junked cars begin. . . .

As long as man keeps the upper hand with Nature, he is going to strive to bring about a flora once more cosmopolitan. His commerce and exchange of crops and weeds, of garden materials and attendant pests, will break down insularity and provincialism just as technical civilization drives out local customs and costumes, and smooths away dialects in favor of a uniform speech. Like the rest of our future, this promises mixed blessings. On the Mojave it is grateful to rest under the shade of tamarix trees brought in from the Sahara, giving respite where even the native mesquite will not cast its thin umbrage. Upon the prairie, where once the virgin sod was proud with tall native grasses and blazing composites, it is lamentable to feel the foreign weeds crowd harsh about the ankles. To the coming of such changes there is no simple answer.

But there are dreams, there are plans. Already with plant breeding and hybridization man has accomplished miracles beyond Nature's own power. Greater things could yet be done, in afforestation of the tree-starved lands, in cereals that would be clean, once more, of the rusts and smuts that civilization has broadcasted. . . .

But sufficient to our own long day is this modern flora of ours. If I have left no simple impression of what it is like, then I have left the correct impression. There are some hundred thousand species of flowering plants on earth today, and they are scattered through some two hundred and fifty families. Add to these all the mosses and ferns, the Gymnosperms and fungi, seaweeds and algas, and you have some three hundred thousand races of plant life populating the Green Kingdom. All this, out of the first bacteria that colonized the planet. All this brilliant land flora, after naked Psylophyton tentatively trying the new environment of the old Devonian continent.

Never in past geologic time can there have been so complex a vegetation as today, for never were there so many climates, such mountains, such deserts, such seas, such arctics, such island archipelagoes, such insularity everywhere. You could have written a florula of Cambrian times upon a very few pages. Today there breathes no man who can master more than a little portion of the plant world, or a selected group of families. Sir Joseph Dalton Hooker, in his prime, could recognize on sight ten thousand species, because he had collected and identified everywhere, from the Indian jungles to lonely Kerguelen Island in the Pacific, and he knew the diatomaceous flora of the arctic ocean as well as the sweet rustic wild-flowers of England. After the age of ninety his prodigious memory fell off a bit. But he was one of the rare titans of classification, like Linnaeus and De Candolle. A fair-to-middling student is glad to recognize on sight two thousand kinds of plants, and he easily goes rusty without constant practice. I remember best, I find, not the plants I learned most recently, but, like poetry, those I memorized when the tablets of my brain were fresh. It follows therefore that I recall still, with a morning clarity, the inhabitants of my distant glen, those old Tertiary Appalachian aristocrats blooming where no weed ever sets root, where there is neither the gaudy splendor of these California poppies, nor the urban squalor of quitch grass and pigweed and goosefoot. The last plant I shall forget, surely, will be the first I ever taught myself to know—the windflower of those Blue Ridge Woods.

1939

A Lobster; or, The Study of Zoology

T. H. HUXLEY

From *Discourses Biological and Zoological*

CERTAIN BROAD LAWS HAVE A GENERAL APPLICATION throughout both the animal and the vegetable worlds, but the ground common to these kingdoms of nature is not of very wide extent, and the multiplicity of details is so great, that the student of living beings finds himself obliged to devote his attention exclusively either to the one or the other. If he elects to study plants, under any aspect . . . his science is botany. But if the investigation of animal life be his choice, the name generally applied to him will vary according to the kind of animals he studies, or the particular phenomena of animal life to which he confines his attention. If the study of man is his object, he is called an anatomist, or a physiologist, or an ethnologist; but if he dissects animals, or examines into the mode in which their functions are performed, he is a comparative anatomist or comparative physiologist. If he turns his attention to fossil animals, he is a palæontologist. If his mind is more particularly directed to the specific description, discrimination, classification, and distribution of animals, he is termed a zoologist.

For the purpose of the present discourse, however, I shall recognise none of these titles save the last, which I shall employ as the equivalent of botanist, and I shall use the term zoology as denoting the whole doctrine of animal life, in contradistinction to botany, which signifies the whole doctrine of vegetable life.

Employed in this sense, zoology, like botany, is divisible into three great but subordinate sciences, morphology, physiology, and distribution, each of which may, to a very great extent, be studied independently of the other.

Zoological morphology is the doctrine of animal form or structure. Anatomy is one of its branches; development is another; while classifica-

378

tion is the expression of the relations which different animals bear to one another, in respect of their anatomy and their development.

Zoological distribution is the study of animals in relation to the terrestrial conditions which obtain now, or have obtained at any previous epoch of the earth's history.

Zoological physiology, lastly, is the doctrine of the functions or actions of animals. It regards animal bodies as machines impelled by certain forces, and performing an amount of work which can be expressed in terms of the ordinary forces of nature. The final object of physiology is to deduce the facts of morphology, on the one hand, and those of distribution on the other, from the laws of the molecular forces of matter.

Such is the scope of zoology. But if I were to content myself with the enunciation of these dry definitions, I shall ill exemplify that method of teaching this branch of physical science, which it is my chief business tonight to recommend. Let us turn away then from abstract definitions. Let us take some concrete living thing, some animal, the commoner the better, and let us see how the application of common sense and common logic to the obvious facts it presents, inevitably leads us into all these branches of zoological science.

I have before me a lobster. When I examine it, what appears to be the most striking character it presents? Why, I observe that this part which we call the tail of the lobster, is made up of six distinct hard rings and a seventh terminal piece. If I separate one of the middle rings, say the third, I find it carries upon its under surface a pair of limbs or appendages, each of which consists of a stalk and two terminal pieces.

If I now take the fourth ring, I find it has the same structure, and so have the fifth and the second; so that, in each of these divisions of the tail, I find parts which correspond with one another, a ring and two appendages; and in each appendage a stalk and two end pieces. These corresponding parts are called, in the technical language of anatomy, "homologous parts." The ring of the third division is the "homologue" of the ring of the fifth, the appendage of the former is the homologue of the appendage of the latter. And, as each division exhibits corresponding parts in corresponding places, we say that all the divisions are constructed upon the same plan. But now let us consider the sixth division. It is similar to, and yet different from, the others. The ring is essentially the same as in the other divisions; but the appendages look at first as if they were very different; and yet when we regard them closely, what do we find? A stalk and two terminal divisions, exactly as in the others, but the stalk is very short and very thick, the terminal divisions are very broad and flat, and one of them is divided into two pieces.

I may say, therefore, that the sixth segment is like the others in plan, but that it is modified in its detail.

The first segment is like the others, so far as its ring is concerned, and though its appendages differ from any of those yet examined in the simplicity of their structure, parts corresponding with the stem and one of the divisions of the appendages of the other segments can be readily discerned in them.

Thus it appears that the lobster's tail is composed of a series of segments which are fundamentally similar, though each presents peculiar modifications of the plan common to all. But when I turn to the forepart of the body I see, at first, nothing but a great shield-like shell, called technically the "carapace," ending in front in a sharp spine on either side of which are the curious compound eyes, set upon the ends of stout movable stalks. Behind these, on the under side of the body, are two pairs of long feelers, or antennae, followed by six pairs of jaws folded against one another over the mouth, and five pairs of legs, the foremost of these being the great pinchers, or claws, of the lobster.

It looks, at first, a little hopeless to attempt to find in this complex mass a series of rings, each with its pair of appendages, such as I have shown you in the abdomen, and yet it is not difficult to demonstrate their existence. Strip off the legs, and you will find that each pair is attached to a very definite segment of the under wall of the body; but these segments, instead of being the lower parts of free rings, as in the tail, are such parts of rings which are all solidly united and bound together; and the like is true of the jaws, the feelers, and the eye-stalks, every pair of which is borne upon its own special segment. Thus the conclusion is gradually forced upon us, that the body of the lobster is composed of as many rings as there are pairs of appendages, namely, twenty in all, but that the six hindmost rings remain free and movable, while the fourteen front rings become firmly soldered together, their backs forming one continuous shield—the carapace.

Unity of plan, diversity in execution, is the lesson taught by the study of the rings of the body, and the same instruction is given still more emphatically by the appendages. If I examine the outermost jaw I find it consists of three distinct portions, an inner, a middle, and an outer, mounted upon a common stem; and if I compare this jaw with the legs behind it, or the jaws in front of it, I find it quite easy to see, that, in the legs, it is the part of the appendage which corresponds with the inner division, which becomes modified into what we know familiarly as the "leg," while the middle division disappears, and the outer division is hidden under the carapace. Nor is it more difficult to discern that, in the appendages of the tail, the middle division appears again and the outer vanishes; while, on the other hand, in the foremost jaw, the so-called mandible, the inner division only is left; and, in the same way, the parts of the feelers and of the eye-stalks can be identified with those of the legs and jaws.

But whither does all this tend? To the very remarkable conclusion that a unity of plan, of the same kind as that discoverable in the tail or abdomen of the lobster, pervades the whole organisation of its skeleton, so that I can return to the diagram representing any one of the rings of the tail and by adding a third division to each appendage, I can use it as a sort of scheme or plan of any ring of the body. I can give names to all the parts of that figure, and then if I take any segment of the body of the lobster, I can point out to you exactly, what modification the general plan has undergone in that particular segment; what part has remained movable, and what has become fixed to another; what has been excessively developed and metamorphosed and what has been suppressed.

But I imagine I hear the question, How is all this to be tested? No doubt it is a pretty and ingenious way of looking at the structure of any animal; but is it anything more? Does Nature acknowledge, in any deeper way, this unity of plan we seem to trace? . . .

Happily, however, there is a criterion of morphological truth, and a sure test of all homologies. Our lobster has not always been what we see it; it was once an egg, a semifluid mass of yolk, not so big as a pin's head, contained in a transparent membrane, and exhibiting not the least trace of any one of those organs, the multiplicity and complexity of which, in the adult, are so surprising. After a time, a delicate patch of cellular membrane appeared upon one face of this yolk, and that patch was the foundation of the whole creature, the clay out of which it would be moulded. Gradually investing the yolk, it became subdivided by transverse constrictions into segments, the forerunners of the rings of the body. Upon the ventral surface of each of the rings thus sketched out, a pair of budlike prominences made their appearance—the rudiments of the appendages of the ring. At first, all the appendages were alike, but, as they grew, most of them became distinguished into a stem and two terminal divisions, to which, in the middle part of the body, was added a third outer division; and it was only at a later period, that by the modification, or absorption, of certain of these primitive constituents, the limbs acquired their perfect form.

Thus the study of development proves that the doctrine of unity of plan is not merely a fancy, that it is not merely one way of looking at the matter, but that it is the expression of deep-seated natural facts. The legs and jaws of the lobster may not merely be regarded as modifications of a common type,—in fact and in nature they are so,—the leg and the jaw of the young animal being, at first, indistinguishable.

These are wonderful truths, the more so because the zoologist finds them to be of universal application. The investigation of a polype, of a snail, of a fish, of a horse, or of a man, would have led us, though by a less easy path, perhaps, to exactly the same point. Unity of plan every- where lies hidden under the mask of diversity of structure—the complex is everywhere evolved out of the simple. Every animal has at first the form of an egg, and every animal and every organic part, in reaching its adult state, passes through conditions common to other animals and other adult parts; and this leads me to another point. I have hitherto spoken as if the lobster were alone in the world, but, as I need hardly remind you, there are myriads of other animal organisms. Of these, some, such as men, horses, birds, fishes, snails, slugs, oysters, corals, and sponges, are not in the least like the lobster. But other animals, though they may differ a good deal from the lobster, are yet either very like it, or are like something that is like it. The cray fish, the rock lobster, and the prawn, and the shrimp, for example, however different, are yet so like lobsters, that a child would group them as of the lobster kind, in contradistinction to snails and slugs; and these last again would form a kind by themselves, in contradistinction to cows, horses, and sheep, the cattle kind.

But this spontaneous grouping into "kinds" is the first essay of the human mind at classification, or the calling by a common name of those things that are alike, and the arranging them in such a manner as best to suggest the sum of their likenesses and unlikenesses to other things.

Those kinds which include no other subdivisions than the sexes, or various breeds, are called, in technical language, species. The English lob- ster is a species, our cray fish is another, our prawn is another. In other countries, however, there are lobsters, cray fish, and prawns, very like ours, and yet presenting sufficient differences to deserve distinction. Naturalists, therefore, express this resemblance and this diversity by grouping them as distinct species of the same "genus." But the lobster and the cray fish, though belonging to distinct genera, have many features in common, and hence are grouped together in an assemblage which is called a family. More distant resemblances connect the lobster with the prawn and the crab, which are expressed by putting all these into the same order. Again, more remote, but still very definite, resemblances unite the lobster with the woodlouse, the king crab, the water flea, and the barnacle, and sep- arate them from all other animals; whence they collectively constitute the larger group, or class, *Crustacea*. But the *Crustacea* exhibit many peculiar features in common with insects, spiders, and centipedes, so that these are grouped into the still larger assemblage or "province" *Articulata*; and, finally, the relations which these have to worms and other lower animals, are expressed by combining the whole vast aggregate into the sub-kingdom of *Annulosa*.

If I had worked my way from a sponge instead of a lobster, I should have found it associated, by like ties, with a great number of other animals into the sub-kingdom *Protozoa*; if I had selected a fresh-water polype or a coral, the members of what naturalists term the sub-kingdom *Cœlenterata*, would have grouped themselves around my type; had a snail been chosen, the inhabitants of all univalve and bivalve, land and water, shells, the lamp shells, the squids, and the sea-mat would have gradually linked themselves on to it as members of the same sub-kingdom of *Mollusca*; and finally, starting from man, I should have been compelled to admit first, the ape, the rat, the horse, the dog, into the same class; and then the bird, the crocodile, the turtle, the frog, and the fish, into the same sub-kingdom of *Vertebrata*.

And if I had followed out all these various lines of classification fully, I should discover in the end that there was no animal, either recent or fossil, which did not at once fall into one or other of these sub-kingdoms. In other words, every animal is organised upon one or other of the five, or more, plans, the existence of which renders our classification possible. And so definitely and precisely marked is the structure of each animal, that, in the present state of our knowledge, there is not the least evidence to prove that a form, in the slightest degree transitional between any of the two groups *Vertebrata*, *Annulosa*, *Mollusca*, and *Cœlenterata*, either exists, or has existed, during that period of the earth's history which is recorded by the geologist. Nevertheless, you must not for a moment suppose, because no such transitional forms are known, that the members of the sub-kingdoms are disconnected from, or independent of, one another. On the contrary, in their earliest condition they are all similar, and the primordial germs of a man, a dog, a bird, a fish, a beetle, a snail, and a polype are, in no essential structural respects, distinguishable. . . .

Turning from these purely morphological considerations, let us now examine into the manner in which the attentive study of the lobster impels us into other lines of research.

Lobsters are found in all the European seas; but on the opposite shores of the Atlantic and in the seas of the southern hemisphere they do not exist. They are, however, represented in these regions by very closely allied, but distinct forms—the *Homarus Americanus* and the *Homarus Capensis*: so that we may say that the European has one species of *Ho-*

marus; the American, another; the African, another; and thus the remarkable facts of geographical distribution begin to dawn upon us.

Again, if we examine the contents of the earth's crust, we shall find in the latter of those deposits, which have served as the great burying grounds of past ages, numberless lobster-like animals, but none so similar to our living lobster as to make zoologists sure that they belonged even to the same genus. If we go still further back in time, we discover, in the oldest rocks of all, the remains of animals, constructed on the same general plan as the lobster, and belonging to the same great group of *Crustacea*; but for the most part totally different from the lobster, and indeed from any other living form of crustacean; and thus we gain a notion of that successive change of the animal population of the globe, in past ages, which is the most striking fact revealed by geology.

Consider, now, where our inquiries have led us. We studied our type morphologically, when we determined its atonomy and its development, and when comparing it, in these respects, with other animals, we made out its place in a system of classification. If we were to examine every animal in a similar manner, we should establish a complete body of zoological morphology. . . .

But you will observe one remarkable circumstance, that, up to this point, the question of the life of these organisms has not come under consideration. Morphology and distribution might be studied almost as well, if animals and plants were a peculiar kind of crystals, and possessed none of those functions which distinguish living beings so remarkably. But the facts of morphology and distribution have to be accounted for, and the science, the aim of which it is to account for them, is Physiology.

Let us return to our lobster once more. If we watched the creature in its native element, we should see it climbing actively the submerged rocks, among which it delights to live, by means of its strong legs; or swimming by powerful strokes of its great tail, the appendages of the sixth joint of which are spread out into a broad fan-like propeller: seize it, and it will show you that its great claws are no mean weapons of offence; suspend a piece of carrion among its haunts, and it will greedily devour it, tearing and crushing the flesh by means of its multitudinous jaws.

Suppose that we had known nothing of the lobster but as an inert mass, an organic crystal, if I may use the phrase, and that we could suddenly see it exerting all these powers, what wonderful new ideas and new questions would arise in our minds! The great new question would be, "How does all this take place?" the chief new idea would be, the idea of adaptation to purpose,—the notion, that the constituents of animal bodies are not mere unconnected parts, but organs working together to an end. Let us consider the tail of the lobster again from this point of view. Morphology has taught us that it is a series of segments composed of homologous parts, which undergo various modifications—beneath and through which a common plan of formation is discernible. But if I look at the same part physiologically, I see that it is a most beautifully constructed organ of locomotion, by means of which the animal can swiftly propel itself either backwards or forwards.

But how is his remarkable propulsive machine made to perform its functions? If I were suddenly to kill one of these animals and to take out all the soft parts, I should find the shell to be perfectly inert, to have no more power of moving itself than is possessed by the machinery of a mill when disconnected from its steam-engine or water-wheel. But if I were to open it, and take out the viscera only, leaving the white flesh, I should perceive that the lobster could bend and extend its tail as well as before. If I were to cut off the tail, I should cease to find any spontaneous motion in it; but on pinching any portion of the flesh, I should observe that it underwent a very curious change—each fibre becoming shorter and thicker. By this act of contraction, as it is termed, the parts to which the ends of the fibre are attached are, of course, approximated; and according to the relations of their points of attachment to the centres of motions of the different rings, the bending or the extension of the tail results. Close observation of the newly-opened lobster would soon show that all its movements are due to the same cause—the shortening and thickening of these fleshy fibres, which are technically called muscles.

Here, then, is a capital fact. The movements of the lobster are due to muscular contractility. But why does a muscle contract at one time and not at another? Why does one whole group of muscles contract when the lobster wishes to extend his tail, and another group when he desires to bend it? What is it originates, directs, and controls the motive power?

Experiment, the great instrument for the ascertainment of truth in physical science, answers this question for us. In the head of the lobster there lies a small mass of that peculiar tissue which is known as nervous substance. Cords of similar matter connect this brain of the lobster, directly or indirectly, with the muscles. Now, if these communicating cords are cut, the brain remaining entire, the power of exerting what we call voluntary motion in the parts below the section is destroyed; and, on the other hand, if, the cords remaining entire, the brain mass be destroyed, the same voluntary mobility is equally lost. Whence the inevitable conclusion is, that the power of originating these motions resides in the brain and is propagated along the nervous cords.

In the higher animals the phenomena which attend this transmission have been investigated, and the exertion of the peculiar energy which resides in the nerves has been found to be accompanied by a disturbance of the electrical state of their molecules.

If we could exactly estimate the signification of this disturbance; if we could obtain the value of a given exertion of nerve force by determining the quantity of electricity; or of heat, of which it is the equivalent; if we could ascertain upon what arrangement, or other condition of the molecules of matter, the manifestation of the nervous and muscular energies depends (and doubtless science will some day or other ascertain these points), physiologists would have attained their ultimate goal in this direction; they would have determined the relation of the motive force of animals to the other forms of force found in nature; and if the same process had been successfully performed for all the operations which are carried on in, and by, the animal frame, physiology would be perfect, and the facts of morphology and distribution would be deducible from the laws which physiologists had established, combined with those determining the condition of the surrounding universe.

There is not a fragment of the organism of this humble animal whose study would not lead us into regions of thought as large as those which I have briefly opened up to you; but what I have been saying, I trust, has not only enabled you to form a conception of the scope and purport of zoology, but has given you an imperfect example of the manner in which, in my opinion, that science, or indeed any physical science, may be best taught. . . .

And if it were my business to fit you for the certificate in zoological science granted by this department, I should pursue a course precisely similar in principle to that which I have taken to-night. I should select a fresh-water sponge, a fresh-water polype or a *Cyanœa*, a fresh-water mussel, a lobster, a fowl, as types of the five primary divisions of the animal kingdom. I should explain their structure very fully, and show how each illustrated the great principles of zoology.

1861

The Life of the Simplest Animals

DAVID STARR JORDAN AND
VERNON LYMAN KELLOGG

From *Animal Life*

*T*HE SIMPLEST ANIMALS, OR PROTOZOA.—THE SIMPLEST
animals are those whose bodies are simplest in structure and which
do the things done by all living animals, such as eating, breathing, moving, feeling, and reproducing in the most primitive way. The body of a
horse, made up of various organs and tissues, is complexly formed, and
the various organs of the body perform the various kinds of work for
which they are fitted in a complex way. The simplest animals are all
very small, and almost all live in the water; some kinds in fresh water
and many kinds in the ocean. Some live in damp sand or moss, and still
others are parasites in the bodies of other animals. They are not familiarly
known to us; we can not see them with the unaided eye, and yet there
are thousands of different kinds of them, and they may be found wherever there is water.

In a glass of water taken from a stagnant pool there is a host of animals.
There may be a few water beetles or water bugs swimming violently
about, animals half an inch long, with head and eyes and oar-like legs;
or there may be a little fish, or some tadpoles and wrigglers. These are
evidently not the simplest animals. There will be many very small active
animals barely visible to the unaided eyes. These, too, are animals of
considerable complexity. But if a single drop of the water be placed
on a glass slip or in a watch glass and examined with a compound microscope, there will be seen a number of extremely small creatures which
swim about in the water-drop by means of fine hairs, or crawl slowly
on the surface of the glass. These are among our simplest animals. There
are, as already said, many kinds of these "simplest animals," although,
perhaps strictly speaking, only one kind can be called simplest. Some of
these kinds are spherical in shape, some elliptical or football-shaped, some

conical, some flattened. Some have many fine, minute hairs projecting from the surface; some have a few longer, stronger hairs that lash back and forth in the water, and some have no hairs at all. There are many kinds and they differ in size, shape, body covering, manner of movement, and habit of food-getting. And some are truly simpler than others. But all agree in one thing—which is a very important thing—and that is in being composed in the simplest way possible among animals.

The animal cell.—The whole body of any one of the simplest animals or Protozoa is composed for the animal's whole lifetime of but a single *cell*. The bodies of all other animals are composed of many cells. The cell may be called the unit of animal (or plant) structure. The body of a horse is complexly composed of organs and tissues. Each of these organs and tissues is in turn composed of a large number of these structural units called cells. These cells are of great variety in shape and size and general character. The cells which compose muscular tissue are very different from the cells which compose the brain. And both of these kinds of cells are very different from the simple primitive undifferentiated kind of cell seen in the body of a protozoan, or in the earliest embryonic stages of a many-celled animal.

The animal cell is rarely typically cellular in character—that is, it is rarely in the condition of a tiny sac or box of symmetrical shape. Plant cells are often of this character. The primitive animal cell consists of a small mass of a viscid, nearly colorless, substance called *protoplasm*. This protoplasm is differentiated to form two parts or regions of the cell, an inner denser mass called the *nucleus*, and an outer, clearer, inclosing mass called the *cytoplasm*. . . .

What the primitive cell can do.—The body of one of the minute animals in the water-drop is a single cell. The body is not composed of organs of different parts, as in the body of the horse. There is no heart, no stomach; there are no muscles, no nerves. And yet the protozoan is a living animal as truly as is the horse, and it breathes and eats and moves and feels and produces young as truly as does the horse. It performs all the processes necessary for the life of an animal. The single cell, the single minute speck of protoplasm, has the power of doing, in a very simple and primitive way, all those things which are necessary for life, and which are done in the case of other animals by the various organs of the body.

Amœba.—The simple and primitive life of these Protozoa can be best understood by the observation of living individuals. In the slime and sediment at the bottom of stagnant pools lives a certain specially interesting kind of protozoan, the *Amœba*. Of all the simplest animals this is as simple or primitive as any. The minute viscous particle of protoplasm which forms its body is irregular in outline, and its outline or shape slowly but constantly changes. It may contract into a tiny ball; it may become almost star-shaped; it may become elongate or flattened; short, blunt, finger-like projections called pseudopods extend from the central body mass, and these projections are constantly changing, slowly pushing out or drawing in. The single protoplasmic cell which makes up the body of the *Amœba* has no fixed outline; it is a cell without a wall. The substance of the cell or body is protoplasm, semiliquid and colorless. The changes in form of the body are the moving of the *Amœba*. By close watching it may be seen that the *Amœba* changes its position on the glass slip. Although provided with no legs or wings or scales or hooks—that is, with no special organs of locomotion—the *Amœba* moves. There are no muscles in this tiny body; muscles are composed of many contractile cells massed together, and the *Amœba* is but one cell. But it is a contractile cell; it can do what the muscles of the complex animals do.

If one of the finger-like projections of the *Amœba*, or, indeed, if any part of its body comes in contact with some other microscopic animal or plant or some small fragment of a larger form, the soft body of the *Amœba* will be seen to press against it, and soon the plant or animal or organic particle becomes sunken in the protoplasm of the formless body and entirely inclosed in it. The absorbed particle soon wholly or partly disappears. This is the manner in which the *Amœba* eats. It has no mouth or stomach. Any part of its body mass can take in and digest food. The viscous, membraneless body simply flows about the food and absorbs it. Such of the food particles as can not be digested are thrust out of the body.

The *Amœba* breathes. Though we can not readily observe this act of respiration, it is true that the *Amœba* takes into its body through any part of its surface oxygen from the air which is mixed with water, and it gives off from any part of its body carbonic-acid gas. Although the *Amœba* has no lungs or gills or other special organs of respiration, it breathes in oxygen and gives out carbonic-acid gas, which is just what the horse does with its elaborately developed organs of respiration.

If the *Amœba*, in moving slowly about, comes into contact with a sand grain or other foreign particle not suitable for food, the soft body slowly recoils and flows—for the movement is really a flowing of the thickly fluid protoplasm—so as to leave the sand grain at one side. The *Amœba* feels. It shows the effects of stimulation. Its movements can be changed, stopped, or induced by mechanical or chemical stimuli or by changes in temperature. The *Amœba* is irritable; it possesses irritability, which is sensation in its simplest degree.

If food is abundant the *Amœba* soon increases in size. The bulk of its body is bound to increase if new substance is constantly assimilated and added to it. The *Amœba* grows. But there seem to be some fixed limits to the extent of this increase in size. No *Amœba* becomes large. A remarkable phenomenon always occurs to prevent this. An *Amœba* which has grown for some time contracts all its finger-like processes, and its body becomes constricted. This constriction or fissure increases inward, so that the body is soon divided fairly in two. The body, being an animal cell, possesses a nucleus imbedded in the body protoplasm or cytoplasm. When the body begins to divide, the nucleus begins to divide also, and becomes entirely divided before the fission of the cytoplasm is complete. There are now two *Amœbæ*, each half the size of the original one; each, indeed, being actually one half of the original one. This splitting of the body of the *Amœba*, which is called fission, is the process of reproduction. The original *Amœba* is the parent; the two halves of the parent are the young. Each of the young possesses all of the characteristics and powers of the parent; each can move, eat, feel, grow, and reproduce by fission. It is very evident that this is so, for any part of the body or the whole body was used in performing these functions, and the young are simply two parts of the parent's body. But if there be any doubt about the matter, observation of the behavior of the young or new *Amœbæ* will soon remove it. Each puts out pseudopods, moves, ingests food particles, avoids sand grains, contracts if the water is heated, grows, and finally divides in two.

Paramœcium.—Another protozoan which is common in stagnant pools and can be readily obtained and observed is *Paramœcium*. The body of the *Paramœcium* is much larger than that of the *Amœba*, being nearly one fourth of a millimeter in length, and is of fixed shape. It is elongate, elliptical, and flattened, and when examined under the microscope seems to be a very complexly formed little mass. The body of the *Paramœcium* is indeed less primitive than that of the *Amœba*, and yet it is still but a single cell. The protoplasm of the body is very soft within and dense on the outside, and it is covered externally by a thin membrane. The body is covered with short fine hairs or cilia, which are fine processes of the dense protoplasm of the surface. There is on one side an oblique shallow groove that leads to a small, funnel-shaped depression in the body which serves as a primitive sort of mouth or opening for the ingress of food. The *Paramœcium* swims about in the water by vibrating the cilia which cover the body, and brings food to the mouth opening by producing tiny currents in the water by means of the cilia in the oblique groove. The food, which consists of other living Protozoa, is taken into the body mass only through the funnel-shaped opening, and that part of it which is undigested is thrust out always through a particular part of the body surface. (The taking in and ejecting of foreign particles can be seen by putting a little powdered carmine in the water.) Within the body there are two nuclei and two so-called pulsating vacuoles. These pulsating vacuoles (*Amœba* has one) seem to aid in discharging waste products from the body. When the *Paramœcium* touches some foreign substance or is otherwise irritated it swims away, and it shoots out from the surface of its body some fine long threads which when at rest are probably coiled up in little sacs on the surface of the body. When the *Paramœcium* has taken in enough food and grown so that it has reached the limit of its size, it divides transversely into halves as the *Amœba* does. Both nuclei divide first, and then the cytoplasm constricts and divides. Thus two new *Paramœcia* are formed. One of them has to develop a new mouth opening and groove, so that there is in the case of the reproduction of *Paramœcium* the beginnings of developmental changes during the course of the growth of the young. The young *Amœbæ* have only to add substance to their bodies, to grow larger, in order to be exactly like their parent.

The new *Paramœcia* attain full size and then divide, each into two. And so on for many generations. But it has been discovered that this simplest kind of reproduction can not go on indefinitely. After a number of generations the *Paramœcia*, instead of simply dividing in two, come together in pairs, and a part of one of the nuclei of each member of a pair passes into the body of and fuses with a part of one of the nuclei of the other member of the pair. In the meantime the second nucleus in each *Paramœcium* has broken up into small pieces and disappeared. The new nucleus composed of parts of the nuclei from two animals divides, giving each animal two nuclei just as it had before this extraordinary process, which is called conjugation, began. Each *Paramœcium*, with its nuclei composed of parts of the nuclei from two distinct individuals, now simply divides in two, and a large number of generations by simple fission follow.

Paramœcium in the character of its body and in the manner of the performance of its life processes is distinctly less simple than the *Amœba*, but its body is composed of a single structural unit, a single cell, and it is truly one of the "simplest animals." . . .

Marine Protozoa.—If called upon to name the characteristic animals of the ocean, we answer readily with the names of the better-known ocean fishes, like the herring and cod, which we know to live there in enormous numbers; the seals and sea lions, the whales and porpoises, those fish-like animals which are really more like land animals than like the true fishes; and the jelly-fishes and corals and star-fishes which abound along the ocean's edge. But in naming only these we should be omitting certain animals which in point of abundance of individuals vastly outnumber all other animals, and which in point of importance in helping maintain the complex and varied life of the ocean distinctly outclass all other marine forms. These animals are the marine Protozoa, those of the "simplest animals" which live in the ocean.

Although the water at the surface of the ocean appears clear, and on superficial examination devoid of life, yet a drop of this water taken from certain ocean regions examined under the microscope reveals the fact that this water is inhabited by Protozoa. Not only is the water at the very surface of the ocean the home of the simplest animals, but they can be found in all the water from the surface to a great depth beneath it. In a pint of this ocean water from the surface or near it there may be millions of these animals. In the oceans of the world the number of them is inconceivable. Dr. W. K. Brooks says that the "basis of all the life in the modern ocean is found in the micro-organisms of the surface." By micro-organisms he means the one-celled animals and the one-celled plants. For the simplest plants are, like the simplest animals, one-celled. "Modern microscopical research," he says, "has shown that these simple plants, and the Globigerinæ and Radiolaria [kinds of Protozoa] which feed upon them, are so abundant and prolific that they meet all demands and supply the food for all the animals of the ocean."

The Globigerinæ and Radiolaria.—The Globigerinæ and Radiolaria are among the most interesting of all the simplest animals. Their simple one-celled body is surrounded by a microscopic shell, which among the Globigerinæ is usually made of lime (calcium carbonate), in the case of Radiolaria of silica. These minute shells present a great variety of shape and pattern, many being of the most exquisite symmetry and beauty. The shells are usually perforated by many small holes, through which project long, delicate, protoplasmic threads. These fine threads interlace when they touch each other, thus forming a sort of protoplasmic network outside of the shell. . . .

Most of the myriads of the simplest animals which swarm in the surface waters of the ocean belong to a few kinds of these shell-bearing Globigerinæ and Radiolaria. Large areas of the bottom of the Atlantic Ocean are covered with a slimy gray mud, often of great thickness, which is called globigerina-ooze, because it is made up chiefly of the microscopic shells of Globigerinæ. As death comes to the minute proto-plasmic animals their hard shells sink slowly to the bottom, and accumu-late in such vast quantities as to form a thick layer on the ocean floor. Nor is it only in present times and in the oceans we know that the Globigerinæ have flourished. All over the world there are thick rock strata which are composed chiefly of the fossilized shells of these simplest animals. Where the strata are made up exclusively of these shells the rock is chalk. Thus are composed the great chalk cliffs of Kent, which gave to England the early name of Albion, and the chalk beds of France and Spain and Greece. The existence of these chalk strata means that where now is land, in earlier geologic times were oceans, and that in the oceans Globigerinæ lived in countless numbers. Dying, their shells accumu-lated to form thick layers on the sea bottom. In later geologic ages this sea bottom has been uplifted and is now land, far perhaps from any ocean. The chalk strata of the plains of the United States, like those in Kansas, are more than a thousand miles from the sea, and yet they are mainly composed of the fossilized shells of marine Protozoa. Indeed, we are acquainted with more than twice as many fossil species of Globigerinæ as species living at the present time. The ancestors of these Globigerinæ, from which the present Globigerinæ differ but little, can be traced far back in the geologic history of the world. It is an ancient type of animal structure.

The Radiolaria, too, which live abundantly in the present oceans, especially in the marine waters of the tropical and temperate zones, are found as fossils in the rocks from the time of the coal age on. The siliceous shells of the Radiolaria sinking to the sea bottom and accumulat-ing there in great masses form a radiolaria-ooze similar to the globiger-inæ-ooze; and just as with the Globigerinæ, the remains of the ancient Radiolaria formed thick layers on the floor of the ancient oceans, which have since been uplifted and now form certain rock strata. That kind of rock called Tripoli, found in Sicily, and the Barbados earth from the island of Barbados, both of which are used as polishing powder, are composed almost exclusively of the siliceous shells of ancient and long-extinct Radiolaria. . . .

The primitive but successful life.—Living consists of the performing of certain so-called life processes, such as eating, breathing, feeling, and multiplying. These processes are performed among the higher animals by various organs, special parts of the body, each of which is fitted to do some one kind of work, to perform some one of these processes. There is a division or assignment of labor here among different parts of the body. Such a division of labor, and special fitting of different parts of the body for special kinds of work does not exist, or exists only in slightest degree among the simplest animals. The *Amœba* eats or feels or moves with any part of its body; all of the body exposed to the air (air held in the water) breathes; the whole body mass takes part in the process of reproduction.

Only very small organisms can live in this simplest way. So all of the Protozoa are minute. When the only part of the body which can absorb oxygen is the simple external surface of a spherical body, the mass of that body must be very small. With any increase in size of the animal the mass of the body increases as the cube of the diameter, while the surface increases only as the square of the diameter. Therefore the part of the body (inside) which requires to be provided with oxygen increases more rapidly than the part (the outside) which absorbs oxygen. Thus this need of oxygen alone is sufficient to determine the limit of size which can be attained by the spherical or subspherical Protozoa.

That the simplest animals, despite the lack of organs and the primitive way of performing the life processes, live successfully is evident from their existence in such extraordinary numbers. They outnumber all other animals. Although serving as food for hosts of ocean animals, the marine Protozoa are the most abundant in individuals of all living animals. The conditions of life in the surface waters of the ocean are easy, and a simple structure and simple method of performance of the life processes are wholly adequate for successful life under these conditions. That the character of the body structure of the Protozoa has changed but little since early geologic times is explained by the even, unchanging character of their surroundings. The oceans of former ages have undoubtedly been essentially like the oceans of to-day—not in extent and position, but in their character of place of habitation for animals. The environment is so simple and uniform that there is little demand for diversity of habits and consequent diversity of body structure. Where life is easy there is no necessity for complex structure or complicated habits of living. So the simplest animals, unseen by us, and so inferior to us in elaborateness of body structure and habit, swarm in countless hordes in all the oceans and rivers and lakes, and live successfully their simple lives.

1905

Secrets of the Ocean

WILLIAM BEEBE

—————

From *Log of the Sun*

I. INTEREST OF THE SEASHORE

WHETHER CONSIDERED FROM THE STANDPOINT OF the scientist, the tourist, or the enthusiastic lover of Nature, the shore of the sea—its sands and waters, its ever-changing skies and moods—is one of the most interesting spots in the world. The very bottom of the deep bays near shore—dark and eternally silent, prisoned under the restless waste of waters—is thickly carpeted with strange and many-colored forms of animal and vegetable life. But the beaches and tide-pools over which the moon-urged tides hold sway in their ceaseless rise and fall, teem with marvels of Nature's handiwork, and every day are restocked and replanted with new living objects, both arctic and tropical offerings of each heaving tidal pulse.

Here on the northeastern shores of our continent one may spend days of leisure or delightful study among the abundant and ever-changing variety of wonderful living creatures. It is not unlikely that the enjoyment and absolute novelty of this new world may enable one to look on these as some of the most pleasant days of life. I write from the edge of the restless waters of Fundy, but any rock-strewn shore will duplicate the marvels.

2. THE SEASHORE AT HIGH TIDE

At high tide the surface of the Bay is unbroken by rock or shoal, and stretches glittering in the sunlight from the beach at one's feet to where the New Brunswick shore is just visible, appearing like a low bluish cloud on the horizon. At times the opposite shore is apparently brought nearer and made more distinct by a mirage, which inverts it, together with any ships which are in sight. A brig may be seen sailing along keel upward, in the most matter-of-fact way. The surface may anon be torn by those fearful squalls for which Fundy is noted, or, calm as a mirror, reflect the blue sky with an added greenish tinge, troubled only by the gentle alighting of a gull, the splash of a kingfisher or occasional osprey, as these dive for their prey, or the ruffling which shows where a school of mackerel is passing. This latter sign always sends the little sailing dories hurrying out, where they beat back and forth, like shuttles traveling across a loom, and at each turn a silvery struggling form is dragged into the boat. . . .

If we watch awhile we will see a line of blackish seaweed and wet sand appearing along the edge of the water, showing that the tide has turned and begun to recede. In an hour it has ebbed a considerable distance, and if we clamber down over the great weather-worn rocks the hardy advance guard of that wonderful world of life under the water is seen. Barnacles whiten the top of every rock which is reached by the tide, although the water may cover them only a short time each day. But they flourish here in myriads, and the shorter the chance they have at the salt water the more frantically their little feathery feet clutch at the tiny food particles which float around them. These thousands of tiny turreted castles are built so closely together that many are pressed out of shape, paralleling in shape as in substance the inorganic crystals of the mineral kingdom. The valved doors are continually opening and partly closing, and if we listen quietly we can hear a perpetual shuss! shuss! Is it the creaking of the tiny hinges? As the last receding wave splashes them, they shut their folding doors over a drop or two and remain tightly closed, while perhaps ten hours of sunlight bake them, or they glisten in the moonlight for the same length of time, ready at the first touch of the returning water to open wide and welcome it.

A little lower down we come to the zone of mussels,—hanging in clusters like some strange sea-fruit. Each is attached by strands of thin silky cables, so tough that they often defy our utmost efforts to tear a specimen away. How secure these creatures seem, how safe from all harm, and yet they have enemies which make havoc among them. At high tide fishes come and crunch them, shells and all, and multitudes of carnivorous snails are waiting to set their file-like tongues at work, which mercilessly drill through the lime shells, bringing death in a more subtle but no less certain form. Storms may tear away the support of these poor mollusks, and the waves dash them far out of the reach of the tides, while at low water, crows and gulls use all their ingenuity to get at their toothsome flesh.

3. THE SEASHORE AT LOW TIDE

There are no ant-hills in the sea, but when we turn over a large stone and see scores upon scores of small black shrimps scurrying around, the resemblance to those insects is striking. These little creatures quickly hitch away on their sides, getting out of sight in a remarkably short time.

The tide is going down rapidly, and following it step by step novel sights meet the eye at every turn, and we begin to realize that in this narrow strip, claimed alternately by sea and land, which would be represented on a map by the finest of hair-lines, there exists a complete world of animated life, comparing in variety and numbers with the life in that thinner medium air. We climb over enormous boulders, so different in appearance that they would never be thought to consist of the same material as those higher up on the shore. These are masses of wave-worn rock, twenty or thirty feet across, piled in every imaginable position, and completely covered with a thick padding of seaweed. Their drapery of algæ hangs in festoons, and if we draw aside these submarine curtains, scenes from a veritable fairyland are disclosed. Deep pools of water, clear as crystal and icy cold, contain creatures both hideous and beautiful, somber and iridescent, formless and of exquisite shape.

4. SEA-ANEMONES

The sea-anemones first attract attention, showing as splashes of scarlet and salmon among the olive-green seaweed, or in hundreds covering the entire bottom of a pool with a delicately hued mist of waving tentacles. As the water leaves these exposed on the walls of the caves, they lose their plump appearance and, drawing in their wreath of tentacles, hang limp and shrivelled, resembling pieces of water-soaked meat as much as anything. Submerged in the icy water they are veritable animal-flowers. Their beauty is indeed well guarded, hidden by the overhanging seaweed in these caves twenty-five feet or more below high-water mark.

Here in these beautiful caverns we may make aquariums, and transplant as many animal-flowers as we wish. Wherever we place them their fleshy, snail-like foot spreads out, takes tight hold, and the creature lives content, patiently waiting for the Providence of the sea to send food to its many wide-spread fingers.

Carpeted with pink algæ and dainty sponges, draped with sea-lettuce like green tissue paper, decorated with strange corallines, these natural aquariums far surpass any of artificial make. Although the tide drives us from them sooner or later, we may return with the sure prospect of finding them refreshed and perhaps replenished with many new forms. For often some of the deep-water creatures are held prisoners in the lower tidepools, as the water settles, somewhat as when the glaciers receded northward after the Ice Age there were left on isolated mountain peaks traces of the boreal fauna and flora.

If we are interested enough to watch our anemones we will find much entertainment. Let us return to our shrimp colonies and bring a handful to our pool. Drop one in the center of an anemone and see how quickly it contracts. The tentacles bend over it exactly as the sticky hairs of the sun-dew plant close over a fly. The shrimp struggles for a moment and is then drawn downward out of sight. The birth of an anemone is well worth patient watching, and this may take place in several different ways. We may see a large individual with a number of tiny bunches on the sides of the body, and if we keep this one in a tumbler, before long these protuberances will be seen to develop a few tentacles and at last break off as perfect miniature anemones. Or again, an anemone may draw in its tentacles without apparent cause, and after a few minutes expand more widely than ever. Suddenly a movement of the mouth is seen, and it opens, and one, two, or even a half-dozen tiny anemones shoot forth. They turn and roll in the little spurt of water and gradually settle to the rock alongside of the mother. In a short time they turn right side up, expand their absurd little heads, and begin life for themselves. These animal "buds" may be of all sizes; some minute ones will be much less developed and look very unlike the parent. These are able to swim about for a while, and myriads of them may be born in an hour. Others, as we have seen, have tentacles and settle down at once.

5. FISH AND JELLY-FISH

Fishes, little and big, are abundant in the pools, darting here and there among the leathery fronds of "devils' aprons," cavernous-mouthed angler fish, roly-poly young lump-suckers, lithe butter-fish and many others.

Moving slowly through the pools are many beautiful creatures, some so evanescent that they are only discoverable by the faint shadows which they cast on the bottom, others suggest animated spheres of prismatic sunlight. These latter are tiny jelly-fish, circular hyaline masses of jelly with eight longitudinal bands, composed of many comb-like plates, along which iridescent waves of light continually play. The graceful appearance of these exquisite creatures is increased by two long, fringed tentacles streaming behind, drifting at full length or contracting into numerous coils. The fringe on these streamers is a series of living hairs—an aquatic cobweb, each active with life, and doing its share in ensnaring minute atoms of food for its owner. When dozens of these *ctenophores* (or comb-bearers) as they are called, glide slowly to and fro through a pool, the sight is not soon forgotten. To try to photograph them is like attempting to portray the substance of a sunbeam, but patience works wonders, and even a slightly magnified image of a living jelly is secured, which shows very distinctly all the details of its wonderfully simple structure; the pouch, suspended in the center of the sphere, which does duty as a stomach; the sheaths into which the long tentacles may be so magically packed, and the tiny organ at the top of this living ball of spun glass, serving, with its minute weights and springs, as compass, rudder, and pilot to this little creature, which does not fear to pit its muscles of jelly against the rush and might of breaking waves. . . .

Other equally beautiful forms of jelly-fish are balloon-shaped. These are *Beröe* fitly named after the daughter of the old god Oceanus. They, like others of their family, pulsate through the water, sweeping gracefully along, borne on currents of their own making.

6. STARFISH AND SEA-URCHINS

Passing to other inhabitants of the pools, we find starfish and sea-urchins everywhere abundant. Hunched-up groups of the former show where they are dining in their unique way on unfortunate sea-snails or anemones, protruding their whole stomach and thus engulfing their victim. The urchins strain and stretch with their innumerable sucker-feet, feeling for something to grasp, and in this laborious way pull themselves along. The mouth, with the five so-called teeth, is a conspicuous feature, visible at the center of the urchin and surrounded by the greenish spines. Some of the starfish are covered with long spines, others are nearly smooth. The colors are wonderfully varied,—red, purple, orange, yellow, etc.

The stages through which these prickly skinned animals pass, before they reach the adult state, are wonderfully curious, and only when they are seen under the microscope can they be fully appreciated. A bolting-cloth net drawn through some of the pools will yield thousands in many stages, and we can take eggs of the common starfish and watch their growth in tumblers of water. At first the egg seems nothing but a tiny round globule of jelly, but soon a dent or depression appears on one side, which becomes deeper and deeper until it extends to the center of the egg-mass. It is as if we should take a round ball of putty and gradually press our finger into it. This pressed-in sac is a kind of primitive stomach and the entrance is used as a mouth. After this follows a marvellous succession of changes, form giving place to form, differing more in appearance and structure from the five-armed starfish than a caterpillar differs from a butterfly. . . .

7. SEA-WORMS, SHRIMPS, AND PRAWNS

But to return to our tide-pools. In the skimming net with the young starfish many other creatures are found, some so delicate and fragile that they disintegrate before microscope and camera can be placed in position. I lie at full length on a soft couch of seaweed with my face close to a tiny pool no larger than my hand. A few armadillo shells and limpets crawl on the bottom, but a frequent troubling of the water baffles me. I make sure my breath has nothing to do with it, but still it continues. At last a beam of sunshine lights up the pool, and as if a film had rolled from my eyes I see the cause of the disturbance. A sea-worm—or a ghost of one—is swimming about. Its large, brilliant eyes, long tentacles, and innumerable waving appendages are now as distinct as before they had been invisible. A trifling change in my position and all vanishes as if by magic. There seems not an organ, not a single part of the creature, which is not as transparent as the water itself. The fine streamers into which the paddles and gills are divided are too delicate to have existence in any but a water creature, and the least attempt to lift the animal from its element would only tear and dismember it, so I leave it in the pool to await the return of the tide.

Shrimps and prawns of many shapes and colors inhabit every pool. One small species, abundant on the algæ, combines the color changes of a chameleon with the form and manner of travel of a measuring-worm, looping along the fronds of seaweed or swimming with the same motion. Another variety of shrimp resembles the common wood-louse found under pieces of bark, but is most beautifully iridescent, glowing like an opal at the bottom of the pool. The curious little sea-spiders keep me guessing for a long time where their internal organs can be, as they consist of legs with merely enough body to connect these firmly together. The fact that the thread-like stomach and other organs send a branch into each of the eight legs explains the mystery and shows how far economy of space may go. Their skeleton-forms, having the appearance of eight straggling filaments of seaweed, are thus, doubtless, a great protection to these creatures from their many enemies. Other hobgoblin forms with huge probosces crawl slowly over the floors of the anemone caves, or crouch as the shadow of my hand or net falls upon them.

The larger gorgeously colored and graceful sea-worms contribute not a small share to the beauty of Fundy tide-pools, swimming in iridescent waves through the water or waving their Medusa-heads of crimson tentacles at the bottom among the sea-lettuce. These worms form tubes of mud for themselves, and the rows of hooks on each side of the body enable them to climb up and down in their dismal homes.

8. HYDROIDS

Much of the seaweed from deeper bottoms seems to be covered with a dense fur, which under a hand lens resolves into beautiful hydroids,—near relatives of the anemones and corals. Scientists have happily given these most euphonious names—*Campanularia, Obelia,* and *Plumularia.* Among the branches of certain of these, numbers of round discs or spheres are visible. These are young medusæ or jelly-fish, which grow like bunches of currants, and later will break off and swim around at pleasure in the water. Occasionally one is fortunate enough to discover these small jellies in a pool where they can be photographed as they pulsate back and forth. When these attain their full size they lay eggs which sink to the bottom and grow up into the plant-like hydroids. So each generation of these interesting creatures is entirely unlike that which immediately precedes or follows it. In other words, a hydroid is exactly like its grandmother and granddaughter, but as different from its parents and children in appearance as a plant is from an animal. Even in a fairy-story book this would be wonderful, but here it is taking place under our very eyes, as are scores of other transformations and "miracles in miniature" in this marvellous underworld.

9. UNDER THE SURFACE

Now let us deliberately pass by all the attractions of the middle zone of tide-pools and on as far as the lowest level of the water will admit. We are far out from the shore and many feet below the level of the barnacle-covered boulders over which we first clambered. Now we may indeed be prepared for strange sights, for we are on the very border-land of the vast unknown. The abyss in front of us is like planetary space, unknown to the feet of man. While we know the latter by scant glimpses through our telescopes, the former has only been scratched by the hauls of the dredge, the mark of whose iron shoe is like the tiny track of a snail on the leaf mould of a vast forest.

The first plunge beneath the icy waters of Fundy is likely to remain long in one's memory, and one's first dive of short duration, but the glimpse which is had and the hastily snatched handfuls of specimens of the beauties which no tide uncovers, is potent to make one forget his shivering and again and again seek to penetrate as far as a good-sized stone and a lungful of air will carry him. Strange sensations are experienced in these aquatic scrambles. It takes a long time to get used to pulling oneself *downward*, or propping your knees against the *under* crevices of rocks. To all intents and purposes, the law of gravitation is partly suspended. and when stone and wooden wedge accidentally slip from one's hand and disappear in *opposite* directions, it is confusing, to say the least.

When working in one spot for some time the fishes seem to become used to one, and approach quite closely. Slick-looking pollock, bloated lump-fish, and occasionally a sombre dog-fish roll by, giving one a start, as the memory of pictures of battles between divers and sharks of tropical waters comes to mind. One's mental impressions made thus are somewhat disconnected. With the blood buzzing in the ears, it is only possible to snatch general glimpses and superficial details. Then at the surface, notes can be made, and specimens which have been overlooked, felt for during the next trip beneath the surface. Fronds of laminaria yards in length, like sheets of rubber, offer convenient holds, and at their roots many curious creatures make their homes. Serpent starfish, agile as insects and very brittle, are abundant, and new forms of worms, like great slugs,— their backs covered with gills in the form of tufted branches.

In these outer, eternally submerged regions are starfish of still other shapes, some with a dozen or more arms. I took one with thirteen rays and placed it temporarily in a pool aquarium with some large anemones. On returning in an hour or two I found the starfish trying to make a meal of the largest anemone. Hundreds of dart-covered strings had been pushed out by the latter in defense, but they seemed to cause the starfish no inconvenience whatever.

In my submarine glimpses I saw spaces free from seaweed on which hundreds of tall polyps were growing, some singly, others in small tufts. The solitary individuals rise three or four inches by nearly straight stalks, surmounted by many-tentacled heads. These droop gracefully to one side and the general effect is that of beds of rose-covered flowers. From the heads hang grape-like masses, which on examination in a tumbler are seen to be immature medusæ. Each of these develop to the point where the four radiating canals are discernible and then their growth comes to a standstill, and they never attain the freedom for which their structure fits them.

When the wind blew inshore, I would often find the water fairly alive with large sun-jellies or *Aurelia*,—their Latin name. Their great milky-white bodies would come heaving along and bump against me, giving a very "crawly" sensation. The circle of short tentacles and the four horse-shoe-shaped ovaries distinguish this jelly-fish from all others. When I had gone down as far as I dared, I would sometimes catch glimpses of these strange beings far below me, passing and repassing in the silence and icy coldness of the watery depths. These large medusæ are often very abundant after a favorable wind has blown for a few days, and I have rowed through masses of them so thick that it seemed like rowing through thick jelly, two or three feet deep. In an area the length of the boat and about a yard wide, I have counted over one hundred and fifty *Aurelias* on the surface alone.

When one of these "sun-fish," as the fishermen call them, is lifted from the water, the clay-colored eggs may be seen to stream from it in myriads. In many jellies, small bodies the size of a pea are visible in the interior of the mass, and when extracted they prove to be a species of small shrimp. These are well adapted for their quasi-parasitic life, in color being throughout of the same milky semi-opaqueness as their host, but one very curious thing about them is, that when taken out and placed in some water in a vial or tumbler they begin to turn darker almost immediately, and in five minutes all will be of various shades, from red to dark brown.

I had no fear of *Aurelia*, but when another free-swimming species of jelly-fish, *Cyanea*, or the blue-jelly, appeared, I swam ashore with all speed. This great jelly is usually more of a reddish liver-color than a purple, and is much to be dreaded. Its tentacles are of enormous length. I have seen specimens which measured two feet across the disc, with streamers fully forty feet long, and one has been recorded seven feet across and no less than one hundred and twelve feet to the tip of the cruel tentacles! These trail behind in eight bunches and form a living, tangled labyrinth as deadly as the hair of the fabled Medusa—whose name indeed has been so appropriately applied to this division of animals. The touch of each tentacle to the skin is like a lash of nettle, and there would be little hope for a diver whose path crossed such a fiery tangle. The untold myriads of little darts which are shot out secrete a poison which is terribly irritating.

On the crevice bottoms a sight now and then meets my eyes which brings the "devil-fish" of Victor Hugo's romance vividly to mind,— a misshapen squid making its way snakily over the shells and seaweed. Its large eyes gaze fixedly around and the arms reach alternately forward, the sucking cups lined with their cruel teeth closing over the inequalities of the bottom. The creature may suddenly change its mode of progression and shoot like an arrow, backward and upward. If we watch one in its passage over areas of seaweed and sand, a wonderful adaptation becomes apparent. Its color changes continually; when near sand it is of a sober brown hue, then blushes of color pass over it and the tint changes, corresponding to the seaweed or patches of pink sponge over which it swims. The way in which this is accomplished is very ingenious and loses nothing by examination. Beneath the skin are numerous cells filled with liquid pigment. When at rest these contract until they are almost invisible, appearing as very small specks or dots on the surface of the body. When the animal wishes to change its hue, certain muscles which radiate from these color cells are shortened, drawing the cells out in all directions until they seem confluent. It is as if the freckles on a person's face should be all joined together, when an ordinary tan would result.

10. THE DEPTHS

From bottoms ten to twenty fathoms below the surface, the dredge brings up all manner of curious things; basket starfish, with arms divided and sub-divided into many tendrils, on the tips of which it walks, the remaining part converging upward like the trellis of a vine-covered summer house. Sponges of many hues must fairly carpet large areas of the deep water, as the dredge is often loaded with them. The small shore-loving ones which I photographed are in perfect health, but the camera cannot show the many tiny currents of water pouring in food and oxygen at the smaller openings, and returning in larger streams from the tall funnels on the surface of the sponge, which a pinch of carmine dust reveals so beautifully. From the deeper aquatic gardens come up great orange and yellow sponges, two and three feet in length, and around the bases of these the weird serpent stars are clinging, while crabs scurry away as the mass reaches the surface of the water.

Treasures from depths of forty and even fifty fathoms can be obtained when a trip is taken with the trawl-men. One can sit fascinated for hours, watching the hundreds of yards of line reel in, with some interesting creature on each of the thirty-seven hundred odd hooks. At times a glance down into the clear water will show a score of fish in sight at once, hake, haddock, cod, halibut, dog-fish, and perhaps an immense "barn-door" skate, a yard or more square. This latter will hold back with frantic flaps of its great "wings," and tax all the strength of the sturdy Acadian fishermen to pull it to the gunwale.

Now and then a huge "meat-rock," the fishermen's apt name for an anemone, comes up, impaled on a hook, and still clinging to a stone of five to ten pounds full weight. These gigantic scarlet ones from fifty fathoms far surpass any near shore. Occasionally the head alone of a large fish will appear, with the entire body bitten clean off, a hint of the monsters which must haunt the lower depths. The pressure of the air must be excessive, for many of the fishes have their swimming bladders fairly forced out of their mouths by the lessening of atmospheric pressure as they are drawn to the surface. When a basket starfish finds one of the baits in that sunless void far beneath our boat, he hugs it so tenaciously that the upward jerks of the reel only make him hold the more tightly.

Once in a great while the fishermen find what they call a "knob-fish" on one of their hooks, and I never knew what they meant until one day a small colony of five was brought ashore. *Boltenia,* the scientists call them, tall, queer-shaped things; a stalk six to eight inches in length, with a knob or oblong bulb-like body at the summit, looking exactly like the flower of a lady-slipper orchid and as delicately colored. This is a member of that curious family of Ascidians, which forever trembles in the balance between the higher back-boned animals and the lower division, where are classified the humbler insects, crabs, and snails. The young of *Boltenia* promises everything in its tiny backbone or notochord, but it all ends in promise, for that shadow of a great ambition withers away, and the creature is doomed to a lowly and vegetative life. If we soften the hard scientific facts which tell us of these dumb, blind creatures, with the humane mellowing thought of the oneness of all life, we will find much that is pathetic and affecting in their humble biographies from our point of view. And yet these cases of degeneration are far from anything like actual misfortunes, or mishaps of nature, as Buffon was so fond of thinking. These creatures have found their adult mode of life more free from competition than any other, and hence their adoption of it. It is only another instance of exquisite adaptation to an unfilled niche in the life of the world.

1906

The Warrior Ants

CARYL P. HASKINS

From *Of Ants and Men*

WHENEVER A SOCIAL GROUP HAS BECOME SO EFFI-ciently organized that it has gained access to an adequate supply of food and has learned to distribute it among its members so well that wealth considerably exceeds immediate demands, it can be depended upon to utilize its surplus energy in the attempt to enlarge the sphere in which it is active. This condition, of course, parallels that of any growing organism, and it inevitably leads to expansionist policies. Expansion may be internal, as in the democratic human states and in very loosely-knit colonial organizations among ants, wherein the "interstices" of the social structure, so to speak, are large enough to permit considerable growth without the resistance of external pressure. Among more closely-knit societies of ants and men, however, this opportunity for internal growth is absent, and the only alternative is the subjugation of additional territory as feeding ground, and, at times, the domination of other organisms to aid in the program of expansion.

The structure of ant colonies renders them particularly prone to this sort of expansionist policy. With very few exceptions, ants of any given colony are hostile to those of any other community, even of the same species, and this condition is bound to produce preliminary bickering among colonies which are closely associated, even when they are very young. Beautiful examples of this sort of thing can be seen in the tropics among ants which habitually nest in cavities of plants, such as the ants of the genus *Azteca*, which nest in the hollow twigs of trees of the genus *Cecropia*. While the trees are quite young and inconspicuous members of the forest, their older twigs are entered by numbers of young, newly deälated queens of *Azteca*, seeking convenient and secluded spots in which to begin their colonies. The branches of many species of *Cecropia* are by habit spongy in the interior, but are supported at intervals by more solid woody septa. The

406

young queens hollow out the pithy portions to make their chambers, but leave the septa intact, thus isolating themselves from one another. This condition suits their purpose well, for, with very few exceptions, young queens dislike one another's society after the marriage flight, even though they be from the same colony. They are far from aggressive, however, and their natural inclination, when thrown together, is merely to build up walls between themselves. This represents the only truly tolerant phase in the life of the normal ant colony. Numbers of *Azteca* queens may come thus to reside side by side in a young developing *Cecropia*. Although they live in close proximity to one another, they have no communication. To all intents and purposes they are completely unaware of one another's existence.

This condition is too good to last. Young first broods of workers shortly come to maturity in each of the incipient communities, and perforate the walls of their homes to obtain egress to the surface of the twig. Their business in life is to bring home as much food as possible from the outside world. In this effort, all the workers of all the colonies are immediately brought into sharp competition for food sources, and the members of each colony are implacably hostile to those from any other. This condition shortly leads to much individual combat and the loss of very many workers, to the detriment of the growth of all the colonies. If the colonies be numerous, and of about the same age and strength, minor conflicts of this sort may persist for a long time, and the development of all the groups be seriously affected; for at this stage the loss of a single worker is a tremendous disadvantage to colonial growth. No one community will dare to invade the nest-chamber of another, because their relative strength is so nearly equal as to make the undertaking a highly hazardous one.

Eventually, however, as the *Cecropia* tree grows and emerges into the sunlight, as the number of its branches increases, as the foraging space upon it expands and the quantity of insect life parasitic upon it and available to the *Azteca* ants as food becomes greater, the condition of equilibrium in strength among colonies is bound to be disturbed. Some one or two communities become more favorably situated than the rest with respect to food supplies, and the numbers composing the groups increase correspondingly more rapidly. Pressure for room is felt by the fortunate colony in its narrow internodal chamber, and, emboldened by its increased numbers, it perforates the septum which sets it apart from its neighboring community. Immediate warfare ensues, in which the entire colony participates, and there are usually very considerable losses on both sides. Ultimately, the weaker colony is forced to flee the site and to seek dwelling elsewhere, usually entirely off the tree. With it will be carried such of its young as its surviving members can transport. The rest, abandoned in cavities of the deserted nest, will be found by the invaders. The young of alien colonies of ants are usually accepted and adopted by other members of the species, so these are quite likely to be added to the brood pile of the invaders, to swell the numbers of their next developing generation. The adopted insects, since their whole learning period as young adults will be spent in the company of the invaders, will become loyal members of their foster community.

The invading colony now settles in its new territory, re-excavates it, redesigns it to suit its own ends, and proceeds as before. Expansion of numbers is now quickened by the new opportunities for food-gathering which its conquest has brought. Later, the pressure of numbers is again felt, and the colony undertakes the raiding of a third community of its neighbors, with results similar to the second raid. The new territory, food-supply, and breeding and foraging grounds are appropriated in the same manner. In the meantime, similar strife has been going on among local neighboring communities on other parts of the tree, resulting in the selective elimination of all but a very few colonies. The interval between wars is longer now, for there is more room for development, and warfare, among ants as among men, is rarely undertaken for the fun of it. However, it is inevitable that the few remaining colonies, now enormously strengthened in numbers, should come into intolerable rivalry. The campaigns are now on a very much larger scale, are more elaborately carried forward, are more boldly waged, and last much longer. Finally, however, a single community will win and will dominate the entire tree. By the time the *Cecropia* has attained a large stature, it will be completely controlled by one colony of ants, and life for any alien upon it will be made so unpleasant that henceforward no young queens will attempt to start colonies there, and ant communities of other trees will not find it worth while to attempt campaigns there. The domination of the world, so far as the world lies within the ken of *Azteca*, has been completed, and henceforward a totalitarian state pursues a peaceful course, up to the point of its ultimate dissolution from internal causes.

The course of the conflicts just referred to is characteristic of the wars of the majority of ants. It is equally characteristic of the soil-nesting species which occur about our homes, although here the greater opportunities to find food, while avoiding neighboring colonies, allow stronger communities to coexist near to one another. However, the raiding spirit may be emphasized in many ants, to the extent that they become habitual pillagers of the colonies of aliens. In such cases, they quickly rob the domicile and as quickly depart, making no attempt at a permanent occupation. This habit is widely distributed among ants in general, and is particularly characteristic of the first of the slave-makers.

Such colonial warfare finds innumerable parallels in human society. It is especially characteristic of early tribal life the world over, and every young culture is featured by tribal wars similar to the intercolonial wars of young ant communities. So far, however, we have presented no analogue of the large-scale warfare which occupies mankind in its maturer years.

Before large-scale warfare can appear among ants, it is necessary that some sort of coöperation be exhibited between neighboring colonies of the same species. For the biological structure of ant society presages that the numbers of any single group must be limited by the fertility of one or a very few queens, and single colonies cannot hope to be great enough to accomplish any sort of world domination so long as they are without allies.

The first step in the changing of this condition is to be seen among certain rather benign earth-loving ants of the Formicine subfamily, notably in the genus *Acanthomyops*. These ants possess a very strong odor, so pronounced as to be readily sensed by human beings and to possess a marked resemblance to oil of citronella. Perhaps because of the strength of this odor, the far more delicate, presumably odoriferous, differences between ants of different colonies of the same species are not perceived. In any event, it has been noticed by many observers that differing colonies of this insect rather readily and peacefully fuse to form super-communities. This fact can easily be checked by any reader, since the ant is commonly found about many houses and gardens. Fusion results in the formation of a peaceful, giant community, and has very little if any effect upon the expansionist policy of the group. These ants are slow-moving and subterranean, largely vegetarian in habit, and are in the pastoral stage of development. They keep great numbers of root aphids, which are carefully attended, and whose cultivation provides a satisfactory store of nutriment in a restricted feeding territory, and absorbs so much of the energies of the nurses that little effort is spent in acquiring more than a modest portion of soil, considering the size of the community. The tendency of these ants to mix with one another is of great significance, however, for as soon as any species of ant acquires the power to form a large state of ants of that species, its power of world domination becomes very greatly increased.

Pheidole megacephala is a small yellow Myrmicine ant, now known in the tropics around the world. The ant possesses the sharp differentiation into soldier and worker castes characteristic of its genus, and is distinctly aggressive. It appears originally to have been a grain-harvesting species, at least in part, like so many of its allies, and the structure of the mandibles of the soldiers, admirably fitted to act as crushers for hard objects, is still retained. In times of need it reverts, even today, to its ancient habits. Its original home was in the tropics of the Old World, presumably in some relatively dry region in which its grain-harvesting habits would be of particular value. The island of Madagascar seems its most likely homeland, since the greatest numbers of its varieties are found there. *Megacephala*, however, seems to have been characterized by a degree of energy, as a race, and a degree of acuteness, as an exploiter of its environment, which are astonishing. Within the last century it began a campaign of exploitation which has left it racially predominant in the tropics throughout the world. This is a very different sort of conquest from the simple colonial warfare which we have surveyed, and is worth careful analysis.

Abandoning the seed-harvesting habits which have for thousands of years been characteristics of its genus, *megacephala* took up two new habits which have been of tremendous significance. It began to cultivate aphids and other coccids, thus reverting from an agricultural to a pastoral existence, and it became adapted to nesting in ships and other conveyances used by man. While it retained its ability to survive in dry areas, it sought environments, such as man-made structures, which were practically free from the social competition of other species. Once it had undertaken the role of the house and ship ant, it was literally transported to the ends of the earth. It was introduced into many islands of the Atlantic and Pacific, and proceeded in its conquest in a very definite way. We have a particularly good picture of the way in which this happened in Madeira, thanks to the observations of Heer.

Pheidole megacephala apparently came into Madeira early in the nineteenth century. At first it confined its nesting sites and its foraging activities almost wholly to the houses and gardens of the settlers, where food was abundant and the competition of foreign species small. New types of bulbs and other plants appeared in the settlers' gardens, and before long they became infested with aphids and such sweet-excreting insects. *Pheidole* promptly took charge of these insects, encouraged their increase, and fed largely upon the manna which they produced. Gradually, as the pressure within its own species increased, and as the native ants weakened with the advent of man, *Pheidole* pushed back into unsettled territory. It first established itself in the bleaker, less hospitable regions of the Island, in which it alone was fitted to survive. With these regions as a base, it shortly raided more attractive ground, and began a

steady, deadly push against the less hardy, less adaptable, and less organized types. Mass raids are the rule with *Pheidole*, and hosts of the tiny
creatures evidently invaded nest after nest of larger but more loosely
organized species, killing the queens, and forcing the workers to evacuate.
Their own losses in workers were terrific, but the great fecundity of their
queens maintained the pressure of numbers, and the race pushed onward.
When Heer visited Madeira in 1852, no species of ant save *Pheidole*
could be found. It had occupied every crack and cranny from the shore
line to the highest crest of the Island, and had become a serious house
pest. Outdoors it fed on dead insects, occasionally on seeds, and cultivated
aphids and other forms of nectar-producing insects. Indoors it abandoned
every form of raiding and cultivation and subsisted quite simply on
human food stuffs.

Once the conquest of the Old World was fairly under way, *Pheidole*
crossed the Atlantic and established itself in various places in the West
Indies and elsewhere in the New World. And here it may now be seen
in the process of establishing its conquest. The Bermuda Islands, in 1929,
were rather extensively occupied by a handsome species of *Odontomachus*,
known as *Odontomachus hæmatoda*, var. insularis. This genus of ant
represents one of the most active, resourceful, and aggressive of the
Ponerines of today—one of the very few which is in any sense dominant
among modern ants. It is probably of relatively recent origin among
Ponerines, as the evolution of that ancient subfamily goes, and is distributed, in one species or another, around the world, *hæmatoda* being especially widespread. The ants are large, active, and aggressive, and in all
probability represent the remains of a fauna which was nearly dominant
among the Ponerines in late Tertiary times. Individually, it is far superior
in size, strength, and sense-organs to *Pheidole*. Its colonies, however,
although large and closely-knit for a Ponerine, are still far inferior in
numbers and powers of coördination to those of the tiny *megacephala*.
In 1929, *Odontomachus* was quite abundant on the higher parts of the
main island of Bermuda, nesting particularly under stones and logs in
the rich, grassy vales of the cedar groves. Along the shore line, existing
in the most inhospitable situations in shifting sands and between blocks
of coral, almost exposed to the salt spray, were numerous active communities of *Pheidole megacephala* which had probably come on a ship not
long before. Today *Odontomachus hæmatoda* is almost extinct in its
former haunts among the cedars, and instead *Pheidole* colonies are to be
found in every patch of sod. In the few *Odontomachus* colonies remaining
on the Islands great numbers of *Pheidole* workers are to be found killing

and carrying off the larvæ, fastening themselves in myriads to the bodies of the workers, and forcing their early abandonment of the site.

Within another ten years, the Ponerine species, which has inhabited Bermuda as its undisturbed Arthropod mistress for millennia, and has in fact developed a characteristic variety there, will have been exterminated. Such are the powers which lie in close social organization and large-scale concerted action among ants, as among men.

Pheidole megacephala, while far inferior in strength and senses, as an individual, to *Odontomachus*, is much superior in organization. It is, however, a Myrmicine ant, and the Myrmicine organizations are excelled as a whole by those of the Formicines and certain Dolichoderines. This is true of the Dolichoderine genus *Iridomyrmex*, and a species of this group, *humilis*, recently undertook a drive for world domination which has been even more striking and successful than that of *Pheidole*.

The workers of *Iridomyrmex humilis* are tiny, soft-bodied, dark-colored insects of extremely active, nervous habit. They are somewhat smaller than the workers even of the tiny *Pheidole*, and, instead of being protected by a heavy chitinous armor, they are very fragile and easily destroyed. Unlike *Pheidole*, they have no sting whatever, and the only means of individual defense which they possess is a white, sticky secretion which can be emitted from the anal glands, but which is of very dubious value as a weapon. Altogether this creature would seem much less able than *Pheidole* to cope with the world. *Humilis*, however, possesses certain social advantages over *Pheidole*. The members of its colony are more closely coördinated than those even of *Pheidole*. They habitually forage in column, and their sensitiveness enables them to exploit new advantages more readily than the more stolid Myrmicine. Of particular advantage to them is the distribution of their reproductive function. *Pheidole* has retained the ancient Myrmicine habit of rearing very large, bulky queens, expensive to produce and to maintain, but well adapted to the foundation of colonies in the classical fashion. Consistent with this behavior-pattern is the fact that individual colonies of *Pheidole* ordinarily recognize only the single queens which founded them. They are therefore highly vulnerable, for it is only necessary for an invader to slaughter this single queen to cause the destruction of the colony. *Iridomyrmex* has remedied this condition to a remarkable degree. The queens of *Iridomyrmex* are tiny, soft-bodied, and active, but little larger in stature than the workers. Very many are permitted to coexist in a single colony. Queens of this type are easily and inexpensively reared in large numbers. They are, of course, unable to found their colonies in the ancient, independent way prevalent among most ants, but this method is no longer necessary under the new living conditions of the *humilis* community. Instead, colonies of these ants bud and divide again and again, each new division taking a few queens with it, and thereby rendering itself nearly impregnable against extermination. The old division of colony from colony, so long prevalent among ants, has nearly been broken down, and a world-state of a single species, through which queens may be uniformly distributed, is being substituted.

Armed with these social weapons, *Iridomyrmex humilis* a few years ago undertook a campaign of expansion which has left almost no part of the tropical world which is inhabited by humans unknown to it. Its original home seems to have been Argentina. Like *Pheidole*, it became an adept at living within houses and ships, and has made extremely good use of man in extending its range. It apparently entered the United States at New Orleans several years ago, and thence has spread eastward and westward along the southern tier of states until today it is known and detested from Florida to California. It has crossed the Atlantic and has appeared in such widely separated localities as Portugal and Cape Colony. It has arrived and established itself in Sicily and in southern Italy, about Naples. It has infested the Canary Islands, and has made its appearance in France and in the vicinity of Hamburg in Germany. More clever than *Pheidole* in taking full advantage of human habitations, it has used them to extend its climatic range, and has established itself in Guernsey and in various parts of the British Isles, even penetrating as far north as Edinburgh. Considering the size of the organism, its colonizing travels and conquests, which have carried it from Argentina to England, and south and eastward into Asia within a period of little more than fifty years, are impressive indeed.

Madeira is a crossroads for the traffic of the South Atlantic, and as such it could hardly better be missed by *Iridomyrmex*, coming from the western New World, than by *Pheidole* in its march from the East. Accordingly, the former arrived some time between 1852 and 1898, and immediately came into conflict with *Pheidole*, which had by 1852 exterminated all of the native ants of its environment, as we have seen. Nowhere could a better theatre of action have been found for the observation of this conflict of two world-conquering races. Proceeding by methods almost identical with those employed by *Pheidole* on the same soil a half-century or less earlier, but undoubtedly with the superior strategy born of its more complex organization, *Iridomyrmex* completely displaced the earlier invader, and today Madeira is overrun with the foraging columns of the tiny brown "Argentine ant" pest, while the *Pheidole* colonies of yore are not to be found. The conquest is complete, and the relative merits of this

Myrmicine and this Dolichoderine ant as world-conquerors have been determined for all time.

The analogies to human behavior in the local wars and the general wars of conquest of ants are numerous and obvious. Small tribal warfare and general wars of replacement have featured human history ever since society became complex. The analogies in these cases, moreover, seem to be real throughout, and do not require qualifications. This is true, of course, because the fundamental aims of conquest—increased food and shelter—are identical for ants and men, and the means of obtaining them are similar for both races.

It is less easy to see among ants than among men why some races should suddenly take up an expansionist policy, and shortly come to dominate very large tracts, when hitherto their existence had followed the same quiet pattern as that of surrounding related groups. *Pheidole megacephala* is but one species of a huge, structurally homogeneous genus that is rather thoroughly distributed over both hemispheres. Why should it alone, of all its contemporaries, suddenly have abandoned the traditional, peace-loving, grain-harvesting mode of life, and become extremely fecund and aggressive?

The genus *Iridomyrmex*, and the allied genus *Tapinoma*, contain many species of closely similar insects, all of whose opportunities and excuses for world expansion would seem to be as obvious as those of *humilis*. Yet no one of them has behaved in a fashion even remotely similar to its brilliant and dramatic, if destructive, relative.

1939

The Vampire Bat

RAYMOND L. DITMARS
AND
ARTHUR M. GREENHALL

———

THE STUDIES OF THE VAMPIRE BAT, DESMODUS
rotundus, outlined here were suggested to the senior author in the
summer of 1932 during a collecting trip in Central America. The trip was
concluded with a call upon Dr. Herbert C. Clark, Director of the Gorgas
Memorial Laboratory in Panama. . . . Several vampires were under
observation at the Memorial Laboratory. They had been maintained for
a number of months on a diet of blood obtained at a nearby slaughter-
house and defibrinated to keep it in fluid condition. Here was a demonstration of the practicability of maintaining this highly interesting species
as an exhibit at the Zoological Park. Dr. Clark, however, could spare none
of his specimens. . . .

The senior author decided to return to Panama the following summer
and search the caves where vampires had been captured. Hence in August
of 1933, accompanied by Arthur M. Greenhall, then a student at the University of Michigan, Panama was again visited and Dr. Clark provided
guides to explore the Chilibrillo Caves in the Chagres Valley. We were
informed that the caves were of limestone formation, with horizontal
tunnels. In some parts these gave way to large chambers, from which again
other tunnels led into the mountain. We were equipped with headband
lamps and batteries carried on our belts.

In a shack near the caves was an illustration of the frequency with which
humans may be bitten by vampire bats. A boy about 10 years old had been
bitten five times during a week, and always on the under surface of his
toes while he slept. He had bled profusely, and the earthen floor beneath
his slatted bed was blood-stained each morning.

The route to the caves led through cattle trails in low, green tangle, with
ankle-deep mud most of the way, as the period was the rainy season. There

was a steep slope near the caves and a growth of rain forest. The Panaman guides, pushing through barricades of vines, disclosed a hole in the ground. It appeared to be little more than the entrance to a coal chute. We slid in and found ourselves in a horizontal tunnel in which we could walk upright in single file. The tunnel soon grew wider and higher, the floor slippery with red mud. Through portions of this entering gallery there was swiftly flowing water, knee deep in places. It appeared to come through the sides, then to seep through crevices in the floor. By pointing a light overhead, a double procession of big bats could be seen, the two streams flying in opposite directions.

After we had worked forward a fair fraction of a mile, the subterranean stream gave way again to the slippery floor. The hallway became larger and now showed side galleries. The guides stopped there to assemble the handles of the nets by which the bats were to be taken. The atmosphere was unlike that of caves in the temperate latitudes; the air was hot, heavy, and sweetish, the latter condition resulting from the odor of thousands of bats. Common on the limestone walls were huge roaches, of pale, straw color. Another insect denizen, not apparent without search of nearby crevices, but possibly common enough, was a small, reddish, blood-sucking bug, coming under strong suspicion in recent studies of carrying the organism of Chagas fever, a disease produced by a trypanosome in human blood, diagnosed and discovered by Dr. Emilio Chagas. Here and there, in startling contrast on the walls, were spiderlike creatures with a spread of limbs of 5 inches or more....

We finally entered a big chamber, the arched ceiling of which appeared to rise about 50 feet. The ceiling looked smooth, yet it was rough enough to provide a hanging foothold for thousands of bats of several kinds. Each species hung in a cluster of its own, the smaller, insectivorous kinds and smaller fruit bats on the sides. Near the dome of the ceiling was a mass of spear-nosed bats in a cluster about 15 feet in diameter. These bats have a wing spread of about 20 inches and bodies the size of a rat. Our lights disturbed them and caused a great shuffling of wings and movement of innumerable faces. There was considerable chattering from these larger bats, and their teeth showed plainly.

The side galleries were also full of bats and we inspected these in search of the big carnivorous spear-nosed bats which could not be captured in the high chamber. We caught 18 and "fought" them into a mesh cage. All the while we were watching for vampires, which may be distinguished by their habit of running along the vertical walls and darting into crevices to hide. In a deep side gallery we found bats of a kind not noted in the large chamber, but again no vampires. After several hours we retraced our way along the subterranean stream until, with a feeling of relief from the oppressive atmosphere, we saw a faint glow that showed we were close to the entrance of the cave.

After a breathing spell we sought and found the entrance to another cave shown on our chart. The route sloped easily toward a circular chamber fully 100 feet in diameter, though not more than 8 feet high. Here were hundreds of bats hanging in clusters, and all of one kind—a medium-sized spear-nosed bat of a fruit-eating species. They were not timid and could be closely approached before they took flight. When a hand was waved close to them the result was a pouring of winged bodies from the ceiling until the air was filled. Again we made an unsuccessful search of the walls for vampires.

The third cavern had an almost vertical entrance through a well-like shaft. There was not room enough to get down with the nets. We lowered ourselves into the hall, reached a horizontal turn-off, and on flashing our lamps against the wall, saw several bats run like rodents along the vertical surface, then dart into crevices. We immediately identified them as vampires, but all escaped.

With lights turned out we waited a half hour, but the bats did not reappear. We explored another gallery and found a spot where a slender man might squeeze through. We were too fatigued to continue, however.

The only other passage sheered off at a ledge beneath which ran a channel of water, from wall to wall, which looked as if it were quite deep. There the day's reconnoiter ended.

The following morning we returned to the cave where the vampires had been seen and with much caution descended to the widened area, keeping the lights out and feeling our way. Ready with some small nets we had prepared the previous evening, we flashed the lights on the wall where the bats had been seen, but no vampires were anywhere in sight.

We reasoned that the vampires had retreated into the recesses of the tunnel with the deep water, or into the narrow shaft where only a slender man could get through. Greenhall worked into this small, horizontal shaft and saw several vampires in a widened space ahead. He captured two and the others made their way into the tunnel with the deep water, which connected with a passage ahead.

Of the two vampires captured, one soon died. It was half grown and possibly had been injured in the net. The other, an adult female, lived for approximately 4 months after capture and, slightly more than 3 months after being caught, gave birth to a single vigorous infant. While as yet we do not know the period of gestation, the length of time from capture of the mother to birth of the young shows a surprisingly long period of pregnancy for such a small mammal.

After obtaining the female vampire, we left for the Atlantic side of the Canal Zone. Dr. Clark provided two quarts of defibrinated blood, fresh from the automatic refrigerator of his laboratory, but from that moment until we reached New York the vampire was a problem. We were naturally very keen to get it back alive. We were not worried about the 18 big carnivorous bats; they were feeding ravenously and fresh meat could be readily obtained. With an assortment of crates containing reptiles and amphibians, and cases of preserved specimens for the museums, we boarded a train for Colon. The defibrinated blood was in a package beside us, and the cage containing the vampire was swathed in black cloth. Dr. Clark had cautioned us to get the blood on ice again as soon as possible.

On the Atlantic side it was necessary for the senior author to stop 2 days at the Navy Submarine Base at Coco Solo to deliver several lectures. The commanding officer invited us to stay at his residence and here the defibrinated blood was placed on ice, while the bat was domiciled in the garage. That night some of the blood was measured out in a flat dish. The amount would have filled a fair-sized wine-glass. The bat hung head downward from the top of its cage when the dish was placed inside and would not come down to drink while we were there. Early the next morning we inspected the cage and found the dish nearly empty.

That routine never varied during the 10 days' voyage to New York, with stops at Colombian ports. We never saw the bat drink the blood, but in the quiet of the night she took her meal. At the Park the senior author decided to keep the vampire in the reptile house where the temperature was automatically maintained and the atmosphere was damp, like a greenhouse. In roomy quarters she quickly settled down. Blood was defibrinated in the Park's research laboratory and the dish was never placed in the cage until dark. For several weeks, however, despite cautious inspections with a flashlight, no observations of her visits to the dish could be made, although at some time during the night the blood was consumed.

At last the vampire became tame enough to show a lively interest when the dish was placed in the cage. She would crawl down the mesh side a few steps, peer at the dish, then creep back to her favorite nook in a corner, where she would hang head downward, by one leg. Each night she came further down and wandered along the sides of the cage before retreating. Her deliberate motions were surprising: A slow stalk, head downward, and a retreat equally deliberate. Her subsequent actions added much to information gleaned from the history of the species.

When the blood had been set in the cage, the observer took his stand in what developed into a series of nightly vigils. Finally there came a night when the bat descended the side of the cage with her usual deliberation. Reaching the bottom, she started across the floor with wings so compactly held that they looked like slender forelimbs of a 4-footed animal. Her rear limbs were directed downward. In this way her body was reared a full two inches from the floor. She looked like a big spider and her slow gait increased that effect. Her long thumbs were directed forward and outward, serving as feet. Anyone not knowing what she was would have been unlikely to suspect her of being a bat. In this trip to the dish it appeared that an unpublished habit of the vampire had been observed, and this, possibly, was the method the bat used for prowling over a sleeping victim in seeking a spot to use the highly perfected teeth in starting a flow of blood.

But other revelations were in store. Bending over the dish, the bat darted her tongue into the sanguineous meal. Her lips were never near the blood. The tongue was relatively long. It moved at the rate of about four darts a second. At the instant of protrusion it was pinkish, but once in action it functioned so perfectly that a pulsating ribbon of blood spanned the gap between the surface of the fluid and the creature's lips. In 20 minutes nothing remained but a red ring at the bottom of the dish. The bat's body was so distended that it appeared spherical. She backed off from the dish, appeared to squat, then leap, and her wings spread like a flash. She left the floor and in a flying movement too quick for the eye to follow hooked a hind claw overhead and hung, head down, in her usual position of rest. Gorged and inverted, she preened herself like a cat, stopping occasionally to peer out of the cage in the light of the single, shielded lamp to which she had become accustomed.

Summarized, these observations appear to add much to the history of Desmodus. In less than half an hour it had been demonstrated that the vampire can assume a walking gait as agile as a 4-legged animal; that the reason for its long thumb is its use as a foot on the wing stalk; that it is not a blood-sucking creature as has long been alleged; that it can gorge itself prodigiously and assume an inverted position to digest its meal.

The problem of recording these actions on motion picture film was at once considered. The outlook was doubtful. If the vampire had been hesitant about performing up to that evening in the illumination of a single, shielded light, it appeared that lights of enough actinic power for photography, yet tolerable upon the bat, would necessitate a slow introduction and increasing the strength of the lamps. The observer's plan was to build up the illumination, night after night, through a resistance coil, or dimmer.

Two weeks were spent in gradually increasing the strength of the light. Ultimately the bat tolerated three 500 watt bulbs, with a reflector. The scenes were exposed on 35 mm pancromatic film. The lens employed was a 4-inch Zeiss, with long light-cone. Results were clear and satisfactory.

Since contentions as to new habits, based upon a single specimen, are far more satisfactory if they are afterward substantiated by observations of additional individuals, it was determined that field observations should be continued and additional vampires obtained during the summer of 1934. Meanwhile the junior author started a search of the literature for observations other than the mere statement that the vampire is a blood-sucking animal. . . .

Charles Darwin appears to have been the first scientist to observe a vampire in the act of drawing blood and note its procedure with satisfactory clarity. He secured a bat and definitely recorded the sanguineous habits of Desmodus. Previous to this, several larger species of bats had been under suspicion. Darwin's (1890) observation, however, did not change the belief that Desmodus was a blood-sucking type. Nor could anything to the contrary be found in comparatively recent writing until the publication of an article by Dr. Dunn (1932) containing the following:

> The vampire does not suck blood, as popularly believed, but takes it up with its tongue, seldom placing its mouth on the wound except when the latter is first made or when the bleeding is very slow. If the wound bleeds freely, the bat simply laps up the blood, hardly touching the tissues, while if the bleeding is scant the bat licks the wound.

Thus Dunn's observation, but a few years past, takes precedence, as far as could be found, in rectifying a long procession of erroneous inferences about the feeding habits of the vampire.

In further elucidation is a letter from Dr. Clark, dated April 18, 1934, and reading in part:

> Our vampire does not suck the blood. It uses its tongue to collect the blood, in a back and forth motion, rather than as a dog or cat laps up water and milk. I have seen them feed from the edge of cuts on horses, but, of course, never got close enough under these conditions to see the tongue in action. Animal feedings offered the bats under laboratory conditions establish the fact that they lick the blood.

As to the quadrupedal gait of the vampire, apparently the first mention of it is in the works of the Rev. J. G. Wood (1869), who states that vampires can walk, rather than grovel like other bats, but the description is insufficient in indicating the habit.

Dr. William Beebe (1925), in his book outlining experiences in British Guiana, states:

We ascertained, however, that there was no truth in the belief that they (vampires) hovered or kept fanning with their wings * * *. Now and then a small body touched the sheet for an instant, then, with a soft little tap, a vampire alighted on my chest.

Slowly it crept forward, but I hardly felt the pushing of the feet and pulling of the thumbs as it crawled along. If I had been asleep, I should not have awakened.

Dr. Beebe's observation, though made in the dark, is good substantiation of the senior author's surmise about the soft gait of the bat in reconnoitering its prey. Dr. Beebe's description of the pushing of the feet and pulling with the thumbs does not however, define the actual action of the vampire, which walks, with body well elevated from the ground and the elongated thumbs used as feet.

In further substantiation of the observation that the bat has a walking gait, the senior author was informed by Sacha Siemel, an explorer of the Brazilian jungle, that while he was conducting a party close to the Bolivian frontier, a number of vampires attacked the horses. Mr. Siemel, with a flashlight, carefully noted the actions of the bats. Some he saw lapping blood from fresh wounds, while others, as yet undecided upon areas to bite, stalked back and forth over the animals' backs, walked among the matted leaves of the forest floor, or hopped from one spot to another.

OBSERVATIONS DURING 1934

For the tropical reconnoiter of this year, the senior author planned a trip along the entire chain of the West Indies, terminating at its southerly end in collecting work in Trinidad and British Guiana. The junior author left a month ahead, on July 19, bearing a letter which put him in contact in Trinidad with Prof. F. W. Urich of the Imperial College of Tropical Agriculture. Professor Urich he found engaged in an investigation, operating on a government grant, of the transmission of paralytic rabies by vampire bats. . . . Several days after arrival in Trinidad the junior author, accompanied by William Bridges, captured seven vampire bats in the Diego Martin Cave.

The newly captured bats were taken to the Government stock farm and placed in a small framework building with sides of wire screen. In this building was another vampire that had been under the observation of Professor Urich for about 3 months. He had studied its feeding habits on goats and fowls. This bat was tame enough to come down and feed while observers stood quietly in the room. Notes made by Professor Urich during the studies by himself and his field assistant appeared in the monthly reports of the Board of Agriculture of Trinidad and Tobago. From these, Professor Urich granted permission to quote as follows:

May report. (Observation on May 19, 1934.) When I got there at 9:40 p. m., found the bat feeding on the left foot of the cock, about 1 inch below the spur. The bat does not suck the blood, but laps it. Bat fed for 12 minutes from the time I arrived, the cock standing absolutely still. Then the cock started to walk, the bat following along the ground, and fed again. The cock became restless and walked away. Then it went into a corner of the cage, on the ground. [Observation by Wehekind.]

June report. (Observation on June 27, 1934.) Bat started feeding at 8:30 p. m. and finished at 8:40 p. m., being so gorged that he could scarcely fly. Bat dropped straight on goat and started to feed. No hovering. [Observation by Wehekind.]

In a later report.

As the Desmodus fed readily in captivity on fowls or goats, Mr. Wehekind was able to ascertain the method of feeding of these bats on fowls. It is quite different as stated in some records, the principal features of which are that the bat does not hover around its victims, does not suck blood, and does a fair amount of walking around on the victim to secure a suitable place for feeding. This is carried out by making a narrow groove in the place selected and lapping up the blood as it exudes from the wound. The bat always returns to an old wound on the same animal on its daily feeding. All these observations were verified by me (F. W. Urich) on several occasions.

The junior author of the present review adds the following notes from observations made in the screened house where the bats were quartered:

On Friday, August 3, 1934, at 6 p. m., Prof. F. W. Urich and myself went to the Government stock farm to see the condition of the captive vampire bats. One male vampire has been under Professor Urich's observation since May 18. It is known as "Tommy." When we caught seven additional vampires, Tommy was placed in a cage by himself, as it was known that he was free from paralytic rabies. Professor Urich then attempted to feed Tommy with defibrinated blood. The bat was used to feeding upon goats and fowls that were introduced into the cage and evidently did not relish the diet of prepared blood in a small dish. It seems to have taken a small quantity, but we thought it best to release it with the others after the necessary quarantine.

At the time we entered the bat cage we found that a goat had been placed inside for the other vampires to feed on. The goat had been freshly bitten, as I noted three open wounds, two on the left side of the neck and one on the right, from which blood was oozing.

The goat was calm, standing in one corner and no bats were feeding when we entered. Tommy was released from his quarantine quarters, flew and attached himself by the hind foot on the screening of the house, about a foot and a half from the sill. The goat was standing not far away from the vampire. The bat remained hanging for about 5 minutes, the thumbs bracing the body, the wings folded close to the arms. After a short interval, the bat showed signs of movement. The head nodded; the lips were drawn back, exposing the large canines and protruding incisor teeth. The bat's gaze finally rested upon the goat. I was watching approximately 4 feet away from the bat and the goat was nearer to me. Slowly the bat moved down the screen, a deliberate stalk. The fore and hind feet were lifted high from the wiring and the body was well above the mesh. The bat stalked down and I noticed that the movement of the forearm in the stride was exceptionally slow, the wings folded tightly. From 2 to 3 minutes were required to traverse the distance from the original position to the sill. Upon arriving at the edge of the sill, the vampire hung from its hind feet and dangled over the edge into space. There, it remained for about 2 more minutes. The goat was still standing in the same position. Suddenly and silently the vampire launched itself into the air and lightly landed on the middle portion of the goat's back. There was still no movement on the part of the goat. I moved quietly forward until I was but 2 feet from the goat. Tommy stalked to the shoulder and neck regions of the animal. After a minute or so of searching, the bat buried its head close to the skin of the goat. There were a few up and down motions of the bat's head (the act of pushing aside the pelage and of biting). The goat then took a few steps forward and turned its head to the right and left. The bat drew itself up but continued the nodding motions. The goat walked around the room rather rapidly, the vampire hanging on and thus riding its host. The goat passed by me, then stopped, and I noticed that blood was exuding from a small wound and the bat was lapping it with a rapid darting of the tongue. The goat started to walk again and passed under a sort of table, a board of which brushed heavily against the animal's back. The goat was, in fact, obliged to slightly lower itself to pass under. The vampire quickly scuttled down the shoulder of the goat to avoid being brushed off. When the goat cleared the table the bat as quickly returned to the wound and continued lapping. We then forced the goat to go back under the table several times, the bat dextrously avoiding being hit by dodging down the shoulder. The movement was very agile and reminded me somewhat of the behavior of a crab. The bat could move both forward, backward, and sideways, but seemingly preferred head first.

I then reached out my hand and succeeded in touching the vampire, which attempted to dodge. It did not, however, make any movement to fly. The goat by now was exceptionally restless and ran back and forth around the room. It was a timid animal and it was of us that it was afraid. When we left, the bat was still riding the goat.

Later visits to the enclosure showed some of the other bats flying down from the ceiling, landing on "all fours" upon the floor, then hopping like toads from one spot to another, instead of assuming the walking gait. On one occasion a bat was seen to be so gorged and heavy from its sanguineous meal that it slid off the back of a goat to the floor. It was unable to launch itself in flight from the floor, hence climbed the wall, with head inverted, and when midway up launched itself in flight, returning to its customary hanging place on a ceiling beam.

When the senior author arrived in Trinidad, he spent considerable time observing the bats during the early evening, in the screened room. His notes on feeding actions would be nothing more than repetition of what has already been brought out. What he noted particularly was the general tolerance of the goat to bats which crawled over its back or even wandered up the neck to the head. For a time after alighting on a goat, the vampire was not inclined to bite, but rested on the dorsal area, a bit forward of the shoulder, or clung to the side, where it looked like a big spider. The wandering of the bat upon the strangely tolerant host, the occasional lifting of the bat's head, the leer that disclosed its keen teeth, and the observer's realization that all of this pointed to a sanguineous meal, produced a sinister and impressive effect.

When the wound had been made, the tongue of the bat seemed to move slower than when lapping blood from a dish, and was extended far enough to come well in contact with the tissue. Goats of the laboratory herd, which had been previously bitten while heavily haired, showed bare spots surrounding the area of former wounds. The wounds themselves had healed as a slightly indicated ridge, from three-sixteenths to a quarter of an inch in length, but the area devoid of hair was as large as, or larger than, one's thumbnail. Apparently the hair had been shed in the area of the wound. Here may be a condition of "desensitization" in a vampire bite, with attending destruction of hair follicles. It has been suggested, though not with satisfactory evidence, that the saliva of the bat contains an anticoagulant, which might account for many bites bleeding for several hours. The term "desensitization," as here used, may be rather a loose one, but it signifies that something abnormal has happened to the tissue besides the opening of a mere wound by specialized and lancing incisor teeth. There can certainly be no injection of an anticoagulant, but there is a possibility of the application of some salivary secretion during the action of the bat's lapping tongue—a secretion retarding the formation of a clot about the wound.

Field observations in Trinidad indicated vampire bats to be fairly common, but not generally distributed. Near the base of the Aripo heights, particularly, frequent bites were reported. The bats attacked cattle, swine, and poultry. Sows were bitten upon the teats and the wounds in healing so shriveled these members that the animals were unable to nurse their young. Most fowls were unable to survive the loss of blood and were found dead in the morning.

Around a dish of defibrinated blood, the feeding motions of the four vampires brought back from Trinidad duplicated the notes made upon the Panama specimen of the preceding year, though the latter represented a different subspecies. The animals so gorge themselves that their bodies become almost spherical. This gorging consumes from 20 to 25 minutes.

In some experiments with large fowls, weighing up to 8 pounds, the bats were observed to be extremely cautious in their approach, slowly stalking in a circle wide enough to keep out of reach of the bird's bill. An action of that kind might readily kill a light-bodied bat. After several circular maneuvers, an approach was made to the fowl's feet, the bat feeling its way forward inch by inch, and finally nibbling gently at the under surface of the toe. This appeared to serve the purpose of getting the fowl accustomed to its toe being touched. If the fowl made an abrupt move, the bat would dart backward, then slowly stalk forward to resume its attack. Whether any slight "shaving" of the tissue was taking place and a salivary secretion was being applied by the tongue it was impossible to determine, as the bats were too timid to bear extremely close inspection. After these preliminaries, however, the mouth was rather slowly opened as if to gauge precisely the sweep of the incisor teeth, and then there was a quick and positive bite. While it has been customary to allege the utter painlessness of vampire bites, in several instances where fowls were under observation, there was a decided reaction of motion on the birds' part, showing that the bite was sharply felt. If the fowl moved, the bat darted back, but immediately returned to the wound, now freely bleeding. From this point the bat continued its meal and the fowl paid no further attention to it.

. . . Experiences of reliable observers point to a remarkable painlessness of the average vampire bite. There are statements that victims knew nothing of the attack, and would have remained ignorant of such a happening had they not found blood stains the following morning. An expedition from the University of Michigan in Santa Marta, Colombia, may be cited (Ruthven, 1922):

. . . We had been raided during the night by vampire bats, and the whole party was covered with blood stains from the many bites of these bats. It may seem unreasonable to the uninitiated that we could have been thus bitten and not be disturbed in our sleep but the fact is that there is no pain produced at the time of the bite, nor indeed for some hours afterward.

In a previous paragraph it has been noted that a fowl, introduced into a cage with vampires, flinched upon being bitten, this observation being made by the senior author. Examining some of the recent studies of Dunn, it appears that the younger bats are not so expert in effecting their bites and that experimenters testing the bites of various specimens upon the human forearm occasionally found bats that dealt decidedly painful bites.

1935

Ancestors

GUSTAV ECKSTEIN

THE FIRST MORNING OF MY VISIT TO THE STATION A doctor took me on his rounds—not from room to room but from cage to cage. We started at the Maternity Building. One mother was a giantess. A hundred and seventy-five pounds she weighed. Mona was her name. Next her was another who, the doctor said, might give birth as early as to-morrow. The third never had had a baby, yet waited with a quiet as if she had had a hundred. Suddenly Mona shuffled foward to the chain-link netting, chewed thoughtfully at a straw, and her infant that lay low against her abdomen dug its scrawny feet into her groin and its thin fingers caught at the hair at either side of her breast. That infant had the oldest face I think I ever saw.

The birth of an ape—the process does not seem like the birth of a calf or a kitten, but more like that of a child, the female period long like ours, the gestation long like ours, the creature that comes forth almost the wrinkly thing that we see in our obstetrical wards. It is light brown to black, pink-palmed, pink-soled. There is of course none of our excitement, no family in a dither, no waiting pacing father. It all goes more unobtrusively, more swiftly. A blunt laboratory record reads: "At 3:30 p.m. the outcries of an infant in a cage adjoining Cuba's attracted attention, and the newborn Peter was discovered."

This Maternity Building is one of a neat group that make up the southern division of the Yale Laboratories of Primate Biology. The buildings began to spring up in 1930, on a spot that had been sand and disorderly sub-tropical foliage, a mile from Orange Park, fifteen miles from Jacksonville. The hollow tile and stucco were bought with Rockefeller money, wisely spent, but the dream, the patience, the energy were Robert Mearns Yerkes', world-known animal psychologist. Northern Florida was chosen because it would be healthful, fairly warm for the apes and not too hot for the scientists, far enough into the country not to have every passerby drop in, and close enough to a city to have supplies near at hand and a railroad that ran you as promptly as possible back to New York or to the parent laboratories in New Haven. The purchase was two hundred acres, only eight of them fenced in, Mrs. Yerkes herself overseeing the gardening, so that to-day these anthropoid experimental laboratories are a place where it is pleasant to live and stimulating to work. The purpose of the Station is to breed the chimpanzee, study it, mind and body, make both the records and the bred animals available for a great range of investigations not only at Yale but everywhere in the country.

The Station's firstborn was a female. They called her Alpha. Her mother, Dwina, died of childbed fever. Thus the director had an orphan on his hands. He called into consultation a pediatrician, who made out a diet list used for human infants. They were to start Alpha on water, corn syrup, evaporated milk, lemon juice. At the fourth month cooked cereals were to be added, at the sixth month puréed vegetables, at the twelfth, banana and Chimcracker, this last with ground bone baked in. In all her earliest performances Alpha was just a little faster than the human infant, otherwise much the same, called impatiently for her food, played with her bottle when it was empty, sucked her thumb when there was not enough. She weighed 4.97 pounds at birth, lost up to the sixth day, regained her original weight by the fifteenth, doubled her weight by the ninetieth, tripled it by the one hundred and eighty-second. In short, she was an all-round model baby.

We left the Maternity Building. We crossed a grassy court to the Nursery. We approached its first cage. Two were plastered against the inside like two bats and a third was swinging on the ceiling. They were Ami, four years old, Cap, two years, Dan, a year. The doctor opened the cage. Ami threw her arms around his neck. He carried her off, weighed her (all nursery inmates are weighed every day of their first year), brought her back. Cap was weighed, brought back. But while Dan was on the scales the doctor stopped to talk with me, told me of some experiments that the scientists are performing on the chimpanzee mind. They are producing neuroses, with the hope that something may be learned from the chimpanzee concerning insanity in man. This talk lasted only about five minutes, but the two left in the cage were in a fury when the doctor returned. They scolded him, welcomed Dan, overdid the welcome, walked arm in arm with him, dramatized everything, treated him as if he had been off for seven months to the South Seas.

We went on to the next cage. This next one's name was Ben. He looked me over. I was wearing a white silk suit. He waited till he had me at the right distance, then between his two front teeth shot a stream of water that caught me head to foot. He kept back a little and let me have that later. Six years old. Born clown. I went into his cage. He threw himself down on to the floor, rolled at full length, lumpy as a sack of potatoes. Suddenly out of the roll he hurled his forty pounds against me, and when he saw that I staggered he made insulting noises with his mouth. He should be sold to a circus. Later I heard his family history, and it was one to warm the heart of a social worker. "Mother, Pati, a bad health risk, relatively inactive, not trustworthy. Father, Pan, heavy, apathetic, of a low intelligence." There was a slum child, unmistakably.

In a building to the left on the second floor is the beginning of an Experimental Nursery. All were taken from their mothers at birth. All will be kept two or three years. All will be exposed to a minimum of childhood infections. All will be washed in a tub. All will wear diapers. I once saw a chimpanzee baby in diapers, and a shock of pain it gave me for that little foreigner so far from its own country.

II

Orang-utan, chimpanzee, gorilla, those are the great apes. Below them in scale are the Old World monkeys and the New World monkeys. Below those are the tarsiers and the lemurs. Put man at the head of the list, and you have them, the primates. They are mammals, nursed by their mothers and come from their mothers, not from eggs. You can see the whole primate parade in any good-sized zoo.

Man has an unsatisfiable curiosity in man. He digs up fossil man. He pries into the races of himself, the black, the brown, the yellow, the white. He believes that beyond fossil man and beyond the great apes, a million years ago, there was once a form, lost now, with more both of ape and man than any form we know, from which both sprang. The ape branch changed comparatively little in that million years, the man branch comparatively much.

Now what you can learn from fossil man is limited, and when you try to study living man his prides get in the way, so the chimpanzee is an increasingly valuable piece of living material. Many things can be learned from it. Many practical human problems can be attacked through it, problems of disease, of the uses of drugs, problems of inheritance, even of social behavior. The records at the Station already go from fingerprints to intelligence quotients. Yet if you are not a specialist, if you are just visiting at Orange Park, watching what goes on in the cages, you find yourself soon becoming a bit contemplative and philosophical.

Could these really be your ancestors? When you are at home with your friends you can feel lighthearted about an objectionable relative, but if the relative drops in on you, and especially if he looks a bit like you, it is another story. In other words, face to face with a gallery of chimpanzees, all ages, thirty-two living portraits, you are bound to ask yourself: "Can these after all be that close to me in the line of man's descent?" You know the arguments. You have decided one way or another. But with the opportunity in front of you you cannot resist a somewhat unscientific search for evidence. I myself even imagined I saw signs of those great steps by which we are thought to have arrived where we are. I mention three. (1) The Rise to the Erect Posture. (2) The Free Use of Hands. (3) Speech.

III

On the second day of my visit I was standing by the Enclosure—a space run round with a 14-foot fence, part galvanized chain-link netting, part steel plate. The Enclosure was a test project. There was to be a much larger one if it worked. Grass and trees were to be planted, a family of chimpanzees to be let in, and to be studied as in its native haunts. The Enclosure was made ready. The chimpanzees were let in. Promptly they removed leaves, branches, bushes, stripped the little jungle. So there was left the space. A shelter was built in the middle of it, and two mature ones, Pan and Josie, were established out there, might stay out all winter, develop fine furs.

It was late afternoon when I was standing by the Enclosure. The buzzards were floating blackly in the Florida sky, a carcass somewhere below. I began picturing to myself the African brush, a chimpanzee trail, a chimpanzee nest, four or ten together, a leader, all for the moment munching at some edible roots. Then, from the shack, Pan leaned out his head and shoulders. He saw me. Noiselessly he dropped to the grass, approached me by that shifty walk that goes forward by going left and right, reached the chain-link netting, lifted his humanoid head from between his shoulders, and, slowly, solemnly, significantly, rose from four feet to two, rose to the erect posture, rose through half a million years of history, and, as if to emphasize what he had done, lifted high his right arm and rested his hand against the chain-link. Back in the shelter, Josie, thinking perhaps that her old man was getting into trouble, now also leaned out, saw me, noiselessly dropped to the grass, came forward by the same shifty walk, reached the chain-link netting, slowly, solemnly, significantly, rose from four feet to two, lifted high her right arm and rested her hand against the chain-link. Male and Female. They might have been Adam and Eve.

I had by now got my eyes so full of chimpanzee that when a man passed me I realized that I had seen him pass me on his two hind feet.

Pan and Josie would not have found it comfortable long to stand that way. They would not have found it comfortable to walk that way. That little silent scene was only a preview ages in advance, and the interpretation only me amusing myself. Yet when the anthropologist explains to us how he thinks the thing actually did take place you can get the impression that he is amusing himself too.

There were trees over Asia, and the apes swung in the branches, and that was their mode of locomotion. Then the Himalayan mountains pushed up out of the earth. The land to the south continued treed, and the apes continued to swing in the branches. But the land to the north was barren, and the apes there went mostly on all fours. However, one ape tried to go on two, tried hard enough and long enough, and therefore, if you take the Lamarckian point of view, finally was able to do it, and had the satisfaction of looking out over all the others. Or, one ape was just able to do it, was born that way, and having that advantage was selected, if you take the Darwinian point of view, anyway also had the satisfaction of looking out over all the others. What that ape did not know was that it possessed the beginning of the domination of the earth.

IV

For there was something of more importance in this than the mere satisfaction. There was something more valuable even than the erect posture. That ape henceforth had its two hands free.

Freedom of the hands, and from that shortly the use of tools, and from that by stages the world that a man knows—a place where he could begin henceforth magnificently to create and appallingly to destroy.

Each chimpanzee apartment at Orange Park consists of a cage partly roofed, and behind it a small living room. Thus a chimpanzee can be out-of-doors in the sun, out-of-doors in the shade, or if he is chilly can go back into his room which is artificially heated and crawl into his box to sleep. A heavy gravity door divides cage from room. Every chimpanzee is able to operate his gravity door, even to slam it if he is in a temper, or to throw it open and give a cold to the whole dormitory, or jam his arm between if man attempts to shut it from the outside, and otherwise so neatly to control it that not once in the ten years of the Station's history has a chimpanzee baby got caught by its hand or foot. Now, to operate a gravity door is a very simple thing to do, but—it is the use of a tool.

When Doctor Yerkes laid out these apartments he needed to get drinking water into them. He considered fountains with plungers. He was advised against this, nevertheless trusted his chimpanzees, sank the drinking fountains into the concrete. Then the big day came. The first chimpanzee pushed his plunger, had his drink, and the knowledge ran like fire through dry wood. Every chimpanzee pushed his plunger, had his drink. To push a plunger is a very simple thing to do, but—it is the use of a tool.

In the psychological experiments that are the chief work at the Station chimpanzees turn knobs, press electric buttons—have an air of doing this only for a serious purpose, like a man sounding the horn of his car when traffic gives him an excuse, but with the same secret joy that no observant eye misses. They also pull ropes, stack boxes, fit pegs into holes, and so on. Yet these hands that are on many occasions so capable may on others be as wild and purposeless.

Wendy is a middle-aged female. Wendy had got hold of a piece of iron pipe. How she got hold of it nobody knew, but it must be taken away from her. The way you do that is trade for a banana. So you may have a scientist on one side of the chain-link, a chimpanzee on the other, bargaining—give me the pipe, I'll give you the banana. This with Wendy was a long affair. Several times she seemed ready to make the trade, but each time withdrew the pipe again, suddenly waxed angry, seized the scientist's hand, sank her teeth into a finger, the flesh tearing out along the bone as he pulled away. He drew his revolver. She rushed at him in a rage. He fired the blank cartridge straight at her. A neighboring chimpanzee fled off in terror. Wendy merely carried the pipe to the back of her cage and glowered from there. Eventually the pipe was taken away, had to be, for sooner or later intelligent Wendy might begin in a most unintelligent manner to beat, beat, beat, in a few hours might hammer through the concrete floor of her cage, beat, beat, beat, without purpose to her, without purpose to anyone, reminding you of some of the actions of our own insane, beat, beat, beat, no more purpose in the machine, but the machine chugs on.

In the twilight I saw Wendy squatting in the shadow of her door. She was like a sculpture of Rodin. Lifted in front of her were her hands. She seemed bored. The hands were there, Wendy was there, but the full rich nervous connections between the hands and Wendy were not yet there. So Wendy waited. You could hardly say she waited impatiently, for no one can wait impatiently through several hundred thousand years, nevertheless with some look of eternal expectance in her face—waited on those hands to establish further connection with that brain, when stone implements would rise, then bronze, then a Stuka bomber or the iron gates of Benvenuto Cellini.

v

The brain of a small chimpanzee will weigh as little as 300 grams. The brain of a large gorilla as much as 650 grams. The brain of the lowest fossil man, Pithecanthropus erectus, less than 1000 grams. Our brains, the human male brain, 1300 to 1500 grams. The brain of the Neanderthal man, 1700 grams. The brain of Ivan Turgenev, 2100 grams. So the chimpanzee brain is at one extreme with 300 grams, the brain of the great Russian at the other with 2100 grams, yet the smaller is in many respects an almost exact replica of the larger. The chimpanzee's is lacking especially in that part that gives to us our noble brow. There is doubtless less of that area of brain with which we do the more intelligent acts of our hands. And there is definitely an almost entire absence of that other man-cherished area—the area of speech.

I was brought to a consideration of speech one morning when I stepped out of the Administration Building. I heard a mewing. I knew the voice. Bokar's. A fine male. I reached his cage. He tipped the top of his head toward me, wanted me to scratch his pate. I did. Abruptly he tipped the top of his head away from me, I should give some attention under his chinless jaw. I did. He pushed one hand through the chain-link netting. I subjected the top of two of his fingers to the most exquisite tactile stimulation—both of us thought that. The next moment, however, the lower reflex animal in him got the better of him, and he clutched my hand, and, having clutched it, his dignity forbade him to return it, so, by way of keeping everything pleasant between us, he presented me his sensitive abdomen. I did. All of this was accompanied by tones, many modulations, very intimate, very friendly, almost amorous. Speech. Private conversation.

Suddenly he backed off to the middle of the cage. He smacked his lips.

He clapped his hands. He shaped a fist. A heavy automobile tire was suspended by a chain from the ceiling. He sent the tire up there with a boom. He liked that. He drove it up again. He leapt forward, grabbed hold of his cage, shook it till you knew why everything down there is anchored in concrete, at the same time spoke, *uh, uh, uh, uh,* his pursed lips belching like a gun mouth. She in the cage beyond pounded with her bare feet. He in the cage beyond hers pounded with his bare hands. Then in a faraway cage someone smothered all this noise in one high scream that was taken up on every side till the whole Station reverberated. It was that extension of zoo that is Africa. Social conversation.

Doctor Yerkes once tried to teach a chimpanzee to speak. The results are published in a small interesting book. A hole was cut into the wall of the observing room, a chute made to lead from the hole for pieces of banana, the observer placing himself by the hole, dropping in a piece and repeating a syllable, *ba, ba, ba, ba,* and doing this day after day. Other devices, other syllables, but the chimpanzee did not learn to speak. The chimpanzee has a vocal apparatus like ours, but cannot be made to imitate us in tones. The experiment was reversed. A worker with a good ear went among the chimpanzees, wrote out on music paper the notes, rests, rhythms, that accompanied actions, food, persons. The conclusion drawn was that, though the chimpanzee does not speak in our sense, it does have a meager substitute, a limited vocabulary.

Think what speech has done for man. It has given him the earth. Report of a small invention in Chicago is printed in a Tokyo newspaper, in that way it becomes added to a small invention made in Tokyo, to another made in London, to another made in Rome, and an airplane in consequence is accelerated fifty miles an hour. On Thursday last a discovery is completed in the Rockefeller Institute, is telephoned to Shanghai, and on the following Tuesday in consequence a life is saved in China. And though a chimpanzee in a moonlit lane may have some definitely moonlit feelings, at least it cannot transmit them next day at noon to someone who was not there, in a radiogram. One suspects, further, that since a chimpanzee mother in her inexperience may crush her infant, and since down the whole biological line mothers may destroy their young when it is not convenient to sustain them, the human mother also might kill more often than she does except for tutorage. And man's monopoly on tutorage he owes to speech. That is, moral quality also comes out of speech. Without speech no religion. Without speech no philosophy. No science. No art. No Shakespeare. No voting. No daily newspaper. No stock market quotation. No propaganda. No war. To be sure, a day may come when man will go back into silence again and be no less great on that account, think more, bear his own company better, settle his problems more honestly and more wisely. Feelings in such a man might stay with him longer than ours do with us, not so quickly escape in sound.

VI

It was my last night at Orange Park. Doctor and Mrs. Yerkes were driving me after supper from their house toward the laboratories. The road goes in and out of a corridor of Spanish moss pinned up on the branches of the water oaks. There was a half moon, a mystic light. We arrived outside the fence that surrounds the eight acres. In there they slept.

Toward five o'clock that afternoon I had stood in front of a cage. One came out of her door. She looked at me. Possibly she wanted me to go away. I stayed. She lay down on her back on the floor. She looked at me. I stayed. She drew both her knees up on to her belly, as I have done with my own knees in my own bed. She looked at me. Would I not have the good breeding to go away? I stayed. She put one hand up under her head, and her disgust with me now was plain, turned away her face, soon snored.

In there they slept. Some on their left sides, some on their right, some on their backs, some on their bellies.

If they were to escape?

They would be shot, Doctor Yerkes quickly assured me. The young ones, Ami, Cap, Dan, people might think them monkeys and not shoot them. But Pan with his low intelligence, and Bokar with his sensitive abdomen, and Wendy the shrew, they would be shot. People would flee from them in terror—but also in outrage—these living testimonials to their own source, these antique breathing fossils, that they should presume to walk abroad among men.

1940

C. THE EVOLUTION OF LIFE

Darwinisms

DARWIN'S FATHER:

"You care for nothing but shooting, dogs, and rat-catching, and will be a disgrace to yourself and all your family."

T. H. HUXLEY ON "THE ORIGIN OF SPECIES":

"It is doubtful if any single book, except the 'Principia,' ever worked so great and so rapid a revolution in science, or made so deep an impression on the general mind."

DARWIN:

"I think that I am superior to the common run of men in noticing things which easily escape attention, and in observing them carefully. My industry has been nearly as great as it could have been in the observation and collection of facts."

"Accuracy is the soul of Natural History. It is hard to become accurate; he who modifies a hair's breadth will never be accurate. . . . Absolute accuracy is the hardest merit to attain, and the highest merit."

"Facts compel me to conclude that my brain was never formed for much thinking."

"I have steadily endeavored to keep my mind free so as to give up any hypothesis, however much beloved (and I cannot resist forming one on every subject), as soon as the facts are shown to be opposed to it."

"If I am wrong, the sooner I am knocked on the head and annihilated so much the better."

"I had, also, during many years followed a golden rule, namely, that whenever a published fact, a new observation or thought came across me, which was opposed to my general results, to make a memorandum of it without fail and at once; for I had found by experience that such facts and thoughts were far more apt to escape from the memory than favorable ones."

"I am very poorly to-day, and very stupid, and hate everybody and everything. One lives only to make blunders."

"I have been speculating last night what makes a man a discoverer of undiscovered things; and a most perplexing problem it is. Many men who are very clever—much cleverer than the discoverers—never originate anything. As far as I can conjecture, the art consists in habitually searching for the causes and meaning of everything which occurs."

". . . I think I can say with truth that in after years, though I cared in the highest degree for the approbation of such men as Lyell and Hooker, who were my friends, I did not care much about the general public. I do not mean to say that a favorable review or a large sale of my books did not please me greatly, but the pleasure was a fleeting one, and I am sure that I have never turned one inch out of my course to gain fame."

"I look at it as absolutely certain that very much in the *Origin* will be proved rubbish; but I expect and hope that the framework will stand."

"It is a horrid bore to feel as I constantly do, that I am a withered leaf for every subject except Science. It sometimes makes me hate Science, though God knows I ought to be thankful for such a perennial interest, which makes me forget for some hours every day my accursed stomach."

"I do not believe any man in England naturally writes so vile a style as I do."

"Now for many years I cannot endure to read a line of poetry: I have tried lately to read Shakespeare, and found it so intolerably dull that it nauseated me."

"What a book a devil's chaplain might write on the clumsy, wasteful blundering, low, and horribly cruel works of nature!"

Darwin and "The Origin of Species"

SIR ARTHUR KEITH

WHEN H.M.S. *BEAGLE*, "OF 235 TONS, RIGGED AS A barque, and carrying six guns," slipped from her moorings in Devonport harbour on 27 December, 1831, the events which were to end in the writing of "*The Origin of Species*" were being set in train. She had on board Charles Darwin, a young Cambridge graduate, son of a wealthy physician of Shrewsbury, in the rôle of naturalist. On the last day of February 1832 the *Beagle* reached South America and Darwin, just entered on his twenty-fourth year, stepped ashore on a continent which was destined to raise serious but secret doubts in his mind concerning the origin of living things. He was not a naturalist who was content merely to collect specimens, to note habits, to chart distributions, or to write accurate descriptions of what he found; he never could restrain his mind from searching into the reason of things. Questions were ever rising in his mind. Why should those giant fossil animals he dug from recent geological strata be so near akin to the little armour-plated armadillos which he found still alive in the same place? Why was it, as he passed from district to district, he found that one species was replaced by another near akin to it? Did every species of animal and plant remain just as it was created, as was believed by every respectable man known to him? Or, did each and all of them change, as some greatly daring sceptics had alleged?

In due course, after surveying many uncharted coasts, the *Beagle* reached the Galapagos Islands, five hundred miles to the west of South America. Here his doubts became strengthened and his belief in orthodoxy shaken. Why was it that in those islands living things should be not exactly the same as in South America but yet so closely alike? And why should each of the islands have its own peculiar creations? Special creation could not explain such things. South America thus proved to be a second University to Charles Darwin; after three and a half years spent in its laboratories he graduated as the greatest naturalist of the nineteenth century. It had taken him even longer to obtain an ordinary pass degree from the University of Cambridge.

The first stage in the preparation of *The Origin of Species* thus lies in South America. The second belongs to London. The *Beagle* having circumnavigated the world returned to England in October 1836, and by his twenty-ninth birthday, 12 February, 1837, Darwin was ensconced in London with his papers round him working hard at his *Journal and Reports*, but at the same time determined to resolve those illicit doubts which had been raised by his observations in South America and which still haunted him, concerning the manner in which species and animals had come into the world. He knew he was treading on dangerous ground; for an Englishman to doubt the truth of the Biblical record in the year 1837 was to risk becoming a social outcast; but, for Darwin, to run away from truth was to be condemned by a tender conscience as a moral coward. He was a sensitive man, reflective, quiet, warm-hearted, ever heeding the susceptibilities of his friends. Added to this he was also intensely modest and as intensely honest, fearing above all things even the semblance of a lie in thought or in act. The facts he had observed in South America merely raised his suspicions. They suggested to him that animals and plants might become, in the course of time, so changed as to form new species. At first they were but suspicions, but as he proceeded to collect evidence in London, the suspicions deepened. More particularly was this the case when he inquired into the methods employed by breeders to produce new varieties of pigeons, fowls, dogs, cattle and horses. He soon realised that for the creation of new domestic breeds two factors were necessary—first there must be a breeder or selector, and secondly the animals experimented on must have in them a tendency to vary in a desired direction. Given those two factors, a new breed, having all the external appearances of a new species, could be produced at will.

Having satisfied himself on this point, he turned again to animals and plants living in a state of nature and found that they too tended to vary. "But where," he had to ask himself, "is Nature's selector or breeder?" At this juncture he happened to read an *Essay* written by the Rev. T. R. Malthus, first published in 1798, *On the Principle of Population*, and as he read, realised that the breeder he was in search of did exist in Nature. It took the form, he perceived, of a self-acting mechanism—a mechanism of selection. Among the individuals of every species, there goes on, as Malthus had realised, a competition or struggle for the means of life, and Nature selects the individuals which vary in the most successful direction. The idea that living things had been evolved had been held by many men before Darwin.came on the scene; it was already well known that animals tended to vary in form and in habit, but the realisation that Nature had set up in the world of living things an automatic breeder, which utilised variations as a means of progress, was entirely Darwin's discovery.

And thus it came about that during his second year in London (1838) and before he had completed the thirtieth of his life, Darwin had wrested from Nature one of her deepest secrets—a secret which gave him a clue to one of her many unsolved mysteries. Great ideas, if they are to come at all, usually come before a man is thirty and it was so in Darwin's case. In South America he had merely had doubts about the orthodox belief; the revelation which came in London convinced him that the real story of creation was quite different from the one usually told and accepted. With the discovery of the law of Natural Selection in 1838 *The Origin of Species* entered its second stage of preparation, and it is convenient to regard this stage as ending in January 1839, when Darwin married his cousin Emma Wedgwood.

The third stage opened in September 1842, when he resolved to find peace for study and for health by removing his family from London to Down in the chalky uplands of Kent, where he lived until his death on 14 April, 1882. He had inherited money and resolved to devote his life to the solution of the old problem of creation, instead, as is so often the case with men of his class, to leisure and to sport. On his arrival at Down he believed he was in possession of a secret of momentous import—and so unholy that he determined to say nothing of it until he had attained complete certainty. He had at that time many researches in hand and, as he worked at them, he was ever on the outlook for evidence to prove the truth or untruth of his theory. We know that, just before he left London, he had permitted himself the luxury of seeing what his theory looked like when reduced to paper; that sketch, written in June 1842, is really the first outline of *The Origin of Species,* but it then filled only thirty-five pages of manuscript. It was not until 1844, when he had been two years at Down, and had amassed much additional evidence, that he committed to writing a complete exposition of his theory; this time he succeeded in filling 230 pages of manuscript. This third stage—the stage of accumulating evidence —continued with many intermissions until 1854, when the preparation of *The Origin of Species* entered its fourth stage.

In 1854 he completed his research on Barnacles—a seven years' task, and was thus free to set in systematic order the immense amount of evidence he had accumulated—all of it bearing upon the problem of transmutation or evolution of every form of life. This he now proceeded to do, but there were many interruptions. From time to time, while busy with many inquiries and experiments and sadly hindered by indifferent health, a chapter of his projected work was written and as his self-imposed task proceeded it became apparent to him it was to be a big book—three volumes at least. And so he went along until the summer of 1858 was reached, when on a day early in June the rural postman pushed into his letter-box a missive which gave him the shock of his life and brought his projected book to a sudden end. The postmark showed that the missive had been dispatched from an address in the Celebes Islands. In this sudden manner we pass from the fourth to the fifth and final stage in the preparation of *The Origin of Species*.

In the history of Science there is no episode so dramatic as that which compelled Charles Darwin to pass so abruptly to the fifth and final stage in the preparation of *The Origin of Species*. He was no longer a young man; he was in his fiftieth year. Let us look for a moment at the staging of this drama and the actors who took part in it. In February 1858, when Darwin, in his study at Down, was suffering from his "accursed stomach" and struggling painfully with his proofs of transmutation, another Englishman, Alfred Russel Wallace, was lying in the small island of Ternate, in the Malay Archipelago, suffering from bouts of malarial fever, and puzzling over the same problem as engaged Darwin's attention at Down. The writer has experienced these bouts of ague and knows how vivid is the imagery that then races through the brain and how nimbly the mind hunts along a train of ideas. Such a bout brought Wallace his revelation. He was fourteen years Darwin's junior. He was also a poor man, being dependent for a livelihood on the collections he made as a travelling naturalist. He, too, had visited South America just as Darwin had, and it was while collecting on the Amazon that he became impressed by the tendency of animals and plants to vary. Soon after his arrival in Borneo he had read, just as Darwin had done eighteen years before him, Malthus's *Essay on Population*. He had, before then, begun to suspect that species were not immutable, and as his brain raced along during his attack of fever in Ternate it stumbled across the idea which came to Darwin in London—the idea that the struggle would favour those individuals which tended to vary in an advantageous direction and that such individuals might continue to change until a new species was brought into existence. As soon as the attack of fever was over and his temperature had returned to normal he began to write, and at one sitting finished an account of his discovery—an idea which would explain the origin of new species without calling in the aid of any supernatural agency whatsoever. Having written his sketch, he thereupon addressed it to a man who was almost a stranger to him—*Charles Darwin Esq., F.R.S., Down House, Down, Kent*, where it duly arrived in the third week of June 1858.

On opening this missive Darwin found that the fears of his best friends, Sir Charles Lyell and Dr. Joseph Hooker of Kew Gardens, had come only too true; he had been forestalled. By a curious stroke of fate, the favourite child of his brain, which he had nursed and tended in secret for over twenty years, was suddenly deprived of that which is so dear to the heart of a father—the birthright of priority. Wallace's sketch, he found, was almost a replica of the one he himself had penned after his arrival at Down; and how much had he discovered and added to the original sketch in the intervening years! Darwin knew that if he acted rationally, and he was as nearly rational as men are made, he ought to welcome Wallace's communication. It was a confirmation of his own conclusions. He was ashamed to find himself troubled at heart over this paltry matter of priority. It is a long way from Kent to the land of Moriah and from Darwin's day to that of Abraham, but distant as are the places and the times, they are linked together by the same human nature. Abraham with his knife and bundle of faggots was resolved to make the supreme sacrifice and so was Darwin, and he would have done it had not his friends Lyell and Hooker intervened. They exercised a judgment worthy of Solomon; justice was to be done to both authors by a conjoint communication to a learned society. They asked Darwin to supply them with a brief abstract of his theory and this, with Wallace's sketch, they sent to the Linnean Society of London. The two papers were read at a meeting held on 1 July, 1858, and caused no great commotion.

This communication having been made, Lyell and Hooker insisted that Darwin must now prepare for publication, and he then began to work on *The Origin of Species* as we now know it. He set himself to abstract and to condense what he had already written. The opening chapters were finished in September 1858 but it took him fully twelve months of toil and tribulation before he could write *finis*. On 24 November, 1859, the book was published and thus ended the fifth stage in the preparation of *The Origin of Species*.

The publishers apparently did not expect a big demand for *The Origin*; at least they printed only 1250 copies. A second edition was called for in 1860—one of 3000 copies. A third appeared in 1861, a fourth in 1866, a fifth in 1869 and a sixth and final edition in 1872. Darwin lived for ten years after the issue of the sixth edition, but so thoroughly had he winnowed his data, so fully had he met the expert criticism of his time, that he did not feel called upon to make any further alteration in its text.

Such is a brief account of how *The Origin of Species* came to be written. Its preparation occupied, from first to last, a period of forty years, for its foundation was being laid in 1832 when Darwin began his researches in

South America, and its building was not finished until the last edition appeared in 1872. The book came into being during a period when Europe was in a state of intense intellectual activity, and the effect it produced was immediate and profound. The generation which felt its first shock is dying or dead. The generation which has grown up, like every new generation, is passing the household gods inherited from its predecessor through the fiery furnace of criticism. How is *The Origin of Species* to emerge from this ordeal? Having served its day and generation is it now dead? Or does it possess, within itself, the seeds of eternal youth and is it thus destined to become one of the world's perpetual possessions? The latter, I am convinced, is its destiny. On the foundations laid by Darwin in this book his successors have erected a huge superstructure which will be infinitely extended and modified as time goes on. Yet I feel certain that as long as men and women desire to know something of the world into which they have been born, they will return, generation after generation, to drink the waters of evolutionary truth at the fountain-head.

The Origin of Species is still freely abused and often misrepresented, just as it was when Darwin was alive. In his final edition he entered a mild protest—a luxury he rarely indulged in—against a misrepresentation to which his theory was persistently subjected. "But as my conclusions have lately been much misrepresented," he wrote, "and it has been stated that I attribute the modification of species exclusively to *natural selection*, I may be permitted to remark, that in the first edition of this work, and subsequently, I placed in a most conspicuous position—namely, at the close of the Introduction—the following words: *I am convinced that natural selection has been the main, but not the exclusive means of modification.* This has been of no avail. Great is the power of steady misrepresentation, but the history of science shows that fortunately this power does not long endure."

The power of error to persist is more enduring than Darwin thought; the misrepresentation of which he complained is being made now more blatantly than ever before. It is being proclaimed from the housetops that *The Origin of Species* contained only one new idea, and that this idea, the conception of natural selection, is false. Natural selection, some of his modern critics declare, is powerless to produce new forms of either plant or animal. Darwin never said it could. In his book the reader will find him giving warning after warning that by itself selection can do nothing. To effect an evolutionary change two sets of factors, he declared, must be at work together—those which bring about variations or modifications in animal or in plant and those which favour and select the individuals which vary or become modified in a certain direction. Why should so many critics continue to misunderstand the essentials of Darwin's theory of evolution?

Men do not wilfully persist in misrepresentation; there must be some explanation of their error. The truth is that Darwin himself was at fault; the full title he gave to his book was *The Origin of Species by Means of Natural Selection*. Plainly such a title was a misnomer, his book was and is much more than such a title implies; it was much more than a mere demonstration of the action of natural selection, it was the first complete demonstration that the law of evolution holds true for every form of living thing. It was this book which first convinced the world of thoughtful men and women that the law of evolution is true. Long before Darwin's time men had proclaimed the doctrine of evolution, but they failed to convince their fellows of its truth, both because their evidence was insufficient and because they had to leave so much that was unexplained. Darwin, on the other hand, brought forward such an immense array of facts in this book and set them in such a logical sequence that his argument proved irresistible. He never resorted to any kind of special pleading, but permitted facts to speak for themselves. However longingly his readers clung to age-long beliefs. Darwin compelled them to face facts and draw conclusions, often at enmity with their predilections. We all desire to be intellectually honest, and sooner or later truth wins. It was this book which won a victory for evolution, so far as that victory has now been won. When it appeared in the nineteenth century the Why and the How of evolution were immaterial issues. What had to be done then was to convince men that evolution represented a mode of thinking worthy of acceptance and in that *The Origin of Species* succeeded beyond all expectation. Nor has it finished its appointed mission. No book has yet appeared that can replace it; *The Origin of Species* is still the book which contains the most complete demonstration that the law of evolution is true.

This, then, is Darwin's essential service to the world—not that he discovered the law of Natural Selection—but that he succeeded in effecting a complete revolution in the outlook of mankind on all living things. He wrought this revolution through *The Origin of Species*. Darwin himself formed a true estimate of what the nature of this revolution was. In the last paragraph of his Introduction, he writes, "Although much remains obscure and will long remain obscure, I can entertain no doubt, after the most deliberate study and dispassionate judgment of which I am capable, *that the view which most naturalists until recently entertained, and which I formerly entertained—namely, that each species has been independently created—is erroneous. I am firmly convinced that species are not immutable.*" From this statement we see that Darwin's aim was to replace a belief in special creation by a belief in evolution and in this he did succeed, as every modern biologist will readily admit. No one was in a better position to measure what Darwin succeeded in doing than his magnanimous contemporary and ally Alfred Russel Wallace. Writing to Professor Newton of Cambridge in 1887, five years after Darwin's death, he penned the following passage: "I had the idea of working it out [the theory of natural selection], so far as I was able, when I returned home, not at all expecting that Darwin had so long anticipated me. I can truly say now, as I said many years ago, that I am glad it was so, for I have not the love of work, experiment and detail that was so preeminent in Darwin and without which anything I could have written *would never have convinced the world*." Darwin succeeded in convincing the world not only by his superabundance of proof but by the transparently honest way in which he presented his case. No one can read *The Origin of Species* without feeling that Darwin had the interests of only one party at heart—his client, Truth.

Darwin succeeded in convincing scientific men that the law of evolution is true of all living things and yet the manner in which evolution takes place—the machinery of evolution, described in his book—may be totally wrong. If this were really so, *The Origin of Species* would be altogether out of date. Some critics have insinuated as much.—But was Darwin wrong in his conception of the mode of evolution? . . . The machinery involved—is it out of date? My deliberate opinion is that the machinery of evolution described in his work is not out of date and never will be. Darwin perceived that two factors are concerned in evolution—one is "productive," the other is "selective." The productive factor gives rise to the materials of evolution—the points or characters wherein one individual differs from another—whether that individual be a plant or a human being. Such differences Darwin names "variations." How are such variations produced? In every chapter of his book the reader will find Darwin declaring that he does not know; the only point of which he felt certain was that individual differences do not arise by chance. He was of opinion that food, climate, and habit are concerned in the production of variations, but he also realised that there were other causes of variation inherent in the living tissues of plants and animals. Every year we are coming to know more and more concerning the production of variations; we begin to see that development and growth are regulated by an extremely complicated series of interacting processes. When we have come to a full knowledge of these processes and can explain how "variations" are produced, will *The Origin of Species* then pass out of date? It will *not*, because Darwin made full allowance for the ignorance of his time and for future knowledge; what we discover now and what our successors will find out about the production of "variations" serves and will serve to add fuel to the fire kindled by Darwin; further discoveries cannot extinguish that fire.

Our knowledge of the laws of heredity increases rapidly; Darwin expected such an increase and made allowance for it. He knew nothing of Mendel but he exemplifies the law now known by Mendel's name. However much our knowledge of heredity may progress, Darwin's position, as established in this book, will be but strengthened.

Thus we may regard the "productive" factor of Darwin's theory of evolution as fully established, but what of his "selective" factor? It has been often assailed, and many critics believe they have demolished it. Let readers judge for themselves. Let them watch the flock of sparrows which year after year frequents their gardens and note the dangers to which its members are exposed, and draw their own conclusion as to the "survival of the fittest." Or let them read the travels of observant naturalists, and judge whether or not a struggle is a condition of all living things in a state of nature. The law is said not to hold true in the world of mankind. We may do our best to debrutalise and to humanise the struggle, but competition prevails. Even Trades Unions compete with one another for increase of membership. One business house unites with other business houses so that the combination may compete the more successfully with all rivals. There is competition between nations and between human races. We increase our knowledge not merely for the glory of knowing, but that we may compete the more successfully. No one who views mankind with unprejudiced eyes can say that Darwin's law of selection is out of date. There is competition and struggle throughout the whole of Nature's realm. Nor do I think it can ever pass out of date in any form of human society unless man deliberately resolves to give up the struggle of life. As to what will happen in such a case the law of evolution leaves us in no doubt. The species which gives up the struggle becomes extinct. The revolution in outlook, effected by this book, was not confined to men who study the history of animals and of plants. Its conquest gradually spread until every department of knowledge was affected. No matter what a man's line of study might be—the stars, the earth, the elements, industry, economics, civilisation, theology or man himself—the inquirer soon began to realise that he must take the law of evolution as his guide. It was Darwin who changed the outlook of all gatherers of knowledge and made them realise that behind the field of their immediate inquiry lay an immense evolutionary or historical background which had to be explored before further progress was possible. Nay, it was Darwin who made men see that evolution is now everywhere at work—in all things material, moral and spiritual, and will continue in operation, so far as the human mind can anticipate, to the very end of time.

1928

Gregor Mendel and His Work

HUGO ILTIS

IT IS 120 YEARS SINCE, IN A SMALL VILLAGE ON THE northern border of what was called Austria at that time, a boy was born in a farmer's house who was destined to influence human thoughts and science. Germans, Czechs and Poles had been settled side by side in this part of the country, quarreling sometimes, but mixing their blood continually. During the Middle Ages the Mongolic Tatars invaded Europe just there. Thus, the place had been a melting pot of nations and races and, like America, had brought up finally a splendid alloy. The father's name was Anton Mendel; the boy was christened Johann. He grew up like other farmers' boys; he liked to help his father with his fruit trees and bees and retained from these early experiences his fondness for gardening and beekeeping until his last years. Since his parents, although not poor compared with the neighbors, had no liquid resources, the young and gifted boy had to fight his way through high school and junior college (Gymnasium). Finally he came to the conclusion, as he wrote in his autobiography, "That it had become impossible for him to continue such strenuous exertions. It was incumbent on him to enter a profession in which he would be spared perpetual anxiety about a means of livelihood. His private circumstances determined his choice of profession." So he entered as a novice the rich and beautiful monastery of the Augustinians of Bruenn in 1843 and assumed the monastic name of Gregor. Here he found the necessary means, leisure and good company. Here during the period from 1843 to 1865 he grew to become the great investigator whose name is known to every schoolboy to-day.

On a clear cold evening in February, 1865, several men were walking through the streets of Bruenn towards the modern school, a big building still new. One of those men, stocky and rather corpulent, friendly of countenance, with a high forehead and piercing blue eyes, wearing a tall hat, a long black coat and trousers tucked in top boots, was carrying a manuscript under his arm. This was Pater Gregor Mendel, a professor at the modern school, and with his friends he was going to a meeting of the Society of Natural Science where he was to read a paper on "Experiments in Plant Hybridization." In the schoolroom, where the meeting was to be held, about forty persons had gathered, many of them able or even outstanding scientists. For about one hour Mendel read from his manuscript an account of the results of his experiments in hybridization of the edible pea, which had occupied him during the preceding eight years.

Mendel's predecessors failed in their experiments on heredity because they directed their attention to the behavior of the type of the species or races as a whole, instead of contenting themselves with one or two clear-cut characters. The new thing about Mendel's method was that he had confined himself to studying the effects of hybridization upon single particular characters, and that he didn't take, as his predecessors had done, only a summary view upon a whole generation of hybrids, but examined each individual plant separately.

The experiments, the laws derived from these experiments, and the splendid explanation given to them by Mendel are to-day not only the base of the modern science of genetics, but belong to the fundamentals of biology taught to millions of students in all parts of the world.

Mendel had been since 1843 one of the brethren of the beautiful and wealthy monastery of the Augustinians of Bruenn, at that time in Austria, later in Czechoslovakia. His profession left him sufficient time, and the large garden of the monastery provided space enough, for his plant hybridizations. During the eight years from 1856 to 1864, he observed with a rare patience and perseverance more than 10,000 specimens.

In hybridization the pollen from the male plant is dusted on the pistils of the female plant through which it fertilizes the ovules. Both the pollen and the ovules in the pistils carry hereditary characters which may be alike in the two parents or partly or entirely different. The peas used by Mendel for hybridization differed in the simplest case only by one character or, better still, by a pair of characters; for instance, by the color of the flowers, which was red on one parental plant and white on the other; or by the shape of the seeds, which were smooth in one case and wrinkled in the other; or by the color of the cotyledons, which were yellow in one pea and green in the other, etc. Mendel's experiments show in all cases the result that all individuals of the first generation of hybrids, the F_1 generation as it is called to-day, are uniform in appearance, and that moreover only one of the two parental characters, the stronger or the dominant one, is shown. That means, for instance, that the red color of the flowers, the smooth shape of the seeds or the yellow color of the cotyledons is in evidence while the other, or recessive, character seems to have disappeared.

From the behavior of the hybrids of the F_1 generation, Mendel derived the first of the experimental laws, the so-called "Law of Uniformity," which is that all individuals of the first hybrid generation are equal or uniform. The special kind of inheritance shown by the prevalence of the dominant characters in the first hybrid generation is called alternative inheritance or the pea type of inheritance. In other instances, however, the hybrids show a mixture of the parental characteristics. Thus, crossing between a red-flowered and a white-flowered four o'clock (*Mirabilis*) gives a pink-flowered F_1 generation. This type of inheritance is called the intermediate, or Mirabilis, type of inheritance.

Now, Mendel self-fertilized the hybrids of the first generation, dusting the pistils of the flowers with their own pollen and obtained thus the second, or F_2 generation of hybrids. In this generation the recessive characters, which had seemingly disappeared, but, which were really only covered in the F_1 generation, reappeared again and in a characteristic and constant proportion. Among the F_2 hybrids he found three red-flowered plants and one white-flowered plant, or three smooth-seeded and one-wrinkled-seeded plant, or three plants with yellow cotyledons and one with green ones. In general, the hybrids of the F_2 generation showed a ratio of three dominant to one recessive plants. Mendel derived from the behavior of the F_2 generation his second experimental law, the so-called "Law of Segregation." Of course, the characteristic ratio of three dominant to one recessive may be expected only if the numbers of individuals are large, the Mendelian laws being so-called statistical laws or laws valid for large numbers only.

The third important experimental law Mendel discovered by crossing two plants which distinguished themselves not only by one but by two or more pairs of hereditary characters. He crossed, for instance, a pea plant with smooth and yellow seeds with another having green and wrinkled seeds. The first, or F_1, generation of hybrids was of course uniform, showing both smooth and yellow seeds, the dominant characters. F_1 hybrids were then self-fertilized and the second hybrid, or F_2, generation was yielded in large numbers, showing all possible combinations of the parental characters in characteristic ratios and that there were nine smooth yellow to three smooth green to three wrinkled yellow to one wrinkled green. From these so-called polyhybrid crossings, Mendel derived the third and last of his experimental laws, the "Law of Independent Assortment."

These experiments and observations Mendel reviewed in his lecture. Mendel's hearers, who were personally attached to the lecturer as well as appreciating him for his original observations in various fields of natural science, listened with respect but also with astonishment to his account of the invariable numerical ratios among the hybrids, unheard of in those days. Mendel concluded his first lecture and announced a second one at the next month's meeting and promised he would give them the theory he had elaborated in order to explain the behavior of the hybrids.

There was a goodly audience, once more, at the next month's meeting. It must be admitted, however, that the attention of most of the hearers was inclined to wander when the lecturer became engaged in a rather difficult algebraical deduction. And probably not a soul among the audience really understood what Mendel was driving at. His main idea was that the living individual might be regarded as composed of distinct hereditary, characters, which are transmitted by distinct invisible hereditary factors—to-day we call them genes. In the hybrid the different parental genes are combined. But when the sex cells of the hybrids are formed the two parental genes separate again, remaining quite unchanged and pure, each sex cell containing only one of the two genes of one pair. We call this fundamental theoretical law the "Law of the Purity of the Gametes." Through combination of the different kinds of sex cells, which are produced by the hybrid, the Law of Segregation and the Law of Independent Assortment can be easily explained.

Just as the chemist thinks of the most complicated compound as being built from a relatively small number of invariable atoms, so Mendel regarded the species as a mosaic of genes, the atoms of living organisms. It was no more nor less than an atomistic theory of the organic world which was developed before the astonished audience. The minutes of the meeting inform us that there were neither questions nor discussions. The audience dispersed and ceased to think about the matter—Mendel was disappointed but not discouraged. In all his modesty he knew that by his discoveries a new way into the unknown realm of science had been opened. "My time will come," he said to his friend Niessl.

Mendel's paper was published in the proceedings of the society for 1866. Mendel sent the separate prints to Carl Naegeli in Munich, one of the outstanding biologists of those days, who occupied himself with experiments on plant hybridization. A correspondence developed and letters and views were exchanged between the two men. But even Naegeli didn't appreciate the importance of Mendel's discovery. In not one of his books or papers dealing with heredity did he even mention Mendel's name. So, the man and the work were forgotten.

When Mendel died in 1884, hundreds of mourners, his pupils, who remembered their beloved teacher, and the poor, to whom he had been always kind, attended the funeral. But although hundreds realized that they had lost a good friend, and other hundreds attended the funeral of a high dignitary, not a single one of those present recognized that a great scientist and investigator had passed away.

The story of the rediscovery and the sudden resurrection of Mendel's work is a thrilling one. By a peculiar, but by no means an accidental, coincidence three investigators, in three different places in Europe, DeVries in Amsterdam, Correns in Germany, Tschermak in Vienna, came almost at the same time across Mendel's paper and recognized at once its great importance.

Now the time had arrived for understanding, now "his time had come" and to an extent far beyond anything of which Mendel had dreamed. The little essay, published in the great volume of the Bruenn Society, has given stimulus to all branches of biology. The progress of research since the beginning of the century has built for Mendel a monument more durable and more imposing than any monument of marble, because not only has "Mendelism" become the name of a whole vast province of investigation, but all living creatures which follow "Mendelian" laws in the hereditary transmission of their characters are said to "Mendelize."

As illustrations, I will explain the practical consequences of Mendelian research by two examples only. The Swede, Nilsson-Ehle, was one of the first investigators who tried to use Mendelistic methods to improve agricultural plants. In the cold climate of Sweden some wheat varieties, like the English square-hood wheat, were yielding well but were frozen easily. Other varieties, like the Swedish country wheat, were winter-hard but brought only a poor harvest. Nilsson-Ehle knew that in accordance with the Mendelian Law of Independent Assortment, the breeder is able to combine the desired characters of two different parents, like the chemist who combines the atoms to form various molecules or compounds. He crossed the late-ripening, well-yielding, square-hood wheat with the early-ripening, winter-hard, but poor-yielding Swedish country wheat. The resulting F_1 generation, however, was very discouraging. It was uniform, in accordance with Mendel's first law, all individuals being late-ripe and poor-yielding, thus combining the two undesirable dominant characters. In pre-Mendelian times the breeder would have been discouraged and probably would have discontinued his efforts. Not so Nilsson-Ehle, who knew that the F_1 generation is hybrid, showing only the dominant traits, and that the independent assortment of all characters will appear only in the F_2 generation. Self-fertilizing the F_1 plants he obtained an F_2 generation showing the ratio of nine late-ripe poor-yielding to three late-ripe well-yielding, to three early-ripe poor-yielding, to one early-ripe, well-yielding wheat plants. The desired combination of the two recessive characters, early-ripe, well-yielding, appeared only in the smallest ratio, one in sixteen

—but because recessives are always true-breeding, or as it is called "homozygote," Nilsson-Ehle had only to isolate these plants and to destroy all others in order to obtain a new true breeding early-ripe and well-yielding variety which after a few years gave a crop large enough to be sold. Thus, by the work of the Mendelist, Nilsson-Ehle, culture of wheat was made possible even in the northern parts of Sweden and large amounts heretofore spent for imported wheat could be saved.

Another instance shows the importance of Mendelism for the understanding of human inheritance. Very soon after the rediscovery of Mendel's paper it became evident that the laws found by Mendel with his peas are valid also for animals and for human beings. Of course, the study of the laws of human heredity is limited and rendered more difficult by several obstacles. We can't make experiments with human beings. The laws of Mendel are statistical laws based upon large numbers of offspring, while the number of children in human families is generally small. But in spite of these difficulties it was found very soon that human characters are inherited in the same manner as the characters of the pea. We know, for instance, that the dark color of the iris of the eye is dominant, the light blue color recessive. I remember a tragi-comic accident connected with this fact. At one of my lecture tours in a small town in Czechoslovakia, I spoke about the heredity of eye color in men and concluded that, while two dark-eyed parents may be hybrids in regard to eye color and thus may have children both with dark and blue eyes, the character blue-eyed, being recessive, is always pure. Hence two blue-eyed parents will have only blue-eyed children. A few months later I learned that a divorce had taken place in that small town. I was surprised and resolved to be very careful even with scientifically proved statements in the future.

Even more important is the Mendelian analysis of hereditary diseases. If we learn that the predisposition to a certain disease is inherited through a dominant gene, as diabetes, for instance, then we know that all persons carrying the gene will be sick. In this case all carriers can be easily recognized. In the case of recessive diseases, feeblemindedness, for instance, we know that the recessive gene may be covered by the dominant gene for health and that the person, seemingly healthy, may carry the disease and transmit it to his children.

With every year the influence of Mendel's modest work became more widespread. The theoretical explanation given by Mendel was based upon the hypothesis of a mechanism for the distribution and combination of the genes. To-day we know that exactly such a mechanism, as was seen by the prophetic eye of Mendel, exists in the chromosome apparatus of the nucleus of the cells. The development of research on chromosomes, from the observations of the chromosomes and their distribution by mitosis to the discovery of the reduction of the number of chromosomes in building the sex cells and finally to the audacious attempt to locate the single genes within the chromosomes, is all a story, exciting as a novel and at the same time one of the most grandiose chapters in the history of science. A tiny animal, the fruit-fly, Drosophila, was found to be the best object for genetical research. The parallelism between the behavior of the chromosomes and the mechanism of Mendelian inheritance was studied by hundreds of scientists, who were trying to determine even the location of the different genes within the different chromosomes and who started to devise so-called chromosome maps. . . .

From 1905 to 1910, I tried by lectures and by articles to renew the memory of Mendel in my home country and to explain the importance of Mendelism to the people. This was not always an easy task. Once I happened to be standing beside two old citizens of Bruenn, who were chatting before a picture of Mendel in a book-seller's window. "Who is that chap, Mendel, they are always talking about now?" asked one of them. "Don't you know?" replied the second. "It's the fellow who left the town of Bruenn an inheritance!" In the brain of the worthy man the term "heredity" had no meaning, but he understood well enough the sense of an inheritance or bequest.

1943

The Courtship of Animals

JULIAN HUXLEY

From *Man Stands Alone*

WE MEN LIKE TO SEE ANIMALS COURTING. IT AMUSES us to see them thus imitating humanity, and throws something at once romantic and familiar into those dumb and hidden lives which they veil so closely from us. "One touch of Nature makes the whole world kin," we murmur, and find a new pleasure in the hackneyed words. They are really not quite apropos, however; for what we in our heart of hearts mean to say is one touch of *human* nature. Man is a vain organism, and likes to stand surrounded by mirrors—magnifying mirrors if it be possible, but at any rate mirrors. And so we read the ideas of our own mind into the animals, and confidently speak of "suitors" and "coy brides to be won" and "jealous rivals" and what not, as if birds or even spiders or newts were miniature human beings, in fancy dress no doubt, but with the thoughts of a twentieth-century inhabitant of London or New York.

Some of the more reflective, perhaps, may wonder how far we are justified in our assumptions as to the motives and meaning of animal courtship; while others, with maybe some biological knowledge behind them, may try to look at it all from the other side of the gulf between man and beast, imagine how our own courtship would look to an external and dispassionate intelligence, wonder whether much of human behaviour had better not be interpreted from the animal side rather than the animal's from ours, and how much we are walled in by our biological heritage.

Animal courtship is an unfashionable topic among biologists at present; and I do not exaggerate when I say that it is also one on which both ignorance and prejudice prevail. My own real interest in the subject began when, one spring in Wales, I observed the beautiful courtship of the redshank, a common shore bird, and when I got back to libraries, could find no ordered account of it, or indeed of bird courtship in general. And

453

now, after some twenty-five years of reading and thinking about the subject, interspersed with a number of pleasant if strenuous holidays in Britain, in Louisiana, in Holland, in Spitsbergen, trying to find out what really does happen with this or that common bird, I can confidently assert that Darwin's theory of sexual selection, though wrong in many details, yet was essentially right: that there is no other explanation for the bulk of the characters concerned with display, whether antics, song, colour, or special plumes or other structures, than that they have been evolved in relation to the mind of the opposite sex; that *mind* has thus been the sieve through which variations in courtship characters must pass if they are to survive.

Down at the base of the animal scale courtship of course does not exist. Jelly-fish or sponges or sea-urchins simply shed their reproductive cells into the water and trust to luck for fertilization. It is only when male and female must actually co-operate for fertilization to be effected, that we can expect to find courtship; and even so it will not exist unless there is a fairly elaborate brain and nervous system.

Perhaps the first adumbration of courtship is seen in the nuptial dances of certain marine bristle-worms (Polychaetes), in which at certain seasons of the year and phases of the moon the creatures swim up out of their crannies in the rocks and gather in groups, excited males wriggling round the females. It is possible that the presence of the dancing males in some way stimulates the females to lay their eggs, upon which the male elements are discharged in milky clouds. Snails too have a primitive courtship, which is complicated by the fact that they are bi-sexual and each in its rôle of male attempts to stimulate the other in its rôle of female.

But the first actions to which the name *courtship*, and not merely perhaps direct stimulus to fertilization, must be given are those of a few crabs and most spiders. Among the crustaceans, the fiddler-crab is characterized by the presence in the male of one enormously enlarged claw, which may weigh almost as much as the rest of the body, and is often brightly coloured. It used to be supposed that with this the males stopped their burrows, or fought other males, or seized and carried off the females. However, the careful studies of Dr. Pearce show that its main function is one of display. In the mating season, when a female comes past, the males throw themselves into a tiptoe attitude, with big claw rigidly held aloft. If the female takes no notice, the male runs again to where she can see him, and again strikes the statuesque pose: if she goes too far, he returns to his burrow. The observer summed up his impressions thus: "One could only say that the males appeared to be displaying their maleness."

There we have the clue to the origins of courtship in a nutshell. Once the brain reaches a certain complexity, it controls behaviour. A crab can react to various situations—a food-situation, a hunger-situation, a fear-situation, a sex-situation; and the statuesque male with his uplifted claw is the sign and symbol of the sex-situation, just as the coming of a man or other large animal among the burrows constitutes an enemy-situation, with resultant scuttling. Doubtless even without such male advertisement, mating would eventually occur; but, as Darwin so clearly saw, the advantage may be to the male and not to the race—the male who did not display himself as such would not get mated and would leave no descendants.

In the spiders, we find a very interesting difference between the hunters and the web-spinners. Among the former, who catch their prey by sight and stalking, males perform strange dances before the females, and often have the parts they thus display brightly coloured. The latter are almost blind; and in them there are no dances, but the male comes up to the web of the female and vibrates one of the threads in a special manner, quite different from the vibrations made by trapped prey. In both cases it seems clear that the courtship's primary function is to indicate the existence of a "sexual situation." But here, to do so is a good deal more important than in the crab, for all the evidence goes to show that if this indication were not made, the female would simply treat the male like any other small living object, and eat him! In many species she actually does so after the act of mating (and this occurs too in the scorpions); and in some others she is definitely hostile at first, while the male, who is usually much smaller than she is, is always obviously very ready to run away during the early phases of courtship.

In one hunting spider the male offers the female a nice fly, neatly wrapped in silk. If put in a box by himself with a fly, he will eat it; but if with a fly and a female, he will wrap and offer it; and if in a box from which a female has recently been removed, and in which her odour still presumably lingers, he will still wrap it, and search, like Shelley with his bouquet, "That he might there present it!—Oh, to whom?"

In the carnivorous flies of the family *Empidae,* strange developments of the love-gift have taken place. In some species the male offers an unadorned carcass to the female. In others, however, the prey is stuck in the front end of a glistening "balloon," made of bubbles of viscous liquid secreted by the male, larger than his own body, and carried in his legs as he flies to and fro; doubtless this makes the "sexual situation" more conspicuous from afar. Finally, in a few species there has been a refinement. The balloon is there, but prey is no longer carried in it; instead, the males stick a leaf or flower-petal in it—and indeed they will dart down and pick up any small conspicuous objects, such as fragments of paper, that you may choose to sprinkle on the surface of the water over which they hover. Here, in quite a different evolutionary line from our own, we find quite definitely the employment of a non-utilitarian "present" as gift from male to female.

When we come to the vertebrates, matters become even more interesting, for it is among them, especially in the birds, that courtship and display reach their highest elaboration. Only in a few fish is there much of a courtship, as would be expected from the fact that most species produce large numbers of eggs which are only fertilized after laying. The frogs and toads that make night pulse with sound in the warm regions of the earth use their voices, as do the grasshoppers their legs or wings, in the interests of reproduction; and if the grasshoppers were life's first instrumentalists, the frogs were the first vocalists.

The male frog, however, merely broadcasts an advertisement of his presence; it is among the tailed amphibians that true display is found. Our common newts in the breeding season take to the water and develop a high fin all along the back and tail. This is much larger in the males, who in addition change their winter livery for one of brighter colours. They may also be seen performing their courtship—actively moving in front of the females, often scraping up against them, all the time vibrating the bent tail. The strange fact about this procedure, however, is that they do not begin their display until after they have emitted their fertilizing elements. These are deposited on the bottom of the pond or aquarium inside a special packet or spermatophore, which the female must pick up for fertilization to occur; and courtship begins when this deposition is completed.

Here we see that display may have a racial function, adjuvant to successful fertilization, and is not an affair between rival males. For even the most hardened Darwinian would hardly maintain that a female, if two males simultaneously deposited spermatophores and then began their display before her, would be able to remember which male had deposited which spermatophore even were she to be better pleased or more stimulated by the display of one rather than of the other; and of course unless the approved male were also to be the father of the young, his pleasing of the female could have no evolutionary effect. No: it seems clear that here the function of display has again to deal with the "sexual situation"; with the difference that it is not merely to advertise the male's presence and masculinity, but to generate a sexual situation in the mind of the female. As a matter of fact, Finkler has by experiment shown that in the absence of a male's display, the female will not pick up spermatophores, so that this conception of courtship's function being to facilitate fertilization via the mind, by stimulating the mental mechanism into the right phase, seems justified.

There is one species of bird for which Darwin's original theory has been definitely shown to hold good. That is the well-known shore bird, the ruff (*Machetes*). In the winter the sexes are only to be told apart by size, but in the breeding season the males grow a magnificent ruff—a tippet or collar—round the cheeks and neck, and two fine ear-tufts above. What is more, it is hard to find two males alike; not only do they develop different ground-colours in their plumage, but the collar and ear-tufts may either or both be of some special colour or marking, one black, the other white; or chestnut, pepper and salt, buff, sandy, grey, sepia, and what not. Arrived at their breeding places, the males assemble at a definite spot, usually known as a "hill," though it may be but a dry area in the marsh. The females visit the hill from time to time, but the males never go near the nests out in the marshes, nor take any share in brooding or the cares of the young. On the hill each male usually keeps to a little private area of his own. When no females are present, the male birds will be dancing, whirring round like Dervishes, and sparring and jousting with each other. On the arrival of a female, the scene is changed. The males crouch down, immobile, sometimes flat on the ground with spread wings The hen may simply stroll round and fly away again—on which the cock birds rise rather sheepishly from their prostrate posture, as if pretending that nothing had been going on. Or she may approach a male and nibble at his neck, on which mating will be consummated.

Edmund Selous watched one particular ruff hill in Holland for weeks, arriving at his hide at or before dawn. Every male on the hill was distinguishable by his appearance; and so Selous was able to discover that some were more successful than others.

Here is Darwin's theory in practice, working itself out in every detail—the adornments developed only by the male in the breeding season, and used only in sexual combat and sexual display; the male with no power to enforce his desires, the female completely arbiter of her choice; and, finally, the evidence that choice is exercised. The only puzzling point is the extreme variability of the males. This may be explained by some later discoveries. Various biologists, as we shall see later, have found that display, combat, and threat have a direct physiological effect on birds of both sexes, actually helping to ripen the reproductive organs. And Fraser Darling and others have recently shown that this effect is cumulative, some stimulus resulting from the sight of other birds courting or fighting. This at once explains the frequent occurrence of communal display-grounds; they are arrangements for heightening reproductive efficiency. But it also explains the ruff's variability. If, as seems reasonable, the unfamiliar is more exciting than the familiar, variety will have a greater mass-stimulating effect than uniformity. So, granted a tendency to marked variation, variety will be encouraged and preserved.

This clear-cut case is of importance, because it enables us to draw pretty definite conclusions in other similar cases. In the blackcock, for instance, a handsome member of the grouse tribe, there are similar assembly-places for mating—veritable temples of Venus. Here the individual males cannot be distinguished, but each again appears to have his own definite pitch or stand, and, both from direct watching and by analogy with the ruff, it seems that here, too, there is true selection. Finally in some Birds of Paradise there are also mating-places, but in the trees, where the males dance and display their gorgeous plumes.

It is interesting to note that the evolution of such special mating-places with assemblies of males and visits by females has taken place at least three separate times in birds—in the waders, the game-birds, and the Birds of Paradise. The influence of mode of life on type of courtship is another problem that can be followed out in birds. Where there is polygamy and where the female alone broods the eggs and cares for the young, there we find the greatest disparity in colour and courtship-behaviour between the sexes. The female is generally drab, protectively coloured; the male, *per contra*, brilliant, and alone participating in display. Since there is polygamy (or promiscuity), the successful male will imprint his characters on a larger number of descendants—and so display-brilliance will be at a premium; while, since he plays no biologically useful rôle after fertilization is once effected, there is less need for protective colour, since it does not much matter whether he be killed or no.

Most birds are monogamous, however, at least for the season (or sometimes only for a single brood—like the American wren, which as bird-banding experiments have shown, usually changes partners between the first and second broods of a single year). Most of the largest group of monogamous birds, the song-birds proper, have their whole sex-life hinge on what we may call the territorial system. They have their young hatched naked and helpless, needing abundant food for their growth, and liable to die of cold if left too long unbrooded. Hence it is necessary, first, for both parent birds to feed the young; second, for the presence round the nest of an area sufficiently large to supply the young's needs, and not trespassed upon by other food-seeking parents of the same species. This is ensured through an extension of the instinct, nearly universal among birds, to resent intrusion into the area round the actual or future nest-site.

Even in colonial nesters, like egrets or guillemots, the defended area exists, though it may be only a couple of feet across. In what we may call the true territorial birds, or birds with feeding as well as nesting territory, the course of events is as follows (I follow in this particular Eliot Howard's admirable description of the course of events in the European warblers or *Sylviidae*). The males are first on the breeding-grounds. If the species be a spring migrant, the males generally migrate north a week or so ahead of the females. Arrived, they take possession of an area—a territory—sometimes without dispute, sometimes after a fight with a simultaneous arrival or a bird already in possession. Then they begin their singing. Contrary to usual belief, the song of most song-birds is at its best before the mate has even arrived. As Howard has I think convincingly shown, the prime function of song is an advertisement. It is an advertisement of eligibly-occupied territory, which serves the double purpose of attracting females and warning off other males. Similarly, many of the special display-characters of males are used in threat-display against other males as well as in courtship-display to females.

When the females arrive on the scene, no immediate courtship on the part of the males is to be observed. If the female is alone, she simply takes her place in the territory, and the two are a pair for the season. Nature abhors a vacuum, and this particular vacuum, the absence of the female from a territory, is filled with the least possible fuss. If two rival females arrive together, it is they who fight for the possession of territory-plus-male, while he hovers about, an interested and even excited spectator, but without participating. Then follows the strange fact, which at first sight seems to upset the whole Darwinian apple-cart, namely that courtship and display now begin vigorously—only now, after the two birds are mated for the season. The male vibrates his wings, spreads his tail, puffs his feathers, bows and scrapes, runs before his mate, often with a leaf or twig or other piece of nest material in his beak, and his antics may be so extravagant as to testify to the most ardent excitement within. How can this be fitted in with Darwin's view that these antics and displays have been evolved in large measure through the female's selection? To this, what we have learned from the lowly newt provides the answer. Court-ship and display need not always have as their chief result the choosing of a mate. They may be, and indeed normally appear to be, accessory to the act of pairing and fertilization itself. The mind of a bird is a complex thing, and so is its life; the bird cannot always be tuned to a sexual situation. The simplest way, it would appear, of ensuring that it is not always so tuned (with consequent excessive pairing), and yet of ensuring that both sexes shall be simultaneously ready to mate often enough, is that one sex—the male—shall be more constantly in the phase of sexual preparedness, and by his display shall both advertise the fact and also help to stimulate the female to the proper emotional level.

Finally, as we have mentioned, there is a more direct biological advantage in display. It appears that in seasons which have been inclement just before and during egg-laying, the number of eggs is often reduced and the percentage of infertility raised. It is also known that all the reproductive processes of birds are very much under the control of the higher, emotional centres of the brain. For instance, a female dove brought up in isolation from infancy will usually lay no eggs; but the presence of a male bird in a near-by cage, or even the caressing of her neck with a human finger in a way reminiscent of the caresses of the male's nibbling beak, will almost always cause an egg to be laid. It has now been demonstrated that display and threat promote the ripening of the reproductive organs; this will be of advantage, and especially in bad seasons, since birds' emotions are very much at the mercy of the weather.

Before leaving this group, mention should be made of the curious fact that in all-the-year residents who are also territory-birds, there is an "engagement" period in the spring. For some weeks after the pair are in possession of a territory, fertilization is not effected. The biological reason for this is plain—it is advantageous for a bird to be on its territory early, or it may not find one; but it must not breed before a date which will give the probability of there being plenty of food for the young. The physiological machinery by which it is effected resides in the females; it is only at a certain season (probably depending on a certain mean temperature) that the eggs in her ovary start to grow rapidly, and only then that her full sex-instincts arise.

Finally, we come to the large group of birds in which both male and female not only help look after the young, but also share in incubation and in the building of the nest. Such are the herons, the pelicans, the grebes, the divers, and many others. In them, neither parent is biologically the more precious; so that if protective colour is needed, it is needed by both. Furthermore, their instincts have to be so similar in regard to nest, eggs, and young that the similarity, it appears, has spread to their courtship habits, too. For it is at any rate a fact that in a large number of this group of birds, and nowhere else, we find what we must call mutual courtship—both sexes developing bright colours and special structures for the breeding season, and both using them simultaneously in a mutual display (which, as with other monogamists among birds, begins only after pairing-up).

Anyone who, like myself, has watched such birds by the hour day after day, must be struck by the fact of their enjoyment of the courtship ceremonies for their own sake, and the further fact that the ceremonies are often what we may call biologically self-exhausting, in that the birds' emotional tension is often liberated through them, instead of being stimulated and leading on to actual pairing. It would seem as if these strange and romantic displays—head-shaking, or diving for weed, or aquatic dances breast to breast, or relieving guard on the nest with ceremonies of parade, or presentation of a twig with wings and crest a-quiver,—as if they constituted a bond between the two birds of the pair, binding them together so long as the breeding season lasted by emotional links. And after all, why not? Does not something similar obtain in human society? And does it not there play a valuable rôle, in cementing with love and joy the racially important edifice of the family? And if it has this value in man, why not in these birds, for whom too the co-operation of both parents for the good of the family is essential?

Here then we see display pressed, not merely into the service of one male against the rest, not merely facilitating fertilization, but into that of the super-individual unit, the family. And it is interesting that the family life of birds attains its highest development in these forms which have, we may say, equal sex rights and duties.

In yet other cases we see display becoming social, and courtship tending (as again sometimes in man) to be again diverted from its original character of individual wooing, this time toward the publicity of the dance. Among birds I myself have investigated, this is best seen in the oyster-catcher, the bold black-and-white shore bird, with red bill, sometimes known as sea-pie. Gatherings of eight or ten birds of this species may be seen in spring, all careering around together in their stiff courtship attitude with neck outthrust and long bill pointing vertically downwards, and a piercing noise of trilled piping issuing from their throats. Observation revealed that this is not only the commonest form of display, but the only one used while on the ground; that it may be employed by the male alone, or mutually by male and female together; and that, in addition to its courtship function, it expresses jealous hostility of other trespassing birds, whether trespassing on territorial or sexual rights. When, in a flock in early spring, courtship begins, other birds may join in the excitement; hostility re-enforces love, and soon the whole number are careering round in frenzied excitement which is, it seems, neither sexual nor hostile, but social. Here the social dance appears to have little or no special function, but is rather a biological accident.

Psychologically, one of the most interesting things about bird courtship is the frequency with which in display the birds will carry in their beaks a piece of the material of which their nest is built. This holds good even for the Adélie penguins, charmingly described by Dr. Levick. Here the nest is nothing but a rim of stones round a depression; and accordingly the male presents stones to his mate as part of his courtship. Interestingly enough, this action sometimes becomes diverted to serve other instincts and emotions, such as wonder—the birds will present stones to dogs and to men; and Dr. Levick confesses to having felt quite embarrassed the first time he was the recipient! Still another tale hangs by these stones. The sitting birds are all the time stealing stones from each other's nests. Levick painted a number of stones different colours, and placed them at one margin of the nesting area. After this he could mark the rate of their progress (all by theft!) across the colony; and found that the red stones travelled much quicker than the rest. This is of great theoretical interest, for red is a colour which is to all intents and purposes absent in the penguin's environment—and yet they prefer it above all others. If a male penguin could grow a red patch he would probably be very quick to gain a mate.

Such an example also shows in what sort of way the extraordinary bowers of the bower-bird can have developed. These are a blend between art gallery and museum, usually a tunnel of twigs with a collection of shells, bones, berries, and flowers at one end. In one species a space of ground is cleared, and large leaves laid upon it, their silvery undersurface upwards. As they wither, they are replaced; if they are blown over, the silver side is turned up once more.

Among the mammals, there is on the whole little courtship or display by the males, but correspondingly more fighting. This probably depends on the fact that the reproductive instincts of the female mammal are more rigidly under a definite physiological control, less under the fluid control of higher, emotional centres; the male deer or elephant-seal has but to guard his harem, and they will automatically accept him in due time. There is, however, a great deal still to be discovered of the courtships of monogamous mammals—a difficult subject, because so many are nocturnal or burrowers, but one that would well repay study. Among some intelligent quadrupeds, however, such as the elephant, a pleasant mutual courtship, of trunk-caresses, has been described; and when we move up towards *Homo sapiens* and reach the monkeys and apes, we find a number of display and threat characters among the males. Some are to us repulsive, like the naked scarlet and azure cheeks of the Mandril, or the blue of Stevenson's

> . . . blue-behinded ape that skips
> about the trees of Paradise.

But others, like the orang or some of the marmosets with their mustachios, or the Satan monkey with his fine beard, are curiously reminiscent of ourselves, and we are reminded of Mr. Hilaire Belloc's baboon—

> The Bib Baboon who lives upon
> The plains of Caribou
> He goes about with nothing on
> —A shocking thing to do.

> But if he dressed respectably
> And let his whiskers grow,
> How like that Bib Baboon would be
> to Miser—So-and-So!

Courtship in animals is the outcome of four major steps in evolution. First, the development of sexuality; secondly, the separation of the sexes; thirdly, internal fertilization, or at least the approximation of males and females; and finally, the development of efficient sense-organs and brains. Without any one of these, there would never have existed that host of strange and lovely features of life, summed up under the head of courtship, which beautify the appearance and variegate the existence of so many of the higher animals, including our own species.

1940

Magic Acres

ALFRED TOOMBS

THIS IS THE PLACE WHERE THE HENS LAY COLORED eggs, where the tomatoes sprout whiskers, and the apples defy the law of gravity. Here magicians grow a hog that won't sunburn or a chicken with superdrumsticks or a bee with a better disposition. They keep a psychologist in attendance on the dogs; they wake up the chrysanthemums at midnight for a stretch and a yawn, and they carefully count a bug's heartbeat.

This is the Wonderland of Agriculture, where scientists build birds, beasts, bugs to order. It is the United States Department of Agriculture's Research Center at Beltsville, Md., where new types of plants and animals are turned out to blueprint specifications, just like new-model automobiles or airplanes.

The Beltsville Research Center is a great laboratory, like those run by big manufacturers, where elements are constantly being fused to bring forth new products. But, instead of experimenting with chemicals or electricity, the scientists at Beltsville are redesigning and remodeling nature to meet modern needs—putting a supercharger on the process of evolution.

As a result, you can dream up just about any kind of animal or plant you'd like, and Beltsville can turn it out for you. There is the case of Lady Burke Ormsby Gerbem Cola Ollie, for instance. Lady B.'s name won't be found in *Burke's Peerage*, but she's a lot more important than many whose titles are recorded there. She is a cow, but a mighty important cow, because, by breeding her, Beltsville has proved that you can get a good herd of milk cows by selecting their sires carefully. Lady B. and all her sisters give an average of eight hundred pounds of butterfat a year, which is twice as much as the average cow yields. Thus Beltsville has pointed a way toward doubling milk production.

The men in the fruit and vegetable department are so far advanced in working wonders that they consider it child's play to grow pears on an

464

apple tree or to grow red and yellow apples on the same tree. They are concentrating on more important things, such as fuzz-free peaches, tearless onions, and the family-size watermelon.

If Newton had parked himself under a Beltsville apple tree, waiting for the idea for the law of gravity to bounce off his head, he'd be sitting there yet. Apples don't drop off the trees there.

For a long time the applegrowers had been up against a tough proposition. Just when their crops were getting ripe, along would come the law of gravity and dump about one third of the apples on the ground. Apples that fall aren't worth much on the market, so when they started dropping the growers hurried and picked the rest. As a result, many of the apples were picked before they had reached the peak of their perfection. With one third on the ground and most of the rest of the apples imperfectly colored and ripened, the growers didn't get much out of the crop.

The apple men at Beltsville began experimenting with plant hormones after they had heard that their fellows in the holly-wreath department had been using a hormone mixture to make the leaves stick on Christmas wreaths. They discovered that they could spray a little of the mixture on the apple trees just when the fruit showed signs of getting ready to drop and keep it on the branches for another two weeks. Thus the growers could pick the apples when they had achieved just the proper rosy color.

It takes only half a teaspoonful of the plant hormones to one hundred gallons of water to make the apples hang on like an obnoxious drunk. If you repeat the treatment at regular intervals the apples will never fall. One tree at Beltsville had fruit hanging from its limbs in January, with snow on the ground.

The truck farmers of the South could tell the story of the tomatoes with whiskers which saved the ten-million-dollar-a-year tomato-growing industry from what looked like sudden death. In this case Beltsville beat odds of forty thousand to one to succeed.

Some years ago the tomato growers found that their plants were being wiped out inexorably by a blight known as tomato rust. Beltsville began to experiment and finally, after raising thousands of plants, came through with a new model that paid no attention to rust blight. But the end was not in sight, for along came a new disease, known as wilt, which attacked the new-type plant. The growers sent another S O S to Beltsville.

About this time some dreamer in the horticulture station at Beltsville remembered a funny little wild tomato that grew in Peru. This plant had defied all comers in the disease line for hundreds of years, and if anything could stand off the rust and the wilt this looked like the one. There was only one minor drawback: the Peruvian tomato wasn't edible, and it was covered with a fine, thick growth of whiskers.

They began the work of crossbreeding, which made the Peruvian tomato bigger and better. But for a long time they couldn't get rid of the whiskers.

Nobody stopped to figure the odds against success until it was all over. But when they finally succeeded in growing a big, tasty, smooth-shaven tomato on the Peruvian disease-resistant stock they checked back and discovered it had been necessary to turn out forty thousand different kinds of plants before they got what they wanted.

Beltsville's work of improving upon nature has carried the scientists on some excursions into strange realms. After years of crossing, recrossing, and double-crossing they turned out a streamlined turkey, nearly all white meat, designed for small families. This new turkey enables the average family to reach the hash stage in about three days. How do you like your chickens? Beltsville can fix one up with almost all white meat or all dark meat. It also produces a fowl with drumsticks big enough to ring bells and hens that lay eggs in standard colors.

The building up of big drumsticks is more a question of environment than heredity. These chickens are turned loose in a big enclosure, where the feed has been scattered all over. The chickens keep running from dawn to dusk in search of food, and this builds up their leg muscles.

The colored eggs were developed during nutritive experiments. It was discovered that certain foods and dyes transmitted color to the eggs. It was also found that special qualities could be developed in eggs for special purposes. For instance, they have chickens which do nothing but lay eggs especially designed for poaching. There is a peculiar quality in the white of these eggs which makes them poach to the taste of the goutiest customer.

One of the big problems which vexes poultry breeders is separating baby chicks by sex, so they can concentrate on the hens-to-be. Beltsville has been working on this problem, trying to get an arrangement whereby all male chicks will be hatched with some identifying mark. They've bred a line now where the male chicks all have a black stripe, and it looks as if the trouble is licked.

There's a kind of college course for canines, with a psychologist in attendance, at Beltsville. This experiment has two objectives—to produce a better farm dog and, secondly, to determine whether special abilities and traits of character can be transmitted with certainty from one generation to another.

The dog experiment started about four years ago, with four types of dogs. There were Pulis, a breed of talented Hungarian sheep dog; Border collies and German shepherds, chosen for their intelligence, aggressiveness, and sheepherding ability, and, for contrast, chows which had no record as shepherds but were stable and smart. Pure-bred pups were bred from each type, and the young dogs were given extensive tests.

The objective of the first tests was to determine the character, personality, and abilities of each individual dog. It was discovered that some of the dogs were not very bright; some were mean; some were obedient, and some just didn't give a hang about school. Some of the Pulis knew as puppies, without being trained, how to handle sheep. When the characteristics of each dog had been established and recorded the work of crossbreeding began—to find out whether the new generation would pick up the parents' virtues or faults. Would a pup born of a Puli-chow union have the Puli's sheepherding ability and the chow's stability? Or would it inherit the less desirable characteristics, such as the chow's lack of talent as a shepherd and the Puli's excitability?

Ada was one of the dogs born of this second generation. Her mother was a German shepherd—a former Seeing-Eye dog—and her father was a Puli. Ada was bright, her psychology tests demonstrated, but she wasn't so hot as a shepherd. She was mated to Paul, a pure Puli, which had scored fairly well on intelligence and had proved himself an ace among the sheepherders. A litter of nine blessed this union, and when they had completed their final exams it was found that four of the dogs had maintained Ada's extraordinary intelligence and that all the rest stood near the head of the class. What was more significant, they were all very handy at herding sheep.

Farmer, one of the best of these, was mated to another good dog and became the father of six pups. The returns aren't all in on Farmer's offspring, but the early reports indicate that they have inherited all the family talents. If so, and if the pups can become the proud parents of another generation of prodigies, Beltsville will be well on its way toward breeding a superdog.

More important, these experiments may establish that it is possible to breed certain desirable talents and traits of character into a line of dogs, just as good points are developed in show dogs. Beltsville doesn't have too high an opinion of "show dogs," by the way. Early in the game many of the fancy thoroughbreds turned out to be morons. Beautiful but dumb.

The job of building a better bee recently engrossed Beltsville. Redesigning the bee for modern needs is just as intricate a task as planning a new fighting plane. Not so long ago there came an insistent demand from beekeepers for a new model with a longer tongue. A bee with a long tongue can dig deep down into the big flowers and get honey that other bees can only dream about. Beltsville turned out some test models, but they learned that they were going to have to make a lot of changes in the fundamental design of the bee. They're still working on it.

They know what they want—a bee with a gentle disposition, a love of its home, ability to fly in cold weather, extra storage space for honey, and some distinguishing characteristics—like stars on the wings—that will make it possible to distinguish the new bee from the old. Not only the bee-keepers, but farmers in general—especially those owning orchards—are demanding a new-model bee. Beltsville showed how much bees, which increase pollination, can mean to the owner of a fruit orchard. They ordered some special bees into action in the Northwest fruit country recently at blossomtime, and production went up faster than an anti-aircraft shell.

The entomology division, where the bee designers are at work, has other departments, where scientists are figuring out some improved methods of killing off other kinds of insects. Here are men who patiently feed the best tweeds to the moths, who count the heartbeat of bugs to see how long it takes different poisons to act, who raise millions of mosquitoes to find out the best way to kill them. These men all share a common ideal—better bugs and fewer of them.

In the animal division they are working with fifty Persian lambs, a breed with which the American farmer has had little luck. They were bred at Beltsville and they are as good as any Persian lambs that have been born anywhere. Beltsville is seeking to establish a strain of karakul sheep which will flourish in this country and has worked out a formula of three quarters karakul and one quarter native sheep which looks good. If the experiment is successful and the precious wool begins to sprout on native sheep the American farmer will have another source of income.

A few years ago vegetable oils began to replace lard, and the farmers suddenly realized that their hogs were devoting a large part of their time to turning out fat that nobody wanted. That got Beltsville started on re-modeling the hog, and they've now produced a porker with the weight transferred back into the bacon-and-ham department, where it gets a nice round price. While they were at it Beltsville threw in a few other innovations. The result is a superhog which, in addition to its meat-giving virtues, is nimble on its feet, immune to sunburn, and safe from nervous breakdowns.

Pigs, you see, is not just pigs. There are many kinds, all of which have their virtues. The Danish Landrace, for instance, is one of the best meat-producing hogs in the world. The Danes have been raising them for years but have been reluctant to let them out of the country. In 1934 a Department of Agriculture man persuaded the Danes to allow a couple of dozen of their prize pigs to pay a visit to the United States, and most of these wound up at Beltsville. The Danes would never know them now.

For Beltsville began to incorporate their virtues in the general design of the superhog. The Landrace, of itself, was not the ideal hog for this country—it had a weak back, weak feet, and a white complexion which would be subject to sunburn in most of the hog-raising states of this country.

To get rid of these weaknesses Beltsville began to breed the Danish hogs to such American strains as the Poland China and Duroc-Jersey. Now, after several generations, the main characteristics of the new hog have been pretty well established. It has a strong, arched back, laden with pork chops and roasts, and the Landraces' long, streamlined body and thick legs, heavy with bacon and hams. The new hog will be red, able to stand the summer sun of Kansas or Florida, and nimble in the barnyard.

They've even tested the temperament of the new piggie. Nervous prima-donna hogs, you see, spend so much time fretting that they don't get fat as quickly as they should. By giving the hogs tests for nerves Beltsville is trying to eliminate the flighty porkers and breed an animal which can look on life with tranquillity and a good appetite.

Just about the time Beltsville got the new lardless hog ready the war got tough and the English found they were short on lard. It was suddenly discovered that this country would have to turn out a lot of lard. Beltsville turned its attention to this problem, but it's keeping the streamlined hog under cover until the fighting blows over and the bottom drops out of the lard market again.

Just as with lard, America is constantly being called upon to make sudden changes in its farm economy to meet new tactics in the war. This country has to improve the model of its crops, just as it must improve airplane models, to keep up with new developments. But new-model crops, like new-model planes, don't just grow. There must be research behind them. And behind our new agriculture is Beltsville—where life is made to order. *1941*

PART FIVE

THE WORLD OF MAN

Synopsis

A. FROM APE TO CIVILIZATION

FROM APE TO CIVILIZATION IS IN SOME WAYS A LONG ROAD, in others a very short one. From life in the trees to that in a modern skyscraper is a big jump, but it has been taken by animals which are closely allied to their cousins. The controversy on the subject is still fresh, as witness the Tennessee trial, but Darwin suggests the evidence which disposes of it in his classic Evidence of the Descent of Man. When he wrote it, the road man has taken was not completely understood, nor is it yet. But what we now know is indicated in two selections. Hooton of Harvard describes man's relation to the primitive primates and later apes in The Upstart of the Animal Kingdom. Ruth Moore tells how recent discoveries in anthropology have completely revolutionized our thinking about the relationship between man and his primitive ancestors.

Man himself varies enormously in the scale from savagery to civilization. Changing from one part of the scale to another can be a bitter step. In Lessons in Living from the Stone Age, the Arctic explorer Stefansson watches the undermining of a co-operative form of society, with nothing to take its place. He wonders, as we may also, which is the "good" life: the primitive or the modern competitive form.

Primitive races are still widespread. Even the various civilized races have diverged in form of skull and shape of body. No one is better qualified than Sir Arthur Keith, the great British authority, to tell us how typical Germans, Englishmen, Chinese and Negroes differ among themselves, as he does in Racial Characters of the Body.

B. THE HUMAN MACHINE

The greatest steps in our knowledge of the human body and how it works were taken in the sixteenth and seventeenth centuries, when Andreas Vesalius published his monumental "Structure of the Human Body," and William Harvey first demonstrated the circulation of the blood. The story of those great days, and of the fundamental discoveries on which rests the edifice of modern medicine, are told in Vesalius and Harvey, by one of the greatest modern teachers of physiology, Sir Michael Foster. The human attributes of the choleric little man who explained how the blood moved are illuminated in The Only Contemporary Character Sketch of William Harvey by John Aubrey.

In our own day, of course, observation of bodily functions is done with microscopic exactness. One example of this meticulous understanding is Margaret Shea Gilbert's Biography of the Unborn, which carries us from the entry of the male sperm into the female egg through the first nine months of our lives as individuals.

So we are born, the most marvelous machines in creation. Even today the greater part of our functioning is imperfectly understood. In How the Human Body Is Studied, Sir Arthur Keith takes us back to the method which first began to give us scientific knowledge. Here in the dissecting room, we catch a glimpse of the arrangement of bones and muscles, the circulation of the blood (the wonderful process discovered by William Harvey), the tendons and nerves. Sir Arthur tells us too little about the hormones and the glands. In his space, he can give us only a fleeting glimpse of human anatomy. But he does show us that whatever else man is, he is a machine.

Man, then, is the product of the process of evolution, of the laws of life and heredity, of a chemical and physical machinery. This is the man that Julian Huxley considers in Variations on a Theme by Darwin, showing that for all the incredible complexity of his actions and reactions, man must be studied as a product of his environment.

C. THE CONQUEST OF DISEASE

Infested by parasites, surrounded by bacteria, a prey to viruses, the human machine fills us with a persisting amazement. How can it function so well so much of the time? Much of the answer lies in man's understanding of his own bodily enemies. The quest goes back to the most primitive of medicine men. But as Clendening shows in Hippocrates, the Greek—the End of Magic, there came a moment when the order of nature and not the whim of the gods was recognized as causing disease. Perhaps Hippocrates was not the first to make this initial discovery, perhaps his Oath, which still hangs in doctors' offices, was the work of others. Whatever his identity, the man who did it was the intellectual father of the investigators of today.

We have space for only a few of the highlights of the subsequent story. Jenner, whose classic paper An Inquiry into the Causes and Effects of the Variolae Vaccinae shows the steps in his discovery of the methods of inoculation against smallpox, was a far greater man than Waterhouse of Massachusetts. Yet in The History of the Kine Pox, Waterhouse, with his scientific detachment, his willingness to face any eventuality in his search for the truth, was an outstanding human figure in the conquest of disease. Perhaps that passionate love of truth reached its acme in Louis Pasteur. Vallery-Radot's story of his life is one of the greatest biographies in any field. The blend of scientific insight and human emotion contained in Louis Pasteur and the Conquest of Rabies makes it an indispensable contribution.

The story is brought up to date with two selections on modern medicine. Sir Alexander Fleming has won world-wide recognition for his discovery of penicillin, still the most effective and the most widely used of the antibiotics. In Chemotherapy, he discusses for the layman not only his own discovery but also the sulfonamides, streptomycin and others. The search for new "magic bullets" goes on at a feverish pace. One reason is that astonishingly enough, some of them, such as aureomycin, when fed to animals like pigs and chicks, result in phenomenal increases in growth.

Our final selection in this section is by Dr. Frank G. Slaughter, who is not only a successful novelist but a physician of note. In The New Science of Surgery he explains how surgical feats such as operations on the heart, which were unheard of a few years ago, have now become commonplace. Present accomplishments indicate that even the valves of the heart, the site of our most often fatal forms of heart disease, are the subject of surgery. We refer the reader also to a number of selections dealing with radiation which appear in the final section of the book. Here are studies of radiation the cause of horrible disease and death, and radiation the new tool for understanding and curing bodily ills.

D. MAN'S MIND

One of the most tragic and difficult problems of modern war is the increase in mental disease among those returned from the front. It may be, as has recently been stated, that nobody is fitted to fight in a modern war. Normal mental functioning must mean a fair balance in man's processes of thinking as well as a balance between mind and body.

In his analysis of Thinking, James Harvey Robinson shows the importance of conscious knowledge, of reverie, of decision, of rationalization and above all of creative thought. In Imagination Creatrix, this last is analyzed more fully, out of his long study of the creative processes of men of genius, by John Livingston Lowes. This whole Treasury is an example of what Lowes describes. We follow it in the work of Copernicus and Darwin. We see it in the laboratories of Madame Curie and Pasteur, the quarry of Hugh Miller, the garden of Gregor Mendel.

We see it too in the Psychology of Sigmund Freud, described by Dr. Brill. After many centuries, a new voice has been heard in the understanding of mental processes and the treatment of abnormality.

A. FROM APE TO CIVILIZATION

The Evidence of the Descent of Man from Some Lower Form

CHARLES DARWIN

From *The Descent of Man*

THE BODILY STRUCTURE OF MAN

IT IS NOTORIOUS THAT MAN IS CONSTRUCTED ON THE same general type or model as other mammals. All the bones in his skeleton can be compared with corresponding bones in a monkey, bat, or seal. So it is with his muscles, nerves, blood-vessels and internal viscera. The brain, the most important of all the organs, follows the same law, as shewn by Huxley and other anatomists. Bischoff, who is a hostile witness, admits that every chief fissure and fold in the brain of man has its analogy in that of the orang; but he adds that at no period of development do their brains perfectly agree; nor could perfect agreement be expected, for otherwise their mental powers would have been the same. But it would be superfluous here to give further details on the correspondence between man and the higher mammals in the structure of the brain and all other parts of the body.

It may, however, be worth while to specify a few points, not directly or obviously connected with structure, by which this correspondence or relationship is well shewn.

Man is liable to receive from the lower animals, and to communicate to them, certain diseases, as hydrophobia, variola, the glanders, syphilis, cholera, herpes etc., and this fact proves the close similarity of their tissues and blood, both in minute structure and composition, far more plainly than does their comparison under the best microscope, or by the aid of the best chemical analysis.

Man is infested with internal parasites, sometimes causing fatal effects;

and is plagued by external parasites, all of which belong to the same genera or families as those infesting other mammals.

The whole process of that most important function, the reproduction of the species, is strikingly the same in all mammals, from the first act of courtship by the male, to the birth and nurturing of the young. Monkeys are born in almost as helpless a condition as our own infants: and in certain genera the young differ fully as much in appearance from the adults, as do our children from their full-grown parents. It has been urged by some writers, as an important distinction, that with man the young arrive at maturity at a much later age than with any other animal: but if we look to the races of mankind which inhabit tropical countries the difference is not great, for the orang is believed not to be adult till the age of from ten to fifteen years. Man differs from woman in size, bodily strength, hairiness, etc., as well as in mind, in the same manner as do the two sexes of many mammals. It is, in short, scarcely possible to exaggerate the close correspondence in general structure, in the minute structure of the tissues, in chemical composition and in constitution, between man and the higher animals, especially the anthropomorphous apes.

EMBRYONIC DEVELOPMENT

Man is developed from an ovule, about the 125th of an inch in diameter, which differs in no respect from the ovules of other animals. The embryo itself at a very early period can hardly be distinguished from that of other members of the vertebrate kingdom. At this period the arteries run in arch-like branches, as if to carry the blood to branchiae which are not present in the higher vertebrata, though the slits on the sides of the neck still remain, marking their former position. At a somewhat later period, when the extremities are developed, "the feet of lizards and mammals," as the illustrious Von Baer remarks, "the wings and feet of birds, no less than the hands and feet of man, all arise from the same fundamental form." "It is," says Prof. Huxley, "quite in the later stages of development that the young human being presents marked differences from the young ape, while the latter departs as much from the dog in its developments, as the man does. Startling as this last assertion may appear to be, it is demonstrably true."

After the foregoing statements made by such high authorities, it would be superfluous on my part to give a number of borrowed details, shewing that the embryo of man closely resembles that of other mammals. It may, however, be added, that the human embryo likewise resembles in various points of structure, certain low forms when adult. For instance, the heart at first exists as a simple pulsating vessel; the excreta are voided through a cloacal passage; and the os coccyx projects like a true tail, "extending considerably beyond the rudimentary legs." In the embryos of all air-breathing vertebrates, certain glands, called the corpora Wolffiana, correspond with, and act like the kidneys of mature fishes. Even at a later embryonic period, some striking resemblances between man and the lower animals may be observed. Bischoff says that the convolutions of the brain in a human foetus at the end of the seventh month reach about the same stage of development as in a baboon when adult. The great toe, as Prof. Owen remarks, "which forms the fulcrum when standing or walking, is perhaps the most characteristic peculiarity in the human structure," but in an embryo, about an inch in length, Prof. Wyman found "that the great toe was shorter than the others; and, instead of being parallel to them, projected at an angle from the side of the foot, thus corresponding with the permanent condition of this part in the quadrumana." I will conclude with a quotation from Huxley, who after asking, Does man originate in a different way from a dog, bird, frog, or fish? says, "the reply is not doubtful for a moment; without question, the mode of origin, and the early stages of development of man, are identical with those of the animals immediately below him in the scale: without a doubt in these respects, he is far nearer to apes than the apes are to the dog."

RUDIMENTS

Not one of the higher animals can be named which does not bear some part in a rudimentary condition; and man forms no exception to the rule. Rudimentary organs are eminently variable; and this is partly intelligible, as they are useless, or nearly useless, and consequently are no longer subjected to natural selection. They often become wholly suppressed. When this occurs, they are nevertheless liable to occasional reappearance through reversion—a circumstance well worthy of attention.

Rudiments of various muscles have been observed in many parts of the human body; and not a few muscles, which are regularly present in some of the lower animals can occasionally be detected in man in a greatly reduced condition. Every one must have noticed the power which many animals, especially horses, possess of moving or twitching their skin; and this is effected by the *panniculus carnosus*. Remnants of this muscle in an efficient state are found in various parts of our bodies; for instance, the muscle on the forehead, by which the eyebrows are raised.

Some few persons have the power of contracting the superficial muscles on their scalps; and these muscles are in a variable and partly rudimentary condition. M. A. de Candolle has communicated to me a curious instance of the long-continued persistence or inheritance of this power, as well as of its unusual development. He knows a family, in which one member, the present head of the family, could, when a youth, pitch several heavy books from his head by the movement of the scalp alone; and he won wagers by performing this feat. His father, uncle, grandfather, and his three children possess the same power to the same unusual degree. This family became divided eight generations ago into two branches; so that the head of the above-mentioned branch is cousin in the seventh degree to the head of the other branch. This distant cousin resides in another part of France; and on being asked whether he possessed the same faculty, immediately exhibited his power. This case offers a good illustration how persistently an absolutely useless faculty may be transmitted.

The sense of smell is of the highest importance to the greater number of mammals—to some, as the ruminants, in warning them of danger; to others, as the carnivora, in finding their prey; to others, again, as the wild boar, for both purposes combined. But the sense of smell is of extremely slight service if any, even to savages, in whom it is much more highly developed than in the civilized races. It does not warn them of danger, nor guide them to their food; nor does it prevent the Esquimaux from sleeping in the most fetid atmosphere, nor many savages from eating half-putrid meat. Those who believe in the principle of gradual evolution, will not readily admit that this sense in its present state was originally acquired by man, as he now exists. No doubt he inherits the power in an enfeebled and so far rudimentary condition, from some early progenitor, to whom it was highly serviceable, and by whom it was continually used. We can thus perhaps understand how it is, as Dr. Maudsley has truly remarked, that the sense of smell in man "is singularly effective in recalling vividly the ideas and images of forgotten scenes and places"; for we see in those animals, which have this sense highly developed, such as dogs and horses, that old recollections of persons and places are strongly associated with their odour.

Man differs conspicuously from all the other Primates in being almost naked. But a few short straggling hairs are found over the greater part of the body in the male sex, and fine down on that of the female sex. There can be little doubt that the hairs thus scattered over the body are the rudiments of the uniform hairy coat of the lower animals.

It appears as if the posterior molar or wisdom-teeth were tending to become rudimentary in the more civilised races of man. These teeth are rather smaller than the other molars, as is likewise the case with the corresponding teeth in the chimpanzee and orang; and they have only two separate fangs. They do not cut through the gums till about the seventeenth year, and I have been assured by dentists that they are much more liable to decay, and are earlier lost, than the other teeth. It is also remarkable that they are much more liable to vary both in structure and in the period of their development, than the other teeth. In the Melanian races, on the other hand, the wisdom-teeth are usually furnished with three separate fangs, and are generally sound; they also differ from the other molars in size less than in the Caucasian races. Prof. Schaffhausen accounts for this difference between the races by "the posterior dental portion of the jaw being always shortened" in those that are civilised, and this shortening may, I presume, be safely attributed to civilised men habitually feeding on soft, cooked food, and thus using their jaws less.

With respect to the alimentary canal, I have met with an account of only a single rudiment, namely the vermiform appendage of the caecum. The caecum is a branch or diverticulum of the intestine, ending in a cul-de-sac, and is extremely long in many of the lower vegetable-feeding mammals. In the marsupial koala it is actually more than thrice as long as the whole body. It is sometimes produced into a long gradually-tapering point and is sometimes constricted in parts. It appears as if, in consequence of changed diet or habits, the caecum had become much shortened in various animals, the vermiform appendage being left as a rudiment of the shortened part. That this appendage is a rudiment, we may infer from its small size, and from the evidence which Prof. Canestrini has collected of its variability in man. It is occasionally quite absent, or again is largely developed. The passage is sometimes completely closed for half or two-thirds of its length, with the terminal part consisting of a flattened solid expansion. In the orang this appendage is long and convoluted; in man it arises from the end of the short caecum, and is commonly from four to five inches in length, being only about the third of an inch in diameter. Not only is it useless, but it is sometimes the cause of death, of which fact I have lately heard two instances; this is due to small hard bodies, such as seeds, entering the passage, and causing inflammation.

The os coccyx in man, though functionless as a tail, plainly represents this part in other vertebrate animals. At an early embryonic period it is free, and projects beyond the lower extremities. In certain rare and anomalous cases, it has been known to form a small external rudiment of a tail.

The bearing of the three great classes of facts now given is unmistakable. But it would be superfluous here fully to recapitulate the line of argument given in detail in my *Origin of Species*. The homological construction of the whole frame in the members of the same class is intelligible, if we admit their descent from a common progenitor, together with their subsequent adaptation to diversified conditions. On any other view, the similarity of pattern between the hand of a man or monkey, the foot of a horse, the flipper of a seal, the wing of a bat, &c., is utterly inexplicable. It is no scientific explanation to assert that they have all been formed on the same ideal plan. With respect to development, we can clearly understand, on the principle of variation supervening at a rather late embryonic period, and being inherited at a corresponding period, how it is that the embryos of wonderfully different forms should still retain, more or less perfectly, the structure of their common progenitor. No other explanation has ever been given of the marvellous fact that the embryos of a man, dog, seal, bat, reptile, &c., can at first hardly be distinguished from each other. In order to understand the existence of rudimentary organs, we have only to suppose that a former progenitor possessed the parts in question in a perfect state, and that under changed habits of life they became greatly reduced, either from simple disuse, or through the natural selection of those individuals which were least encumbered with a superfluous part.

Thus we can understand how it has come to pass that man and all other vertebrate animals have been constructed on the same general model, why they pass through the same early stages of development, and why they retain certain rudiments in common. Consequently we ought frankly to admit their community of descent; to take any other view, is to admit that our own structure, and that of all the animals around us, is a mere snare laid to entrap our judgment. This conclusion is greatly strengthened, if we look to the members of the whole animal series and consider the evidence derived from their affinities or classification, their geographical distribution and geological succession. It is only our natural prejudice, and that arrogance which made our forefathers declare that they were descended from demi-gods, which leads us to demur to this conclusion. But the time will before long come, when it will be thought wonderful, that naturalists, who were well acquainted with the comparative structure and development of man, and other mammals, should have believed that each was the work of a separate act of creation.

Edition of 1875

The Upstart of the Animal Kingdom

EARNEST A. HOOTON

THE PRINCIPAL PUBLIC FUNCTION OF THE ANTHRO-
pologist is to instill into man a proper humility, by reminding him of
his humble origin and by demonstrating to him how short a distance he
has come from his lower mammalian forbears and in how prodigiously
long a time . . .

Through the long middle ages of life on the earth multifarious reptiles had dominated the scene—aquatic, aerial, and terrestrial, herbivorous
and carnivorous, tiny and gigantic, but generally slimy. I think that by
the end of the Mesozoic Age nature had grown tired of dinosaurs—fed up
with their eggs—and felt ready for a leadership of brains. Throughout
this period there had been lying low, or rather sitting high in the tree
tops, some little long-snouted insectivores who reproduced their young in
higher mammalian fashion and suckled them at the breast instead of laying eggs *passim* like reptiles. In the fullness of time and at the beginning
of the Paleocene, perhaps sixty million years ago, there sprang from this
order of insectivores the first primitive primates, called lemurs.

These early lemurs were animals of small pretensions and apparently
slight evolutionary promise. They had longish snouts, laterally directed
eyes and very modest brains but they possessed the most precious of animal endowments, adaptability. This adaptability is essentially the faculty
of grasping an environmental opportunity and following, not the line of
least resistance but that of greatest opportunity. Literally and corporeally
this ability to grasp an object and a situation was centered in the prehensile
pentadactyle hands and feet, equipped with flat nails instead of claws and
with thumbs and great toes which could be opposed to the other digits.
These sensitive members could encircle a bough, pluck a leaf, pick a flea
or convey an edible object to the eyes for examination, to the snout for
smelling and to the mouth for tasting. These hands and feet were not only
prehensile but also tactile organs which enabled their small tree-dwelling
owners to explore the world and to become conscious of the various parts

481

of their own bodies inaccessible to most quadrupeds. Their greatest importance was not in being conveyors merely of food to the mouth but rather
of messages to the brain, which now began to be something more than a
sensory receptacle and a coordinator of muscular movements. The lemur
brain began to record associations, to register visual and tactile impressions and to allocate to specific areas of its nervous cortex definite functions
—motor, sensory and associative. In short, these lemurs began really to
exercise their brains and to manifest intelligence. The hands called to the
brain and the latter responded, assuming the function of direction and
guidance.

Let us pause for a few moments to consider the advantages of arboreal
life to a small and weak animal. A tiny terrestrial animal has to depend
largely upon its sense of smell to warn it of the approach of enemies and
to enable it to find food. Its visual sense is of comparatively slight utility
because its horizon is restricted by its nearness to the ground. It lives in
a world of tall grass and underbrush. It "noses its way through life." Now
suppose this small animal climbs a tree. It gets up out of the wet and
away from the clutch of enemies; it has a chance to sit up and look around.
Arboreal life puts a premium upon the visual sense and the olfactory function diminishes in importance. The animal begins to look for its food
rather than to sniff for it. Agility and motor coordination are essential for
moving about in the trees and avoiding falls. On the whole no nursery
school could be more ideal for a small mammal with prehensile extremities. The original equipment of five-digited hands and feet with opposable
thumbs and great toes allowed the animal to grasp an object of whatever
shape and size and the absence of protrusive claws encouraged the use of
the finger bulbs for tactile discrimination.

The dietary afforded by the tropic forest was varied and stimulated an
omnivorous habit—extremely useful for evolutionary survival as anyone
who has lived in a boarding-house should know. Nuts, fruits, berries,
leaves and shoots for salads, birds' eggs, grubs and even birds themselves
if these could be caught—here were plenty of vitamins; and sufficient sunlight was handy for those disposed to climb to the top of the trees.

Parental care, too, was necessitated by the arboreal habitat since the
young of mammals are relatively helpless. Those secondarily adapted for
arboreal life must be reared in a nest or carried on their mothers' bodies
until they attain the strength, agility and experience to pursue their precarious aerial lives.

Nature then had provided these primitive lemurine primates with a bodily equipment suitable for arboreal life, and necessity, or less probably
choice, had driven them into the trees. Here was offered, to those who

could grasp it, the educational opportunity for evolutionary advancement. Now the most mystifying feature of evolution and of modern human life is the variation of individuals in their capacity to utilize opportunities. Why do some people absorb and assimilate an education and others merely excrete it? The arboreal habitat for some of these early primates was a catalytic agent for evolutionary progress and for others merely a lotus-eating existence. Students of organic evolution dismiss the question by asserting that some animals are progressive and adaptive whereas others are conservative and rigid. As a matter of fact the secret of progress appears to be the ability of the animal to utilize the advantages of an environment without molding its organism too narrowly to the requirements of any particular mode of life. The really progressive animal must if possible adapt environment to itself and not become too malleable to its influence. It must maintain its organic independence, it must possess a certain initiative whereby it picks and chooses, and when choice is narrowed to its extreme disadvantage it needs to move on in search of better things. There are today, of course, plenty of lemurs in Madagascar, Africa, and Indonesia, and they are probably very little changed from their original proto-primate status in bodily form and in habits. These, however, are the stultified and backward children of the Order—the perennial kindergarteners.

Practically contemporary with the early lemurs, possibly an offshoot from some gifted lemuroid stock, were other and more precocious primates, the tarsioids. To see what they were like we have had to study their few relatively unmodified modern descendants, confined to the islands of Indonesia. These tarsioids differed from the lemurs in a number of significant and promising features and habits. First, instead of running on all fours through the trees they hopped on their hind legs. An animal which has to use all four limbs for locomotion and support is necessarily dependent upon its snout for tactile and feeding purposes, but these little arboreal tarsioids have "emancipated their fore-limbs" for purposes of prehension, exploration and hand-feeding. Release from the function of bough-gripping foreshadowed tool-using, tool-making and the ultimate genesis of material culture. Further, the hopping tarsier sits up and looks around; it carries the long axis of its body perpendicular to the ground instead of parallel with it. It takes a vertical rather than a horizontal view of life.

It is a principle of Nature that organs increase in size when their functions are enlarged and atrophy when their activity is diminished. In the tarsioids there took place an elongation of the tarsus (that portion of the foot which supports the hopping animal). Far more important, however, were changes in the face, the brain case and the brain itself, associated with the upright sitting posture and the freedom of the fore-limbs. For an animal largely dependent upon its olfactory sense, the snout, terminating in a moist muzzle or rhinarium, not only serves as the principal tactile organ; it also collects the scents and odors by which the animal's existence is guided. Furthermore the snout includes inferiorly the jaws, the incisive front ends of which are projected forward of the eyes in order that the animal can graze and still see what it is eating and what is going on around it. But with the free use of prehensile hands as organs of touch and conveyors of food a projecting snout loses its function. Thus we find the snout greatly shortened in the tarsier. Furthermore, the visual sense in this animal has become wholly dominant over the olfactory. The brain has swollen enormously and particularly those portions of the cortex or nervous covering in which vision is represented; the neopallium, or new cloak of the brain, has spread like a tent over the primitive olfactory bulbs, covering, obscuring and dwarfing them. To accommodate this larger brain the skull has grown backward so that now it nearly balances upon the vertical spinal column. The tarsier can hold up its head without straining the neck muscles with the weight of the thrust-out and over-balancing snout.

Lemurs and lower mammals have eyes laterally directed on each side of a protrusive snout. They see with one eye at a time and the fields of vision do not overlap. Such wall-eyed brutes lack stereoscopic vision whereby the eyes can focus simultaneously upon the same object and without which there can be no depth of perception and but little perspective. The tarsier, in contrast, has formed the habit of holding objects in front of its eyes for examination. Whether for this reason or another, its eyes have tended to swivel forward toward the frontal plane so that their axes of vision are less divergent although not yet parallel. Probably the fields of vision overlap to some extent but true stereoscopic sight has not yet been realized. Moreover this little animal displays certain anatomical precocities of the reproductive system which foreshadow the higher primates and determine the consensus of zoölogical opinion that monkeys, apes and even man must own some progressive Eocene form of this arboreal hopper as their ultimate primate ancestor.

It would have taken a zoölogist gifted with extraordinary evolutionary foresight to predict from the generalized Eocene tarsioids the final emergence of Homo. But if we move on to the Oligocene period, not more than thirty-five millions of years ago, we find in the dried up lake bed of the Fayum west of the Nile ample evidence of the great evolutionary strides which the primates had taken in their first quarter of a hundred million years. Primitive and generalized Old World monkeys appear—

and from a tarsioid to a monkey is a bigger jump than from an ape to a man. The monkeys have much larger and better developed brains than tarsioids. Instead of being smooth and probably devoid of well-defined association areas, the surface of the cerebral hemispheres, or forebrain, is now wrinkled or convoluted, affording more nervous cortical surface. The occipital lobes of the forebrain in monkeys overhang the hind brain or cerebellum, which in the tarsiers is naked and exposed. The greatest expansion in the monkey brain has occurred in the so-called association areas, especially in the frontal and parietal regions. The visual and general sensory areas are now widely separated and well differentiated. Binocular or stereoscopic vision exists; there is an advanced method of intra-uterine nourishment of the young; without doubt there are enhanced mental faculties such as better memory, clearer association of ideas, intensified emotional activity, more acute tactile discrimination and sharper attention— above all, perhaps, the genesis of a certain curiosity, a tendency to poke into and investigate things. The faculty which makes a monkey mischievous is precisely that which in man has created something unique in the world of life—a material culture. It manifests itself in lower primate forms in an irresistible inclination to pull things apart; in man it puts things together. The monkey uses his agile fingers and his restless brain in play; man puts them to work.

We know little of these Oligocene monkeys except that they were small, primitive and generalized ancestors of the simian troops which people the forests of Asia and Africa today. However, just as the precocious tarsier appears in the same Eocene deposits with the less advanced lemur, so in the Oligocene beds of the Fayum the first tiny anthropoid ape is a contemporary of the ancestral Old World Monkey. The rise of this small ape was the second greatest achievement of organic evolution—the explicit promise of a reasoning animal which should create a civilization. There remains of Propliopithecus, ape of the dawn, only the half of a lower jaw and some teeth but these bespeak incontrovertibly a form which must have stood at the very point of divergence of the anthropoid-humanoid stock from that of the monkeys.

You may inquire how paleontologists and zoölogists are able to trace descent through teeth, which seem small and inadequate pegs upon which to hang whole genealogies. The expert upon fossil remains has to work with those parts of the body which best resist the attacks of time. In most animals these happen to be the teeth and the lower jaws—relatively tough and indigestible morsels which no beast of prey can stomach. The teeth are composed of dentine, coated on the crowns and necks with hard enamel, and they normally outlast all other skeletal parts. One of the most sinister signs of degression in civilized man is that he holds the undesirably unique position of being the only animal whose teeth commonly decay so early in life that his open mouth reveals a charnel house—an inadequately whitened sepulchre of rotting dentition.

The number and kind of teeth and the details of their cusp pattern have been found to be the most reliable criteria of relationship which comparative anatomy affords. Not only does the architecture of the teeth furnish a substantial clue as to the diet of the owner; it also indicates his descent. Thus the molar teeth of the little Propliopithecus show substantially the same five-cusped pattern as those of later fossil anthropoids, the present great apes and man. That is about all that we know of Propliopithecus except that he stands closer to the line of the modern gibbon than to that of the giant primates which ultimately gave rise to man, gorilla, chimpanzee and orang-utan. We may, however, postulate that this common ancestor of apes and man had a much larger brain relative to his body size than any existing monkey although in actual bulk he could have been no larger than a human suckling. It is probable also that Propliopithecus was an arboreal brachiator—i.e. he moved about the trees by taking long swings with his arms, the body suspended in an upright position and the legs trailing in the air. This brachiating habit, with consequent elongation of the arms, is characteristic of all existing anthropoid apes and there are ample traces of its former presence in the ancestral line of man. With it developed the vertical suspension of the viscera by means of sheets of membrane which hold the organs in place and prevent them from slumping into the pelvic cavity when the trunk is upright. Such suspension is a prerequisite for the biped erect posture on the ground, afterwards adopted by the hominids. Propliopithecus still lived on a generalized and mainly frugivorous diet such as the trees of the tropical forest afford; he was no predatory carnivore.

Our next glimpse of primate evolution is at the beginning of the Miocene period, perhaps nineteen million years ago. By this time the Old World monkeys are well developed and the anthropoid ape line has differentiated a full-fledged gibbon and the first of the generalized *giant* apes. The present gibbons are restricted to the southeastern portion of Asia and adjacent islands of the Indonesian archipelago. They are small arboreal anthropoids standing about three feet in height and very slender in build. With their prodigious arms (so long that they touch the ground when the animal stands erect) they swing from bough to bough and from tree to tree, easily clearing spaces of twenty to thirty feet. Like monkeys and tarsiers they produce only one offspring at a birth and take very good care of that single infant. When on the ground they run on their hind legs, keeping the knees bent and holding their arms aloft like a sprinter about to breast the tape. They have big and complicated brains, somewhat projecting jaws with long, sabre-like teeth, elongated and slender hands and feet with opposable thumbs and great toes. The Miocene gibbons were somewhat less specialized than those of the present day but were otherwise substantially like them.

Much more important are the remains of the generalized giant anthropoid apes of the Lower and Middle Miocene, which are often lumped together into one big group—the Dryopithecus family. The earliest of these apes appear on the Mediterranean edge of the Libyan desert but later they are distributed through Europe and along the southern foothills of the Himalayas, in the Siwalik deposits. These anthropoids are represented for the most part by isolated teeth and fragments of mandibles, with an occasional long bone. From these bits, however, it may be inferred that there were many genera and species—some already clearly ancestral to the orang-utan (the giant ape of Borneo and Sumatra), some showing dental features foreshadowing the African apes, the gorilla and the chimpanzee, and others displaying dentitions that make them possible ancestors of man.

Meanwhile what of man? It is generally postulated that his separation from the common anthropoid-humanoid stock occurred at least as early as the middle of the Miocene period—at a guess, thirteen million years ago. A strong body of opinion, in which I do not concur, would even go so far as to derive the humanoid line from a small ground ape which diverged from the anthropoid stocks back in the Oligocene, before there were any giant primates. This view is inacceptable to me because man bears in his molar teeth the pattern of his Dryopithecus heritage and because he manifests more numerous and detailed resemblances to the present great African apes than can be explained plausibly by convergence or by such a remote relationship as is implied in the theory of the small Oligocene ground-ape ancestor.

Geologists generally agree that the uplifting of the Central Asiatic plateau and the formation of the Himalayas and other encircling mountain chains occurred in the Miocene period. According to one theory this uplift was accompanied by a desiccation and deforestation of the elevated regions which left the ancestral generalized anthropoids under the necessity of migrating to some area where the forests were intact or of taking to the ground. Whether our ancestors made a virtue of a necessity by adopting a terrestrial life because there were no more trees or whether they took a chance on the ground out of sheer initiative can be argued but not proved. It may be noted that arboreal life, so advantageous for small primates, becomes a very cramping and precarious existence when an animal attains the body bulk of man and the great anthropoid apes. Firstly, the struggle against gravity increases with increments of weight. The orang-utan or gorilla is forced to keep to the larger boughs and the trunks of the trees and cannot flip lightly from the terminal branches of one tree to the next as does the gibbon. Big anthropoids must move slowly and cautiously, testing out the strength of branches before entrusting their weight to them. They have to waste a good deal of energy trying not to fall out of the trees. Again, tree life provides a sufficient diet for a small primate but the two-hundred-pound ape has rather lean pickings. He has to devour vast quantities of fruits and roughage in order to keep going at all and spends most of his life in a vain pursuit of his appetite.

Is it then incomprehensible that a giant primate, endowed with some-what more courage and initiative than his fellows, should have taken a chance upon the ground? There a fall means merely getting up again, there food is infinitely more plentiful and varied, there progress is a matter of putting one foot in front of another instead of a precarious climbing from bough to bough, which gets one nowhere but out on the end of the limb. Zaccheus of the biblical story showed great perspicacity in climbing a tree but greater intelligence still in that he chose the auspicious moment in which to come down.

Here and then was the crucial event of primate evolution—the trans-formation of a tree-dwelling ape into a terrestrial biped. When our anthropoid ancestor took to the ground alternatives of posture and locomo-tion were offered him. The first was quadrupedal progression, the habitual gait of the gorilla, the chimpanzee and the orang-utan when they leave the trees. This habit would have involved a loss of the free use of the fore-limbs and might even have necessitated a re-development of the snout as, seemingly, in the dog-faced baboons. Such a choice might have resulted in our continuance as apes. Erect posture, on the contrary, offered every pos-sible advantage, except that of stability. Moreover our anthropoid forbears were probably already adjusted for the upright position by their previous habit of suspending the body from the arms in brachiating and by climbing up and down the trunks of trees. It has even been suggested that our arboreal line may have been somewhat deficient in arm development, so that its members were not efficient brachiators.

At any rate a series of far-reaching anatomical adaptations was necessary before man attained his present efficiency in standing, walking and running as an "erect and featherless biped." In the first place his center of gravity had to shift to a position above the supporting hind limbs—a result effected naturally by erecting the trunk. In order to accomplish this straightening of the body axis, the spine had to be bent in its free region between the rib cage and the pelvis. Thus originated the lumbar curve, a concavity of the vertebral column in the small of the back which converts the spine into a graceful sigmoid shape and incidentally gives rise to innumerable back-aches. Then, since the entire body weight was now transmitted to the hind limbs through the pelvis, the form of the latter had to be modified to serve this purpose, and so changed also as to provide suitable surfaces for attachment of the muscles which balance the body in the upright posture. To dispense with technical detail, it may be said that the pelvis was broadened and flattened from a funnel to a basin shape. The legs became enormously elongated and strengthened in accordance with the new demands made upon them as the exclusive organs of support and locomotion. But the most radical changes occurred in the foot, which had to be transformed from a mobile prehensile member, much like a hand, to a more stable and rigid organ. Apes and monkeys can oppose their great toes (which protrude inward like thumbs) to the tips of their long outer digits. Such a movement is essential for the encircling foot grasp of boughs. It is quite useless for a flat-footed walker. The great toe was brought into line with the long axis of the foot and converted into a main point of pedal support. The outer toes, no longer used for grasping, were shortened. The tarsus, originally composed of loose and mobile bones like those of the wrist, was molded into a springy vault of wedge-shaped elements. The heel bone was prolonged backward to give more leverage to the great calf muscles which lift the body to the balls of the feet in walking. Thus originated the makeshift organ we call the human foot, with its easily broken down arches and its vestigial outer toes. It is essentially human; it serves its purpose more or less efficiently; but it is rarely beautiful and usually looks like a mutilated slab terminating in degenerate digits like external vermiform appendices.

Other bodily changes consequent upon the assumption of the erect standing posture include a flattening of the chest, a broadening of the shoulders, a slight shortening of the arms and a refinement of the hands for skilled manual movements—especially an elongation and perfected opposability of the thumbs. A great transformation was wrought in the face. The protruding snout, already regressive from the transfer of its major function to the hands in prehuman primates, continued to shrink back, particularly in the region of the teeth, as these dental elements became reduced in size because they were no longer needed for defense, for offense or for the tearing of tough food. All these duties were assumed by the hands and subsequently by the sharpened tools or weapons the hands created and manipulated. Partly as a result of dental shrinkage, the chin was left outthrust and the soft tip of the nose was protruded in degenerative exuberance. An esthetic ape would shudder at the human face, which proclaims itself a product of regressive evolution and atrophy of function. But the most remarkable change of all was effected in a prodigious swelling of the brain and its skeletal envelope. The forehead, previously non-existent, swelled up into a bulbous arch; the whole vault of the skull rose like an inflated bladder, bulged laterally and protruded posteriorly into a bun-shaped occiput. . . .

During the Pliocene period, which lasted at least six million years and terminated with the onset of the glacial epoch, perhaps a million years B.C., it seems certain that our ancestors, who now deserved the name of man, flourished like the green bay tree. Unfortunately we have as yet no skeletal remains of human beings which can be attributed with certainty to this early period. We know, however, that before its close man had already begun to make stone implements, somewhat crude and amorphous but definitely recognizable as human artifacts. The elements of material culture had been formed. Social organization may well have existed. Anatomical evidence suggests that a number of different physical types of man were present, some more apelike than others but all essentially human, and that several of the types were possessed of such ability to dominate their physical environments as to ensure survival through the rigors of the ensuing glacial epoch.

The million-year Pleistocene or glacial period witnessed four advances of the ice sheets with three genial climatic intervals of varying duration in terms of scores of thousands of years. Throughout this whole period we have nearly continuous records of man's stone work in the gravel deposits laid down by rivers and in the inhabited caves. Flint-working evolved slowly to a pitch of skill which can be appreciated only if one attempts to produce similar tools from the same refractory material.

Geological deposits of the earlier and middle portions of the Pleistocene have yielded occasional skeletal remains of man, for the most part fragmentary, but enormously instructive. All these men seem to have been erect walkers, with feet fully adapted for support. Some had rather small brains, low foreheads, great bars of bone above the eye sockets, protrusive jaws and receding chins. Such anatomical reminders of ape ancestry did not prevent them from fabricating a great variety of stone tools, efficient and, in many cases, symmetrical to the point of beauty. Low brows did not preclude the clear development of family life around the hearth of cave habitations, or the reverent burial of the dead, with funeral gifts that suggest belief in a future life.

Before the end of the glacial period, perhaps 25,000 years ago, anatomically modern types of men were dwelling in the caves of Europe and were decorating the walls of their abodes with realistic polychrome frescoes of the animals they hunted. These men of the Old Stone Age also carved statuettes of their lady friends or their mother goddesses—rather frank representations of Rubensian females. They had invented a number of skillful devices used in fishing and hunting. They were almost civilized and altogether human.

1936

Evolution Revised

RUTH MOORE

———

SINCE 1950 THE SCIENTIFIC EVIDENCE HAS POINTED inescapably to one conclusion: man did not evolve in either the time or the way that Darwin and the modern evolutionists thought most probable. The physicists and the geologists by 1950 had clearly shown that the world is older and man is younger than anyone had dared to estimate before.

By that year, the men who dug into the ancient caves of South Africa and China, looking for traces of early man and the part-human, part-anthropoid races that had preceded him had succeeded. All the major steps in the evolution of man were for the first time filled in; the hitherto missing link had been found. But the missing link was not what science had expected; no one had imagined a being with the head of an ape and the body of a man.

What did it mean? The physicists and geologists and fossil-hunters did not say. They merely presented their dates and materials. . . .

The question was insistent: what did it mean? How did the new findings affect the theory of evolution? This was a problem for the anthropologist, because the whole problem of man's origins and evolution was affected.

The surprising and almost unbelievable fossils that came from the banks of the Solo River, from Dragon-bone Hill, and from the Sterkfontein caves indicated that man had developed according to a new pattern, and that the pattern given him in the past—and currently, in many cases—was wrong at some critical points. The fossils supplied disconcerting proof that the development of the body came first, and the typical development of the brain later—that we had human bodies long before we reached human intelligence.

At first, such evidence from the ground was disbelieved, as evidence

492

is likely to be when it runs counter to what the world has always thought.

When Eugène Dubois found an undeniably human leg bone close by the skull of *Pithecanthropus erectus,* the world cried: "They can't belong together." The ridicule heaped upon his find, in large part because of this "discrepancy," drove the Dutch physician into his thirty-year retreat.

The skepticism was almost as strong when similar bones began to be found with the skulls of Peking man.

Broom ran headlong into the same feeling that there must be a mix-up when he discovered human-like pelvic bones in the same deposits with the unquestionably apelike skulls of the South African ape-men. For a number of years his work was not taken seriously because he ventured to claim that the ape-like creatures could have had near-human bodies and walked like men.

The conviction that the first men began as replicas, however crude and primitive, of modern man was so deep that the evidence to the contrary long was discredited and discounted. It was a staple belief that many millions of years ago some of the anthropoids developed better brains, and that as they became smarter they came down out of the trees and gradually evolved into modern man.

Weidenreich was perhaps the first authority to point out that man's development might have followed a different course. In 1941 he wrote: "Little is known about the development of other parts of the skeleton, but it can be taken as definitely established that the erect posture and all that is connected with its adoption were attained long before [man reached his definitive form]. Thus the subsequent change of the skull, and above all that of the brain case, morphologically viewed, crowns the transformation in the true sense of the word, both in time and position."

But not until after the publication of the South African monographs and their appraisal by Clark of Oxford did science generally begin to grant that the body reached human form long before the brain.

Laboratory work at the University of Chicago and Harvard strongly confirmed the new pattern of evolution evinced by the fossils. Washburn, at Chicago, made a close study of the different body "complexes" of man and the apes.

In the arms, the ribs, and the shoulder girdle, he found, the two are very much alike. The important middle part of the body had changed little; there men still were essentially apes. The specialist can recognize the technical differences between the shoulders of modern man and the ape, but the differences are not great.

The most noticeable departure is in the hands, which Washburn, from the long-term anthropological viewpoint, considered of lesser importance.

Once man had become a biped, selection inevitably would have favored a hand differing from that of the tree-living primates. Even so, the human hand still shows a remarkable amount of the primitive grasping adaptation, particularly in the long fingers and nails.

As Washburn and a number of other anthropologists now see it, the middle part of the body, the trunk and arms, began to take on its essential form millions of years ago, at the time when the earliest primates climbed up into the trees. The story as they trace it goes, in outline, something like this:

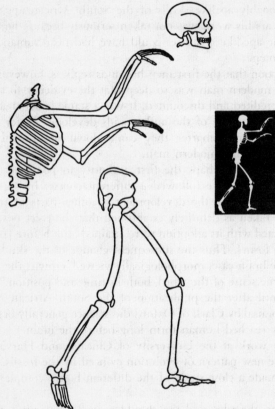

The three great body "complexes" of·man. Each section evolved differently. The arms, shoulders, and ribs changed little. In this middle part of the body men still are essentially apes. There was an all-important change in the pelvis-legs complex, a change that started man on a distinctive line of evolution. Man's ability to walk on two legs freed his hands for the use of tools. The development of the third great complex, the brain, then followed.

The development of the ability to grasp with the hands and feet set the first primates apart from all the other primitive mammals and made it possible for them to take up life in the trees.

But life on the leafy green world above was a fairly restricted, though safe one. Without the great ranges over which the ground-living animals could move and mix, the tree-living primates came to differ widely from each other.

Many of them developed differences in the senses. In the trees, the strong sense of smell, the ears that cocked to the least sound, the hair that stood on end at the threat of danger, were not so important as on the ground. The monkeys with better eyes and color vision were the ones that survived and left descendants. And gradually the brain changed from a primitive "smell-brain" to a more advanced "sight-brain."

The monkeys thus equipped became abundantly successful in the Old World tropical forests and in most of the other areas to which they spread.[1]

Some of the numerous small bands of primates then began to develop a different mode of locomotion. Instead of hopping or running along, holding fast with hands and feet, they would swing along with a different motion of the arms. This mode of progress, called brachiation, involved anatomical changes in the wrist, elbow, shoulder, and thoracic region.

And thus the apes arose, and the shoulder, arms, and ribs took on the form that has been carried along almost unchanged to all of us today.

Washburn points out that no monkey anywhere in the world has such arms and shoulders. But every essential detail of this "complex" is shared by man and ape. He believes this crucially important change occurred about ten million years ago.

As the eons rolled by, the story continues, some of the apes that ate a more varied diet came down to the ground to live. Like their present-day descendants, they could take a few steps upright, perhaps even while holding a stick in one hand. But when they wanted to cover space, down went the knuckles and they proceeded on all fours.

About a million years ago there came what many anthropologists regard as the most important of all the changes in the evolution of man, a change that forever afterward was to set man apart from his anthropoid ancestors.

Some of the big ground-living apes were born with a different kind of pelvis. It meant that they could walk upright, on two legs! For the first time, in all of time, the hands were free. They no longer had to be used

---

[1] The older, more primitive forms soon were replaced, except where they were especially protected, or retreated to a nocturnal life. The safety of the island of Madagascar, for example, saved the lemurs. The tarsiers, the lorises, and the galagos found refuge in the night.

for locomotion. These ground-living apes could use tools, for any implement held in the hands no longer had to be dropped every time more
than a few steps were taken. "The fact that we number more than a few
thousand bipeds living in the Old World tropics is due to the development
of tools," said Washburn.

Gibbon, gorilla, and spider monkey. The gibbon and gorilla swing along with
the arms—brachiate. The monkey, lacking the arm and shoulder development of the
apes and man, runs along holding fast with arms, legs, and, in the case of the
new world monkey, with the tail too.

From this point on, all was changed; a new future had been cast.
Natural selection was on a new basis, for a premium had been placed on
brains as well as brawn. The most intelligent of the biped man-apes, the
ones that could most effectively use sticks and stones to beat off their
enemies and kill their food, were the survivors and the parents of the
next generation.

The pelvis that precipitated this all-important turn in evolution has a
number of functions. It not only connects the legs and trunk in such a
way that it controls gait; it gives origin to many muscles and serves as a
bony birth canal.

How any living creature stands and moves depends in large part upon
the length of the pelvis and upon the angle at which it is inclined. In the
apes it is long and slanting. In the ape-men and men it is shorter and more
nearly upright.

Washburn believes that this whole vital evolutionary cycle began when some of the big ground-living apes were born with a shorter pelvis. When this basic genetic change occurred, the bone had to take on a more upright position to assure a safe birth for offspring. And once the pelvis is brought into such a position, the thigh muscles that attach to it are directly affected. These muscles make the human step.

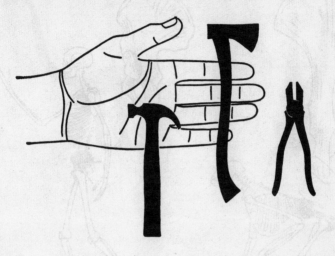

Hand and tools.

Washburn argues that the real difference between the walk of man and ape is not in the extent of the motion, but in the ability to finish the step with a drive. The muscle that provides the drive and swings back the thigh is the gluteus maximus, the muscle that arises from the posterior part of the pelvis. When the pelvis is short, the gluteus maximus pulls hard. A vigorous step is possible.

Negative evidence of how important the muscle is appears when it becomes paralyzed. A man who suffers such an accident cannot walk normally, though he can get around easily with a flexed gait similar to that of the apes. "The paralysis of the single muscle makes the human type of bipedal locomotion impossible," wrote Washburn. "It shows that the form and function of this particular muscle is critical in the evolution of man's posture and gait."

Carrying this argument back to what may have happened when the first apes began to walk, Washburn maintains that since selection is for function, the animals able to walk and use the hands most freely were the ones to survive. Hence selection favored the new type of pelvis. "It is my belief," the Chicago anthropologist concludes, "that this single change is the thing that initiates human evolution."

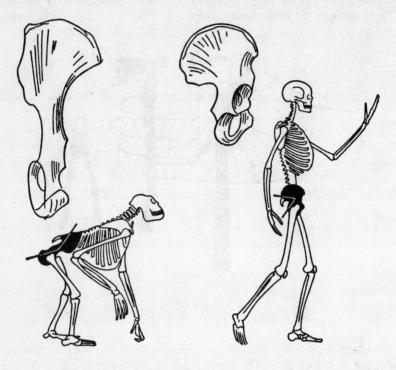

One great change forever afterward set man apart from his anthropoid ancestors. It was in the pelvis. The apes, with their long slanting pelvis, can take only a few steps upright and must use the hands for locomotion. Man, because of his shorter pelvis, can stand and walk—he is a biped. His hands are then no longer needed for locomotion.

And the evidence backs up this theory with enlightening and revealing regularity. No living ape ever has been found with a human-type pelvis. Nor has any man or any of the fossil remains of man ever been discovered with an ape-type pelvis. In Java, in China, in South Africa, the pelvic bones found with the fossils placed in the human line were either human or near-human in type. There has been no exception, though the world long wanted to believe otherwise.

To put the point to the final test, Washburn has proposed a bold and intriguing experiment. He would like to operate on a laboratory ape and change its pelvis, much as the pelvis must have changed in evolution. If the operation succeeded, the ape would be able to walk on two legs! Its hands would be freed for the use of tools. The studies that could be made as this one animal relived in part a change through which the human race passed about a million years ago would hold exciting possibilities.

Preliminary studies have indicated that the operation is anatomically possible. Only the lack of laboratory funds has halted work along this amazing and promising line.

It was only after the trunk and the pelvis and legs had developed much as they are today that the brain began the spectacular growth that eventually was to change ape-man and primitive man into modern man. Until the 1940's science assumed that the growth of the brain always came first. Supposedly it was a better brain that enabled the mammals as a group to triumph over the reptiles when the two contended for the control of that ancient world of sea and jungle.

And supposedly it was again the development of a better brain that led the apes out of the trees and onto the ground. Even Weidenreich, though he recognized that the evolution of the body came first, rated the development of the brain as the primary factor in evolution.

The faith in the priority of the brain was first seriously jarred in 1948. In that year Professor Tilly Edinger of Harvard showed that the growth of the brain tends to follow in evolution. The earliest mammals, their fossil remains revealed, had brains no more advanced than those of the reptiles. Only later, after they had become typical mammals, did the brains reach modern mammalian proportions.

The horse, which Edinger studied in particular, attained its characteristic form, its long legs and teeth, well before the brain reached its final size.

And so it was with man. A comparison of the brain capacity of man and his forerunners sharply etches the pattern:

	CRANIAL CAPACITY
Chimpanzee and gorilla	325–650 (cubic centimeters)
South African ape-man	450–650
Java man	790–900
Peking man	900–1,200
Neanderthal man	1,100–1,500
Modern man	1,200–1,500

The South African ape-men—despite their near-human bodies and upright posture—were in the brain range of the apes.

"There is no doubt that all human fossils described so far have human pelves and limb bones, and the man-apes were remarkably human in these features," Washburn emphasized. "Therefore it appears that the differences in the brain between apes and man, just as those in dentition, were attained after full human status had been achieved in the limbs and trunk."

In its final evolution the change in the brain was large. Between the ape-men and the emergence of modern man, the brain more than doubled in size. It grew from the 650-cubic-centimeter maximum of the apes and the ape-men to the modern top average of 1,500 cubic centimeters.

Some of the Neanderthal men of Europe had a brain capacity very close to that of modern man, if not within the modern range. They were well along the way. . . .

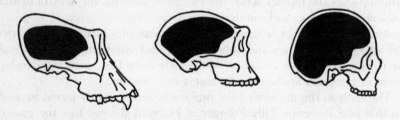

The growth of the brain. The ape (left) had a brain averaging less than 650 cubic centimeters. Primitive man reached a brain of 900 to 1,200 cubic centimeters. Modern man often has a brain of 1,500 cubic centimeters. The brain of modern man is more than twice as large as that of the ape.

It should be remembered, too, that many of the other fossils that once appeared to date man with a fairly sizable brain back in the shadowy stretches of 500,000 to 1,000,000 years ago were also shown to belong to comparatively recent years.

How recent? Here Carbon-14 comes in. Although the Carbon-14 dates do not go beyond 25,000 years, they clearly indicate that the ice last extended down from the north both in Europe and in North America about 11,000 years ago. If this is correct, geologists hold that the final glaciation began less than 50,000 years ago.

This is an assumption, unsupported as yet by any absolute system of dating, but with the date of the final advance of the ice fixed, and with all the wealth of evidence left by the glaciers themselves, there is little speculation in estimating the duration of the last ice age.

The new timing indicates therefore that humans who had the requisite intelligence to be called men did not reach that high status until about 50,000 years ago. Modern man, then, is only about 50,000 years old.

The 50,000 years, of course, are approximate. But even if this estimate should later be enlarged to 75,000 or 100,000 years, modern man still would be the veriest of newcomers by all evolutionary standards. And if our 50,000-year tenure of the earth must be adjusted, the chances are that it will be shortened. Unpublished work and studies now going on in a number of universities are tending to pull the time of man's emergence as man even closer to today.

At the same time, the work of Washburn, Dice, and others demonstrated that man could have made the steep climb from ape-man to modern man in the shorter time now allotted.

In the light of these new understandings, much that has been taught about the time of man and his development must now be changed. Books must be rewritten and courses revised. For the new timing, the new fossil finds, the new pattern of evolution are bringing about a new and major revision in the theory of the origin of man.

The theory of evolution is not being weakened by this correction of past errors and misconceptions and by the opening of new understandings. On the contrary, the basic truths developed by Darwin and the brilliant succession of evolutionists who came after him are strengthened.

1953

Lessons In Living from the Stone Age

VILHJALMUR STEFANSSON

SLIGHTLY LESS EMBARRASSING THAN OWNING TO A philosophy of life is confessing that you have some idea, though vague and changing, as to what constitutes the good life. My ideas of it come chiefly from a comparison between civilization and primitive culture.

I feel that when Shaw intentionally speculates in his *Back to Methuselah* on the good life in coming millenniums he describes unintentionally the lives of some groups of our ancestors during millenniums of the remote past. For Shaw pictures the nearly ideal condition of the future in a way that has little relation to civilization as we find it about us to-day but which is reminiscent of a great deal that we call the lowest savagery. . . .

My party of one white and three "Americanized" western Eskimos reached the Stone Age Eskimos of Coronation Gulf in late winter, traveling by sledge in a manner to which the local people were accustomed. We wore fur garments similar to their own, and gave the impression of being not foreign, though strangers. We were able to converse from the first day; for Eskimo is one language from Greenland to Bering Sea across the northern frontier of the New World.

In culture the Gulf Eskimos went back not thousands but tens of thousands of years; for they were just emerging from the age of wood and horn into the earliest period of stone. They knew that certain berries and roots could be eaten, although they did not consider them as real food, but only as a substitute for food in an emergency. Their proper diet was wholly animal tissues. Through two-thirds of the year it was chiefly seal, with an occasional polar bear. During the summer they lived mainly on caribou, with some fish. There was no clothing except from the skins of animals. The tents were of skin and so were the boats. There were kayaks, the small boats used for hunting; there were none of the large skin boats in which other groups of Eskimos travel. The only domestic beast was the dog, and he was mainly a hunting animal. There was usually not more than one dog for each hunter; so that, although the dogs were hitched to sledges in traveling, there were so few of them in comparison with the people that essentially the Eskimos themselves were the draft animals.

The Coronation Eskimos knew of the Bear Lake forest but did not like it as a country to live in and made journeys to it only to secure timber for sledges, tent poles, and for a few other uses. They considered the treeless prairie north of the forest the best possible land in summer, and they considered the ice of the gulf and strait a proper and desirable home in winter. They were satisfied, then, with both their country and their climate, believing that any change would be for the worse.

These Stone Age people considered not only that the one proper food is meat but also that the most delicious things in the world are the preferred parts of animals. They had the highest average of good health which I have ever found in any community of like size; most of the deaths among them came from accident or old age. They had a religion by which they believed themselves able to control their environment; but it was a religion neither of hope nor of fear. There was no permanent future life; there was nothing resembling heaven or hell. The spirits were powerful but they were not in themselves good or evil, though they might do the good or evil bidding of men or women who controlled them—this Stone Age attitude toward spirits was something like the modern attitude toward explosives or steam power: things neutral in themselves but capable of being used for good or ill. They had as much desire to live as any of us but less fear of dying than most of us have.

Of the seven hundred or so Stone Age people about two hundred had been in contact with whaling ships for a few days each of two years, 1906-7 and 1907-8. Our visit to them was in 1910. There were a dozen or less who had seen David Hanbury when he passed along the southern edge of their district in 1902. Another dozen had seen for an hour or two at close range some Slavey Indians a few years before our visit, and of course they had seen groups of them frequently at a distance. But at least four hundred had never heard the noise which gunpowder makes when it explodes or seen the lighting of a match. They had seen pieces of cloth and believed them to be skins of animals. They had received many guns by tribe-to-tribe trade, but had secured them only when the neighbor groups had run out of ammunition. They hammered and cut up the guns to make things which they wanted, such as knives, spear points, and especially needles.

When we first lived with these people they envied us greatly just one thing we had with us, our sewing needles. Among themselves the most valuable single possession was a dog. I purchased a dog for a large knife, worth about three dollars at American wholesale prices. Later that day the man returned with the knife and with a second dog—if I would take the knife back he would give me two dogs for one needle. They explained that, although they had seen the Eskimo woman member of our party sewing before we made the first trade of the knife for the dog, they had not then realized that she possessed two needles. Now they understood that she had not only two but several, and she had told them that, with my consent, she was willing to give up one.

We inquired and found that by local standards a No. 1 size sewing needle was worth much more than any knife and was well worth, in the common estimation, two good dogs. So we made the trade.

The point of the trading story is that these Stone Age Eskimos were as yet not discontented with their copper knives, although they had been familiar for decades with the better iron knives which they themselves had made through Stone Age technic from rifle barrels and other pieces of iron. But they were far from content with their copper needles, for the shafts were necessarily stout in comparison with the size of the eye, which made it difficult to sew a waterproof seam.

Waterproof sewing is apparently one of the early discoveries of man. There may not be any people on earth to-day except the Eskimos who still remember how to make, and do make, a really waterproof seam. For most or all other sewers rub grease into a seam to waterproof it, or use some trick of that sort; but the women of the Stone Age Eskimos considered it an insult if they saw anybody rubbing grease on the seam of a water boot which they had made. However, in spite of their skill, waterproof sewing was difficult with the use of a copper needle; but it was easy with one of our steel needles.

Perhaps we have gone too far already before saying that we have no thought of deriving the health, happiness, and other details of the good life of the Copper Eskimos from their backward state—from their being still thousands of years behind us in technological development. We are merely trying to sketch briefly, and without any necessary causal relation, how these people lived who were to all appearances so much happier than any other people whom I have ever known.

We were the first of European civilization to live with these Eskimos, and we saw during the first year the gradual, and later rapid, increase of discontent—which was a decrease of happiness. Discontent grew not always along lines that might have been expected. For instance, you would think that our matches would have been coveted, but this was not the case. Their method of lighting fires by knocking together two pieces of iron pyrite had advantages which to their minds (and even to mine later on) compensated for the disadvantages. Certainly a match is handier for a cigarette; also for lighting a fire in good weather our matches were better. The advantage of the pyrite we discovered when we had to kindle a fire in a gale or in a rainstorm. It came to be our practice when we traveled with the Stone Age people to light fires with matches in good weather and to borrow their technic when the weather was bad. Then another advantage of pyrite was of course that two pieces of it, each the size of a lemon, would last you for years, if not for a lifetime. Nor did you have to worry about keeping these lumps of rock dry.

The Stone Age people had been discontented with their needles before we came. The first discontent after that was connected with the insect pests. They had never conceived of a mosquito net that would protect your face during the day and that might be used to cover your bed at night. As first they considered our face nets and bed nets frivolous. But after a few weeks of association they began to say what a fine thing it would be if a white trader should come in with enough mosquito nets so that everybody could buy one.

There were also the black flies. Eskimo garments are loose, somewhat as if the coat were a Russian blouse and the trousers in the style of our pajamas. Besides, in the heat of the summer, with temperatures sometimes running above 90° in the shade, they practically had to have rents and holes in their skin clothing. Through these holes, up their sleeves and down their necks would crawl the black flies as if they were fleas, stinging so that the hurt was greater than the itch. Against these pests we wore knitted cotton shirts and drawers, with long arms and long legs, the elasticity making them tight and flyproof round the wrist and ankle. A longing for this kind of underwear to use in summer was perhaps the basis of the second of the new discontents.

There grew slowly through the first summer an appreciation that a cloth tent was better than one of skins—lighter, less bulky, and less difficult to preserve from decay. It was not until perhaps the second or third year that there was any real discontent with the bow and arrow for caribou hunting and a desire for rifles. The appreciation of the value of fish nets, as compared with spears and hooks, developed somewhat more rapidly than the longing for guns. During the first few years of Copper Eskimo association with Europeans there was no discontent on the score of diet. The local conception was, as said, that meat is real food and that things like cereals and vegetables are makeshifts.

II

The picture of Stone Age life which we have begun to sketch might not seem attractive to the reader even if we could spread it over a large canvas

with the details completely presented. We endeavor to bring out our meaning in part by making a contrast between the Copper Eskimos of 1910
and those of 1939.

Perhaps the only thing with which the Coronation people are still content is their climate. You cannot describe to them the weather of Hawaii
or California in such terms as to get a more favorable reply than that no
doubt Europeans like that sort of thing but they themselves would never
like it. They still prefer boiled meat to any imported food; but they now
feel ashamed if they do not have, especially for visitors, a few of the
costly imports to offer, among them tea, coffee, sugar, salt, bread, and syrup.
They are as discontented now with the sewing machines which they own
as they formerly were with the copper needles. They are less content with
the best rifles they can get than they were with their bows and arrows.
They still enjoy their own songs most, but they feel a social need of phono-
graphs, and there is a developing need for the radio. They know that their
skin clothes are best for the climate, but fashion has laid such hold upon
them that they must have clothes of silk and other materials.

In 1910 they believed in keeping up with the Joneses. In this they used
to be approximately successful; for under their communistic anarchy
everyone shared the best of the foods and the best of all materials. There
was scarcely any difference between garments except that one woman
could make a more attractive dress than another out of a given material,
or a man correspondingly could make a slightly superior bow or spear.
To-day keeping up with the Joneses wears a different aspect. Formerly in
that contest they had no problems which we classify as economic; now
they compete, or want to compete, in things which are beyond their economic reach, some of them known through hearsay but not obtainable in
their country.

The breakdown in native economy, and thereby in self-respect, is more
easily described, at least so far as my own experience goes, from the
Mackenzie River district, several hundred miles to the west of the Copper
Eskimos.

Mackenzie habits of life began to change with the entrance of the
New England whaling fleet in 1889. I arrived there in 1906. Between that
year and 1918 I saw much change; the rest to date is known to me from
dependable reports.

Comparing the reports of Sir John Franklin with what I saw a hundred
years later, I would conclude that two thousand delta people had decreased
in a century to less than two hundred. The chief cause was measles, one
epidemic of which, in the memory of those still living, had killed something like two out of three within a few weeks. Tuberculosis had been

rare or absent; now it was prevalent. Digestive troubles had been few, but now they were common. Tooth decay had been unknown, but now their teeth were as bad as ours. There is no reasonable doubt that in 1820 the Mackenzie people, then in the Stone Age, were on the average as healthy as my Copper Eskimos were in 1910; but when I reached the Mackenzie district in 1906 the average Mackenzie health was probably not better than that of our worst slum districts.

The Mackenzie people, however, were not living under a slum level of poverty in 1906. They still had their economic independence and the respect which goes with it. How this later broke down can be shown by the story of Ovayuak, who still held to the old ways of life and who was still a heathen.

Steamers come down the Mackenzie River in midsummer, usually arriving at Macpherson during early July. The first steamer brought the Bishop. It was known among the converts in the Mackenzie district that the Bishop wanted to see them on his annual pastoral visits. The people liked the Bishop, they wanted to purchase goods that had been brought by the steamer, and they enjoyed the outing of the two-hundred-mile trip south to the Hudson's Bay post. So they streamed to Macpherson in late June.

But, said Ovayuak, the Bishop's visit came in a fishing season. Not being a convert, he stayed behind and fished all summer with his family and a few who still took their lead from him. Most of the others went to meet the Bishop and the traders. By the time the religious ceremonies, the feasting, and the trading were completed and the return journey made to the coast, the fishing was nearly over.

But that was only part of the difficulty. The trader had said to the Eskimo husbands that they ought to dress their wives in the best possible garments. When the reply was that the Eskimos had nothing with which to pay, the trader said that he knew them well, that they were reliable, that he would be glad to trust them, and that they could take as much cloth as they wanted, paying him next year.

However, when the cloth had been sold the trader would give these men a talking-to of another sort. He would remind them that now they were in honor bound to pay for the goods a year later. They must not, therefore, spend all their time down on the coast fishing and gorging themselves; they would now have to go up into the forest or to certain promontories on the coast so as to catch the mink of the woodland or the white foxes that frequent the shore floe. These would now have to be their chief concern; for they were pledged to see that the dealer should not suffer through having trusted them.

Accordingly, said Ovayuak, when the people returned from their sum-

mer visit to Macpherson they would explain to him that they had made
promises not to stay very long at the fishing but to go to the promontories
or the forest in time to be ready for the trapping season. And, said
Ovayuak, naturally he could not argue against this; for, like them, he
believed that a promise ought to be kept. So most of the families would
scatter for the trapping districts, leaving him and his few adherents still
at the fishing.

Ovayuak told me this just after the New Year. He forecast that when
the midwinter days began to lengthen, visitors would begin to arrive.
The trappers would now be running short of food and they would say to
one another, "Let us go to Ovayuak; he has plenty of fish."

Sure enough, they began to gather. At first we took them into our
house, where twenty-three of us had been living in one room; but that
accommodation could not be stretched for more than ten extras. So the
others had to pitch tents or to build snowhouses in the neighborhood of
our cabin. The stores of fish that seemed inexhaustible began to melt
rapidly. There was not merely a steady increase of people; they all had
their dog teams to feed, also.

Everybody went out fishing every day, we locals and the visitors, but we
caught perhaps only one-tenth as much as was being consumed. This went
on till the fish store was nearly gone. Thereupon everybody who had a
sledge loaded it heavy with the last of the fish and then we scattered in all
directions, to hunting and fishing districts. We went in small detachments,
for it is a principle of the hunting life that you must not travel in large
groups.

The system which I watched breaking down under the combined
influence of Christianity and the fur trade was on its economic side communism. Natural resources and raw materials were owned in common,
but made articles were privately owned. The blubber of a seal that was
needed for light and heat, or lean and fat that were needed for meals,
belonged no more to the man who secured them than to anyone else.
A pair of boots belonged to the woman who made them until she
presented or sold them to somebody else. A meal that had been cooked
was in a sense private property, but it was open to everyone under the
laws of hospitality—it was very bad form to start a meal in any village
without at the least sending a youngster outdoors to shout at the top of
his voice that the family were about to dine or breakfast. If the houses were
scattered and the people indoors, then messengers, usually children, would
be sent to every household. People would come and join the family at their
meal, either because they wanted the food or else for sociability. If the

house was too small to accommodate everybody, then portions of cooked food were sent out to the other houses.

It is a usual belief with us that this type of communism leads to shiftlessness. But that was certainly not the case in any Eskimo community known to me so long as they still followed the native economy.

Among the Eskimos of northern Canada there was no law except public opinion. Although no one had authority, each person had influence according to the respect won from a community which had intimate knowledge of everybody. Nobody was supposed to work if he was sick; and still the permanently handicapped were expected to work, each according to his ability. Among the Copper Eskimos, for instance, I saw a man of about forty who had been blind since childhood. He was one of the most cheerful and constant workers, but naturally could do only a few special things.

It has been a part of European ethics that a debt of honor should be paid before other debts. Thus a debt which could not be collected through legal machinery was a heavier obligation than one which had behind it the penalties of the state. With the Stone Age Eskimos every debt was a debt of honor; for there were no police, judges, prisons, or punishment.

The same force which compelled the Eskimo to pay his debts compelled him to do his share of the work according to his recognized abilities. I never knew even one who didn't try his best, although there were of course the same differences of energy and aptitude which we find among ourselves. If there had been a shirker he would have received the same food; but even in a circle of punctilious courtesy he would have felt that he was not being fed gladly. It is nearly impossible, when you know how primitive society works under communistic anarchy, to conceive of anyone with the combination of indolence and strength of character which would make it possible for a healthy man to remain long a burden on the community.

In the few cases where strength of character is enough for running against public opinion the issue is seldom or never on any such low plane as that of indolence. I have known one situation where a man was condemned to death. For there was no punishment among the Stone Age Eskimos except the disapproval of the community or death—nothing in between.

III

We may now summarize those things in the Stone Age life which we judge make for happiness more than do the corresponding elements of our own civilization:

The successful man stood above his fellows in nothing but their good opinion. Rank was determined by the things you secured and turned over to the common use. Your importance in the community depended on your judgment, your ability, and your character, but notably upon your unselfishness and kindness. Those who were useful to the community, who fitted well into the community pattern, were leaders. It was these men who were so often wrongly identified by the careless early civilized traveler and the usual trader as chiefs. They were not chiefs, for they had no authority; they had nothing but influence. People followed their advice because they believed it to be sound. They traveled with them because they liked to travel with them.

There was of course the negative side. If you were selfish you were disliked. If you tried to keep more than your share you became unpopular. If you were persistently selfish, acquisitive, and careless of the general good you gradually became too unpopular. Realizing this, very likely you would try moving to another community and starting life there over again. If you persisted in your ways and stayed where you were there would come a period of unanimous disapproval. You might survive for a year or even a few years as an unwanted hanger-on; but the patience of the community might at any time find its limit, and there would be one more execution of a troublemaker.

Because few understand the workings of a communistic anarchy it is necessary to insist that most of the supposed difficulties which fill our theoretical discussions of communism and of anarchy do not arise in practice.

Under the communism we are describing you don't have to accumulate food, apart from the community's store; for you are welcome to all you reasonably need of the best there is. You do not have to buy clothes; for they will be made for you either by some woman member of your family or by some woman friend who will feel about your wearing a coat of hers just the way any number of our women feel when they see their men friends wearing a garment they have knit or a tie they have sent as a Christmas gift. You do not have to accumulate wealth against your old age; for the community will support you as gladly when you are too old to work as it would if you had never been able to work at all—say because you had been blind from infancy.

One common arrangement of ours, however, is useful under communism, though not quite as necessary there as under rugged individualism. It is a good thing to have a family, for your children and grandchildren will look after you even more thoughtfully than mere friends.

The nearest thing to an investment among the Stone Age Eskimos, the one means of providing against old age, is children. For that reason a widow without a child would have to be loved for herself alone. A widow with one child would be a desirable match. To marry a widow with three or four children was, among the Stone Age people of Coronation Gulf, the New York equivalent to marrying the widow of a millionaire.

On the basis of my years with the Stone Age Eskimos I feel that the chief factor in their happiness was that they were living according to the Golden Rule.

It is easier to feel that you can understand than to prove that you do understand why it is man gets more happiness out of living unselfishly under a system which rewards unselfishness than from living selfishly where selfishness is rewarded. Man is more fundamentally a co-operative animal than a competitive animal. His survival as a species has been perhaps through mutual aid rather than through rugged individualism. And somehow it has been ground into us by the forces of evolution to be "instinctively" happiest over those things which in the long run yield the greatest good to the greatest number.

My hope for the good life of the future, as I have seen it mirrored from the past by the Stone Age of northern America, does not rest wholly on a belief in cycles of history. It rests in part on the thought that a few more decades or centuries of preaching the Golden Rule may result in its becoming fashionable, even for the civilized, to live by the Golden Rule. Perhaps we could live as happily in a metropolis as in a fishing village if only we could substitute the ideals of co-operation for those of competition. For it does not seem to be inherent in "progress" that it shall be an enemy to the good life.

1939

Racial Characters of the Body

SIR ARTHUR KEITH

From Man: A History of the Human Body

IF I WERE TO DECLARE OPENLY THAT THIS IS NOTHING
more or less than an attempt to expound the "Principles of Physical
Anthropology," I fear that I should turn my readers away with the
declaration that they do not wish to know anything of a subject which
has such a forbidding title. The subject, however, is really not uninterest-
ing, and the reader will be surprised to discover he knows much more
of it than he is aware. Modern commerce and our world-wide enterprise
have brought all the races of the earth as visitors to our shores. We see
them plentifully in our great seaports, and even in the most remote
country villages we have now and then an opportunity of making their
acquaintance. It is on those occasions we discover that we do know
something of Anthropology—or Ethnology as it is sometimes named.
How otherwise did we recognize that the stranger who drew the eyes
of the village on him was a Chinaman, a Red Indian or a Negro? If,
however, we are asked how we knew, we find we are not quite certain,
and that our knowledge of the subject is rather subconscious. Those
who study the bodily characters of the varieties of mankind are seeking
to make this subconscious knowledge into a system of well-defined facts
to which the name of Physical Anthropology is given. We collect these
facts not only to ascertain how one race differs from another in structure
of body, but we have a larger aim in view, we wish to know how and
when the earth became populated with a diverse humanity.

It is always well to begin our study at home. When we see a regiment
in full dress march past we recognize it as the "Suffolks," the "Gordons,"
the "Connaughts," or the "Welsh Fusiliers," as the case may be. When,
however, the soldiers file silently past, dressed alike in a fighting uniform,
without a number or a badge, can we distinguish the nationality? I doubt
if one could, and I hold the opinion that, however many racial stocks

have been planted from time to time within the bounds of Britain, the condition at the present day is such that we cannot tell—except from speech, temperament or local mannerisms—whether a given batch of men are English, Scotch, Welsh or Irish. It is possible that the professed anthropologist, by making a series of measurements as regards height, proportion, and shape of head, and other observations on colour of skin, and eyes and hair, could tell the part of the country from which each batch came. Our difficulty lies in the fact that in every county we see that there are many types of body and face and many shades in the colour of hair and skin. It is true that in some counties certain types prevail and other types are uncommon, while in other counties these same types occur in an opposite proportion. At the present time there is a tendency to suppose that a pure race is made up of individuals having the same form of body, and that, if within the bounds of a country or of a county several types are found, there has been a mixture of races in that country or county in past times. Such an opinion seems quite reasonable, especially when we remember how many invading peoples have settled in Britain from first to last. When, however, we begin to survey even the purest human races we find within their communities just as great a variety of bodily form as is to be seen in any part of Britain. Nay, I am quite certain that the reader can recall families in which some were tall and some short, some dark and some fair, some with a narrow face and some with a wide face. The existence of numerous types and varieties inside even the purest race is a most important fact, for it is easy to see how the characters of the race might be changed if certain types flourished and increased in numbers, while other types were gradually repressed and ultimately disappeared. So far as we know there is no selection of any special type in progress in Britain.

If, however, we were to pick a man from the streets of Strassburg, and set him side by side with the first man we met in Nottingham, we should probably see the two chief types of mankind in Western Europe. We have nothing to do with the national spirit, the speech, the hairdressing and tailoring which mark the one off from the other; these are of the greatest importance, but they are outside the bounds of physical anthropology. The colour of hair and complexion of skin, hue of eye, may be the same in these two individuals drawn from towns so far apart; their faces may be of the same type; it is probable, however, that the Englishman's face is the longer and narrower. Their stature may be the same—possibly the Englishman is the taller by about half an inch, but not heavier. The form of head, however, is totally different. When we take the length and breadth of the Englishman's head we shall probably find that its breadth is between seventy-four and seventy-six per cent. of its length, or if we wish to give our knowledge a learned turn we say that his "cephalic index" is between seventy-four and seventy-six. In the Strassburger's head the cephalic index is probably between eighty and eighty-two. When we look at his head in profile it appears as if it had been compressed from back to front, so that the width of the head has been increased and the brain pushed forwards, thus coming to occupy a more anterior position above and in front of the ears. The height of the head is increased. The Englishman's head has been compressed from side to side and rather flattened on the top, so that it does not appear to be so high as the German head. We find then that the best mark to distinguish the typical Englishman from the typical German is the shape of the head. It must not be forgotten, however, that in Nottingham, as in Strassburg, there are all forms of heads, but the rounded type prevails in the one and the long type in the other. It is possible, but very unlikely, that two individuals, selected by chance, may have the same types of head.

If we estimate the capacity of the skull in these two selected types of man, we shall probably find that in size of brain chamber they are about equal, each containing from 1,480 to 1,500 cubic centimetres of brain. When, however, the reader asks me why the head is long in one and round in the other, I must confess that no satisfactory answer can be given to the question at the present time. We know, however, that the head is artificially and grossly distorted in infancy by many races of mankind —indeed the custom was once common in Europe—without producing any marked mental change. The brain also suffers a change in shape in those cases of distortion, but travellers have noted that the men with the altered heads are just as intelligent as those whose heads have escaped constriction. The brain seems to work as well in one shape of skull as in another. As a matter of daily experience we have no reason to think that the round-headed man is more capable than the long-headed, and yet when we come to trace the history of long-headed races in Europe we meet with facts which give matter for thought.

If we make a survey of modern Europe we find the long-headed races scattered along her western shores—in Norway, in Britain, in those parts of Denmark, Germany and Holland which flank the North Sea; in Spain, and to a less degree in parts of France and Italy. Round-headed peoples dominate the great central region of Europe. If, however, we go back 5,000 years and examine the graves of that remote period, we obtain a different picture of head and racial distribution in Europe. The German, the Swiss, the French graves of that time contain the bones of men who were of the long-headed type; we must suppose them to represent the people of the country at that period. We know from history and from tradition that waves of round-headed races have pressed westwards and southwards in Europe, and all the evidence goes to show that these waves issued from that part of Europe now included in the Russian Empire. We know, too, that an advance guard of the round-head invasion reached our shores some 4,000 years ago, when bronze was the metal employed by civilized races. Graves of these people have been found from Yorkshire to Kent, and in Scotland. They were conquerors and yet they could not save their head-form; in the course of generations the round head merged in the long, not perhaps without some effect on our modern head-form. We have every reason to think, then, that in Europe the round head is the prevailing type. Indeed, had it not been for the discovery of America and of Australia the long-headed type of European would have been sparsely represented in the modern world.

We now set out to enquire which of these two types of head, the round or the long, is the older or more primitive. We turn first to the anthropoid skull to see in which mould it is cast. In the adults we find that the shape of the essential part of the skull—the part which contains the brain—is masked by a great bony framework which was formed during the years of youth to give attachment to the muscles of mastication. We must, therefore, measure the skulls of the young, and in them we find the breadth amounts to eighty per cent. or more of the length of the skull. The anthropoids are round-headed, especially the orangs. When we look more closely we see that the roundness of the anthropoid head is altogether different in character from the roundness of the modern European head. We see at once that the anthropoid's skull is wide, because the width is increased at the price of height; it gives the impression of having been compressed from above downwards into a bun-shaped form, the width being thus increased and not the length. The apparent compression of the human skull is rather from behind forwards as in round-headed races of men, or from side to side, as in long-headed races. Thus we cannot say that the round type of human head is more anthropoid than the long one.

When, however, we examine the skulls of the most ancient men yet discovered, the evidence is very definite; all of them have the long form of head. In the oldest and most primitive type yet found—the fossil man of Java—the breadth of the skull is seventy-two or seventy-three per cent. of the length; he is long-headed. We note in this skull, however, a very remarkable feature—it is flattened or compressed from crown to base, as we have seen to be the case in anthropoid skulls. In another very ancient skull from Gibraltar we notice this anthropoid character and also that the breadth is seventy-four per cent. of the length. In the Neanderthal race, which lived in Europe during the glacial period, the head is also of the long type, and indeed the length of their skulls is much above the modern average. The Cro-Magnon race, which came long after the Neanderthal and yet were inhabitants of France before the glacial period had closed, were remarkably long-headed. The oldest man yet discovered in England —the Galley Hill man, who also apparently belongs to the glacial period— had a remarkably narrow and long head; the breadth is only sixty-nine per cent. of its length. From all these facts we must conclude that the long head is the older type. Indeed, all the evidence points to the round form of skull we have seen in the citizen of Strassburg as a comparatively recent product in the evolution of human races. The evolution of the form of human skull seems to have taken place in the following order. The anthropoid skull, short, wide, flat, seems to be the oldest form. In the early human stock it became long, moderately wide, and flattened; later it became long, narrow, and high, and lastly short, wide, and high.

We have been comparing opposite types of head-form, and we now propose to contrast the most widely divergent types of mankind. As one of these we select again the man from Strassburg, premising that he is of the short-headed or brachycephalic type, with blond hair, blue eyes, and a fair clear skin. Beside him we propose to place, for purposes of contrast, a negro from the heart of Africa. Here I would beg of the reader to break away from the common habit of speaking and thinking of various races as high and low. When we meet the native of the Congo in his home we find that he does not share our opinion that we are of a superior race and type; indeed, his candid opinion is the reverse. High and low refers to civilization; it does not refer to the human body. When we have placed a Central European and a Central African side by side, we see before us the end stems of the two most divergent branches of humanity. They are equally old in type, and we may truthfully say equally specialized. We believe they have arisen from a common stock, but that must be a million of years ago or more. The mere diversity of their bodily features indicates an evolutionary period of great length. We note the difference in their head-form; the negro has a long narrow head; its cranial capacity is less, and on the average the brain is simpler in its pattern. It is the difference in colour that impresses us most. In the negro the skin and eyes are laden with black pigment, which is being constantly absorbed and constantly renewed. Even the deeper parts of the body show scattered patches of pigment. In the Central European there are pigment granules in the skin, but the skin must be cut in fine sections and examined with the microscope before they are plainly visible. The contrast in colour in the two types is so great that it seems scarcely credible that we are dealing with the same species of being. Indeed, there are many who maintain that they belong to different species. Yet we know that intermixture of these two types produces children which in urn are fertile for generation after generation.

When, too, we cross from Central Europe to Central Africa, we see that these two extreme types of mankind are linked together by all the intervening shades between fair and dark. In Southern Europe the skin and hair become more pigmented; in Northern Africa the skin is dark brown or black. Whenever we find an intermediate series which carries us from one extreme to the other, we believe that those extremes may have arisen from a common stock. We see, too, how the inhabitants of the same country or even of the same parish, may show many shades of pigmentation—but for each country there is a certain average, and the variation in shade is bounded by definite limits. When we wish to explain why the Central European is fair and the Central African is black, we are brought at once to a dead stop by our ignorance. We do not know what service pigment performs in the human body. We cannot suppose it to be a useless substance. It is true that it is most developed in those who live in hot climates, yet the ancient Tasmanians, the natives of a very temperate climate, were black. There is no definite proof that negroes become less black in temperate countries, nor that fair men become more pigmented in tropical lands. Yet it seems most reasonable to suppose that the pigment of the skin does protect the body from certain rays of the sun.

Anthropologists have always presumed that the primitive human stock must have been dark-skinned. Certainly the degree of pigmentation seen amongst the great anthropoids lends support to this theory. The gorilla is black; there are various races or varieties of chimpanzee, and all of them show a degree of black pigmentation. In one variety the skin becomes totally black; in another, pigmentation of the face and of other parts is delayed until late in life; in others the face never becomes absolutely black. The skin of the orang is also deeply pigmented, but the black granules are masked by the presence of a red element. The evidence supplied by anthropoids points to a common stock with dark pigmented skins. It is very possible, however, that in the progress of evolution, the degree of pigmentation has somewhat increased in the pure negro races, while in the Central European it has become greatly diminished. One is led to form such an opinion from the skin colour of the natives of Australia. They have so many primitive features in the structure of their bodies that it is also possible that their skin colour is likewise primitive. Their skins are not so deeply pigmented as in the typical negro. On the whole, the evidence points to the stock from which human races have arisen as having had brown pigmented skins. The very black African and very fair European races may represent comparatively recent products in the evolution of modern races.

We must return to the consideration of the African and European types of mankind now standing before us. We shall admit, I think, that in character of skull and of brain, and in colour of skin, the negro shows the older type, but in the character of his hair this is not so. The woolly hair, coiled naturally into little isolated locks, is unlike the hair of ape or man. It is a feature of the negro or negroid races, and was evolved with them. The straight black or wavy brown hair of the European appears to be more primitive in character. There are two other features of the negro's face which appear to be specializations or departures from the primitive type. The thick everted lips are very different from the thin straight lips of the anthropoid apes. The thin European lips seem a more primitive type, and yet when sections are made of the lips of Europeans and Africans certain features are seen which make us hesitate to endorse this opinion. Then, again, there are the characters of the forehead. It is true that in the West Coast of Africa we meet natives with prominent supraorbital ridges and receding foreheads. In the typical African negro this is not the case; the forehead as a rule is high, narrow, often prominent or bulging, and the supraorbital ridges are moderately or slightly developed—distinctly less prominent than in the European. There is not a shadow of doubt that the stock from which modern man is descended had great supraorbital ridges. They are still to be found in a fairly primitive form in native Australians, but to see them at their best one must examine the skulls of those ancient Europeans—the Neanderthal race. In the gorilla especially, and also in the chimpanzee, these supraorbital ridges form prominent bony ledges or shelves above their sunken eyes. The typical negro is destitute of great supraorbital ridges, which are primitive features.

When we compare the negro and European nose it may be a question as to which is the more primitive. Neither the one nor the other is like the nose of the anthropoid, and yet of the two, the sharp, narrow, prominent nose of the European, with its high bridge and compressed wings, must be admitted to be the more specialized type. If, however, we leave the Congo Valley and make our way to Egypt along the Valley of the Nile, we shall meet with various negro tribes in whom the nose is narrow and prominent and almost European in shape.

We have reason to believe that the shape of the nose does depend to a considerable degree on the development of the teeth and jaws. A long, prominent and narrow nose is usually part of a face in which the palate is narrow or contracted and in which the jaws have grown in length rather than in width and strength. In the ancient inhabitants of Europe we find the jaws and teeth well and regularly developed and the nose of fair width. In modern Europeans, especially in those with long heads, we find a tendency to an irregular development of the jaws and to an elongation and narrowing of the face, with the result that the nose also is rendered sharper and more prominent. The jaws and cheeks have retreated and left the nose as a narrow prominent organ on the face of the typical European. In Central Africa we find other tendencies at work; the teeth are big, white, and regularly set in well-developed jaws. The face is broad rather than long. The jaws may be so well grown as actually to give the individual the appearance of having a muzzle. The nose is correspondingly flat and wide. In brief, I conceive it possible that the nose of the negro might assume a European form were his teeth and jaws to undergo those changes which are apparently occurring amongst the civilized peoples of Europe and America.

There are other features of the body we ought to contrast in the European and African—the longer forearm and leg of the latter, the absence of calf and longer heel, the different type of ear, but enough has been said to give some idea of the chief bodily features in which one race of mankind differs from another.

In Eastern Asia we find another distinctive type of modern man. We may take the Chinaman as a representative and place him with the Central European for comparison. They are both short-headed or brachycephalic, but their heads are essentially different in shape. The Mongolian head is really round or ball-shaped. The skin is pigmented—less so than in negro races, but more so than in European. The hair is strong, lank and black. The stature is short—perhaps two inches less than in the European, the shortening being due not to a diminution in length of trunk so much as to a shortening of the legs. In size of brain there is nothing to choose between the two types. The chief difference lies in the face. The cheek bones are prominent, the teeth good, and the jaws strong in the Chinaman, but we note at once that the supraorbital ridges are less developed than in the European. In this the Mongol resembles the negro, but his forehead is wide, not narrow as in the negro. The essential Mongolian feature is the nose—its low sunken bridge over which one eye can almost see its neighbour. With the depression of the nose a peculiar fold of skin—the epicanthic fold—is drawn like a curtain above the inner angle of the eye. The eyes seem set at an oblique angle, a feature which Chinese artists love to emphasize. The Mongolian face, when compared with the European, is remarkably flat and shield-like. The forehead, the prominent cheek bones, the sunken nose and well-developed jaws all take a part in forming this facial plateau.

Thus we find contrasted types of man have been evolved at divergent points or centres of the old world—in Europe, in Africa, in Asia. When we remember that the skulls and limb bones of the inhabitants of Egypt have changed remarkably little during 5,000 years we must conclude that evolution amongst human races does not proceed quickly. One finds the same form of skull among Englishmen of to-day, as occurred in the men who lived in Britain many thousands of years ago. If then, we believe in evolution, it becomes evident that the well marked differences which characterize the races of Europe, Asia, and Africa, must be the result of a very long period of time.

1912

B. THE HUMAN MACHINE

Vesalius and Harvey: The Founding of Modern Anatomy and Physiology

MICHAEL FOSTER

———

THE WHOLE STORY OF THE RISE AND GROWTH OF the art of healing is too vast to be gathered into one set of lectures, too varied to be treated of by one man alone. . . . I will ask you to let me start with the middle of the sixteenth century, and indeed with the particular year 1543. . . .

In this year 1543 the printing-press of J. Oporinus (or Herbst) in Basel gave to the world in a folio volume the *Fabrica Humani Corporis,* the Structure of the Human Body, by Andreas Vesalius. This marked an epoch in the history of Anatomy, and so of Physiology and of Medicine. Who was Andreas Vesalius, and why did his book mark an epoch?

Let me briefly answer the latter question first. In the times of the Greeks mankind had made a fair start in the quest of natural knowledge, both of things not alive and of things living; the search had been carried on into the second century of the Christian Era when Galen expounded the structure and the use of the parts of the body of man. As Galen passed away inquiry, that is to say inquiry into natural knowledge, stood still. For a thousand years or more the great Christian Church was fulfilling its high mission by the aid of authority; but authority, as with the growth of the Church it became more and more potent as an instrument of good, became at the same time more and more potent as a steriliser of original research in natural knowledge.

As spiritual truths were learned by the study of the revealed word, so anatomical and medical truths were to be sought for, not by looking directly into the body of man, not by observing and thinking over the phenomena of disease, but by studying what had been revealed in the writings of Hippocrates and Galen. As the Holy Scriptures were the Bible for all men, so the works of the Greek and Latin writers became the bible for the anatomist and the doctor. Truth and science came to mean simply that which was written, and inquiry became mere interpretation.

The "new birth" of the fifteenth and sixteenth centuries was in essence a revolt against authority as the guide in knowledge; and the work of Andreas Vesalius of which I am speaking marks an epoch, since by it the idol of authority in anatomical science was shattered to pieces never to be put together again. Vesalius described the structure of the human body such as he found it to be by actual examination, by appealing to dissection, by looking at things as they are. He dared not only to show how often Galen was wrong, but to insist that when Galen was right he was to be followed, not because he had said it, but because what he said was in accordance with what anyone who took the pains to inquire could assure himself to be the real state of things. . . .

Who then was this Andreas Vesalius?

He was born at Brussels at midnight as the last day of 1514 was passing into the first of 1515. His family, which had dwelt for several generations at Nymwegen and which originally bore the name of Witing, had produced many doctors and learned men, and his father was apothecary to Charles V. His mother, to judge by her maiden name, Isabella Crabbe, was probably of English extraction.

The young Vesalius (or Wesalius, for so it was sometimes spelt) was sent to school at Louvain and afterwards entered the University there, which then as later was of great renown. Though he diligently pursued the ordinary classical and rhetorical studies of the place, the bent of his mind early showed itself; while yet a boy he began to dissect such animals as he could lay his hands on. Such a boy could not do otherwise than study medicine, and in 1533, a lad of seventeen or eighteen, he went to Paris to sit at the feet of Sylvius, then rising into fame.

The ardent young Belgian was however no docile hearer, receiving open-mouthed whatever fell from the master. Sylvius' teaching was in the main the reading in public of Galen. From time to time however the body of a dog or at rarer intervals the corpse of some patient was brought into the lecture room, and barber servants dissected in a rough, clumsy way and exposed to the view of the student the structures which the learned doctor, who himself disdained such menial, loathsome work, bid them show. This did not satisfy Vesalius. At the third dissection at which he was present he, already well versed in the anatomy of the dog, irritated beyond control at the rude handling of the ignorant barbers, pushing them on one side, completed the dissection in the way he knew it ought to be done.

"My study of anatomy," says he, "would never have succeeded had I when working at medicine at Paris been willing that the viscera should be merely shewn to me and to my fellow-students at one or another public dissection by wholly unskilled barbers, and that in the most superficial way. I had to put my own hand to the business."

Besides listening to Sylvius, he was a pupil of Johannes Guinterius (Günther), a Swiss from Andernach, who also was teaching anatomy and surgery at Paris at the time, and with whom his relations seem to have been closer than with Sylvius.

Neither Sylvius, however, nor Guinterius, nor any one at the time was able to supply Vesalius with that for which he was obviously longing, the opportunity of dissecting thoroughly the human body. Complete dissection was then well-nigh impossible, the most that could be gained was the hurried examination of some parts of the body of a patient who had succumbed to disease. One part of the human body, the foundation of all other parts, the skeleton, could however be freely used for study. In those rude times burial was rough and incomplete, and in the cemeteries bones lay scattered about uncovered. In the burial-ground attached to the Church of the Innocents at Paris Vesalius spent many hours, studying the bones; and he also tells us how in another burial-ground, on what is now "Les Buttes Chaumont," he and a fellow-student nearly left their own bones, being on one occasion attacked and in great risk of being devoured by savage, hungry dogs who too had come there in search of bones. By such a rough, perilous study Vesalius laid the foundation of his great work, a full and exact knowledge of the human skeleton. He tells us how he and a fellow-student were wont to try their knowledge by a test which has been often used since, the recognition of the individual bones by touch alone, with the eyes shut.

After three years the wars drove him back from Paris to Louvain, where he continued to pursue his anatomical studies with unflagging zeal. Here as at Paris he was driven to use strange means to gain the material for his studies. Walking one day with a friend in the outskirts of the city and coming to the public gibbet, where "to the great convenience of the studious, the bodies of those condemned to death were exposed to public view," they came upon a corpse "which had proved such a sweet morsel to the birds that they had most thoroughly cleaned it, leaving only the bones and ligaments." With his friend's help he climbed up the gallows and attempted to carry off the skeleton, but in the hurry of such a theft in open daylight he only succeeded in getting part of it; accordingly that evening he got himself shut out of the city gates, secured in the quiet of night the rest of the skeleton, and returning home by a roundabout way and re-entering the city by a different gate, safely carried it in.

In 1537, after a year's stay at Louvain where, in the February of that year, he put forth his first juvenile effort, a translation of the ninth book of Rhazes, he migrated to Venice, the enlightened if despotic government of which was in all possible ways fostering the arts and sciences, and striving to develop in the dependent city of Padua a University which should worthily push on the new learning. It may be worth while to note, as an instance of how in the web of man's history threads of unlike kind are made to cross, that among the monks who had charge of the Hospital at Venice, at which Vesalius pursued his medical studies, was one who bore the name of Ignatius Loyola. . . .

The brilliant talents of the young Belgian at once attracted the notice of the far-sighted rulers of Venice. He was in December of that same year, 1537, made Doctor of Medicine in their University of Padua, was immediately entrusted with the duty of conducting public dissections, and either then or very shortly afterwards, though he was but a lad of some one or two and twenty summers, was placed in a Chair of Surgery with care of Anatomy.

He at once began to teach anatomy in his own new way. Not to un-skilled ignorant barbers would he entrust the task of laying bare before the students the secrets of the human frame; his own hand, and his own hand alone, was cunning enough to track out the pattern of structures which day by day were becoming more and more clear to him. Following venerated customs he began his academic labours by "reading" Galen, as others had done before him, using his dissections to illustrate what Galen had said. But time after time the body on the table said plainly something different from that which Galen had written.

He tried to do what others had done before him, he tried to believe Galen rather than his own eyes, but his eyes were too strong for him; and in the end he cast Galen and his writings to the winds and taught only what he himself had seen and what he could make his students see too.

Thus he brought into anatomy the new spirit of the time, and the men of the time, the young men of the time answered to the new voice. Students flocked to his lectures, his hearers amounted it is said to some five hundred, and an enlightened Senate recognized his worth by repeatedly raising his emoluments.

Such a mode of teaching laid a strain on the getting of the material for teaching. Vesalius was unwearied in his search for subjects to dissect. He begged all the doctors to allow him to examine the bodies of their fatal cases. He ingratiated himself with the judges, so that when a criminal was condemned to death they gave directions that the sentence should be carried out at such a time, and the execution should be conducted now in this manner, now in that as might best meet the needs of Vesalius' public dissections. Nor did he shrink apparently from robbing the grave, for he relates how, learning of the death and hurried burial of the concubine of a monk, he got possession of the body, and proceeded at once to remove the whole of the skin in order that the peccant holy man, who had got wind of the matter, might be unable to recognize his lost love. And he made dissections in Bologna as well as Padua. . . .

Five years he thus spent in untiring labours at Padua. Five years he wrought, not weaving a web of fancied thought, but patiently disentangling the pattern of the texture of the human body, trusting to the words of no master, admitting nothing but that which he himself had seen; and at the end of the five years, in 1542, while he was as yet not 28 years of age, he was able to write the dedication to Charles V of a folio work, entitled the "Structure of the Human Body," adorned with many plates and woodcuts, which appeared at Basel in the following year, 1543. He had in 1538 published, under the sanction of the Senate of Venice, "Anatomical Tables," and in the same or succeeding year had brought forth an edition of Guinterius, a treatise on blood-letting, and an edition of Galen. There is a legend that the pictures in the great work were by the hand of Titian, but there seems no doubt that they, like the Tables, were done by one John Stephen Calcar, a countryman of Vesalius.

This book is the beginning not only of modern anatomy but of modern physiology.

We cannot, it is true, point to any great physiological discovery as Vesalius' own special handiwork, but in a sense he was the author of discoveries which were made after him. He set before himself a great task, that of placing the study of human anatomy on a sound basis, on the basis of direct, patient, exact observation. And he accomplished it. Galen had attempted the same thing before him; but the times were not then ripe for such a step. Authority laid its heavy hand on inquiry, and Galen's teaching instead of being an example and an encouragement for further research, was, as we have said, made into a bible, and interpretation was substituted for investigation. Vesalius, inspired by the spirit of the new learning, did his work in such a way as to impress upon his age the value not only of the results at which he arrived, but also and even more so, of the method by which he had gained them. He taught in such a way that his disciples, even when they thought him greater than Galen, never made a second Galen of him; they recognized that they were most truly following his teaching as a whole when they appealed to observation to show that in this or that particular point his teaching was wrong. After him backsliding became impossible; from the date of the issue of his work onward, anatomy pursued an unbroken, straightforward course, being made successively fuller and truer by the labours of those who came after.

Vesalius' great work is a work of anatomy, not of physiology. Though to almost every description of structure there are added observations on the use and functions of the structures described, and though at the end of the work there is a short special chapter on what we now call experimental physiology, the book is in the main a book of anatomy, the physiology is incidental, occasional, and indeed halting. Nor is the reason far to seek. Vesalius had a great and difficult task before him. He had to convince the world that the only true way to study the phenomena of the living body was, not to ask what Galen had said, but to see for oneself with one's own eyes how things really were. And not only was a sound and accurate knowledge of the facts of structure a necessary prelude to any sound conclusions concerning function, but also the former was the only safe vantage ground from which to fight against error. When he asserted that such a structure was not as Galen had described it but different, he could appeal to the direct visible proof laid bare by the scalpel. Even then he found it difficult to convince his hearers, so ready were men still to trust Galen rather than their own eyes. Much harder was the task when, in dealing with function, he had to leave the solid ground of visible fact, and to have recourse to arguments and reasoning. . . .

Obviously his vigorous and active young mind was starting many inquiries of a purely physiological kind, and he was aware that much of the physiology which he had put into his book would not stand the test of future research. He knew more particularly that the chapter in that book in which he treated of the use of the heart and its parts was as he says "full of paradoxes." But he was no less aware that his bold attempt to expound the plain visible facts of anatomy, such as they appeared to one who had torn from his eyes the bandages of authority, was of itself enough to raise a storm of opposition; he feared to jeopardize his success in that great effort by taking upon himself further burdens.

Experience showed that in this he was right. Even while he was writing his book, timorous friends urged him not to publish it; its appearance they said would destroy his prospects in life. And in one sense it did. Towards the end of 1542 after the completion of his great task, although in August of that year he had been reappointed to the Chair of Surgery and Anatomy for three years, he, with the sanction of the Senate, left Padua for a while, his pupil Realdus Columbus being appointed his deputy. He made a short stay at Venice; he visited Basel either once or twice, chiefly it would seem to confer with his printers; but while in that city he prepared with his own hands from the body of an executed criminal a complete skeleton which is still religiously preserved there. He also probably made a hurried journey to the Netherlands. During his absence from Padua, after the appearance of his book the storm broke out. The great Sylvius and others thundered against him, reviling him in a free flow of adjectives. Coming back to Padua, after about a year's absence, he found opposition to his new views strong even there. . . . The spirit shewn entered like iron into his soul. If the work on which he had laboured so long and which he felt to be so full of promise met with such a reception, why should he continue to labour? Why should he go on casting his pearls before swine? He had by him manuscripts of various kinds, the embodiment of observations and thoughts not included in the *Fabrica*. What they were we can only guess; what the world lost in their loss we shall never know. In a fit of passion he burnt them all, and the Emperor Charles V, offering him the post of Court Physician, he shook from his feet in 1544 the dust of the city in whose University he had done so much, and still a youth who had not yet attained the thirties, ended a career of science so gloriously begun.

Ended a career; for though in the years which followed he from time to time produced something, and in 1555 brought out a new edition of his *Fabrica,* differing chiefly from the first one, so far as the circulation of the blood is concerned, in its bolder enunciation of his doubts about the Galenic doctrines touching the heart, he made no further solid addition to the advancement of knowledge. Henceforward his life was that of a Court Physician much sought after and much esteemed, a life lucrative and honourable and in many ways useful, but not a life conducive to original inquiry and thought. The change was a great and a strange one. At Padua he had lived amid dissections; not content with the public dissections in the theatre, he took parts at least of corpses to his own lodgings and continued his labours there. No wonder that he makes in his *Fabrica* some biting remarks to the effect that he who espouses science must not marry a wife, he cannot be true to both. A year after his arrival at the Court he sealed his divorce from science by marrying a wife; no more dissections at home, no more dissections indeed at all, at most some few post-mortem examinations of patients whose lives his skill had failed to save. . . .

When in 1556 Charles withdrew from the world and took refuge in the Cloister, Vesalius transferred to the son Philip II the services which he had paid to the father, and in 1559 returned with him to Spain.

Spain, as it then was, could be no home for a man of science. The hand of the Church was heavy on the land; the dagger of the Inquisition was stabbing at all mental life, and its torch was a sterilizing flame sweeping over all intellectual activity. . . .

We cannot wonder that amid such surroundings the feelings that the past years had been years of a wasted life grew strong upon him, and that wistful memories of the earlier happy times gathered head. He was still in the prime of life, a man of some forty-five summers; many years of intellectual vigour were perhaps still before him. Was he to spend all these in marking time to the music of an Imperial Court?

Just at this time, in 1561, there came into his hands the anatomical observations of Falloppius (Gabrielo Falloppio), a man of whom I shall presently have to speak, who in 1551 had after a brief interval succeeded Vesalius in the Chair of Padua. This book came to the wearied and despondent Vesalius, banished to the intellectual desert of Madrid, as a living voice from a bright world outside. Putting everything else on one side, he gave himself, as he says, "wholly up to the instant greedy reading of the pages" which brought vividly back to him the delights of his youth. Calling back from the past the memory of things observed long ago, for new observations, as we have seen, were out of his power, he put together bit by bit some notes criticizing Falloppius' work, put them together hurriedly and rapidly, in order that Tiepolo, the Venetian ambassador, then at Madrid but about to return to Venice, might carry the manuscript with him. In that "Examen," as he calls it, Vesalius says how the reading of Falloppius' notes had raised in him "a glad and joyful memory of that most delightful life which, teaching anatomy, I passed in Italy, the true nurse of intellects." He looks forward, he says, "to see the ornaments of our science continue to bud forth in the school from which I was while yet a youngster dragged away to the dull routine of medical practice and to the worries of continual journeys. I look forward to the accomplishment of that great work for which, to the best of my powers so far as my youth and my then judgment allowed, I laid foundations, such that I need not be ashamed of them."

And even more, he was nursing the idea that his present barren life might be exchanged for a more fruitful one. "I still," says he, "live in hope that at some time or other, by some good fortune I may once more be able to study that true bible, as we count it, of the human body and of the nature of man. . . ."

But it was not to be. In 1563 he suddenly determined to make a pilgrimage to Jerusalem. There are various legends as to the reasons which led him to this step. It is said that in making what was supposed to be a post-mortem examination on a noble man, or according to others a woman suffering from some obscure disease, it turned out that the body was still living, and that the Church insisted upon the pilgrimage as an expiation for an act deemed to be a sacrilege. The truer account is probably that told by the botanist Clusius, that Vesalius, ill in body, and we may add even more sick at heart, wearied of the Court, and harassed by the Church, seized an opportunity, and made the proposed pilgrimage an excuse for bringing to an end his then mode of life.

On his way to Jerusalem he stopped at Venice and renewed his intercourse with scientific friends. He there learnt that the manuscript on Falloppius had never reached that anatomist, who had somewhat suddenly died in 1562, but was still in Tiepolo's hands. His friends at once obtained it from Tiepolo, and it saw the light in the following May.

The Senate at Venice were just then at a loss for a fit successor to Falloppius, and it is possible that Vesalius during his stay in the city made known his willingness to desert the Court and to return to academic life; for it is said, though documentary evidence is lacking, that during his eastern journey he received an invitation to occupy his old Chair. Alas, on his way back in 1564 he was taken ill, or possibly a latent malady openly developed itself, he was put ashore on the island of Zante, and there he passed away.

The influence of Vesalius on the history of science may be regarded on the one hand in its general, on the other in its more special aspect.

Taking the general aspect first we may say that he founded modern anatomy. He insisted upon, and through his early unwearied labours by his conspicuous example he ensured the success of the new method of inquiry, the method of observation as against interpretation; he overthrew authority and raised up experience, he put the book of nature, the true book, in place of the book of Galen, and thus made free and open the paths of inquiry. Others before him, as we have said, Mundinus to wit and Carpi, had made like efforts, but theirs were partial and unsuccessful; Vesalius' efforts were great, complete, and successful. Upon the publi-

cation of the *Fabrica*, the pall of "authority" was once and for ever removed. Vesalius' results were impugned, and indeed were corrected by
his compeers and his followers; but they were impugned and corrected
by the method which he had introduced. Inquirers asserted that in this or
that point Galen was right and Vesalius was wrong, but they no longer
appealed to the authority of Galen as deciding the question, they appealed
now to the actual things as the judge between the two, as the judge of
Galen as of others. And even those who were Vesalius' most devoted disciples never made of him a second Galen; they never appealed to him
as an authority, they were content to show on the actual body that what
he had said was right.

Under a more special aspect he may be regarded as the founder of
physiology as well as of anatomy in as much as he was the distinct fore-
runner of Harvey. For Harvey's great exposition of the circulation of
the blood did, as we shall see, for physiology what Vesalius' *Fabrica* did
for anatomy; it first rendered true progress possible. And Harvey's great
work was the direct outcome of Vesalius' teaching. . . .

When in 1542 after the completion of his great work Vesalius had leave
to absent himself from Padua a young man, Matheus Realdus Columbus,
a native of Cremona, was appointed as his deputy, and when in 1544
Vesalius finally left Padua, the Senate of Venice entrusted for two years
the duty of reading the lectures on Surgery and Anatomy to the same
Columbus. But Columbus did not remain Vesalius' successor even for the
two years; in the next year, 1545, Cosimo de Medici appointed him as the
first Professor of Anatomy in the newly renovated University of Pisa;
and Vesalius' Chair was not adequately filled until 1551, when Gabrielus
Falloppius was placed in it.

Falloppius, born in Modena in 1523, a favourite and a devoted pupil of
Vesalius, an accomplished and travelled scholar, a careful and exact observer and describer, a faithful, modest, quiet man, has left his name in
anatomy in the terms Falloppian canal and Falloppian tubes. We owe to
him many valuable observations on the skeleton, especially on the skull,
on the tympanum, on the muscles, and on the generative organs. But he
made no large contribution to knowledge such as distinctly influenced the
progress of physiology; and he left no mark on the doctrines of the
circulation. I have already spoken of his Anatomical Observations as stirring up Vesalius in his later years to revived anatomical longings; in these
Falloppius says that if he had been able to advance any new truth, that

was largely due to Vesalius "who so showed me the true path of inquiry that I was able to walk along it still farther than had been done before."

Born, in 1537, of humble parents, in the little Tuscan town or rather village bearing that name, Hieronymus Fabricius[1] studied under Falloppius at Padua, and, on the death of his master, in 1565, succeeded him in the Chair of Anatomy, holding it for 40 years, until 1619, when he died at the ripe old age of 82.

A distinguished surgeon and a learned anatomist, well acquainted with the anatomy not only of man but of other vertebrates, he was the author of many treatises, most of which had distinct physiological bearings and which contained many contributions to the advancement of knowledge. He was the first after Aristotle to describe the formation of the chick in the egg; he wrote well on locomotion, on the eye, on the ear, on the skin, on the larynx and on speech; but the one work which concerns the subject which we have in hand is that on the valves of the veins, the book *De venarum ostiolis,* "the little doors of the veins," which saw the light in 1574.

Johannus Baptista Cannanus, Professor at Ferrara, is said to have observed the valves long before, namely in 1547, and indeed to have told Vesalius of his observation; and even before that, these structures it is said were noticed by Sylvius. But they were not really laid hold of until Fabricius published his book. In that work he most carefully and accurately described their structure, position and distribution, illustrating his observations by fairly good figures. He moreover clearly recognized that the valves offered opposition to the flow of blood from the heart towards the periphery, and even gives the now well-known demonstration of their action on the living arm.

He says, *De venarum ostiolis:*

"Little doors of the veins is the name I give to certain very thin little membranes occurring on the inside of the veins, and distributed at intervals over the limbs, placed sometimes one by itself, and sometimes two together. They have their mouths directed towards the root of the veins (*i.e.* the heart), and in the other direction are closed. Viewed from the outside they present an appearance not unlike the swellings which are seen in the branches and stem of a plant. In my opinion they are formed by nature in order that they may to a certain extent delay the blood and so prevent the whole of it flowing at once like a flood either to the feet, or to the hands and fingers, and becoming collected there. For this would

[1] Often spoken of, from the place of his birth, as ab Aquapendente.

give rise to two evils; on the one hand the upper parts of the limbs would suffer from want of nourishment, and on the other the hands and feet would be troubled with a continual swelling. In order therefore that the blood should be everywhere distributed in a certain just measure and admirable proportion for maintaining the nourishment of the several parts, these valves of the veins were formed. . . ."

But he wholly failed to recognize their true function. Still labouring under the influence of the old doctrines and believing that the use of the veins was that of carrying crude blood, blood not vivified by the vital spirits, from the heart to the tissues, he thought that he had fully explained the value of the veins, by pointing out that they opposed the flow from the heart to the tissues, not of all blood but only of an excess of blood; their purpose was to prevent the blood as it flowed along the veins from the heart being heaped up too much in one place. But he also thought that they were the means of furnishing temporary local reservoirs of blood; and he likens them to the devices by which in mills and elsewhere water is dammed up. He left for another, for a pupil of his, the opportunity of putting to its right use the discovery which he had made. . . .

I need not take up time by entering largely into the details of the oft-told story of William Harvey's life.

Born at Folkestone, on the south coast of England, in April 1578, just four years after Fabricius had published his treatise on the valves of the veins, admitted to Gonville and Caius College, Cambridge, in 1593, taking his degree in Arts in 1597, he left England the following year to study medicine under the great master at Padua. There he spent the greater part of four years, years very nearly overlapping the period between the writing and the publication of Fabricius's treatise on Respiration, of which I have just spoken as being, in great measure, an exposition of the Galenic doctrine of the circulation. At the end of the period, in 1602, he received at Padua the degree of Doctor of Medicine, and on his return to England in the same year was incorporated into the Doctorate at Cambridge.

Setting up his abode in London, joining the Royal College of Physicians in 1604, and becoming Physician to St. Bartholomew's Hospital in 1609, he ventured in 1615 to develop, in his Lectures on Anatomy at the College of Physicians, the view which he was forming concerning the movements of the heart and of the blood. But his book, his *Exercitatio,* on that subject did not see the light until 1628.

"The little choleric man," as Aubrey calls him, attained fame among his fellows, and favour at Court. As Physician to King Charles I he accompanied that monarch on his unhappy wanderings, and every one knows the tale or legend of how at the battle of Edgehill, taking care of the Princes, he sat, on the outskirts of the fight under a hedge, reading a book. In 1646, after the events at Oxford, he retired into private life, publishing in 1651 his treatise, *De generatione animalium,* in which he followed up some of the researches of his Paduan master, and on June 3, 1667, he ended a life remarkable for its effects rather than for its events.

It is a fashion to speak of Harvey as "the immortal Discoverer of the Circulation"; but the real character of his work is put in a truer light when we say that he was the first to demonstrate the circulation of the blood. His wonderful book, or rather tract, for it is little more, is one sustained and condensed argument, but an argument founded not on general principles and analogies but on the results of repeated "frequent appeals to vivisection" and ocular inspection. He makes good one position, and having done that advances on to another, and so marches victoriously from position to position until the whole truth is put clearly before the reader, and all that remains is to drive the truth home by further striking illustrations.

His first position is the true nature and purpose of the movements of the heart itself, that is, of the ventricles. When, in the beginning of the inquiry, he "first gave his mind to vivisections" he found the task of understanding the "motions and uses of the heart so truly arduous, so full of difficulties" that he began to think with Fracastorius (a Veronese doctor of the middle of the sixteenth century (1530) and more a poet than a man of science), "that the motion of the heart was only to be comprehended by God." But the patient and prolonged study of many hearts of many animals shewed him that "the motion of the heart consists in a certain universal tension, both of contraction in the line of its fibres, and constriction in every sense, that when the heart contracts it is emptied, that the motion which is in general regarded as the diastole of the heart is in truth its systole," that the active phase of the heart is not that which sucks blood in, but that which drives blood out. Caesalpinus alone of all Harvey's forerunners had in some way or other dimly seen this truth. Harvey saw it clearly and saw it in all its consequences. It is, he says, the pressure of the constriction, of the systole, which squeezes the blood into and along the arteries, it is this transmitted pressure which causes the pulses; the artery swells at this point or that along its course, not in order that it may suck blood into it, but because blood is driven into it, and that by the pressure of the constricting systole of the heart.

With this new light shining in upon him, he was led to a clear conception of the work of the auricles and the ventricles, with their respective valves. He saw how the vena cava, on the one side, and the vein-like artery, the pulmonary veins, on the other side, empty themselves into and fill the ventricles during the diastole, and how the ventricles in turn empty themselves during the systole into the artery-like vein, the pulmonary artery on the one side and the great artery or aorta on the other. And this at once led him to a truer conception of the pulmonary circulation than was ever grasped by Servetus or Columbus. On the old view, only *some* of the blood of the right ventricle passed through the septum into the left ventricle; the rest went back again to the tissues; and it was this "some" only which Servetus and Columbus believed to pass through not the septum but the lungs. Harvey saw that all the reasons for thinking that any of the contents of the ventricle so passed were equally valid for thinking that all passed, and that the latter view alone was consonant with the facts.

This new view, new in reality, though having so much resemblance to old ones that Harvey speaks of it as one "to which some, moved either by the authority of Galen or Columbus or the reasonings of others, will give their adhesion," led him at once to another conception which however "was so new, was of so novel and unheard of a character that in putting it forward he not only feared injury to himself from the envy of a few, but trembled lest he might have mankind at large for his enemies." This new view consisted simply in applying to the greater circulation the same conclusions as those at which he had arrived in regard to the lesser circulation.

It is important to note that to this new view he was guided by distinctly quantitative considerations. He argued in this way. At each beat of the heart a quantity of blood is transferred from the vena cava to the aorta. Even if we take a low estimate (he had made observations with a view to determining the exact amount but he leaves this aside for the present as unessential), say half an ounce, or three drachms, or only one drachm, and multiply this by the number of beats, say in half-an-hour, we shall find that the heart sends through the arteries to the tissues during that period as much blood as is contained in the whole body. It is obvious, therefore, that the blood which the heart sends along the arteries to the tissues cannot be supplied merely by that blood which exists in the veins as the result of the ingesta of food and drink; only a small part can be so accounted for; the greater part of that blood must be blood which has returned from the tissues to the veins; the blood in the tissues passes from the arteries to the veins, in some such way as in the lungs it passes from the veins (through the heart) to the arteries; the blood moves in a circle from the left side of the heart, through the arteries, the tissues and the veins to the right side of the heart, and from thence through the lungs to the left side of the heart.

This is what he says:

"I frequently and seriously bethought me, and long revolved in my mind, what might be the quantity of blood which was transmitted, in how short a time its passage might be effected, and the like; and not finding it possible that this could be supplied by the juices of the ingested aliment without the veins on the one hand becoming drained, and the arteries on the other hand becoming ruptured through the excessive charge of blood, unless the blood should somehow find its way from the arteries into the veins, and so return to the right side of the heart; I began to think whether there might not be *a motion, as it were, in a circle*. Now this I afterwards found to be true; and I finally saw that the blood, forced by the action of the left ventricle into the arteries, was distributed to the body at large, and its several parts, in the same manner as it is sent through the lungs, impelled by the right ventricle into the pulmonary artery, and that it then passed through the veins and along the vena cava, and so round to the left ventricle in the manner already indicated, which motion we may be allowed to call circular."

As the sun of this truly new idea rose in Harvey's mind, this new idea that the blood is thus for ever moving in a circle, the mists and clouds of many of the conceptions of old faded away and the features of the physiological landscape hitherto hidden came into view sharp and clear. This idea once grasped, fact after fact came forward to support and enforce it. It was now clear why the heart was emptied when the vena cava was tied, why it was filled to distension when the aorta was tied. It was now clear why a middling ligature which pressed only or chiefly on the veins made a limb swell turgid with blood, whereas a tight ligature which blocked the arteries made it bloodless and pale. It was now clear why the whole or nearly the whole of the blood of the body could be drained away by an opening made in a single vein. And now for the first time was clear the purpose of those valves in the veins, whose structure and position had been demonstrated doubtless to Harvey, by the very hands of their discoverer, his old master Fabricius, but "who did not rightly understand their use, and concerning which succeeding anatomists have not added anything to our knowledge."

Fabricius, as we have seen, had used the now well-worn experiment of pressing on the cutaneous veins of the bared arm to demonstrate the existence of the valves; but he had used it to demonstrate their existence only. Blinded by the conceptions of his time he could not see that the same experiment gave the lie to his explanation of the purpose of the valves, and demonstrated not only their existence, but also their real use. Harvey, with the light of his new idea, at once grasped the true meaning of the knotty bulgings.

These however were not the only phenomena which now for the first time received a reasonable explanation. Harvey was able to point to many other things, to various details of the structure and working of the heart, to various phenomena of the body at large both in health and in disease as intelligible on his new view, but incomprehensible on any other.

If we trust, as indeed we must do, Harvey's own account of the growth of this new idea in his own mind, we find that he was not led to it in a straight and direct way by Fabricius' discovery of the valves. It was not that the true action of these led to the true view of the motion of the blood, but that the true view of the motion of the blood led to the true understanding of their use. To that true view of the motion of blood he was led by a series of steps, each in turn based on observations made on the heart as seen in the living animal, or as he himself says "repeated vivisections," the great step of all being that one by which he satisfied himself that the quantity of blood driven out from the heart could not be supplied in any other way than by a return of the blood from the arterial endings in the body through the veins. As he himself says: "Since all things, both argument and ocular demonstration, show that the blood passes through the lungs and heart by the action of the ventricles, and is sent for distribution to all parts of the body, where it makes its way into the veins and pores of the flesh, and flows by the veins from the circumference on every side to the centre, from the lesser to the greater veins, and is by them finally discharged into the vena cava and right auricle of the heart, and this in such a quantity or in such a flux and reflux thither by the arteries, hither by the veins, as cannot possibly be supplied by the ingesta, and is much greater than can be required for mere purposes of nutrition; it is absolutely necessary to conclude that the blood in the animal's body is impelled in a circle, and is in a state of ceaseless motion; that this is the act or function which the heart performs by means of its pulse; and that it is the sole and only end of the motion and contraction of the heart. . . ."

The new theory of the circulation made for the first time possible true conceptions of the nutrition of the body, it cleared the way for the chemical appreciation of the uses of blood, it afforded a basis which had not existed before for an understanding of how the life of any part, its continued existence and its power to do what it has to do in the body, is carried on by the help of the blood. And in this perhaps, more than its being a true explanation of the special problem of the heart and the blood vessels, lies its vast importance.

1901

The Only Contemporary Character Sketch of William Harvey

JOHN AUBREY

HE WAS WONT TO SAY THAT MAN WAS BUT A GREAT mischievous baboon. He would say, that we Europaeans knew not how to order or governe our woemen, and that the Turkes were the only people used them wisely.

He was far from bigotry.

He had been physitian to the Lord Chancelor Bacon, whom he esteemed much for his witt and style, but would not allow him to be a great philosopher. "He writes philosophy like a Lord Chancelor," said he to me, speaking in derision; "I have cured him."

About 1649 he travelled again into Italy, Dr. George (now Sir George) Ent, then accompanying him.

At Oxford, he grew acquainted with Dr. Charles Scarborough, then a young physitian (since by King Charles II knighted), in whose conversation he much delighted; and whereas before, he marched up and downe with the army, he tooke him to him and made him ly in his chamber, and said to him, "Prithee leave off thy gunning, and stay here; I will bring thee into practice."

For 20 years before he dyed he tooke no manner of care about his worldly concernes, but his brother Eliab, who was a very wise and prudent menager, ordered all not only faithfully, but better then he could have donne himselfe.

He was, as all the rest of the brothers, very cholerique; and in his young days wore a dagger (as the fashion then was, nay I remember my old schoolemaster, old Mr. Latimer, at 70, wore a dudgeon, with a knife, and bodkin, as also my old grandfather Lyte, and alderman Whitson of Bristowe, which I suppose was the common fashion in their young days), but this Dr. would be to apt to drawout his dagger upon every slight occasion.

He was not tall; but of the lowest stature, round faced, olivaster complexion; little eié, round, very black, full of spirit; his haire was black as a raven, but quite white 20 yeares before he dyed.

I have heard him say, that after his booke of the Circulation of the Blood came-out, that he fell mightily in his practize, and that 'twas beleeved by the vulgar that he was crack-brained; and all the physitians were against his opinion, and envyed him; many wrote against him, as Dr. Primige, Paracisanus, etc. (vide Sir George Ent's booke). With much adoe at last, in about 20 or 30 yeares time, it was received in all the Universities in the world; and, as Mr. Hobbes sayes in his book "De Corpore," he is the only man, perhaps, that ever lived to see his owne doctrine established in his life time.

Seventeenth Century

Biography of the Unborn

MARGARET SHEA GILBERT

A Condensation from the Book

FIRST MONTH
OUT OF THE UNKNOWN

OUT OF THE UNKNOWN INTO THE IMAGE OF MAN—
this is the miraculous change which occurs during the first month
of human life. We grow from an egg so small as to be barely visible,
to a young human embryo almost one fourth of an inch long, increasing
50 times in size and 8000 times in weight. We change from a small round
egg cell into a creature with a head, a body and, it must be admitted, a
tail; with a heart that beats and blood that circulates; with the beginnings
of arms and legs, eyes and ears, stomach and brain. In fact, within the
first 30 days of our life almost every organ that serves us during our
allotted time (as well as some that disappear before birth) has started
to form.

Shortly after fertilization the great activity which was stirred up in the
egg by the entrance of the sperm leads to the division or "cleavage" of the
egg into two cells, which in turn divide into four and will go on so
dividing until the millions of cells of the human body have been formed.

In addition to this astounding growth and development we must also
make our first struggle for food. For this purpose a special "feeding"
layer"—the trophoblast—forms on the outer edge of the little ball of cells,
and "eats its way" into the tissues of the uterus. As these tissues are
digested by the trophoblast, the uterus forms a protective wall—the placenta
—which coöperates with the trophoblast in feeding the growing embryo.
The maternal blood carries food, oxygen (the essential component of the
air we breathe) and water to the placenta, where they are absorbed by
the trophoblast and passed on to the embryo through the blood vessels
in the umbilical cord. In return, the waste products of the embryo are

540

brought to the placenta and transferred to the mother's blood, which carries them to her kidneys and lungs to be thrown out. In no case does the mother's blood actually circulate through the embryo—a prevalent but quite unfounded belief.

Meanwhile the new individual has been moving slowly along the path of changes which it is hoped will make a man of him. While the trophoblast has been creating a nest for the egg in the uterine wall, the inner cell-mass has changed from a solid ball of cells into a small hollow organ resembling a figure 8—that is, it contains two cavities separated in the middle by a double-layered plate called the embryonic disc which, *alone*, develops into a human being. The lower half of our hypothetical figure eight becomes a small empty vesicle, called the yolksac, which eventually (in the second month) is severed from the embryo. The upper half forms a water-sac (called the amnion) completely surrounding the embryo except at the thick umbilical cord. The embryo then floats in a water-jacket which acts as a shock-absorber, deadening any jolts or severe blows which may strike the mother's body.

Having now made sure of its safety, the truly embryonic part of the egg—the double-layered plate—can enter wholeheartedly into the business of becoming a human being. Oddly enough, it is his heart and his brain, in their simplest forms, which first develop.

Almost at once (by the age of 17 days at most) the first special cells whose exact future we can predict appear. They are young blood cells, occurring in groups called blood islands which soon fuse to form a single tube, the heart-tube, in the region that is to be the head end of the embryonic disc. This simple tube must undergo many changes before it becomes the typical human heart, but rather than wait for that distant day before starting work, it begins pulsating at once. First a slight twitch runs through the tube, then another, and soon the heart is rhythmically contracting and expanding, forcing the blood to circulate through the blood vessels in the embryonic disc. It must continue to beat until the end of life.

About the same time the nervous system also arises. In the embryonic disc a thickened oval plate forms, called the neural plate, the edges of which rise as ridges from the flat surface and roll together into a round tube exactly in the middle of what will be the embryo's back. The front end of this tube will later develop into the brain; the back part will become the spinal cord. Thus, in this fourth week of life, this simple tube represents the beginning of the nervous system—the dawn of the brain that is to be man's most precious possession.

The embryo now turns his attention to the food canal. The hungry man calls this structure his stomach, but the embryologist briefly and indelicately speaks of the gut. The flat embryonic disc becomes humped up in the middle into a long ridgelike pocket which has a blind recess at either end. Very shortly an opening breaks through from the foregut upon the under surface of the future head to form the primitive mouth, though a similar outlet at the hind end remains closed for some time.

Within 25 days after the simple egg was fertilized by the sperm, the embryo is a small creature about one tenth of an inch long with head and tail ends, a back and a belly. He has no arms or legs, and he lacks a face or neck, so his heart lies close against his brain. Within this unhuman exterior, however, he has started to form also his lungs, which first appear as a shallow groove in the floor of the foregut; his liver is arising as a thickening in the wall of the foregut just behind the heart; and he has entered on a long and devious path which will ultimately lead to the formation of his kidneys.

The development of the human kidneys presents a striking example of a phenomenon which might be called an "evolutionary hangover." Instead of forming at once the type of organ which he as a human will use, the embryo forms a type which a much simpler animal (say the fish) possesses. Then he scraps this "fish organ" and forms another which a higher animal such as the frog uses. Again the embryo scraps the organ and then, perhaps out of the fragments of these preceding structures, forms his own human organ. It is as if, every time a modern locomotive was built, the builder first made the oldest, simplest locomotive ever made, took this engine apart, and out of the old and some new parts built a later locomotive; and after several such trials finally built a modern locomotive, perhaps using some metal which had gone into the first. Scientists interpret this strange process common to the development of all higher animals as a hasty, sketchy repetition of the long process of evolution.

By the end of the month the embryo is about one fourth of an inch long, curled almost in a circle, with a short pointed tail below his belly, and small nubbins on the sides of his body—incipient arms and legs. On the sides of his short neck appear four clefts, comparable to the gill-slits of a fish—another "evolutionary hangover." Almost all the organs of the human body have begun to form. In the head the eyes have arisen as two small pouches thrust out from the young brain tube. The skin over the front of the head shows two sunken patches of thickened tissue which are the beginning of a nose. At a short distance behind each eye an ear has started to develop—not the external ear, but the sensitive tissue which will later enable the individual to hear. In 30 days the new human being has traveled the path from the mysteriously simple egg and sperm to the threshold of humanity.

SECOND MONTH

THE FACE OF MAN

From tadpole to man: so one might characterize the changes that occur during the second month of life. True, the embryo is not a tadpole, but it looks not unlike one. The tailed bulbous creature with its enormous drooping head, fish-like gill-slits, and formless stubs for arms and legs, bears little resemblance to a human form. By the end of the second month, however, the embryo has a recognizable human character, although it is during this period that the human tail reaches its greatest development. In this month the embryo increases sixfold in length (to almost an inch and a half) and approximately 500 times in weight. Bones and muscles, developing between the skin and the internal organs, round out the contours of the body.

But the developing face and neck are the main features that give a human appearance, however grotesque. The mouth, now bounded by upper and lower jaws, is gradually reduced in size as the fused material forms cheeks. The nasal-sacs gradually move closer together until they form a broad nose. The eyes, which at first lie on the sides of the head, are shifted around to the front. During the last week of the month eyelids develop which shortly afterwards close down.

The forehead is prominent and bulging, giving the embryo a very brainy appearance. In fact, the embryo is truly brainy in the sense that the brain forms by far the largest part of the head. It will take the face many years to overcome this early dominance of the brain and to reach the relative size the face has in the adult.

The limbs similarly pass through a surprising series of changes. The limb "buds" elongate, and the free end of the limb becomes flattened into a paddlelike ridge which forms the finger-plate or toe-plate. Soon five parallel ridges separated by shallow grooves appear within each plate; the grooves are gradually cut through, thus setting off five distinct fingers and toes. At the same time, transverse constrictions form within each limb to mark off elbow and wrist, knee and ankle.

The human tail reaches its greatest development during the fifth week, and the muscles which move the tail in lower animals are present. But from this time it regresses, and only in abnormal cases is it present in the newborn infant. Along with the muscles develop the bones. In most instances of bone development a pattern of the bone is first formed in cartilage, a softer translucent material, and later a hard bony substance is laid down in and around the cartilage model. As a sculptor first fashions his work in clay and then, when he knows that his design is adequate, casts the statue in bronze, so the developing embryo seems to plan out its skeleton in cartilage and then cast it in bone. This process continues through every month of life before birth, and throughout childhood and adolescence. Not until maturity is the skeleton finally cast.

Perhaps the most interesting feature of the second month of life is the development of the sexual organs. At the beginning of the month there is no way of telling the sex of the embryo except by identifying the sex chromosomes. By the end of the month the sex is clearly evident in the internal sex organs and is usually indicated externally. The most surprising aspect of sexual development is that the first-formed organs are identical in the two sexes. Even milk glands start to develop in both sexes near the end of the second month. Nature seems to lay down in each individual all the sexual organs of the race, then by emphasizing certain of these organs and allowing the remainder to degenerate, transforms the indifferent embryo into male or female.

Is each human being, then, fundamentally bisexual with the organs and functions of the apparent sex determined at fertilization holding in abeyance the undeveloped characters of the opposite sex? Laboratory experiments with sex-reversal in lower animals suggest that there may be various degrees of sexual development, even in mankind, and that between the typical male and female there may occur various degrees of inter-sexuality.

So the second month of life closes with the stamp of human likeness clearly imprinted on the embryo. During the remaining seven months the young human being is called a fetus, and the chief changes will be growth and detailed development.

THIRD MONTH
EMERGENCE OF SEX

Now the future "lords of all they survey" assert their ascendency over the timid female, for the male child during the third month plunges into the business of sexual development, while the female dallies nearer the neutral ground of sexual indifference. Or if sexual differences are over-looked, the third month could be marked the "tooth month," for early in this period buds for all 20 of the temporary teeth of childhood are laid down, and the sockets for these teeth arise in the hardening jaw bones.

Although six months must pass before the first cry of the infant will be heard, the vocal cords whose vibrations produce such cries now appear, at present as ineffective as a broken violin string. Only during the first six months after birth do they take on the form of effective human vocal cords. It must be remembered that during the period of life within the uterus no air passes through the larynx into the lungs. The fetus lives in a watery world where breathing would merely flood the lungs with amniotic fluid, and the vocal cords remain thick, soft and lax.

The digestive system of the three-months-old fetus begins to show signs of activity. The cells lining the stomach have started to secrete mucus—the fluid which acts as a lubricant in the passage of food through the digestive organs. The liver starts pouring bile into the intestine. The kidneys likewise start functioning, secreting urine which gradually seeps out of the fetal bladder into the amniotic fluid, although most of the waste products of the fetus's body will still be passed through the placenta into the mother's blood.

Overlying the internal organs are the bones and muscles which, with their steady development, determine the form, contours, and strength of the fetal body. In the face, the developing jaw bones, the cheek bones, and even the nasal bones that form the bridge of the nose, begin to give human contours and modeling to the small, wizened fetal face. Centers of bone formation have appeared in the cartilages of the hands and feet, but the wrists and ankles are still supported only by cartilage.

No longer is there any question about whether or not the fetus is a living, individual member of mankind. Not only have several of the internal organs taken on their permanent functions, but the well-developed muscles now produce spontaneous movements of the arms, legs and shoulders, and even of the fingers.

FOURTH MONTH
THE QUICKENING

Death throws its shadow over man before he is born, for the stream of life flows most swiftly through the embryo and young fetus, and then inexorably slows down, even within the uterus. The period of greatest growth occurs during the third and fourth fetal months, when the fetus grows approximately six to eight inches in length, reaching almost one half its height at birth. Thereafter the rate of growth decreases steadily.

However, the young fetus is not a miniature man, but a gnomelike creature whose head is too large, trunk too broad, and legs too short. At two months the head forms almost one half of the body; from the third to fifth months it is one third, at birth one fourth, and in the adult about one tenth the body height.

Nevertheless, the four-month fetus is not an unhandsome creature. With his head held more or less erect, and his back reasonably straight, he bears a real resemblance to a normal infant. The face is wide but well modeled, with widely spaced eyes. The hands and feet are well formed. The fingers and toes are rather broad, and are usually flexed. At the tip of each finger and toe patterned whorls of skin ridges appear—the basis of future fingerprints and toeprints. As might be expected, the pattern of these skin ridges is characteristically different for each fetus; at four months each human being is marked for life with an individual, unchangeable stamp of identity.

The skin of the body is in general dark red and quite wrinkled at this time; the redness indicates that the skin is so thin that the blood coursing through the underlying vessels determines its color. Very little fat is stored in the fetus's body before the sixth month, and the skin remains loose and wrinkled until underlain by fat.

Now the still, silent march of the fetus along the road from conception to birth becomes enlivened and quickened. The fetus stirs, stretches, and vigorously thrusts out arms and legs. The first movements to be perceived by the mother may seem to her like the fluttering of wings, but before long his blows against the uterine wall inform her in unmistakable terms that life is beating at the door of the womb. For this is the time of the "quickening in the womb" of folklore.

FIFTH MONTH
HAIR, NAILS AND SKIN

Man is an enigma; indivisible and yet complex; he is composed of hundreds of separate parts that are constantly dying and being renewed, yet he retains a mysterious "individuality." The human being may be compared to a coöperative society whose members band together for mutual support and protection, presenting a common front to the external world, and sharing equally in the privileges and responsibilities of their internal world. Division of labor, specialization, and the exchange of produce are just as important in the society of cells and organs as in the society of men. The digestive organs convert the materials taken in as food into the components of living cells. The circulating fluids of the body form an extensive transportation system. Nerves are the cables of the communications system while the brain is the central exchange. The potent endocrine glands determine the speed and constancy of many activities. Overlying all of the body's specialized systems is the skin—the protector, conservator, and inquirer of the society of organs.

Now that the internal organs are well laid down, the skin and the structures derived from it hasten to attain their final form. The surface of the skin becomes covered with tough, dried and dead cells which form a protective barrier between the environment and the soft tissues of the body. Even as in life after birth, the outer dead cells are being constantly sloughed off and replaced from below by the continually growing skin. Sweat glands are formed, and sebaceous glands, which secrete oil at the base of each hair. During the fifth month these glands pour out a fatty secretion which, becoming mixed with the dead cells sloughed off from the skin, forms a cheesy paste covering the entire body. This material, called the *vernix caseosa,* is thought to serve the fetus as a protective cloak from the surrounding amniotic fluid, which by this time contains waste products which might erode the still tender skin.

Derivatives of the skin likewise undergo marked development. Fine hair is generally present all over the scalp at this time. Nails appear on the fingers and toes. In the developing tooth germs of the "milk teeth," the pearly enamel cap and the underlying bonelike dentine are formed.

But the most striking feature of the month's development is the straightening of the body axis. Early in the second month the embryo forms almost a closed circle, with its tail not far from its head. At three months the head has been raised considerably and the back forms a shallow curve. At five months the head is erectly balanced on the newly formed neck, and the back is still less curved. At birth the head is perfectly erect and the back is almost unbelievably straight. In fact, it is more nearly straight than it will ever be again, for as soon as the child learns to sit and walk, secondary curvatures appear in the spinal column as aids in body balance.

The five-month fetus is a lean creature, with wrinkled skin, about a foot long and weighing about one pound. If born (or, strictly speaking, aborted) it may live for a few minutes, take a few breaths, and perhaps cry. But it soon gives up the struggle and dies. Although able to move its arms and legs actively, it seems to be unable to maintain the complex movements necessary for continued breathing.

SIXTH MONTH

EYES THAT OPEN ON DARKNESS

Now the expectant parents of the six-months-old human fetus may become overwhelmingly curious about the sex of their off-spring, especially when they realize that the sex is readily perceived in the fetus. Yet to the external world no sign is given.

During the sixth month the eyelids, fused shut since the third month, reopen. Completely formed eyes are disclosed which, during the seventh month, become responsive to light. Eyelashes and eyebrows usually develop in the sixth or seventh month.

Within the mouth, taste buds are present all over the surface of the tongue, and on the roof and walls of the mouth and throat, being relatively more numerous than in the infant or adult. It seems odd that the fetus, with no occasion for tasting, should be more plentifully equipped, and some biologists believe that this phenomenon is but another evidence of the recurrence of evolutionary stages in development, since in many lower animals taste organs are more widely and generously distributed than they are in man.

The six-month fetus, if born, will breathe, cry, squirm, and perhaps live for several hours, but the chances of such a premature child surviving are extremely slight unless it is protected in an incubator. The vitality, the strength to live, is a very weak flame, easily snuffed out by the first adverse contact with the external world.

SEVENTH MONTH
THE DORMANT BRAIN

Now the waiting fetus crosses the unknown ground lying between dependence and independence. For although he normally spends two more months within the sure haven of the uterus, he is nonetheless capable of independent life. If circumstances require it and the conditions of birth are favorable, the seven-month fetus is frequently able to survive premature birth.

One of the prime causes of the failure of younger fetuses to survive birth is believed to be the inadequate development of the nervous system, especially of those parts concerned in maintaining constant rhythmic breathing movements, in carrying out the sequence of muscular contractions involved in swallowing, and in the intricate mechanism for maintaining body temperature.

The human nervous system consists of a complex network of nerves connecting all the organs of the body with the brain and spinal cord, the centralized "clearinghouse" for all the nervous impulses brought in from the sense organs and sent out to the muscles. By the third month of life special regions and structures have developed within the brain: the cerebellum, an expanded part of the brain that receives fibers coming mostly from the ear; and two large saclike outpocketings, the cerebral hemispheres, which are the most distinctive feature of man's brain. They are destined to become the most complex and elaborately developed structures known in the nervous system of any animal. They are alleged by some to be the prime factor in man's dominance over other animals.

At seven months these hemispheres cover almost all the brain, and some vague, undefined change in the minute nerve cells and fibers accomplishes their maturation. Henceforth the nervous system of the fetus is capable of successful functioning.

The seven-month fetus is a red-skinned, wrinkled, old-looking child about 16 inches long and weighing approximately three pounds. If born he will cry, breathe, and swallow. He is, however, very susceptible to infection and needs extra protection from the shocks which this new life in the external world administers to his delicate body. He is sensitive to a light touch on the palm. He probably perceives the difference between light and dark. Best of all—he has a chance to survive.

EIGHTH AND NINTH MONTHS
BEAUTY THAT IS SKIN-DEEP

Now the young human being, ready for birth, with all his essential organs well formed and able to function, spends two more months putting the finishing touches on his anatomy, and improving his rather questionable beauty. Fat is formed rapidly all over his body, smoothing out the wrinkled, flabby skin and rounding out his contours. The dull red color of the skin fades gradually to a flesh-pink shade. The fetus loses the wizened, old-man look and attains the more acceptable lineaments of a human infant.

Pigmentation of the skin is usually very slight, so that even the offspring of colored races are relatively light-skinned at birth. Even the iris of the eye is affected; at birth the eyes of most infants are a blue-gray shade (which means that very little pigment is present) and it is usually impossible to foretell their future color.

The fetus is by no means a quiet, passive creature, saving all his activity until after birth. He thrashes out with arms and legs, and may even change his position within the somewhat crowded quarters of the uterus. He seems to show alternate periods of activity and quiescence, as if perhaps he slept a bit and then took a little exercise.

EXODUS

Just what specific event initiates the birth sequence remains unknown. For some weeks or even months previous to birth, slow, rhythmic muscular contractions, similar to those which cause labor pains, occur in a mild fashion in the uterus. Why the uterus, after withstanding this long period of futile contractions, is suddenly thrown into the powerful, effective muscular movements which within a few hours expel the long-tolerated fetus remains the final mystery of our prenatal life. It is quite probable that the birth changes occur as a complex reaction of the mother's entire body, especially those potent endocrine glands which may pour into the blood stream chemicals that stimulate immediate and powerful contractions of the uterine muscle.

There is nothing sacrosanct about the proverbial "nine months and ten days" as the duration of pregnancy; but 10 per cent of the fetuses are born on the 280th day after the onset of the last true menstrual period and approximately 75 per cent are born within two weeks of that day.

As soon as the infant is born, he usually gasps, fills his lungs with air and utters his first bleating cry, either under the influence of the shock which this outer world gives to his unaccustomed body or from some stimulus administered by the attending doctor. The infant is still, however, connected through the umbilical cord with the placenta lodged within the uterine wall. Their usefulness ended, the placenta and umbilical cord are cut off from the infant. The stump soon degenerates, but its scar, the defect in the abdominal wall caused by the attachment of the cord to the fetus, remains throughout life as the navel—a permanent reminder of our once parasitic mode of living.

The newborn infant is by no means a finished and perfect human being. Several immediate adjustments are required by the change from intra-uterine to independent life. The lungs at birth are relatively small, compact masses of seemingly dense tissue. The first few breaths expand them until they fill all the available space in the chest cavity, and as the numerous small air sacs are filled with air, the lungs become light and spongy in texture. But it is not yet a complete human lung, for new air sacs are formed throughout early childhood, and even those formed before birth do not function perfectly until several days of regular breathing have passed.

The heart, which is approximately the size of the infant's closed fist, gradually beats more slowly, approaching the normal rate of the human heart. Shortly after birth the material which has been accumulating in the intestine during the last six months of fetal life is passed off. One peculiarity of the newborn infant is that the intestine and its contents are completely sterile; the elaborate and extensive bacterial population present in the intestine of all human beings appears only after birth.

Neither tear glands nor salivary glands are completely developed at birth; the newborn infant cries without tears, and his saliva does not acquire its full starch-digesting capacity until near weaning time. The eyes, although sensitive to light, have not yet acquired the power of focusing on one point so that the newborn infant may be temporarily cross-eyed.

Thus the first nine months of life are completed. The manifold changes occurring during this period form the first personal history of each member of the race. It is the one phase of life which we all have in common; it is essentially the same for all men.

1939

How the Human Body Is Studied

SIR ARTHUR KEITH

From *Man: A History of the Human Body*

IN ALL THE MEDICAL SCHOOLS OF LONDON A NOTICE is posted over the door leading to the dissecting room forbidding strangers to enter. I propose, however, to push the door open and ask the reader to accompany me within, for, if we are to understand the human body, it is essential that we should see the students at work. If we enter in the right spirit—with a desire to learn something of the structure of man's wonderful body with our own eyes—there is nothing in the room which need repel or offend us. The room is lofty, well-lighted and clean; the students in their white coats are grouped round tables on which lie the embalmed bodies of men and women who have run the race of life— often, alas! with but ill fortune. The students are dissecting systematically, each with his text-book placed beside him for consultation and guidance, and with the instruments of dissection in his hands. The human body is to be the subject of their life's work; if they are to recognize and treat its illnesses and injuries they must know each part as familiarly as the pianist knows the notes of the keyboard. We propose to watch them at work. Each student is at his allotted part, and if we observe them in turn we shall, in an hour or less, obtain an idea of the main tissues and structures which enter into the composition of the human body.

By good fortune a dissection is in progress in front of the wrist, which displays, amongst other structures, the radial artery at which the physician feels the pulse and counts the rate of the heart's beat. The skin here is loose and thin, and as the student turns it aside in flaps he uses his knife to free it from the white subcutaneous tissue which binds it down to the deeper parts. He looks at his own wrist and sees why the skin here is loose; as he bends his wrist the skin is thrown into folds; when he extends it, the skin in front of the wrist is stretched; unless it were loosely bound down it would be impossible to move the wrist joint freely. On the palm the skin is different; it is thick and bound firmly by dense subcutaneous tissue to the underlying parts; there would be no firmness of grasp unless the skin of the palm were thick and closely bound down. As the student turns back the skin from the front of the wrist he searches in the loose tissue under it for the nerves which supply the skin with the power of feeling and for small veins which carry the used or venous blood back to the heart. He squeezes the blood backwards in these vessels; they swell out here and there into little knobs owing to the presence of pockets or valves which permit the blood to flow only in one direction, namely, towards the heart. It was the study of the arrangement of these valves, nearly three centuries ago now, which led Harvey to the discovery of the circulation. Beneath the skin and subcutaneous tissue there is another covering which has to be cut through before the sinews or tendons in front of the wrist are exposed to view. This third wrapping— the deep fascia the student will call it—is membranous and strong and keeps the tendons in place; workmen often find it necessary to add additional support by means of a wrist-strap. The tendons are glistening almost white; eight of them go to the fingers (two to each); one goes to the thumb and two act on the bones of the wrist or carpus. Just above the wrist joint the tendons have attached to them the muscles which flex the fingers and the wrist. They look so simple in the dead body; yet one has but to watch the fingers and wrists of the pianist or of the typist to see how quick and complicated they can be in life. As the student traces the tendons into the palm of the hand he sees them become in- folded within a loose sac with its interior lined by a smooth lubricated surface. This synovial sac is an example of the perfect manner in which the human machine is made; a self-oiling mechanism is provided at each point of friction. From overwork or injury fluid may collect in this sac and weaken the power of the workman's wrist.

Lying side by side with the sinews at the wrist there is another cord, somewhat like them in appearance, but very different in nature. It is the median nerve. Our friend the dissector has already seen a patient in the wards of the hospital with a jagged wound at the wrist which has injured the nerve. In that case he noticed that the thumb, fore, middle and part of the ring fingers had lost their usual sense of feeling, and that some of the small muscles of the thumb had no longer the power of movement. For our benefit he traces the nerve upwards in the forearm, arm, through the armpit until it reaches the root of the neck, where it is seen to be formed by five pairs of nerve roots which issue from the spinal cord. In the median nerve we see one of the paths which unite the brain and hand; messages pass by it from the hand which the brain interprets as heat or cold, rough or smooth, sharp or blunt; other messages pass outwards from the brain to start or stop the muscles of the forearm or fingers. The student pays particular attention to the radial artery; on the wrist, just above the root of the thumb, he finds the vessel resting on the lower end of the radius. He places his finger over the artery and observes how easily he can press it against the bone. In life we feel the artery suddenly expand and then subside with each beat of the heart; with a finger on the pulse the physician knows how the heart is working.

We propose to observe the dissector as he traces the radial artery to the heart. Below the bend of the elbow it is seen to issue from the main vessel of the upper arm—the brachial; the brachial in turn is found to be a continuation of the great artery of the armpit—the axillary. From the armpit the great arterial channel is followed across the root of the neck through the upper opening of the chest or thorax until it joins the aorta— the great vessel which springs from the left ventricle of the heart.

It must not be thought that the artery at the wrist is merely an elastic-walled pipe which expands passively as the ventricle discharges its load of blood; it is much more than that. When the student places a very thin section of the artery under the microscope for our particular benefit, we see that it has an exceedingly smooth lining, in order that the blood may flow with a minimum of friction; outside the lining there is seen an inner coat with contains many elastic fibres; then another coat made up of small contractile or muscular fibres. These muscular fibres regulate the size of the artery; they give or yield with each beat of the heart, and then contract, thus assisting the heart to force the blood onwards to nourish the tissues of the hand. The artery we have just seen under the microscope had been continuously expanding and contracting for over seventy years at the rate of seventy or eighty times a minute. No elastic tube yet invented by man could have done that. We note, however, that it has suffered the changes which overtake our arteries when they have been at work for forty years or even less; the elastic tissue and the muscle fibres are clogged with lime-salts; the elasticity of youth is gone. Hence as we grow older we cannot make the violent "spurts" of our youth.

Before leaving the dissection we have been surveying it will be well to see one of those marvelously contrived structures known as a joint. The wrist joint is still hidden by the tendons; even when these are cut through the interior of the joint is not yet visible; it is enclosed by stout bands of tissue or ligaments which become tight when the joint is over-bent. They prevent dislocation of the joint; indeed, so strong are those of the wrist joint that when we stumble forwards, or fall on the out-stretched hand, it is the bones and not the ligaments which are apt to give way. When the ligaments are cut through, the articulating or jointed surfaces of the bones are seen. They are covered by an exceedingly smooth coating of white cartilage. Here, again, there is a self-lubricating mechanism which reduces friction at the joint to a minimum. In those individuals, however, who have the misfortune to suffer from rheumatism the self-lubricating mechanism has failed, the cartilaginous covering has become dry and worn away, and instead of a joint which works smoothly and silently there is one which is rough and creaks like a gate swinging on a rusty hinge.

We have surveyed the anatomy at the wrist in some detail and with a very distinct purpose. At every part of the limbs—upper and lower—we see the same arrangement of parts as at the wrist. There is first a covering of skin, then a layer of subcutaneous tissue, which unites the skin loosely to the third wrapping—the deep fascia. Within the sleeve of deep fascia are packed the muscles which move the limbs, the nerves which control the muscles and supply sensation to the parts; the great arteries which carry the nourishing blood from the left ventricle of the heart, and the great veins which return the used blood to the right ventricle—the pump of the lungs. When the fleshy or perishable parts are removed by dissec-tion or by the corruption which so soon overtakes the soft parts after death, only the bones or skeleton remain to represent what was at one time a marvelous living machine.

We now propose to transfer our attention for a short time to two students who are uncovering the parts in front of the neck between the chin and breastbone or sternum. The windpipe has already been exposed, and is seen issuing from the voice-box or larynx below the chin to dis-appear at the upper opening of the chest on its way to the lungs. On each side of the windpipe the carotid arteries are found passing upwards to supply the head and brain with blood; close by them are the jugular veins carrying the venous blood in an opposite direction. Here we have an opportunity given us of seeing a peculiar feature of man's structure. Just above the larynx the carotid artery divides into two branches, an external one which nourishes the face, and an internal one which supplies the brain with blood. Man has a large brain and a relatively small face, hence in him the internal branch is the larger. In all other animals the external is much the larger, because the face is massive while the brain is small. It has been suggested that our brains are large because of the calibre of our internal carotid arteries; that statement we do not believe any more than the word of the waggoner who assures us that it is the dray which pulls the horse. Our object, however, in examining the anatomy of the neck is to see that curious structure or gland known as the thyroid body. It is made up of two parts or lobes, one on each side of the larynx and upper part of the windpipe; the lobes are united together by a part which crosses in front of the windpipe. Most glands in the body, such as the salivary and liver, have ducts or channels by which is discharged the substances they secrete, but there is no duct connected with the thyroid. The secretion which it forms is discharged directly into the blood stream and hence it is called a ductless gland or a gland of internal secretion. In recent years we have come to recognize that the secretion of the thyroid body is of the greatest importance. In children who suffer from disease of this gland we see that the growth of their bones is delayed or ceases, their skin becomes pasty, puffy and ill-nourished, and what is more serious their brains do not develop properly, and they become cretins or idiots. In some parts of this country—especially in Derbyshire—the thyroid is apt to become enlarged, forming a goitre and giving rise to the condition popularly known as "Derbyshire neck." There are other ductless glands, such as the pituitary body which lies enclosed within the skull and below the brain, and the suprarenal bodies which are situated in the abdomen above the kidneys. Our sense of well-being, our capacity for work and for pleasure, the nourishment and growth of our bony frames depend to a very great extent on the manner in which these small, insignificant-looking ductless glands perform their proper functions.

Our time with the students in the dissecting room has almost expired; there remains only a moment to glance at a dissection which is exposing the important organs which are enclosed within the thorax and abdomen. Part of the front wall of these cavities has been removed. Within the thorax we see the heart enclosed within its fibrous sac—the pericardium. Two great arteries issue from its upper part—the pulmonary artery to convey the impure blood from the right ventricle to the lungs, and the aorta from the left ventricle to nourish the body with pure blood. Two great veins enter the right side of the heart—the upper and lower venæ cavæ; they bring back the impure blood gathered from the various parts of the body. The pulmonary veins convey the pure blood from the lungs to the left side of the heart. Within the thoracic cavity are the two lungs, one on each side of the heart. They are mottled and dark with soot, showing that their owner had breathed the air of those who live in large cities.

At the moment we have chosen to view the students at work two of them are examining that wonderful partition—the diaphragm—which separates the chamber containing the heart and lungs from the lower or abdominal cavity in which the organs concerned with digestion are placed. Thanks to the discovery of Röntgen these students have a decided advantage over their predecessors of fifteen years ago; they can see the diaphragm, which is mainly composed of muscle, actually at work in your body or mine. As we take a breath the domes of the diaphragm are seen to descend, enlarging the cavity of the thorax, and we see the lungs become clearer as they expand and are filled with air. We can also see the dark shadow of the liver descending below the right dome of the diaphragm and the transparency that marks the stomach pushed downwards under the left dome. As we allow our breath to escape we see the domes of the diaphragm again ascend, and if we place our hand on our bodies as we breathe we shall observe that, as the diaphragm ascends, the muscles which enclose the abdomen are at work, pressing the visera and the diaphragm upwards and thus returning the parts to a proper position for taking another breath. All the muscles which we now see connected with the walls of the cavities of the thorax and abdomen are concerned in respiration. At the moment of birth they begin to work and keep on unceasingly all through the years of life until death brings to a final stop one of the most wonderful mechanisms of the human body. We have not the time now to look at the nerves and nerve centres which control the muscles of respiration and keep them at work both when we sleep and when we wake.

There are structures connected with digestion which we might examine, but we must postpone their consideration until another opportunity. It may have occurred, however, to the onlooker that, since we can transilluminate the human body, it is no longer necessary to dissect it. Dissection is still necessary, for we cannot interpret correctly what is seen when the body is lighted up under X-rays unless we already possess an extremely accurate knowledge of the arrangement of parts as they are displayed in the human body after death.

Our cursory visit to the dissecting room has not been in vain if the reader has realized how complex the structure of the human body really is, and how necessary it is that those who have to cure its disorders should try to understand the intricacy of its mechanism. We have seen, however—and this is of more importance for our present purpose—the

manner in which our knowledge of the human body is obtained. What
one generation of anatomists has learned is written in books and thus
handed on. For more than three centuries men have studied the structure
of the human body, and yet to-day there is still much, very much, which
we do not understand, but we live and work in the hope that our knowledge will continue to increase.

1912

Variations on a Theme by Darwin

JULIAN HUXLEY

D URING THE PRESENT CENTURY WE HAVE HEARD SO
much of the revolutionary discoveries of modern physics that
we are apt to forget how great has been the change in the outlook due
to biology. Yet in some respects this has been the more important. For
it is affecting the way we think and act in our everyday existence. Without the discoveries and ideas of Darwin and the other great pioneers in
the biological field, from Mendel to Freud, we should all be different
from what we are. The discoveries of physics and chemistry have given
us an enormous control over lifeless matter and have provided us with
a host of new machines and conveniences, and this certainly has reacted
on our general attitude. They have also provided us with a new outlook
on the universe at large: our ideas about time and space, matter and
creation, and our own position in the general scheme of things, are
very different from the ideas of our grandfathers.

Biology is beginning to provide us with control over living matter—
new drugs, new methods for fighting disease, new kinds of animals and
plants. It is helping us also to a new intellectual outlook, in which man
is seen not as a finished being, single lord of creation, but as one among
millions of the products of an evolution that is still in progress. But
it is doing something more. It is actually making us different in our
natures and our biological behaviour. I will take but three examples.

The application of the discoveries of medicine and physiology is making us healthier: and a healthy man behaves and thinks differently from one who is not so healthy. Then the discoveries of modern psychology have been altering our mental and emotional life, and our system of education: taken in the mass, the young people now growing up feel differently, and will therefore act differently, about such vital matters as sex and marriage, about jealousy, about freedom of expression, about the relation between parents and children. And as a third example, as a race we are changing our reproductive habits: the idea and the practice of deliberate birth-control has led to fewer children. People living in a country of small families and a stationary or decreasing population will in many respects *be* different from people in a country of large families and an increasing population.

This change has not been due to any very radical new discoveries made during the present century. It has been due chiefly to discoveries which were first made in the previous century, and are at last beginning to exert a wide effect. These older discoveries fall under two chief heads. One is Evolution—the discovery that all living things, including ourselves, are the product of a slow process of development which has been brought about by natural forces, just as surely as has to-day's weather or last month's high tides. The other is the sum of an enormous number of separate discoveries which we may call physiological, and which boil down to this: that all living things, again including ourselves, work according to regular laws, in just the same way as do non-living things, except that living things are much more complicated. The old idea of "vital-force" has been driven back and back until there is hardly any process of life where it can still find any foothold. Looked at objectively and scientifically, a man is an exceedingly complex piece of chemical machinery. This does not mean that he cannot quite legitimately be looked at from other points of view—subjectively, for instance; what it means is that so far as it goes, this scientific point of view is true, and not the point of view which ascribed human activities to the working of a vital force quite different from the forces at work in matter which was not alive.

Imagine a group of scientists from another planet, creatures with quite a different nature from ours, who had been dispassionately studying the curious objects called human beings for a number of years. They would not be concerned about what we men felt we were or what we would like to be, but only about getting an objective view of what we actually were and why we were what we were. It is that sort of picture which I want to draw for you. Our Martian scientists would have to consider us from three main viewpoints if they were to understand much about us.

First they would have to understand our physical construction, and what meaning it had in relation to the world around and the work we have to do in it. Secondly, they would have to pay attention to our development and our history. And thirdly, they would have to study the construction and working of our minds. Any one of these three aspects by itself would give a very incomplete picture of us.

An ordinary human being is a lump of matter weighing between 50 and 100 kilograms. This living matter is the same matter of which the rest of the earth, the sun, and even the most distant stars and nebulae are made. Some elements which make up a large proportion of living matter, like hydrogen and especially carbon, are rare in the not-living parts of the earth; and others which are abundant in the earth are, like iron, present only in traces in living creatures, or altogether absent, like aluminum or silicon. None the less, it is the same matter. The chief difference between living and non-living matter is the complication of living matter. Its elements are built up into molecules much bigger and more elaborate than any other known, often containing more than a thousand atoms each. And of course, living matter has the property of self-reproduction; when supplied with the right materials and in the right conditions, it can build up matter which is not living into its own complicated patterns.

Life, in fact, from the "public" standpoint, which Professor Levy has stressed as being the only possible standpoint for science, is simply the name for the various distinctive properties of a particular group of very complex chemical compounds. The most important of these properties are, first, feeding, assimilation, growth, and reproduction, which are all aspects of the one quality of self-reproduction; next, the capacity for reacting to a number of kinds of changes in the world outside—to stimuli, such as light, heat, pressure, and chemical change; then the capacity for liberating energy in response to these stimuli, so as to react back again upon the outer world—whether by moving about, by constructing things, by discharging chemical products, or by generating light or heat; and finally the property of variation. Self-reproduction is not always precisely accurate, and the new substance is a little different from the parent substance which produced it.

The existence of self-reproduction on the one hand and variation on the other automatically leads to what Darwin called "natural selection." This is a sifting process, by which the different new variations are tested out against the conditions of their existence, and in which some succeed better than others in surviving and in leaving descendants. This blind process slowly but inevitably causes living matter to change—in other words, it leads to evolution. There may be other agencies at work in guiding the course of evolution; but it seems certain that natural selection is the most important.

The results it produces are roughly as follows. It *adapts* any particular stream of living matter more or less completely to the conditions in which it lives. As there are innumerable different sets of conditions to which life can be adapted, this has led to an increasing diversity of life, a splitting of living matter into an increasing number of separate streams. The final tiny streams we call species; there are perhaps a million of them now in existence. This adaptation is progressive; any one stream of life is forced to grow gradually better and better adapted to some particular condition of life. We can often see this in the fossil records of past life. For instance, the early ancestors of lions and horses about 50 million years ago were not very unlike, but with the passage of time one line grew better adapted to grass-eating and running away from enemies. And finally natural selection leads to general progress; there is a gradual rising of the highest level attained by life. The most advanced animals are those which have changed their way of life and adapted themselves to new conditions, thus taking advantages of biological territory hitherto unoccupied. The most obvious example of this was the invasion of the land. Originally all living things were confined to life in water, and it was not for hundreds of millions of years after the first origin of life that plants and animals managed to colonize dry land.

But progress can also consist in taking better advantage of existing conditions: for instance, the mammal's biological inventions, of warm blood and of nourishing the unborn young within the mother's body, put them at an advantage over other inhabitants of the land; and the increase in size of brain which is man's chief characteristic has enabled him to control and exploit his environment in a new and more effective way, from which his pre-human ancestors were debarred.

It follows from this that all animals and plants that are at all highly developed have a long and chequered history behind them, and that their present can often not be properly understood without an understanding of their past. For instance, the tiny hairs all over our own bodies are a reminder of the fact that we are descended from furry creatures, and have no significance except as a survival.

Let us now try to get some picture of man in the light of these ideas. The continuous stream of life that we call the human race is broken up into separate bits which we call individuals. This is true of all higher animals, but is not necessary: it is a convenience. Living matter has to deal with two sets of activities: one concerns its immediate relations with the world outside it, the other concerns its future perpetuation. What we call an individual is an arrangement permitting a stream of living matter to deal more effectively with its environment. After a time it is discarded and dies. But within itself it contains a reserve of potentially immortal substance, which it can hand on to future generations, to produce new individuals like itself. Thus from one aspect the individual is only the casket of the continuing race; but from another the achievements of the race depend on the construction of its separate individuals.

The human individual is large as animal individuals go. Size is an advantage if life is not to be at the mercy of small changes in the outer world: for instance, a man the size of a beetle could not manage to keep his temperature constant. Size also goes with long life: and a man who only lived as long as a fly could not learn much. But there is a limit to size; a land animal much bigger than an elephant is not, mechanically speaking, a practical proposition. Man is in that range of size, from 100 lb. to a ton, which seems to give the best combination of strength, and mobility. It may be surprising to realize that man's size and mechanical construction are related to the size of the earth which he inhabits; but so it is. The force of gravity on Jupiter is so much greater than on our own planet, that if we lived there our skeletons would have to be much stronger to support the much increased weight which we would then possess, and animals in general would be more stocky; and conversely, if the earth were only the size of the moon, we could manage with far less expenditures of material in the form of bone and sinew, and should be spindly creatures.

Our general construction is determined by the fact that we are made of living matter, must accordingly be constantly passing a stream of fresh matter and energy through ourselves if we are to live, and must as constantly be guarding ourselves against danger if we are not to die. About 5 per cent of ourselves consists of a tube with attached chemical factories, for taking in raw materials in the shape of food, and converting it into the form in which it can be absorbed into our real interior. About 2 per cent consists in arrangements—windpipe and lungs—for getting oxygen into our system in order to burn the food materials and liberate energy. About 10 per cent consists of an arrangement for distributing materials all over the body—the blood and lymph, the tubes which hold them and the pump which drives them. Much less than 5 per cent is devoted to dealing with waste materials produced when living substance breaks down in the process of producing energy to keep our machinery going—the kidneys and bladder and, in part, the lungs and skin. Over 40 per cent is machinery for moving us about—our muscles; and nearly

20 per cent is needed to support us and to give the mechanical leverage for our movements—our skeleton and sinews. A relatively tiny fraction is set apart for giving us information about the outer world—our sense organs. And there is about 3 per cent to deal with the difficult business of adjusting our behaviour to what is happening around us. This is the task of the ductless glands, the nerves, the spinal cord and the brain; our conscious feeling and thinking is done by a small part of the brain. Less than 1 per cent of our bodies is set aside for reproducing the race. The remainder of our body is concerned with special functions like protection, carried out by the skin (which is about 7 per cent of our bulk) and some of the white blood corpuscles; or temperature regulations, carried out by the sweat glands. And nearly 10 per cent of a normal man consists of reserve food stores in the shape of fat.

Other streams of living matter have developed quite other arrangements in relation to their special environment. Some have parts of themselves set aside for manufacturing electricity, like the electric eel, or light, like the firefly. Some, like certain termites, are adapted to live exclusively on wood; others, like cows, exclusively on vegetables. Some like boa-constrictors, only need to eat every few months; others, like parasitic worms, need only breathe a few hours a day; others, like some desert gazelles, need no water to drink. Many cave animals have no eyes; tapeworms have no mouths or stomachs; and so on and so forth. And all these peculiarities, including those of our own construction, are related to the kind of surroundings in which the animal lives.

This relativity of our nature is perhaps most clearly seen in regard to our senses. The ordinary man is accustomed to think of the information given by his senses as absolute. So it is—for him; but not in the view of our Martian scientist. To start with, the particular senses we possess are not shared by many other creatures. Outside backboned animals, for instance, very few creatures can hear at all; a few insects and perhaps a few crustacea probably exhaust the list. Even fewer animals can see colours; apparently the world as seen even by most mammals is a black and white world, not a coloured world. And the majority of animals do not even see at all in the sense of being given a detailed picture of the world around. Either they merely distinguish light from darkness, or at best can get a blurred image of big moving objects. On the other hand, we are much worse off than many other creatures—dogs, for instance, or some moths—in regard to smell. Our sense of smell is to a dog's what an eye capable of just distinguishing big moving objects is to our own eye.

But from another aspect, the relativity of our senses is even more fundamental. Our senses serve to give us information about changes outside our bodies. Well, what kind of changes are going on in the outside world? There are ordinary mechanical changes: matter can press against us, whether in the form of a gentle breeze or a blow from a poker. There are the special mechanical changes due to vibrations passing through the air or water around us—these are what we hear. There are changes in temperature—hot and cold. There are chemical changes—the kind of matter with which we are in contact alters, as when the air contains poison gas, or our mouth contains lemonade. There are electrical changes, as when a current is sent through a wire we happen to be touching.

And there are all the changes depending on what used to be called vibrations in the ether. The most familiar of these are light-waves; but they range from the extremely short waves that give cosmic rays and X-rays, down through ultra-violet to visible light, on to waves of radiant heat, and so on to the very long Hertzian waves which are used in wireless. All these are the same kind of thing, but differ in wave-length.

Now of all these happenings, we are only aware of what appears to be a very arbitrary selection. Mechanical changes we are aware of through our sense of touch. Air-vibrations we hear; but not all of them—the small wave-lengths are pitched too high for our ears, though some of them can be heard by other creatures, such as dogs and bats. We have a heat sense and a cold sense, and two kinds of chemical senses for different sorts of chemical changes—taste and smell. But we possess no special electrical sense—we have no way of telling whether a live rail is carrying a current or not unless we actually touch it, and then what we feel is merely pain.

The oddest facts, however, concern light and kindred vibrations. We have no sense organs for perceiving X-rays, although they may be pouring into us and doing grave damage. We do not perceive ultra-violet light, though some insects, like bees, can see it. And we have no sense organs for Hertzian waves, though we make machines—wireless receivers—to catch them. Out of all this immense range of vibrations, the only ones of which we are aware through our senses are radiant heat and light. The waves of radiant heat we perceive through the effect which they have on our temperature sense organs; and the light-waves we see. But what we see is only a single octave of the light waves, as opposed to ten or eleven octaves of sound-waves which we can hear.

This curious state of affairs begins to be comprehensible when we remember that our sense organs have been evolved in relation to the world in which our ancestors lived. In nature, there are large-scale electrical discharges such as lightning, and they act so capriciously and violently that to be able to detect them would be no advantage. The same is true of X-rays. The amount of them knocking about under normal conditions is so small that there is no point in having sense organs to tell us about them. Wireless waves, on the other hand, are of such huge wave-lengths that they go right through living matter without affecting it. Even if they were present in nature, there would be no obvious way of developing a sense organ to perceive them.

As regards light, there seem to be two reasons why our eyes are limited to seeing only a single octave of the waves. One is that of the ether vibrations raying upon the earth's surface from the sun and outer space, the greatest amount is centered in this region of the spectrum; the intensity of light of higher or lower wave-lengths is much less, and would only suffice to give us a dim sensation. Our greatest capacity for seeing is closely adjusted to the amount of light to be seen. The other is more subtle, and has to do with the properties of light of different wavelengths. Ultra-violet light is of so short a wave-length that much of it gets scattered as it passes through the air, instead of progressing forward in straight lines. Hence a photograph which uses only the ultra-violet rays is blurred and shows no details of the distance. A photograph taken by infra-red light, on the other hand, while it shows the distant landscape very well, over-emphasizes the contrast between light and shade in the foreground. Leaves and grass reflect all the infra-red, and so look white, while the shadows are inky-black, with no gradations. The result looks like a snowscape. An eye which could see the ultra-violet octave would see the world as in a fog; and one which could see only the infra-red octave would find it impossible to pick out lurking enemies in the jet-black shadows. The particular range of light to which our eyes are attuned gives the best-graded contrast.

Then of course there is the pleasant or unpleasant quality of a sensation; and this, too, is in general related to our way of life. I will take one example. Both lead acetate and sugar taste sweet; the former is a poison, but very rare in nature; the latter is a useful food, and common in nature. Accordingly we most of us find a sweet taste pleasant. But if lead acetate were as common in nature as sugar, and sugar as rare as lead acetate, it is safe to prophesy that we should find sweetness a most horrible taste, because we should only survive if we spat out anything which tasted sweet.

Now let us turn to another feature of man's life which would probably seem exceedingly queer to a scientist from another planet—sex. We are so used to the fact that our race is divided up into two quite different kinds of individuals, male and female, and that our existence largely circles round this fact, that we rarely pause to think about it. But there is no inherent reason why this should be so. Some kinds of animals consist only of females; some, like ants, have neuters in addition to the two sexes; some plants are altogether sexless.

As a matter of fact, the state of affairs as regards human sex is due to a long and curious sequence of causes. The fundamental fact of sex has nothing to do with reproduction; it is the union of two living cells into one. The actual origin of this remains mysterious. Once it had originated, however, it proved of biological value, by conferring greater variability on the race, and so greater elasticity in meeting changed conditions. That is why sex is so nearly universal. Later, it was a matter of biological convenience that reproduction in higher animals became indissolubly tied up with sex. Once this had happened, the force of natural selection in all its intensity became focused on the sex instinct, because in the long run those strains which reproduce themselves abundantly will live on, while those which do not do so will gradually be supplanted.

A wholly different biological invention, the retention of the young within the mother's body for protection led to the two sexes becoming much more different in construction and instincts than would otherwise have been the case. The instinctive choice of a more pleasing as against a less pleasing mate—what Darwin called sexual selection—led to the evolution of all kinds of beautiful or striking qualities which in a sexless race would never have developed. The most obvious of such characters are seen in the gorgeous plumage of many birds; but sexual selection has undoubtedly modelled us human beings in many details— the curves of our bodies, the colours of lips, eyes, cheeks, the hair of our heads, and the quality of our voices.

Then we should not forget that almost all other mammals and all birds are, even when adult, fully sexed only for a part of the year: after the breeding season they relapse into a more or less neuter state. How radically different human life would be if we too behaved thus! But man has continued an evolutionary trend begun for some unknown reason among the monkeys, and remains continuously sexed all the year round. Hunger and love are the two primal urges of man: but by what a strange series of biological steps has love attained its position!

We could go on enumerating facts about the relativity of man's physical construction; but time is short, and I must say a word about his mind. For that too has developed in relation to the conditions of our life, present and past. Many philosophers and theologians have been astonished at the strength of the feeling which prompts most men and women to cling to life, to feel that life is worth living, even in the most wretched circumstances. But to the biologist there is nothing surprising in this. Those men (and animals) who have the urge to go on living strongly developed will automatically survive and breed in greater numbers than those in whom it is weak. Nature's pessimists automatically eliminate themselves, and their pessimistic tendencies, from the race. A race without a strong will to live could no more hold its own than one without a strong sexual urge.

Then again man's highest impulses would not exist if it were not for two simple biological facts—that his offspring are born helpless and must be protected and tended for years if they are to grow up, and that he is a gregarious animal. These facts make it biologically necessary for him to have well-developed altruistic instincts, which may and often do come into conflict with his egoistic instincts, but are in point of fact responsible for half of his attitude towards life. Neither a solitary creature like a cat or a hawk, nor a creature with no biological responsibility towards its young, like a lizard or a fish, could possibly have developed such strong altruistic instincts as are found in man.

Other instincts appear to be equally relative. Everyone who has any acquaintance with wild birds and animals knows how much different species differ in temperament. Most kinds of mice are endowed with a great deal of fear and very little ferocity; while the reverse is true of various carnivores like tigers or Tasmanian devils. It would appear that the amounts of fear and anger in man's emotional make-up are greater than his needs as a civilized being, and are survivals from an earlier period of his racial history. In the dawn of man's evolution from apes, a liberal dose of fear was undoubtedly needed if he was to be preserved from foolhardiness in a world peopled by wild beasts and hostile tribes, and an equally liberal dose of anger, the emotion underlying pugnacity, if he was to triumph over danger when it came. But now they are on the whole a source of weakness and maladjustment.

It is often said that you cannot change human nature. But that is only true in the short-range view. In the long run, human nature could as readily be changed as feline nature has actually been changed in the domestic cat, where man's selection has produced an amiable animal out of a fierce ancestral spit-fire of a creature. If, for instance, civilization should develop in such a way that mild and placid people tended to have larger families than those of high-strung or violent temperament, in a few centuries human nature would alter in the direction of mildness. . . .

Pavlov has shown how even dogs can be made to have nervous breakdowns by artificially generating in their minds conflicting urges to two virtually exclusive kinds of action; and we all know that the same thing, on a higher level of complexity, happens in human beings. But a nervous breakdown puts an organism out of action for the practical affairs of life, quite as effectively as does an ordinary infectious disease. And just as against physical germ-diseases we have evolved a protection in the shape of the immunity reactions of our blood, so we have evolved oblivion as protection against the mental diseases arising out of conflict. For, generally speaking, what happens is that we forget one of the two conflicting ideas or motives. We do this either by giving the inconvenient idea an extra kick into the limbo of the forgotten, which psychologists call suppression, or else, when it refuses to go so simply, by forcibly keeping it under in the sub-conscious, which is styled repression. For details about suppression and repression and their often curious and sometimes disastrous results I must ask you to refer to any modern book on psychology. All I want to point out here is that a special mental machinery has been evolved for putting inconvenient ideas out of consciousness, and that the contents and construction of our minds are different in consequence. . . .

But I have said enough, I hope, to give you some idea of what is implied by calling man a relative being. It implies that he has no real meaning apart from the world which he inhabits. Perhaps this is not quite accurate. The mere fact that man, a portion of the general stuff of which the universe is made, can think and feel, aspire and plan, is itself full of meaning, but the precise way in which man is made, his physical construction, the kinds of feelings he has, the way he thinks, the things he thinks about, everything which gives his existence form and precision— all this can only be properly understood in relation to his environment. For he and his environment make one interlocking whole.

The great advances in scientific understanding and practical control often begin when people begin asking questions about things which up till then they have merely taken for granted. If humanity is to be brought under its own conscious control, it must cease taking itself for granted, and, even though the process may often be humiliating, begin to examine itself in a completely detached and scientific spirit.

1933

C. THE CONQUEST OF DISEASE

The Hippocratic Oath

I SWEAR BY APOLLO PHYSICIAN, BY ASCLEPIUS, BY Health, by Panacea and by all the gods and goddesses, making them my witnesses, that I will carry out, according to my ability and judgment, this oath and this indenture. To hold my teacher in this art equal to my own parents; to make him partner in my livelihood; when he is in need of money to share mine with him; to consider his family as my own brothers, and to teach them this art, if they want to learn it, without fee or indenture; to impart precept, oral instruction, and all other instruction to my own sons, the sons of my teacher, and to indentured pupils who have taken the physician's oath, but to nobody else. I will use treatment to help the sick according to my ability and judgment, but never with a view to injury and wrong-doing. Neither will I administer a poison to anybody when asked to do so, nor will I suggest such a course. Similarly I will not give a woman a pessary to cause abortion. But I will keep pure and holy both my life and my art. I will not use the knife, not even, verily, on sufferers from stone, but I will give place to such as are craftsmen therein. Into whatsoever houses I enter, I will enter to help the sick, and I will abstain from all intentional wrong-doing and harm, especially from abusing the bodies of man or woman, bond or free. And whatsoever I shall see or hear in the course of my profession, as well as outside my profession in my intercourse with men, if it be what should not be published abroad, I will never divulge, holding such things to be holy secrets. Now if I carry out this oath, and break it not, may I gain for ever reputation among all men for my life and for my art; but if I transgress it and forswear myself, may the opposite befall me. *Estimated between Fifth and First Centuries* B.C.

Hippocrates, the Greek—the End of Magic

LOGAN CLENDENING

From *Behind the Doctor*

PHILISCUS, WHO LIVED BY THE WALL IN ATHENS, LAY sick of a fever. The year, according to our reckoning, was 410 B.C. The Battle of Marathon had been fought eighty years before. Athens was still the greatest city in the world—great in the sunset of its golden age.

The members of Philiscus' family were uneasy about him, for the malady had not progressed favourably.

They sat sadly on the doorstep awaiting the report of his wife, who had gone in to help him.

She appeared with an unhappy frown on her brow.

"He doth not know me," she explained. "And he hath not slept. He hath passed water that is black."

"Ah! I have seen that," exclaimed her father. "It is a bad omen." His voice sank to a whisper. "I tell you it is the hounds of Hekate that rend him."

Another elder shook his head.

"It was a sudden affliction that seized him—it came from Pan, or, mayhap, one of the arrows of Apollo," he averred.

"What physicians have treated him?" inquired this sage, after an interval of silence.

"Im-Ram, the Egyptian, came by two days ago and gave him an emetic of white hellebore. But he was no better."

The elder looked stolidly ahead at this. He did not approve of Egyptians or Egyptian remedies. He wanted to placate the angry Apollo.

"Then there was the Babylonian, Mother," the son of Philiscus reminded her.

"What did he do?" inquired the elder.

"He sacrificed a goat and made divination by the liver."

569

"Ah! and what did that show?" asked the elder, somewhat more approvingly.

"He laid the liver out and explained it to me carefully," said the son, eagerly. "There was the lobus dexter and the lobus sinister—and they were inequal."

"The omens were not clear," sighed the wife.

"And the *vesica fellea*," continued the lad—"the gall-bladder—it was full of stones."

"How many?" demanded the old man.

"There were three large ones and many small ones."

"Three?" the elder shook his head, dubiously—"that is grave. One element is missing. There should be four."

"Water, perhaps," suggested the wife, "he cries, when he cries sensibly at all, always for water."

"Fire, air, earth, and water," repeated the old man, sententiously. "The elements of Pythagoras, the Samian. If one is taken away by the demons or the hounds of Hekate, it must be replaced. Now here the sick man is hot and dry—fire is in the ascendancy. Water is cold and moist—just the opposite. It is water he must have." And he nodded his head emphatically, pleased with his own reasoning.

"I give him water morning, noon, and night, every hour," answered the wife, distractedly.

"If we could take him to a temple of Aesculapius," suggested the father-in-law, "and let the priests treat him."

The wife shook her head. "He is too sick to move," she said, "and out of his senses—we could not leave him alone."

"I went to a temple once when I was a young man—for this eye," the old man said, reminiscently. "It was a very good temple, and a very good treatment, to my way of thought. My eye got better soon after; whereas before, it had been painful and running like a sore."

"What temple did you go to?" the other old man inquired.

"At Epidaurus—naturally," the narrator replied. "I remember it very well. The priests of the temple made me cleanse myself first. There was a bath of salt water, too, as well as the clear water which they made me enter. Then I purified my soul with prayer. And then the oblation."

"What was your oblation?"

"I was too poor to offer a sheep or a cock, so I offered a popana—a small cake dipped in oil. The priests sell it to you. Then I starved four days and was allowed to enter the sanctuary for the incubation sleep."

"What was that?" asked the boy.

"Inside the temple—you slept. There was the great image of Aesculapius at the high altar. It was an awe-inspiring sight. The representation of the flesh was of ivory, and the rest was of gold enamelled in colours."

By this time he had acquired the attention of his audience, and he launched into his narrative.

"Sufferers were all over the floor of the temple. Each of us had his pallet. The night came down and we composed ourselves to sleep. And whether it was a dream or not I cannot tell, but it seemed to me the god himself came down from the altar and walked among us. He had two great yellow snakes and a dog. He stopped a moment at my pallet and leaned over me. One of the snakes licked my eye. The god put some ointment in it. And the next day I found a box of ointment at my side. I took it away with me. And soon my eye was well, and I placed a votive tablet in the temple."

The youth laughed incredulously.

"Ay!" the elder reproved, "in this age of doubt you fall away from the old things, but I tell you they are good—those temple rites. I know of things wrought there that would outdo your modern treatments. While I was being cured, Proklos, the philosopher, himself, was also there: he was afflicted with a rheum of his knee—very painful: and he covered it with a cloth. The night he slept in the temple, a sacred sparrow plucked the cloth away, and the pain left with it. His knee was as good as ever."

This account of success seemed to impress his audience.

"Yes, you doubt!" he continued. "You doubt the old ways, and you doubt the old gods. I heard of a new drama of Aristophanes—what is the name of it—*Plutus*—played in the theatre of Dionysus—and what does it amount to? Making fun of a poor sick person who goes to the temple for help—that's what. It jests at the priests—says they steal the offerings of food brought by the patients and eat the food themselves and give it to the sacred serpents—and all this—" the old man's voice rose excitedly— "all this played out in the theatre of Dionysus—and the priests do not interfere. Why, in my time—"

A wild cry from the delirious patient interrupted the discourse. The wife hurried in to attend her patient.

The boy crept to his grandfather's feet and said: "Grandfather, can we not fetch the physician Hippocrates to counsel about father?"

"Hippocrates? Yes, I have heard of this healer," assented his grandfather. "He hath a good name and is highly esteemed."

"He is in Athens now," declared the youth.

"He was the son of a temple priest—I know, I have heard," said the other old man. "His father was a priest in the Temple of Aesculapius at Cos. Ah, that is a wonderful temple for healing! If we cannot take

Philiscus to a temple, the next best thing were to have a priest of the Asclepiadæ come to him."

The wife returned to their circle again, gravely troubled.

"He is worse even than before," she answered their interrogatory glances.

"Think you we could get Hippocrates, the physician, to see him?" asked her father.

A look of hope came to her face.

"I have heard of that Hippocrates," she answered. "Is he not the one who treated the Clazomenian who was lodged by the wall of Phynichides?"

"Yes, that was he—now that you recall it to me."

"The Clazomenian was cured."

"He was indeed—and his case is much like that of Philiscus. He had a pain in the neck and head, and fever. And he could not sleep, and besides, like Philiscus, he became delirious. He was sick for many days, but this Hippocrates came to see him every day and wrote down on his tablets the condition of the patient every day."

"What was his treatment?" asked the elder.

"That I cannot recall, but he prescribed diets and baths, that I know."

"Mayhap he leaves the patient and propitiates a god," suggested the elder.

"Mayhap, but his method was good in the case of the Clazomenian."

"Let us send for him quickly—quickly," cried the wife. "Who will help us?"

"I will run through the streets, Mother, and bring him back," said the boy, eagerly starting off.

The watchers waited impatiently; time seemed to them to pass slowly, but in reality in a short while the boy returned, leading a radiant stranger, the physician Hippocrates. He was between forty-five and fifty years of age—tall, erect, godlike in presence and calmness.

Three young men accompanied him, disciples learning the art. They were his sons Thessalus and Dracon, and one named Dexippus.

He entered the home of Philiscus gravely, greeted the wife and the two older men with a smile, and then walked quickly to the bed where the patient lay.

He put his hand on the sick man's forehead.

"Have you any pain?" he asked.

The patient stared at him vacantly, his lips trembling in a muttering delirium, and then he suddenly started as if to rise from his bed.

The younger physicians restrained him.

"Has he been delirious long?" Hippocrates asked the wife.

"Since yesterday evening," she answered.

"How long has he been sick?"

"This is the third day. He went to the market-place to discuss some matter and stood in the sun, and something he said must have incurred the anger of the god."

Hippocrates lifted his hand to stop her.

"Tell the story just as it happened, without bringing in the gods," he said, somewhat severely.

The woman looked at him with some fear. Then seeing a reassuring smile from the physician, she continued:

"He came home and took to his bed. He sweated and was very uneasy Yesterday, the second day, he was worse in all these points."

"Did he have a stool?" asked Hippocrates.

"Yes, late in the evening—a proper stool from a small clyster."

"Write that down, Dexippus," commanded the master—and "Go on," he said to the wife.

"Today he has been much worse. He has been very hot. He trembles; he sweats and is always thirsty. He hath been delirious on all subjects. He has passed black water."

"Oh! When was that?" asked the physician, suddenly alert.

"This afternoon."

"Let me see some of it."

A slave boy was summoned and brought an earthen vessel with some of the sick man's urine in it.

"Notice, my sons," said the physician to his disciples. "The black water again. We have seen it often this season. And always the prognostic is unfavourable."

"Anything more to tell us?" he asked, turning again to the wife.

"That is all, I think—O mighty physician, invoke the gods to drive this devil from my husband."

"Your husband hath no devil—he hath a disease. We will do our best. More we cannot promise. Pray to the gods, but pray for piety and good works. Do not ask them for things they cannot grant."

He left some instructions about the patient's diet and recommended limewater to drink. He instructed the slave in bathing his master by sponging him with cloth, unless he chilled. He left a draught of medicine to be given for delirium.

"I will return tomorrow and observe the patient," he announced to the family. "Let us see now, Dexippus, if you have that description right." He took the scroll from his pupil and read it.

"Shall we sacrifice to any of the gods?" asked the elder, tremulously.

"I do not practise by the gods," answered Hippocrates. "I try to discover the nature of the disease and to follow that. To read nature—believe me, friend, it is better than relying on the gods."

When he came the next day, the patient was unimproved. The physician noted all points about his condition and ordered Dexippus to write them down—which he did.

On the fifth day, however, the patient was worse. There was something very peculiar about the breathing.

Hippocrates motioned for the members of Philiscus' family to leave the room. Then "What think you of that breathing?" the physician asked his pupils.

"It is passing strange," answered Thessalus.

"How would you describe it?" demanded his father.

The young man watched the patient for a few minutes and then said: "Sometimes it is very rapid and deep—then it becomes shallower."

"Then what?"

"Then it stops altogether for a moment, and then he begins again like a person recollecting himself."

"That is good," approved the master. "Write that down, Dexippus—a splendid description—'like a person recollecting himself.'—Good. There is no better description I ever heard. See, there it is—'like a person recollecting himself.' Have you ever seen it before?"

"Yes—the Thessalonian had something like it."

"Quite true. And what was the outcome of his case?"

"He died."

"So he did. Do you remember anyone else who had it?"

"Was not that woman we saw in the little house yonder breathing in this way?" inquired Dracon, diffidently.

"She was indeed. Do you not all remember? Exactly the same. And what was the outcome of her case?"

"She, too, died," answered Dracon.

"That is the rule," said Hippocrates. "I have never seen one recover. So it will be here. I am sorry, for the wife loves her husband, but the rules of nature are immutable. Feel the spleen, Thessalus."

"It is large and round," answered Thessalus, after placing his hands on the abdomen.

"Extremities altogether cold," dictated Hippocrates, for his notes. "The paroxysms on the even days. Sweats cold throughout. So—"

The physician gave the family such comfort as he could, but his prognosis was fulfilled and Philiscus died that night.

. . . The method of Hippocrates the Greek was to ignore all of the gods. Disease, he preached, was a part of the order of nature, and to conquer it, to understand it, one must study it as one does any other natural event. Many useful facts about treatment and diagnosis and the classification of disease were gathered together before Hippocrates. But with him the doctrine that disease is a natural event and follows natural laws comes out clear and strong.

That is why Hippocrates is called the Father of Medicine. Yet how long it took men to learn the simple thing he taught! How many hundreds of years elapsed between the medicine man and Hippocrates is a matter for the conjecture of anthropologists. Certainly not less than fifty thousand. But from his time to ours his influence extends in a clear stream, never changing in the great essential doctrine that disease is a part of nature.

The case of Philiscus is a good subject of study in order to analyse the elements which Hippocrates contributed to human thought.

Here we see him in the midst of his regular daily life, expounding by precept and example those principles. I have tried to show how far ahead of his time he was—how the older men in the scene harked back to the superstitions and to the ways of the gods of their youth—to Babylonian liver prognostication, to the idea of Apollo as the dealer of death, to the influence of Pan, and to the hounds of Hekate.

How scornful the Hippocratic writings are about the last: "But terrors which happen during the night, and fevers, and delirium, and jumpings out of bed, and frightful apparitions and fleeing away—all these they hold to be the plots of Hekate!"

The case of "Philiscus who lived by the wall," is actual enough. It is the first of those many little case histories found in Hippocrates—that earliest collection of clinical cases recorded from the standpoint of science.

The case is described simply day by day. There is no embroidery—simply the symptoms as they appeared and the outcome of the case.

The name of the patient, the address (by the wall), the circumstances, are all set down. The picture of the sick man tossing through the hot Athenian night comes to us across two thousand years, stabbing us like a personal anxiety.

The peculiarity of breathing which Hippocrates noted—"as of a person recollecting himself"—is now known as Cheyne-Stokes respiration. It is a common symptom of approaching death and is due to exhaustion or lack of oxygenation of the respiratory centre.

Hippocrates as a historical figure, aside from his writings, is very vague. In this he corresponds to Homer in the epic literature of Greece. It is doubtful if there was any single personality known as Hippocrates. The Hippocratic writings are probably the work of many men, the crystallization of the thought of a school.

Tradition dates his birth at 460 B.C. Plato mentions him as if he were a living man known to him. He is said to have travelled widely, teaching as he went. He died at Larissa, it was said, at the age of a hundred and ten.

It is difficult for anyone who reads the Hippocratic writings to escape the conviction that the best of them were the product of a single mind—their unity of thought, their clarity, their radiance, preclude any other idea.

The best are the "Aphorisms"—short, descriptive, clinical facts. The most famous, of course, is the first: "Life is short and art is long."

But "Persons who are naturally very fat are apt to die earlier than those who are slender" might have a place in a modern life-insurance actuary's summary of his studies.

"Consumption most commonly occurs between the ages of eighteen and thirty-five."

"From a spitting of blood there is a spitting of pus" shows that Hippocrates has watched people with tuberculosis of the lungs have as the initial symptom a hemorrhage and then begin ordinary expectoration.

"Eunuchs do not take the gout nor become bald."

"If a dropsical patient be seized with hiccup, the case is hopeless."

"Anxiety, yawning, and rigour—wine drunk with equal proportions of water removes these complaints."

Into the domain of treatment also he tried to bring some order.

His diets, for instance, as Dr. Singer points out, were to be prescribed according to certain sensible rules. First the age of the patient was to be considered—"Old persons use less nutriment than young." Then the season—"In winter abundant nourishment is wholesome; in summer a more frugal diet." The physical state of the patient—"Lean persons should take little food, but this little should be fat; fat persons, on the other hand, should take much food, but it should be lean." Digestibility of the food—"White meat is more digestible than dark."

The typical Greek myth has always seemed to my mind that of Prometheus. He stole the fire of the gods from heaven and brought it down to earth for man's use. The Greeks constantly did that. The Mediterranean basin was hag-ridden and god-ridden until they appeared. They took the drama—a service to the god—and they wrenched it away from the god and subdued it to the services of man. They made it not a service in a temple, but a story to charm the mind; they filled it with music and dancing and song for their fellow-men's entertainment. So with Hippocrates. He took once and for ever "the art"—the art of healing. He wrested it from the gods and made it man's.

With Hippocrates—with all the Greeks—we first find people of our own kind. We come out, as Osler says—"out of the murky night of the East, heavy with phantoms, into the bright daylight of the West." Here are men speaking our words, following our devotions, thinking our thoughts, pursuing objects which seems to us worth gaining and to us understandable.

1933

An Inquiry into the Causes and Effects of the Variolae Vaccinae, Known by the Name of the Cow-Pox

EDWARD JENNER

THE DEVIATION OF MAN FROM THE STATE IN WHICH he was originally placed by nature seems to have proved to him a prolific source of diseases. From the love of splendour, from the indulgence of luxury, and from his fondness for amusement he has familiarized himself with a great number of animals, which may not originally have been intended for his associates.

The wolf, disarmed of ferocity, is now pillowed in the lady's lap. The cat, the little tiger of our island, whose natural home is the forest, is equally domesticated and caressed. The cow, the hog, the sheep, and the horse, are all, for a variety of purposes, brought under his care and dominion.

There is a disease to which the horse, from his state of domestication, is frequently subject. The farriers call it the grease. It is an inflammation and swelling in the heel, from which issues matter possessing properties of a very peculiar kind, which seems capable of generating a disease in the human body (after it has undergone the modification which I shall presently speak of), which bears so strong a resemblance to the smallpox that I think it highly probable it may be the source of the disease.

In this dairy country a great number of cows are kept, and the office of milking is performed indiscriminately by men and maid servants. One of the former having been appointed to apply dressings to the heels of a horse affected with the grease, and not paying due attention to cleanliness, incautiously bears his part in milking the cows, with some particles of the infectious matter adhering to his fingers. When this is the case, it com-monly happens that a disease is communicated to the cows, and from the cows to dairy maids, which spreads through the farm until the most of the cattle and domestics feel its unpleasant consequences. This disease has obtained the name of the cow-pox. It appears on the nipples of the cows in the form of irregular pustules. At their first appearance they are commonly of a palish blue, or rather of a colour somewhat approaching to livid, and are surrounded by an erysipelatous inflammation. These pustules, unless a timely remedy be applied, frequently degenerate into phagedenic ulcers, which prove extremely troublesome. The animals become indisposed, and the secretion of milk is much lessened. Inflamed spots now begin to appear on different parts of the hands of the domestics employed in milking, and sometimes on the wrists, which quickly run on to suppuration, first assum-ing the appearance of the small vesications produced by a burn. Most com-monly they appear about the joints of the fingers and at their extremities; but whatever parts are affected, if the situation will admit, these superficial suppurations put on a circular form, with their edges more elevated than their centre, and of a colour distantly approaching to blue. Absorption takes place, and tumours appear in each axilla. The system becomes affected—the pulse is quickened; and shiverings, succeeded by heat, with general lassitude and pains about the loins and limbs, with vomiting, come on. The head is painful, and the patient is now and then even affected with delirium. These symptoms, varying in their degrees of violence, generally continue from one day to three or four, leaving ulcerated sores about the hands, which, from the sensibility of the parts, are very troublesome, and commonly heal slowly, frequently becoming phagedenic, like those from whence they sprung. The lips, nostrils, eyelids, and other parts of the body are sometimes affected with sores; but these evidently arise from their being heedlessly rubbed or scratched with the patient's infected fingers. No eruptions on the skin have followed the decline of the feverish symp-toms in any instance that has come to my inspection, one only excepted, and in this case a very few appeared on the arms: they were very minute, of a vivid red colour, and soon died away without advancing to matura-tion; so that I cannot determine whether they had any connection with the preceding symptoms.

Thus the disease makes its progress from the horse to the nipple of the cow, and from the cow to the human subject.

Morbid matter of various kinds, when absorbed into the system, may produce effects in some degree similar; but what renders the cow-pox virus so extremely singular is that the person who has been thus affected is forever after secure from the infection of the smallpox; neither exposure to the variolous effluvia, nor the insertion of the matter into the skin, producing this distemper.

In support of so extraordinary a fact, I shall lay before my reader a great number of instances.

Case I. Joseph Merret, now as under gardener to the Earl of Berkeley, lived as a servant with a farmer near this place in the year 1770, and occasionally assisted in milking his master's cows. Several horses belonging to the farm began to have sore heels, which Merret frequently attended. The cows soon became affected with the cow-pox, and soon after several sores appeared on his hands. Swellings and stiffness in each axilla followed, and he was so much indisposed for several days as to be incapable of pursuing his ordinary employment. Previously to the appearance of the distemper among the cows there was no fresh cow brought into the farm, nor any servant employed who was affected with the cow-pox.

In April, 1795, a general inoculation taking place here, Merret was inoculated with his family; so that a period of twenty-five years had elapsed from his having the cow-pox to this time. However, though the variolous matter was repeatedly inserted into his arm, I found it impracticable to infect him with it; an efflorescence only, taking on an erysipelatous look about the centre, appearing on the skin near the punctured parts. During the whole time that his family had the smallpox, one of whom had it very full, he remained in the house with them, but received no injury from exposure to the contagion.

It is necessary to observe that the utmost care was taken to ascertain, with the most scrupulous precision, that no one whose case is here adduced had gone through the smallpox previous to these attempts to produce that disease.

Had these experiments been conducted in a large city, or in a populous neighborhood, some doubts might have been entertained; but here, where population is thin, and where such an event as a person's having had the smallpox is always faithfully recorded, no risk of inaccuracy in this particular can arise.

Case II. Sarah Portlock, of this place, was infected with the cow-pox when a servant at a farmer's in the neighborhood, twenty-seven years ago.

In the year 1792, conceiving herself, from this circumstance, secure from the infection of the smallpox, she nursed one of her own children who had accidentally caught the disease, but no indisposition ensued. During the time she remained in the infected room, variolous matter was inserted into both her arms, but without any further effect than in the preceding case.

Case XVII. The more accurately to observe the progress of the infection I selected a healthy boy, about eight years old, for the purpose of inoculating for the cow-pox. The matter was taken from a sore on the hand of a dairymaid, who was infected by her master's cows, and it was inserted on the 14th day of May, 1796, into the arm of the boy by means of two superficial incisions, barely penetrating the cutis, each about an inch long.

On the seventh day he complained of uneasiness in the axilla and on the ninth he became a little chilly, lost his appetite, and had a slight headache. During the whole of this day he was perceptibly indisposed, and spent the night with some degree of restlessness, but on the day following he was perfectly well.

The appearance of the incisions in their progress to a state of maturation were much the same as when produced in a similar manner by variolous matter. The difference which I perceived was in the state of the limpid fluid arising from the action of the virus, which assumed rather a darker hue, and in that of the efflorescence spreading round the incisions, which had more of an erysipelatous look than we commonly perceive when variolous matter has been made use of in the same manner; but the whole died away (leaving on the inoculated parts scabs and subsequent eschars) without giving me or my patient the least trouble.

In order to ascertain whether the boy, after feeling so slight an affection of the system from the cow-pox virus, was secure from the contagion of the smallpox, he was inoculated the 1st of July following with variolous matter, immediately taken from a pustule. Several slight punctures and incisions were made on both his arms, and the matter was carefully inserted, but no disease followed. The same appearances were observable on the arms as we commonly see when a patient has had variolous matter applied, after having either the cow-pox or smallpox. Several months afterwards he was again inoculated with variolous matter, but no sensible effect was produced on the constitution.

After the many fruitless attempts to give the smallpox to those who had had the cow-pox, it did not appear necessary, nor was it convenient to me, to inoculate the whole of those who had been the subjects of these late trials; yet I thought it right to see the effects of variolous matter on some of them, particularly William Summers, the first of these patients who had been infected with matter taken from the cow. He was, therefore, inoculated from a fresh pustule; but, as in the preceding cases, the system did not feel the effects of it in the smallest degree. I had an opportunity also of having this boy and William Pead inoculated by my nephew, Mr. Henry Jenner, whose report to me is as follows: "I have inoculated Pead and Barge, two of the boys whom you lately infected with the cow-pox. On the second day the incisions were inflamed and there was a pale inflammatory stain around them. On the third day these appearances were still increasing and their arms itched considerably. On the fourth day the inflammation was evidently subsiding, and on the sixth day it was scarcely perceptible. No symptoms of indisposition followed.

"To convince myself that the variolous matter made use of was in a perfect state I at the same time inoculated a patient with some of it who never had gone through the cow-pox, and it produced the smallpox in the usual regular manner."

These experiments afforded me much satisfaction; they proved that the matter, in passing from one human subject to another, through five gradations, lost none of its original properties, J. Barge being the fifth who received the infection successively from William Summers, the boy to whom it was communicated from the cow. . . .

Although I presume it may not be necessary to produce further testimony in support of my assertion "that the cow-pox protects the human constitution from the infection of the smallpox," yet it affords me considerable satisfaction to say that Lord Somerville, the President of the Board of Agriculture, to whom this paper was shown by Sir Joseph Banks, has found upon inquiry that the statements were confirmed by the concurring testimony of Mr. Dolland, a surgeon, who resides in a dairy country remote from this, in which these observations were made. . . .

1798

The History of the Kine-pox, Commonly Called the Cow-pox

WITH AN ACCOUNT OF A SERIES OF INOCULATIONS PERFORMED FOR THE KINE-POX IN MASSACHUSETTS

BENJAMIN WATERHOUSE

***

CHAPTER I

IN THE BEGINNING OF THE YEAR 1799 I RECEIVED FROM my friend Dr. Lettsom of London, a copy of Dr. Edward Jenner's "Inquiry into the causes and effects of the variolae vaccinae, or Cow-pox"; a disease totally unknown in this quarter of the world. On perusing this work I was struck with the unspeakable advantages that might accrue to this, and indeed to the human race at large, from the discovery of a mild distemper that would ever after secure the constitution from that terrible scourge, the smallpox.

As the ordinary mode of communicating even medical discoveries in this country is by newspapers, I drew up the following account of the Cow-pox, which was printed in the Columbian Centinal March 12, 1799.

SOMETHING CURIOUS IN THE MEDICAL LINE

Everybody has heard of these distempers accompanied by pocks and pustules, called the small-pox, and chickenpox and the swinepox, but few have ever heard of the cow-pox, or if you like the term better, the cow small-pox; or to express it in technical language, the variolae vaccinae. There is however such a disease which has been noticed here and there in several parts of England, more particularly in Gloucestershire, for sixty or seventy years past, but has never been an object of medical inquiry until lately.

This variolae vaccinae is very readily communicated to those who milk cows infected with it. This malady appears on the teats of the cows. . . . Those who milk the cows thus affected, seldom or ever fail catching the distemper, *if there be cracks, wounds, or abrasions of the hands*. . . . But what makes this newly discovered disease so very curious, and so extremely important is that every person thus affected is EVER AFTER SECURED FROM THE ORDINARY SMALLPOX, *let him be ever so much exposed to the effluvian of it, or let ever so much ripe matter be inserted into the skin by inoculation.*

Dr. Edward Jenner is the physician in England who has collected and arranged a series of facts and experiments respecting the disease there called the Cow-pox.

CHAPTER II

Under the serious impression of effecting a public benefit, and conceiving it moreover a duty in my official situation in this University, I sent to England for some of the vaccine, or cow-pox matter for trial. After several fruitless attempts, I obtained some by a short passage from Bristol, and with it I inoculated all the younger part of my family.

The first of my children that I inoculated was a boy of five years old, named Daniel Oliver Waterhouse. I made a slight incision in the usual place for inoculation in the arm, inserted a small portion of the infected thread, and covered it with a sticking plaster. It exhibited no other appearances than what would have arisen from any other extraneous substance, until the sixth day when an increased redness called forth my attention. On the eighth day he complained of pain under the inoculated arm and on the ninth the inoculated part exhibited evident signs of virulency. By the tenth anyone much experienced in the inoculated small-pox would have pronounced the arm infected. The pain and swelling under his arm went on gradually encreasing and by the eleventh day from inoculation his febrile symptoms were pretty strongly marked. The sore in the arm proceeded exactly as Drs. Jenner and Woodville described, and appeared to the eye very like the second plate in Dr. Jenner's elegant publication.

The inoculated part in this boy was surrounded by an efflorescence which extended from his shoulder to his elbow, which made it necessary to apply some remedies to lessen it; but the "symptoms," as they are called, scarcely drew him from his play more than an hour or two; and he went through the disease in so light a manner as hardly even to express any marks of peevishness. A piece of true skin was fairly taken out of the arm by the virus, the part appearing as if eaten out by a caustick, a never failing sign of thorough section of the system by the inoculated small-pox.

Satisfied with the appearances and symptoms in this boy I inoculated another of three years of age with matter taken from his brother's arm, for he had no pustules on his body. He likewise went through the disease in a perfect and very satisfactory manner. The child pursued his amusements with as little interruption as his brother. Then I inoculated a servant boy of about 12 years of age, with some of the infected thread from England. His arm was pretty sore and his symptoms pretty severe. He treated himself rather harshly by exercising unnecessarily in the garden when the weather was extremely hot (Fahrt. Therm. 96 in the shade!) and then washing his head and upper parts of his body under the pump, and setting, in short, all rules at defiance in my absence. Nevertheless this boy went through the disorder without any other accident than a sore throat and a stiffness of the muscles of the neck. All which soon vanished by the help of a few remedies.

Being obliged to go from home a few days, I requested my colleague Dr. Warren to visit these children. Dr. Danforth as well as some other physicians, came to Boston out of curiosity, and so did several practitioners from the country. I mention this because it gave rise to a groundless report, that one of the children had so bad an arm that I thought it prudent to take the advice of some of my brethren upon it.

From a full matured pustule in my little boy three years old I inoculated his infant sister, already weaned, of one year. At the same time and from the same pustule, I inoculated its nursery maid. They both went through the disease with equal regularity. . . .

CHAPTER III

Having thus traced the most important facts respecting the causes and effects of the Kine-pox up to their source in England, and having confirmed most of them by actual experiment in America, one experiment only remained behind to complete the business. To effect this I wrote the following letter to Dr. Aspinwall, physician to the smallpox hospital in the neighborhood of Boston.

Cambridge, August 2, 1800

Dear Doctor:

You have doubtless heard of the newly discovered disorder, known in England by the name of cow-pox, which so nearly resembles the smallpox, that it is now agreed in Great Britain, that the former will pass for the latter.

I have procured some of the vaccine matter, and therewith inoculated seven of my family. The inoculation has proceeded in six of them exactly as described by Woodville and Jenner; but my desire is to confirm the doctrine by having some of them inoculated by you.

I can obtain variolous matter and inoculate them privately, but I wish to do it in the most open and public way possible. As I have imported a new distemper, I conceive that the public have a right to know exactly every step I take in it. I write this, then to enquire whether you will on philanthropic principles try the experiment of inoculating some of my children who have already undergone the cow-pox. If you accede to my proposal, I shall consider it as an experiment in which we have co-operated for the good of our fellow citizens, and relate it as such in the pamphlet I mean to publish on the subject.

I am, etc.

B. W.

Hon. William Aspinwall, Esq.
Brookline.

To this letter the doctor returned a polite answer, assuring me of his readiness to give any assistance in his power, to ascertain whether the cow-pox would prevent the small-pox; observing that he had at that time fresh matter that he could depend on, and desiring me to send the children to the hospital for that purpose. Of the three which I offered, the doctor chose to try the experiment on the boy of 12 years of age, whom he inoculated in my presence by two punctures, and with matter taken that moment from a patient who had it pretty full upon him. He at the same time inserted an infected thread and then put him into the hospital, where was one patient with it the natural way. On the fourth day, the doctor pronounced the arm to be infected. It became every hour sorer, but in a day or two it died off, and grew well, without producing the slightest trace of a disease; so that the boy was dismissed from the hospital and returned home the twelfth day after the experiment. One fact, in such cases, is worth a thousand arguments.

1800

Louis Pasteur and The Conquest of Rabies

RENÉ VALLERY-RADOT

From *The Life of Pasteur*

AMIDST THE VARIOUS RESEARCHES UNDERTAKEN IN his laboratory, one study was placed by Pasteur above every other, one mystery constantly haunted his mind—that of hydrophobia. When he was received at the Académie Française, Renan, hoping to prove himself a prophet for once, said to him: "Humanity will owe to you deliverance from a horrible disease and also from a sad anomaly: I mean the distrust which we cannot help mingling with the caresses of the animal in whom we see most of nature's smiling benevolence."

The two first mad dogs brought into the laboratory were given to Pasteur, in 1880, by M. Bourrel, an old army veterinary surgeon who had long been trying to find a remedy for hydrophobia. He had invented a preventive measure which consisted in filing down the teeth of dogs, so that they should not bite into the skin; in 1874, he had written that vivisection threw no light on that disease, the laws of which were "impenetrable to science until now." It now occurred to him that, perhaps, the investigators in the laboratory of the Ecole Normale might be more successful than he had been in his kennels in the Rue Fontaine-au-Roi.

One of the two dogs he sent was suffering from what is called *dumb madness:* his jaw hung, half opened and paralyzed, his tongue was covered with foam, and his eyes full of wistful anguish; the other made ferocious darts at anything held out to him, with a rabid fury in his bloodshot eyes, and, in the hallucinations of his delirium, gave vent to haunting, despairing howls.

Much confusion prevailed at that time regarding this disease, its seat, its causes, and its remedy. Three things seemed positive: firstly, that the rabic virus was contained in the saliva of the mad animals; secondly, that it was communicated through bites; and thirdly, that the period of incubation might vary from a few days to several months. Clinical observation

586

was reduced to complete impotence; perhaps experiments might throw some light on the subject. . . .

One day, Pasteur having wished to collect a little saliva from the jaws of a rabid dog, so as to obtain it directly, two of Bourrel's assistants undertook to drag a mad bulldog, foaming at the mouth, from its cage; they seized it by means of a lasso, and stretched it on a table. These two men, thus associated with Pasteur in the same danger, with the same calm heroism, held the struggling, ferocious animal down with their powerful hands, whilst the scientist drew, by means of a glass tube held between his lips, a few drops of the deadly saliva.

But the same uncertainty followed the inoculation of the saliva; the incubation was so slow that weeks and months often elapsed whilst the result of an experiment was being anxiously awaited. Evidently the saliva was not a sure agent for experiments, and if more knowledge was to be obtained, some other means had to be found of obtaining it.

Magendie and Renault had both tried experimenting with rabic blood, but with no results, and Paul Bert had been equally unsuccessful. Pasteur tried in his turn, but also in vain. "We must try other experiments," he said, with his usual indefatigable perseverance.

As the number of cases observed became larger, he felt a growing conviction that hydrophobia has its seat in the nervous system, and particularly in the medulla oblongata. "The propagation of the virus in a rabid dog's nervous system can almost be observed in its every stage," writes M. Roux, Pasteur's daily associate in these researches, which he afterwards made the subject of his thesis. "The anguish and fury due to the excitation of the grey cortex of the brain are followed by an alteration of the voice and a difficulty in deglutition. The medulla oblongata and the nerves starting from it are attacked in their turn; finally, the spinal cord itself becomes invaded and paralysis closes the scene."

As long as the virus has not reached the nervous centres, it may sojourn for weeks or months in some point of the body; this explains the slowness of certain incubations, and the fortunate escapes after some bites from rabid dogs. The *a priori* supposition that the virus attacks the nervous centres went very far back; it had served as a basis tc a theory enunciated by Dr. Duboué (of Pau), who had, however, not supported it by any experiments. On the contrary, when M. Galtier, a professor at the Lyons Veterinary School, had attempted experiments in that direction, he had to inform the Academy of Medicine, in January, 1881, that he had only ascertained the existence of virus in rabid dogs in the lingual glands and in the buccopharyngeal mucous membrane. "More than ten times, and always unsuccessfully, have I inoculated the product obtained by pressure of the cerebral substances of the cerebellum or of the medulla oblongata of rabid dogs."

Pasteur was about to prove that it was possible to succeed by operating in a special manner, according to a rigorous technique, unknown in other laboratories. When the post-mortem examination of a mad dog had revealed no characteristic lesion, the brain was uncovered, and the surface of the medulla oblongata scalded with a glass stick, so as to destroy any external dust or dirt. Then, with a long tube previously put through a flame, a particle of the substance was drawn and deposited in a glass just taken from a stove heated up to 200° C., and mixed with a little water or sterilized broth by means of a glass agitator, also previously put through a flame. The syringe used for inoculation on the rabbit or dog (lying ready on the operating board) had been purified in boiling water.

Most of the animals who received this inoculation under the skin succumbed to hydrophobia; that virulent matter was therefore more successful than the saliva, which was a great result obtained.

"The seat of the rabic virus," wrote Pasteur, "is therefore not in the saliva only: the brain contains it in a degree of virulence at least equal to that of the saliva of rabid animals." But, to Pasteur's eyes, this was but a preliminary step on the long road which stretched before him; it was necessary that all the inoculated animals should contract hydrophobia, and the period of incubation had to be shortened.

It was then that it occurred to Pasteur to inoculate the rabic virus directly on the surface of a dog's brain. He thought that, by placing the virus from the beginning in its true medium, hydrophobia would more surely supervene and the incubation might be shorter. The experiment was attempted: a dog under chloroform was fixed to the operating board, and a small, round portion of the cranium removed by means of a trephine (a surgical instrument somewhat similar to a fret-saw); the tough fibrous membrane called the dura-mater, being thus exposed, was then injected with a small quantity of the prepared virus, which lay in readiness in a Pravaz syringe. The wound was washed with carbolic and the skin stitched together, the whole thing lasting but a few minutes. The dog, on returning to consciousness, seemed quite the same as usual. But, after fourteen days, hydrophobia appeared: rabid fury, characteristic howls, the tearing up and devouring of his bed, delirious hallucination, and finally, paralysis and death.

A method was therefore found by which rabies was contracted surely and swiftly. Trephinings were again performed on chloroformed animals —Pasteur had a great horror of useless sufferings, and always insisted on anæsthesia. In every case, characteristic hydrophobia occurred after inoculation on the brain. The main lines of this complicated question were beginning to be traceable; but other obstacles were in the way. Pasteur could not apply the method he had hitherto used, *i.e.* to isolate, and then to cultivate in an artificial medium, the microbe of hydrophobia, for he failed in detecting this microbe. Yet its existence admitted of no doubt; perhaps it was beyond the limits of human sight. "Since this unknown being is living," thought Pasteur, "we must cultivate it; failing an artificial medium, let us try the brain of living rabbits; it would indeed be an experimental feat!"

As soon as a trephined and inoculated rabbit died paralyzed, a little of his rabic medulla was inoculated to another; each inoculation succeeded another, and the time of incubation became shorter and shorter, until, after a hundred uninterrupted inoculations, it came to be reduced to seven days. But the virus, having reached this degree, the virulence of which was found to be greater than that of the virus of dogs made rabid by an accidental bite, now became fixed; Pasteur had mastered it. He could now predict the exact time when death should occur in each of the inoculated animals; his predictions were verified with surprising accuracy.

Pasteur was not yet satisfied with the immense progress marked by infallible inoculation and the shortened incubation; he now wished to decrease the degrees of virulence—when the attenuation of the virus was once conquered, it might be hoped that dogs could be made refractory to rabies. Pasteur abstracted a fragment of the medulla from a rabbit which had just died of rabies after an inoculation of the fixed virus; this fragment was suspended by a thread in a sterilized phial, the air in which was kept dry by some pieces of caustic potash lying at the bottom of the vessel and which was closed by a cotton-wool plug to prevent the entrance of atmospheric dusts. The temperature of the room where this desiccation took place was maintained at 23° C. As the medulla gradually became dry, its virulence decreased, until, at the end of fourteen days, it had become absolutely extinguished. This now inactive medulla was crushed and mixed with pure water, and injected under the skin of some dogs. The next day they were inoculated with medulla which had been desiccating for thirteen days, and so on, using increased virulence until the medulla was used of a rabbit dead the same day. These dogs might now be bitten by rabid dogs given them as companions for a few minutes, or submitted to the intracranial inoculations of the deadly virus: they resisted both.

Having at last obtained this refractory condition, Pasteur was anxious that his results should be verified by a Commission. The Minister of Public Instruction acceded to this desire, and a Commission was constituted in May, 1884, composed of Messrs. Béclard, Dean of the Faculty of Med icine, Paul Bert, Bouley, Villemin, Vulpian, and Tisserand, Director of the Agricultural Office. The Commission immediately set to work; a rabid dog having succumbed at Alfort on June 1, its carcase was brought to the laboratory of the Ecole Normale, and a fragment of the medulla oblongata was mixed with some sterilized broth. Two dogs, declared by Pasteur to be refractory to rabies, were trephined, and a few drops of the liquid injected into their brains; two other dogs and two rabbits received inoculations at the same time, with the same liquid and in precisely the same manner.

Bouley was taking notes for a report to be presented to the Minister:

"M. Pasteur tells us that, considering the nature of the rabic virus used, the rabbits and the two new dogs will develop rabies within twelve or fifteen days, and that the two refractory dogs will not develop it at all, however long they may be detained under observation."

On May 29, Mme. Pasteur wrote to her children:

"The Commission on rabies met to-day and elected M. Bouley as chairman. Nothing is settled as to commencing experiments. Your father is absorbed in his thoughts, talks little, sleeps little, rises at dawn, and, in one word, continues the life I began with him this day thirty-five years ago."

On June 3, Bourrel sent word that he had a rabid dog in the kennels of the Rue Fontaine-au-Roi; a refractory dog and a new dog were immediately submitted to numerous bites; the latter was violently bitten on the head in several places. The rabid dog, still living the next day and still able to bite, was given two more dogs, one of which was refractory; this dog, and the refractory dog bitten on the 3rd, were allowed to receive the first bites, the Commission having thought that perhaps the saliva might then be more abundant and more dangerous.

On June 6, the rabid dog having died, the Commission proceeded to inoculate the medulla of the animal into six more dogs, by means of trephining. Three of those dogs were refractory; the three others were fresh from the kennels; there were also two rabbits.

On the 10th, Bourrel telegraphed the arrival of another rabid dog, and the same operations were gone through.

"This rabid, furious dog," wrote Pasteur to his son-in-law, "had spent the night lying on his master's bed; his appearance had been suspicious for a day or two. On the morning of the 10th, his voice became rabietic, and his master, who had heard the bark of a rabid dog twenty years ago, was seized with terror, and brought the dog to M. Bourrel, who found that he was indeed in the biting stage of rabies. Fortunately a lingering fidelity had prevented him from attacking his master. . . .

"This morning the rabic condition is beginning to appear on one of the new dogs trephined on June 1, at the same time as two refractory dogs. Let us hope that the other new dog will also develop it and that the two refractory ones will resist."

At the same time that the Commission examined this dog which developed rabies within the exact time indicated by Pasteur, the two rabbits on whom inoculation had been performed at the same time were found to present the first symptoms of rabic paralysis. "This paralysis," noted Bouley, "is revealed by great weakness of the limbs, particularly of the hind quarters; the least shock knocks them over and they experience great difficulty in getting up again." The second new dog on whom inoculation had been performed on June 1 was now also rabid; the refractory dogs were in perfect health. . . .

Bouley's report was sent to the Minister of Public Instruction at the beginning of August. "We submit to you to-day," he wrote, "this report on the first series of experiments that we have just witnessed, in order that M. Pasteur may refer to it in the paper which he proposes to read at the Copenhagen International Scientific Congress on these magnificent results, which devolve so much credit on French Science and which give it a fresh claim to the world's gratitude."

The Commission wished that a large kennel yard might be built, in order that the duration of immunity in protected dogs might be timed, and that other great problem solved, viz., whether it would be possible, through the inoculation of attenuated virus, to defy the virus from bites.

By the Minister's request, the Commission investigated the Meudon woods in search of a favourable site; an excellent place was found in the lower part of the Park, away from dwelling houses, easy to enclose and presumably in no one's way. But, when the inhabitants of Meudon heard of this project, they protested vehemently, evidently terrified at the thought of rabid dogs, however securely bound, in their peaceful neighbourhood.

Another piece of ground was then suggested to Pasteur, near St. Cloud, in the Park of Villeneuve l'Etang. Originally a State domain, this property had been put up for sale, but had found no buyer, not being suitable for parcelling out in small lots; the Bill was withdrawn which allowed of its sale and the greater part of the domain was devoted by the Ministry to Pasteur's and his assistants' experiments on the prophylaxis of contagious diseases. . . .

. . . Pasteur pondered on the means of extinguishing hydrophobia or of merely diminishing its frequency. Could dogs be vaccinated? There are 100,000 dogs in Paris, about 2,500,000 more in the provinces: vaccination necessitates several preventive inoculations; innumerable kennels would have to be built for the purpose, to say nothing of the expense of keeping the dogs and of providing a trained staff capable of performing the difficult and dangerous operations. And, as M. Nocard truly remarked, where were rabbits to be found in sufficient number for the vaccine emulsions?

Optional vaccination did not seem more practicable; it could only be worked on a very restricted scale and was therefore of very little use in a general way.

The main question was the possibility of preventing hydrophobia from occurring in a human being, previously bitten by a rabid dog. . . .

The successful opposition of the inhabitants of Meudon had inspired those of St. Cloud, Ville d'Avray, Vaucresson, Marnes, and Garches with the idea of resisting in their turn the installation of Pasteur's kennels at Villeneuve l'Etang. People spoke of public danger, of children exposed to meet ferocious rabid dogs wandering loose about the park, of popular Sundays spoilt, picnickers disturbed, etc., etc. . . .

Little by little, in spite of the opposition which burst out now and again, calm was again re-established. French good sense and appreciation of great things got the better of the struggle; in January, 1885, Pasteur was able to go to Villeneuve l'Etang to superintend the arrangements. The old stables were turned into an immense kennel, paved with asphalt. A wide passage went from one end to the other, on each side of which accommodation for sixty dogs was arranged behind a double barrier of wire netting.

The subject of hydrophobia goes back to the remotest antiquity; one of Homer's warriors calls Hector a mad dog. The supposed allusions to it to be found in Hippocrates are of the vaguest, but Aristotle is quite explicit when speaking of canine rabies and of its transmission from one animal to the other through bites. He gives expression, however, to the singular opinion that man is not subject to it. More than three hundred years later we come to Celsus, who describes this disease, unknown or unnoticed until then. "The patient," said Celsus, "is tortured at the same time by thirst and by an invincible repulsion towards water." He counselled cauterization of the wound with a red-hot iron and also with various caustics and corrosives.

Pliny the Elder, a worthy precursor of village quacks, recommended the livers of mad dogs as a cure; it was not a successful one. Galen, who opposed this, had a no less singular recipe, a compound of cray-fish eyes. Later, the shrine of St. Hubert in Belgium was credited with miraculous cures; this superstition is still extant.

Sea bathing, unknown in France until the reign of Louis XIV, became a fashionable cure for hydrophobia, Dieppe sands being supposed to offer wonderful curing properties.

In 1780 a prize was offered for the best method of treating hydrophobia, and won by a pamphlet entitled *Dissertation sur la Rage*, written by a surgeon-major of the name of Le Roux.

This very sensible treatise concluded by recommending cauterization, now long forgotten, instead of the various quack remedies which had so long been in vogue, and the use of butter of antimony.

Le Roux did not allude in his paper to certain tenacious and cruel prejudices, which had caused several hydrophobic persons, or persons merely suspected of hydrophobia, to be killed like wild beasts, shot, poisoned, strangled, or suffocated.

It was supposed in some places that hydrophobia could be transmitted through the mere contact of the saliva or even by the breath of the victims; people who had been bitten were in terror of what might be done to them. A girl, bitten by a mad dog and taken to the Hôtel Dieu Hospital on May 8, 1780, begged that she might not be suffocated!

Those dreadful occurrences must have been only too frequent, for, in 1810, a philosopher asked the Government to enact a Bill in the following terms: "It is forbidden, under pain of death, to strangle, suffocate, bleed to death, or in any other way murder individuals suffering from rabies, hydrophobia, or any disease causing fits, convulsions, furious and dangerous madness; all necessary precautions against them being taken by families or public authorities."

In 1819, newspapers related the death of an unfortunate hydrophobe, smothered between two mattresses; it was said à propos of this murder that "it is the doctor's duty to repeat that this disease cannot be transmitted from man to man, and that there is therefore no danger in nursing hydrophobia patients." Though old and fantastic remedies were still in vogue in remote country places, cauterization was the most frequently employed; if the wounds were somewhat deep, it was recommended to use long, sharp and pointed needles, and to push them well in, even if the wound was on the face.

One of Pasteur's childish recollections (it happened in October, 1831) was the impression of terror produced throughout the Jura by the advent of a rabid wolf who went biting men and beasts on his way. Pasteur had seen an Arboisian of the name of Nicole being cauterized with a red-hot iron at the smithy near his father's house. The persons who had been bitten on the hands and head succumbed to hydrophobia, some of them amidst horrible sufferings; there were eight victims in the immediate neighbourhood. Nicole was saved. For years the whole region remained in dread of that mad wolf. . . .

As to the origin of rabies, it remained unknown and was erroneously attributed to divers causes. Spontaneity was still believed in. Bouley himself did not absolutely reject the idea of it, for he said in 1870: "In the immense majority of cases, this disease proceeds from contagion; out of 1,000 rabid dogs, 999 at least owe their condition to inoculation by a bite."

Pasteur was anxious to uproot this fallacy, as also another very serious error, vigorously opposed by Bouley, by M. Nocard, and by another veterinary surgeon in a *Manual on Rabies*, published in 1882, and still as tenacious as most prejudices, viz., that the word hydrophobia is synonymous with rabies. The rabid dog is *not* hydrophobe, he does *not* abhor water. The word is applicable to rabid human beings, but is false concerning rabid dogs.

Many people in the country, constantly seeing Pasteur's name associated with the word rabies, fancied that he was a consulting veterinary surgeon, and pestered him with letters full of questions. What was to be done to a dog whose manner seemed strange, though there was no evidence of a suspicious bite? Should he be shot? "No," answered Pasteur, "shut him up securely, and he will soon die if he is really mad." Some dog owners hesitated to destroy a dog manifestly bitten by a mad dog. "It is such a good dog!" "The law is absolute," answered Pasteur; "every dog bitten by a mad dog must be destroyed at once." And it irritated him that village mayors should close their eyes to the non-observance of the law, and thus contribute to a recrudescence of rabies.

Pasteur wasted his precious time answering all those letters. On March 28, 1885, he wrote to his friend Jules Vercel—

"Alas! we shall not be able to go to Arbois for Easter; I shall be busy for some time settling down, or rather settling my dogs down at Villeneuve l'Etang. I also have some new experiments on rabies on hand which will take some months. I am demonstrating this year that dogs can be vaccinated, or made refractory to rabies *after* they have been bitten by mad dogs.

"I have not yet dared to treat human beings after bites from rabid dogs; but the time is not far off, and I am much inclined to begin by myself—inoculating myself with rabies, and then arresting the consequences; for I am beginning to feel very sure of my results.". . .

In May, everything at Villeneuve l'Etang was ready for the reception of sixty dogs. Fifty of them, already made refractory to bites or rabic inoculation, were successively accommodated in the immense kennel, where each had his cell and his experiment number. They had been made refractory by being inoculated with fragments of medulla, which had hung for a fortnight in a phial, and of which the virulence was extinguished, after which further inoculations had been made, gradually increasing in virulence until the highest degree of it had again been reached.

All those dogs, which were to be periodically taken back to Paris for inoculations or bite tests, in order to see what was the duration of the immunity conferred, were stray dogs picked up by the police. They were of various breeds, and showed every variety of character, some of them gentle and affectionate, others vicious and growling, some confiding, some shrinking, as if the recollection of chloroform and the laboratory was disagreeable to them. They showed some natural impatience of their enforced captivity, only interrupted by a short daily run. One of them, however, was promoted to the post of house-dog, and loosened every night; he excited much envy among his congeners. The dogs were very well cared for by a retired *gendarme*, an excellent man of the name of Pernin.

A lover of animals might have drawn an interesting contrast between the fate of those laboratory dogs, living and dying for the good of humanity, and that of the dogs buried in the neighbouring dogs' cemetery at Bagatelle, founded by Sir Richard Wallace, the great English philanthropist. Here lay toy dogs, lap dogs, drawing-room dogs, cherished and coddled during their useless lives, and luxuriously buried after their useless deaths, while the dead bodies of the others went to the knacker's yard.

Rabbit hutches and guinea-pig cages leaned against the dogs' palace. Pasteur, having seen to the comfort of his animals, now thought of himself; it was frequently necessary that he should come to spend two or three days at Villeneuve l'Etang. The official architect thought of repairing part of the little palace of Villeneuve, which was in a very bad state of decay. But Pasteur preferred to have some rooms near the stables put into repair, which had formerly been used for non-commissioned officers of the Cent Gardes; there was less to do to them, and the position was convenient. The roof, windows, and doors were renovated, and some cheap paper hung on the walls inside. "This is certainly not luxurious!" exclaimed an astonished millionaire, who came to see Pasteur one dav on his way to his own splendid villa at Marly.

On May 29 Pasteur wrote to his son—

"I thought I should have done with rabies by the end of April; I must postpone my hopes till the end of July. Yet I have not remained stationary; but, in these difficult studies, one is far from the goal as long as the last word, the last decisive proof is not acquired. What I aspire to is the possibility of treating a man after a bite with no fear of accidents.

"I have never had so many subjects of experiments on hand—sixty dogs at Villeneuve l'Etang, forty at Rollin, ten at Frégis', fifteen at Bourrel's, and I deplore having no more kennels at my disposal.

"What do you say of the Rue Pasteur in the large city of Lille? The news has given me very great pleasure."

What Pasteur briefly called "Rollin" in this letter was the former *Lycée Rollin*, the old buildings of which had been transformed into outhouses for his laboratory. Large cages had been set up in the old courtyard, and the place was like a farm, with its population of hens, rabbits, and guinea-pigs.

Two series of experiments were being carried out on those 125 dogs. The first consisted in making dogs refractory to rabies by preventive inoculations; the second in preventing the onset of rabies in dogs bitten or subjected to inoculation. . . .

On Monday, July 6, Pasteur saw a little Alsatian boy, Joseph Meister, enter his laboratory, accompanied by his mother. He was only nine years old, and had been bitten two days before by a mad dog at Meissengott, near Schlestadt.

The child, going alone to school by a little by-road, had been attacked by a furious dog and thrown to the ground. Too small to defend himself, he had only thought of covering his face with his hands. A bricklayer, seeing the scene from a distance, arrived, and succeeded in beating the dog off with an iron bar; he picked up the boy, covered with blood and saliva. The dog went back to his master, Théodore Vone, a grocer at Meissengott, whom he bit on the arm. Vone seized a gun and shot the animal, whose stomach was found to be full of hay, straw, pieces of wood, etc. When little Meister's parents heard all these details they went, full of anxiety, to consult Dr. Weber, at Villé, that same evening. After cauterizing the wounds with carbolic, Dr. Weber advised Mme. Meister to start for Paris, where she could relate the facts to one who was not a physician, but who would be the best judge of what could be done in such a serious case. Théodore Vone, anxious on his own and on the child's account, decided to come also.

Pasteur reassured him; his clothes had wiped off the dog's saliva, and his shirt-sleeve was intact. He might safely go back to Alsace, and he promptly did so.

Pasteur's emotion was great at the sight of the fourteen wounds of the little boy, who suffered so much that he could hardly walk. What should he do for this child? could he risk the preventive treatment which had been constantly successful on his dogs? Pasteur was divided between his hopes and his scruples, painful in their acuteness. Before deciding on a course of action, he made arrangements for the comfort of this poor woman and her child, alone in Paris, and gave them an appointment for 5 o'clock, after the Institute meeting. He did not wish to attempt anything without having seen Vulpian and talked it over with him. Since the Rabies Commission had been constituted, Pasteur had formed a growing esteem for the great judgment of Vulpian, who, in his lectures on the general and comparative physiology of the nervous system, had already mentioned the profit to human clinics to be drawn from experimenting on animals.

His was a most prudent mind, always seeing all the aspects of a problem. The man was worthy of the scientist: he was absolutely straightforward, and of a discreet and active kindness. He was passionately fond of work, and had recourse to it when smitten by a deep sorrow.

Vulpian expressed the opinion that Pasteur's experiments on dogs were sufficiently conclusive to authorize him to foresee the same success in human pathology. Why not try this treatment? added the professor, usually so reserved. Was there any other efficacious treatment against hydrophobia? If at least the cauterizations had been made with a red-hot iron! but what was the good of carbolic acid twelve hours after the accident. If the almost certain danger which threatened the boy were weighed against the chances of snatching him from death, Pasteur would see that it was more than a right, that it was a duty to apply antirabic inoculation to little Meister.

This was also the opinion of Dr. Grancher, whom Pasteur consulted. M. Grancher worked at the laboratory; he and Dr. Straus might claim to be the two first French physicians who took up the study of bacteriology; these novel studies fascinated him, and he was drawn to Pasteur by the deepest admiration and by a strong affection, which Pasteur thoroughly reciprocated.

Vulpian and M. Grancher examined little Meister in the evening, and, seeing the number of bites, some of which, on one hand especially, were very deep, they decided on performing the first inoculation immediately; the substance chosen was fourteen days old and had quite lost its virulence: it was to be followed by further inoculations gradually increasing in strength.

It was a very slight operation, a mere injection into the side (by means of a Pravaz syringe) of a few drops of a liquid prepared with some fragments of medulla oblongata. The child, who cried very much before the operation, soon dried his tears when he found the slight prick was all that he had to undergo.

Pasteur had had a bedroom comfortably arranged for the mother and child in the old Rollin College, and the little boy was very happy amidst the various animals—chickens, rabbits, white mice, guinea-pigs, etc.; he begged and easily obtained of Pasteur the life of several of the youngest of them.

"All is going well," Pasteur wrote to his son-in-law on July 11: "the child sleeps well, has a good appetite, and the inoculated matter is absorbed into the system from one day to another without leaving a trace. It is true that I have not yet come to the test inoculations, which will take place on Tuesday, Wednesday and Thursday. If the lad keeps well during the three following weeks, I think the experiment will be safe to succeed. I shall send the child and his mother back to Meissengott (near Schlestadt) in any case on August 1, giving these good people detailed instruction as to the observations they are to record for me. I shall make no statement before the end of the vacation."

But, as the inoculations were becoming more virulent, Pasteur became a prey to anxiety: "My dear children," wrote Mme. Pasteur, "your father has had another bad night; he is dreading the last inoculations on the child. And yet there can be no drawing back now! The boy continues in perfect health."

Renewed hopes were expressed in the following letter from Pasteur—

My dear René, I think great things are coming to pass. Joseph Meister has just left the laboratory. The three last inoculations have left some pink marks under the skin, gradually widening and not at all tender. There is some action, which is becoming more intense as we approach the final inoculation, which will take place on Thursday, July 16. The lad is very well this morning, and has slept well, though slightly restless; he has a good appetite and no feverishness. He had a slight hysterical attack yesterday.

The letter ended with an affectionate invitation. "Perhaps one of the great medical facts of the century is going to take place; you would regret not having seen it!"

Pasteur was going through a succession of hopes, fears, anguish, and an ardent yearning to snatch little Meister from death; he could no longer work. At nights, feverish visions came to him of this child whom he had seen playing in the garden, suffocating in the mad struggles of hydrophobia, like the dying child he had seen at the Hôpital Trousseau in 1880. Vainly his experimental genius assured him that the virus of that most terrible of diseases was about to be vanquished, that humanity was about to be delivered from this dread horror—his human tenderness was stronger than all, his accustomed ready sympathy for the sufferings and anxieties of others was for the nonce centered in "the dear lad."

The treatment lasted ten days; Meister was inoculated twelve times.

The virulence of the medulla used was tested by trephinings on rabbits, and proved to be gradually stronger. Pasteur even inoculated on July 16, at 11 A.M., some medulla only one day old, bound to give hydrophobia to rabbits after only seven days' incubation; it was the surest test of the immunity and preservation due to the treatment.

Cured from his wounds, delighted with all he saw, gaily running about as if he had been in his own Alsatian farm, little Meister, whose blue eyes now showed neither fear nor shyness, merrily received the last inoculation; in the evening, after claiming a kiss from "Dear Monsieur Pasteur," as he called him, he went to bed and slept peacefully. Pasteur spent a terrible night of insomnia; in those slow dark hours of night when all vision is distorted, Pasteur, losing sight of the accumulation of experiments which guaranteed his success, imagined that the little boy would die.

The treatment being now completed, Pasteur left little Meister to the care of Dr. Grancher (the lad was not to return to Alsace until July 27) and consented to take a few days' rest. He spent them with his daughter in a quiet, almost deserted country place in Burgundy, but without however finding much restfulness in the beautiful peaceful scenery; he lived in constant expectation of Dr. Grancher's daily telegram or letter containing news of Joseph Meister.

By the time he went to the Jura, Pasteur's fears had almost disappeared. He wrote from Arbois to his son August 3, 1885: "Very good news last night of the bitten lad. I am looking forward with great hopes to the time when I can draw a conclusion. It will be thirty-one days to-morrow since he was bitten."

. . . On his return to Paris, Pasteur found himself obliged to hasten the organization of a "service" for the preventive treatment of hydrophobia after a bite. The Mayor of Villers-Farlay, in the Jura, wrote to him that, on October 14, a shepherd had been cruelly bitten by a rabid dog.

Six little shepherd boys were watching over their sheep in a meadow; suddenly they saw a large dog passing along the road, with hanging, foaming jaws.

"A mad dog!" they exclaimed. The dog, seeing the children, left the road and charged them; they ran away shrieking, but the eldest of them, J. B. Jupille, fourteen years of age, bravely turned back in order to protect the flight of his comrades. Armed with his whip, he confronted the infuriated animal, who flew at him and seized his left hand. Jupille, wrestling with the dog, succeeded in kneeling on him, and forcing his jaws open in order to disengage his left hand; in so doing, his right hand was seriously bitten in its turn; finally, having been able to get hold of the animal by the neck, Jupille called to his little brother to pick up his whip which had fallen during the struggle, and securely fastened the dog's jaws with the lash. He then took his wooden *sabot*, with which he battered the dog's head, after which, in order to be sure that it could do no further harm, he dragged the body down to a little stream in the meadow, and held the head under water for several minutes. Death being now certain, and all danger removed from his comrades, Jupille returned to Villers-Farlay.

Whilst the boy's wounds were being bandaged, the dog's carcase was fetched, and a necropsy took place the next day. The two veterinary surgeons who examined the body had not the slightest hesitation in declaring that the dog was rabid.

The Mayor of Villers-Farlay, who had been to see Pasteur during the summer, wrote to tell him that this lad would die a victim of his own courage unless the new treatment intervened. The answer came immediately: Pasteur declared that, after five years' study, he had succeeded in making dogs refractory to rabies, even six or eight days after being bitten; that, he had only once yet applied his method to a human being, but that once with success, in the case of little Meister, and that, if Jupille's family consented, the boy might be sent to him. "I shall keep him near me in a room of my laboratory; he will be watched and need not go to bed; he will merely receive a daily prick, not more painful than a pin-prick."

The family, on hearing this letter, came to an immediate decision; but, between the day when he was bitten and Jupille's arrival in Paris, six whole days had elapsed, whilst in Meister's case there had only been two and a half!

Yet, however great were Pasteur's fears for the life of this tall lad, who seemed quite surprised when congratulated on his courageous conduct, they were not what they had been in the first instance—he felt much greater confidence.

A few days later, on October 26, Pasteur in a statement at the Academy of Sciences described the treatment followed for Meister. Three months and three days had passed, and the child remained perfectly well. Then he spoke of his new attempt. Vulpian rose—

"The Academy will not be surprised," he said, "if, as a member of the Medical and Surgical Section, I ask to be allowed to express the feelings of admiration inspired in me by M. Pasteur's statement. I feel certain that those feelings will be shared by the whole of the medical profession.

"Hydrophobia, that dread disease against which all therapeutic measures had hitherto failed, has at last found a remedy. M. Pasteur, who has been preceded by no one in this path, has been led by a series of investigations unceasingly carried on for several years, to create a method of treatment, by means of which the development of hydrophobia can *infallibly* be prevented in a patient recently bitten by a rabid dog. I say infallibly, because, after what I have seen in M. Pasteur's laboratory, I do not doubt the constant success of this treatment when it is put into full practice a few days only after a rabic bite.". . .

Bouley, then chairman of the Academy, rose to speak in his turn—

"We are entitled to say that the date of the present meeting will remain for ever memorable in the history of medicine, and glorious for French science; for it is that of one of the greatest steps ever accomplished in the medical order of things—a progress realized by the discovery of an efficacious means of preventive treatment for a disease, the incurable nature of which was a legacy handed down by one century to another. From this day, humanity is armed with a means of fighting the fatal disease of hydrophobia and of preventing its onset. It is to M. Pasteur that we owe this, and we could not feel too much admiration or too much gratitude for the efforts on his part which have led to such a magnificent result. . . ."

As soon as Pasteur's paper was published, people bitten by rabid dogs began to arrive from all sides to the laboratory. The "service" of hydrophobia became the chief business of the day. Every morning was spent by Eugène Viala in preparing the fragments of marrow used for inoculations: in a little room permanently kept at a temperature of 20° to 23° C., stood rows of sterilized flasks, their tubular openings closed by plugs of cotton wool. Each flask contained a rabic marrow, hanging from the stopper by a thread and gradually drying up by the action of some fragments of caustic potash lying at the bottom of the flask. Viala cut those marrows into small pieces by means of scissors previously put through a flame, and placed them in small sterilized glasses; he then added a few drops of veal broth and pounded the mixture with a glass rod. The vaccinal liquid was now ready; each glass was covered with a paper cover, and bore the date of the medulla used, the earliest of which was fourteen days old. For each patient under the treatment from a certain date, there was a whole series of little glasses. . . . The date and circumstances of the bites and the veterinary surgeon's certificate were entered in a register, and the patients were divided into series according to the degree of virulence which was to be inoculated on each day of the period of treatment.

Pasteur took a personal interest in each of his patients, helping those who were poor and illiterate to find suitable lodgings in the great capital. Children especially inspired him with a loving solicitude. But his pity was mingled with terror, when, on November 9, a little girl of ten was brought to him who had been severely bitten on the head by a mountain dog, on

October 3, thirty-seven days before! The wound was still suppurating. He said to himself, "This is a hopeless case: hydrophobia is no doubt about to appear immediately; it is much too late for the preventive treatment to have the least chance of success. Should I not, in the scientific interest of the method, refuse to treat this child? If the issue is fatal, all those who have already been treated will be frightened, and many bitten persons, discouraged from coming to the laboratory, may succumb to the disease!" These thoughts rapidly crossed Pasteur's mind. But he found himself unable to resist his compassion for the father and mother, begging him to try and save their child.

After the treatment was over, Louise Pelletier had returned to school, when fits of breathlessness appeared, soon followed by convulsive spasms; she could swallow nothing. Pasteur hastened to her side when these symptoms began, and new inoculations were attempted. On December 2, there was a respite of a few hours, moments of calm which inspired Pasteur with the vain hope that she might yet be saved. This delusion was a short-lived one. Pasteur spent the day by little Louise's bedside, in her parents' rooms in the Rue Dauphine. He could not tear himself away; she herself, full of affection for him, gasped out a desire that he should not go away, that he should stay with her! She felt for his hand between two spasms. Pasteur shared the grief of the father and mother. When all hope had to be abandoned: "I did so wish I could have saved your little one!" he said. And as he came down the staircase, he burst into tears.

He was obliged, a few days later, to preside at the reception of Joseph Bertrand at the Académie Française; his sad feelings little in harmony with the occasion. He read in a mournful and troubled voice the speech he had prepared during his peaceful and happy holidays at Arbois. Henry Houssaye, reporting on this ceremony in the *Journal des Débats*, wrote, "M. Pasteur ended his speech amidst a torrent of applause, he received a veritable ovation. He seemed unaccountably moved. How can M. Pasteur, who has received every mark of admiration, every supreme honour, whose name is consecrated by universal renown, still be touched by anything save the discoveries of his powerful genius?" People did not realize that Pasteur's thoughts were far away from himself and from his brilliant discovery. He was thinking of the child he had been unable to snatch from the jaws of death; his mind was not with the living, but with the dead.

A telegram from New York having announced that four children, bitten by rabid dogs, were starting for Paris, many adversaries who had heard of Louise Pelletier's death were saying triumphantly that, if those children's parents had known of her fate, they would have spared them so long and useless a journey.

The four little Americans belonged to workmen's families and were sent to Paris by means of a public subscription opened in the columns of the *New York Herald*; they were accompanied by a doctor and by the mother of the youngest of them, a boy only five years old. After the first inoculation, this little boy, astonished at the insignificant prick, could not help saying, "Is this all we have come such a long journey for?" The children were received with enthusiasm on their return to New York, and were asked "many questions about the great man who had taken such care of them."

A letter dated from that time (January 14, 1886) shows that Pasteur yet found time for kindness, in the midst of his world-famed occupations.

"My dear Jupille, I have received your letters, and I am much pleased with the news you give me of your health. Mme. Pasteur thanks you for remembering her. She, and every one at the laboratory, join with me in wishing that you may keep well and improve as much as possible in reading, writing and arithmetic. Your writing is already much better than it was, but you should take some pains with your spelling. Where do you go to school? Who teaches you? Do you work at home as much as you might? You know that Joseph Meister, who was first to be vaccinated, often writes to me; well, I think he is improving more quickly than you are, though he is only ten years old. So, mind you take pains, do not waste your time with other boys, and listen to the advice of your teachers, and of your father and mother. Remember me to M. Perrot, the Mayor of Villers-Farlay. Perhaps, without him, you would have become ill, and to be ill of hydrophobia means inevitable death; therefore you owe him much gratitude. Good-bye. Keep well."

Pasteur's solicitude did not confine itself to his two first patients, Joseph Meister and the fearless Jupille, but was extended to all those who had come under his care; his kindness was like a living flame. The very little ones who then only saw in him a "kind gentleman" bending over them understood later in life, when recalling the sweet smile lighting up his serious face, that Science, thus understood, unites moral with intellectual grandeur.

Edition of 1920

Chemotherapy

ALEXANDER FLEMING

SCIENTIFIC CHEMOTHERAPY DATES FROM EHRLICH and scientific chemotherapy of a bacterial disease from Ehrlich's Salvarsan, which in 1910 revolutionized the treatment of syphilis. The story of Salvarsan has often been told, and I need not go further into it except to say that it was the first real success in the chemotherapeutic treatment of a bacterial disease. Ehrlich originally aimed at "Therapia magna sterilisans," which can be explained as a blitz sufficient to destroy at once all the infecting microbes. This idea was not quite realized, and now the treatment of syphilis with arsenical preparations is a long-drawn-out affair. But it was extraordinarily successful treatment, and stimulated work on further chemotherapeutic drugs. While they had success in some parasitic diseases the ordinary bacteria which infect us were still unaffected.

It was in 1932 that a sulfonamide of the dye chrysoidine was prepared, and in 1935 Domagk showed that this compound (Prontosil) had a curative action on mice infected with streptococci. It was only in 1936, however, that its extraordinary clinical action in streptococcal septicaemia in man was brought out. Thus just ten years ago and twenty-six years after Ehrlich had made history by producing Salvarsan, the medical world woke up to find another drug which controlled a bacterial disease. Not a venereal disease this time, but a common septic infection which unfortunately not infrequently supervened in one of the necessary events of life—childbirth.

Before the announcement of the merits of the drug Prontosil, the industrialists concerned had perfected their preparations and patents. Fortunately for the world, however, Téfouel and his colleagues in Paris soon showed that Prontosil acted by being broken up in the body with the liberation of sulfanilamide, and this simple drug, on which there were no patents, would do all that Prontosil could do. Sulfanilamide affected streptococcal, gonococcal and meningococcal infections as well as B. coli infections in the urinary tract, but it was too weak to deal with infections due to organisms like pneumococci and staphylococci.

Two years later Ewins produced sulfapyridine—another drug of the same series—and Whitby showed that this was powerful enough to deal with pneumococcal infections. This again created a great stir, for pneumonia is a condition which may come to every home.

The hunt was now on and chemists everywhere were preparing new sulfonamides—sulfathiazole appeared, which was still more powerful on streptococci and pneumococci than its predecessors, and which could clinically affect generalized staphylococcal infections.

Since then we have had sulfadiazine, sulfamerazine, sulfamethazine and others. But of these we need not go into detail, so much has already been written about them. Meantime there had appeared other sulfonamide compounds, such as sulfaguanidine, which were not absorbed from the alimentary tract, and these were used for the treatment of intestinal infections like dysentery.

The sulfonamides were very convenient for practice, in that they could be taken by the mouth. The drug was absorbed into the blood, where it appeared in concentration more than was necessary to inhibit the growth of sensitive bacteria. From the blood it could pass with ease into the spinal fluid, so it was eminently suited for the treatment of cerebrospinal infections. The sulfonamides were excreted in high concentration in the urine, so that although they were unable to control generalized infections with coliform bacilli they rapidly eliminated similar infections of the urinary tract. In contrast to the older antiseptics they had practically no toxic action on the leucocytes. There were disadvantages in that they were not without toxicity to the patient. . . .

Soon after the sulfonamides came into practice, also, it was discovered that some strains of what were generally sensitive microbes were resistant to their action. The result of widespread treatment was that the sensitive strains were largely displaced by insensitive strains. This was especially noticeable in gonococcal infections, and after a few years something like half of the gonococcal infections were sulfonamide insensitive.

This could be due to one of two things; the sensitive organisms might have been eliminated by treatment with the drug, while the insensitive ones persisted and were passed on from one individual to another; or that by insufficient treatment with the drug a sensitive microbe might have acquired a resistance or "fastness" to the drug.

It is not difficult in the laboratory to make sensitive bacteria resistant to the sulfonamides, but this is not peculiar to the sulfonamides. There is probably no chemotherapeutic drug to which in suitable circumstances the bacteria cannot react by in some way acquiring "fastness."

In the first year of the war the sulfonamides had the field of chemotherapy of septic infections to themselves, but there were always the drawbacks I have mentioned. Later another type of sulfonamide, "Marfanil," was introduced in Germany which for systemic administration had relatively little potency, but which was not inhibited by pus or the usual sulfonamide inhibitors. This was largely used in Germany throughout the war, but there is no doubt that their methods of dealing with sepsis were far behind ours.

The sulfonamides did not directly kill the organisms—they stopped their growth, and the natural protective mechanisms of the body had to complete their destruction. This explained why in some cases of rather long-continued streptococcal septicaemia sulfanilamide failed to save the patient, although the *Streptococcus* was fully sensitive to the drug; the protective mechanism of the body—the opsonic power and phagocytes —had become worn out and failed.

Fildes introduced a most attractive theory of the action of chemotherapeutic drugs. It was that these drugs had a chemical structure so similar to an "essential metabolite" of the sensitive organism that it deluded the organism into the belief that it was the essential metabolite. The organism therefore took it up, and then its receptors became filled with the drug so that it was unable to take up the essential metabolite which was necessary for its growth. Thus it was prevented from growing and died or was an easy prey for the body cells. This theory had been supported by many experimental facts and may give a most profitable guide to future advances in chemotherapy.

But another completely different type of chemotherapeutic drug appeared, namely, penicillin. This actually was described years before the sulfonamides appeared, but it was only concentrated sufficiently for practical chemotherapeutic use in 1940.

The story of penicillin has often been told in the last few years. How, in 1928, a mold spore contaminating one of my culture plates at St. Mary's Hospital produced an effect which called for investigation; how I found that this mold—a *Penicillium*—made in its growth a diffusible and very selective antibacterial agent which I christened Penicillin; how this substance, unlike the older antiseptics, killed the bacteria but it was nontoxic to animals or to human leucocytes; how I failed to concentrate this substance from lack of sufficient chemical assistance, so that it was only ten years afterwards, when chemotherapy of septic infections was a predominant thought in the physician's mind, that Florey and his colleagues at Oxford embarked on a study of antibiotic substances, and succeeded in concentrating penicillin and showing its wonderful therapeutic properties; how this happened at a critical stage of the war, and how they took their information to America and induced the authorities there to produce penicillin on a large scale; how the Americans improved methods of production so that on D-day there was enough penicillin for every wounded man who needed it, and how this result was obtained by the closest co-operation between governments, industrialists, scientists and workmen on both sides of the Atlantic without thought of patents or other restrictive measures. Everyone had a near relative in the fighting line and there was the urge to help him, so progress and production went on at an unprecedented pace.

Penicillin is the most powerful chemotherapeutic drug yet introduced. Even when it is diluted 80,000,000 times it will still inhibit the growth of *Staphylococcus*. This is a formidable dilution, but the figure conveys little except a series of many naughts. Suppose we translate it into something concrete. If a drop of water is diluted 80,000,000 times it would fill over 6,000 whisky bottles.

We have already seen that all the older antiseptics were more toxic to leucocytes than to bacteria. The sulfonamides were much more toxic to bacteria than to leucocytes, but they had some poisonous action on the whole human organism. Here in penicillin we had a substance extremely toxic to some bacteria but almost completely nontoxic to man. And it not only stopped the growth of the bacteria, it killed them, so it was effective even if the natural protective mechanism of the body was deficient. It was effective, too, in pus and in the presence of other substances which inhibited sulfonamide activity.

Penicillin has proved itself in war casualties and in a great variety of the ordinary civil illnesses, but it is specific, and there are many common infections on which it has no effect. Perhaps the most striking results have been in venereal disease. Gonococcal infections are eradicated with a single injection and syphilis in most cases by a treatment of under ten days. Subacute bacterial endocarditis, too, was a disease which until recently was almost invariably fatal. Now with penicillin treatment there are something like 70 per cent recoveries.

So far in this country penicillin has been under strict control, but soon it will be on sale in the chemists' shops. It is to be hoped that it will not be abused as were the sulfonamides. It is the only chemotherapeutic drug which has no toxic properties—in the ordinary sense of the word it is almost impossible to give an overdose—so there is no medical reason for underdosage. It is the administration of too small doses which leads to the production of resistant strains of bacteria, so the rule in penicillin treatment should be to give enough. If more than enough is given there is no harm to the patient but merely a little waste—but that is not serious when there is a plentiful supply.

But I am not giving you a discourse on penicillin. Suffice it to say that it has made medicine and surgery easier in many directions, and in the near future its merits will be proved in veterinary medicine and possibly in horticulture.

The spectacular success of penicillin has stimulated the most intensive research into other antibiotics in the hope of finding something as good or even better.

GRAMICIDIN AND TYROTHRICIN

But even before penicillin was publicized another antibiotic had been introduced by Dubos in 1939. This was a substance made by the *Bacillus brevis*, which had a very powerful inhibitory action on the Gram-positive bacteria. This substance was originally named gramicidin, but later the name was changed to tyrothricin, when it was found to be a mixture of two antibiotic substances—true gramicidin and tyrocidin. Gramicidin has proved to be a very useful local application to infected areas. It has an inhibitory power on bacteria far in excess of its antileucocytic power, but unfortunately it is toxic when injected, so that it cannot be used for systemic treatment. If penicillin had not appeared it is likely that gramicidin or tyrothricin would have been much more extensively used, but penicillin, which is quite nontoxic, can be used either locally or systemically for almost every condition which would be benefited by gramicidin.

STREPTOMYCIN

Waksman in 1943 described this antibiotic, which is produced by *Streptomyces griseus*. This substance has very little toxicity and has a powerful action on many of the Gram-negative organisms. It has been used in tularaemia, undulant fever, typhoid fever, and *B. coli* infections, but the greatest interest has been in its action on the tubercle bacillus. *In vitro* it has a very powerful inhibitory action on this bacillus, and in guinea pigs it has been shown to have a definite curative action. In man, however, the clinical results have not been entirely successful, but in streptomycin we have a chemical which does have *in vivo* a definite action on the tubercle bacillus and which is relatively nontoxic. This is a great advance and may lead to startling results. One possible drawback may be that bacilli appear to acquire rapidly a fastness to streptomycin, much more rapidly than they do to penicillin or even the sulfonamides.

Many other antibiotics have been described in the last five years. Most of them are too toxic for use, but there are some which so far have promise in preliminary experiments. Whether they are going to be valuable chemotherapeutic agents belongs to the future.

TOMORROW

Let us now consider the future. There are now certain definite lines on which research is proceeding in antibacterial chemotherapy.

Fildes's theory of the action of chemotherapeutic drugs has already led to certain results—not sufficiently powerful to have made wonderful advances in practical therapeutics—but the work goes on, and from it at any time some new antibacterial chemical combination may emerge. All this is dependent on further fundamental research on the essential metabolites necessary for the growth of different bacteria.

Bacteriologists and mycologists are, by more or less established methods, investigating all sorts of molds and bacteria to see if they produce antibiotic substances. The chemist concentrates or purifies the active substance, and then the experimental pathologist tests the concentrate for activity and toxicity. There are teams of workers who are thus investigating every bacillus and every mold in the collections which exist in various countries. This is useful team work and may lead to something of practical importance, but it is reminiscent of the momentous German researches lacking in inspiration but which by sheer mass of labor bear some fruit. . . .

It seems likely that in the next few years a combination of antibiotics with different antibacterial spectra will furnish a "cribrum therapeuticum" from which fewer and fewer infecting bacteria will escape.

Then the work on antibiotics has led to the discovery of many new chemical combinations possessing antibacterial power. Most of the antibiotics have certain disadvantages—many of them are too toxic—but it may not be beyond the powers of the organic chemists to alter the formula in such a way that the antibiotic power is retained, but the toxic power reduced to such an extent that these substances can be used therapeutically. . . .

As to chemotherapeutic research in general, I would like to conclude with a quotation from Mervyn Gordon: "No research is ever quite complete. It is the glory of a good bit of work that it opens the way for something still better, and this rapidly leads to its own eclipse. The object of research is the advancement, not of the investigator, but of knowledge."

1946

The New Science of Surgery

FRANK G. SLAUGHTER

———

RECENTLY A SURGEON PUT A PATCH ON THE HEART. A few months later the Surgeon General of the United States Army announced that more than 96 per cent of the wounded who reached medical care in World War II lived.

Both these events were "firsts," for never before had an operation of this type been done, never before had such life-saving results been obtained in treating those wounded in battle. Surgery lists a progression of "firsts" in recent years. First operation for cancer of the pancreas. First removal of an entire lung for malignant disease. First operation upon the great blood vessels that spring from the heart, setting distorted blood channels right. First cure of hypertension by removing two insignificant strands of nerve tissue from the back. These "firsts" aren't just casual occurrences, they are inevitable offspring of a brilliant marriage, the union of science and surgery.

But what has science to do with surgery? Surgery means trained fingers, shining instruments, an amphitheater tense with the drama of life and death, the hush that falls over the audience as the surgeon's hands, trained hands in smooth white rubber gloves, lift the scalpel, and, balancing life and death between long, skilled fingers, make the quick ruthless cut that brings away a malignant tumor, then suture up spurting blood vessels.

Yes, surgery is all this. Without the skill of the surgeon's fingers, there would be no surgery, no lives saved. But without science there would be no way for that skill to operate.

Take, for example, the operation upon the heart. It began with a coronary attack, the sudden blocking of one of the heart's own blood vessels. Such attacks not infrequently come to those who work under a great deal of stress, people whose coronary arteries are in a continual state

of tension from the barrage of nerve impulses that govern the size of
the intricate net of arteries and veins all over the body which doctors
call the "vascular bed." Sometimes there are warning signs, pain in the
chest and left arm, discomfort in the upper abdomen often mistaken for
gall bladder disease. The attack is sudden and sharp, the pain lancinating,
the collapse profound and complete, a dramatic and terrifying thing to
watch. Often the victim dies on the spot. Old-time doctors used to call
it "acute indigestion," and it was common talk that one did not survive
a third attack. Modern heart specialists know that the time element was
right, if the reasoning was wrong. Few patients do survive a third coronary attack.

The original blocking of the coronary artery by spasm and clot is only
the beginning of a series of events which may follow a severe coronary
attack. Slowly, over a period of weeks, there develops an area of heart
muscle which has been weakened by damage to its blood supply. The
muscle fibers may grow thin, fray out, the wall gradually yields to a
pressure of blood surging against it at each heart beat. Looking at such
a heart in a fluoroscope, the specialist sees a localized bulging of the
heart wall in the injured area, thrusting out with each contraction of the
heart itself. Then one day the wall ruptures and all is over.

For years heart specialists looked at such bulging heart walls, the
"aneurysms of the heart" which sometimes occurred after coronary damage. There was nothing to be done, they knew. Surgeons couldn't graft
a new heart wall, and nothing short of that would strengthen the weak
area.

Then one day a surgeon watched just such a case under the fluoroscope.
The story was the same, a coronary attack, severe, the patient barely pulling through it. And then an "aneurysm of the heart." But this time there
was a difference. The surgeon was a specialist in heart surgery, a man
who thought in terms of using the scalpel to help injured and diseased
hearts. He had already devised an operation which promised much as
a new source of blood supply to damaged hearts.

To this surgeon the bulging, weakened heart posed a problem—not in
how long the patient would live, or how best to break the news to the
family, but whether or not it would be possible to splint that damaged
muscle and protect the weakened spot. He thought something could be
done, felt confident enough to attempt the operation, and, most important of all, possessed the necessary skill and was backed up by the same
scientific knowledge and discovery which made possible the ninety-six
per cent figure in saving wounded men.

The operation succeeded. A patch of tough fascia was successfully placed over a bulging, paper-thin aneurysm of the heart wall. The patient lived five weeks and died of a coincident infection, but the heart patch held firmly and did not give away. Dr. Claude Beck of Cleveland, Ohio, achieved the distinction of another "first" in surgery, first to operate and place a patch on the heart. . . .

Advances in surgical knowledge and skill are continually pushing back the frontiers which have from time to time seemed definitely to bar all further surgical progress. One such frontier remains, one which to this time has steadily resisted all battering by surgical experimenters, all devices of ingenious surgical techniques which have made it possible to operate in places which seemed anatomically impossible to reach before. This, to date, uncrossed barrier is the interior of the heart itself, the delicate valves inside it which are so often attacked by the infections of rheumatic fever, syphilis, bacterial endocarditis, and other infections. But even in this restricted field, surgeons have come a long way, as witness the feat of putting a patch on the heart. If they haven't been able to operate successfully inside the heart itself, except in an occasional case which does not establish a precedent upon which to work, surgeons have learned a lot about the heart, about how it works, and in some cases have been able to accomplish a great deal by changing, surgically, other conditions of the circulation which affect the heart.

Generally, a few years after surgeons really decide to tackle a formidable barrier to surgical progress, they surmount all its difficulties. As a result, hundreds of people every year are saved months of misery and pain and the knowledge of a hopeless cancer gnawing unrestrained at their vital organs. Always in the great medical schools, the efficient clinics scattered over the country, research is going forward for new ways to fight disease, new ways to circumvent death. . . .

When surgeons began to look to the last remaining frontier, the heart, they found a lot of the preliminary work already accomplished. Tackling the heart surgically means opening the chest. Positive pressure anesthesia made long operations in the open chest possible.

One drawback to operations on the circulation is clotting, called a thrombosis, wherever a blood vessel is damaged by whatever agent, a bullet or a surgeon's knife. Thrombosis tends to close up the vessel at this point. Worse still, pieces of it break off and travel in the blood stream causing often fatal emboli to the lungs and brain.

That problem was solved with heparin, the clot-preventing substance. Isolated chemically and now prepared for medical use it can be injected into the circulation in intermittent or continuous doses. There it decreases the clotting power of the blood to a remarkable degree, preventing the formation of thrombi where blood vessels are connected together by surgical operation, or where a great artery is opened to remove the clot which may suddenly shut off the circulation of an entire leg of a heart patient. It was a wonderful discovery, one destined to revolutionize the lusty science of blood vessel surgery.

As if heparin weren't enough of an accomplishment, along came another group of scientists, studying the peculiar disease animals got after eating large quantities of sweet clover, in which they hemorrhaged into their own tissues and body cavities and died. This group reasoned that there was in this sweet clover a substance which acted like heparin, but unlike heparin, could be eaten and still do its work. Eat heparin and the stomach digests it immediately, ending its clot-preventing power. But the clover substance withstands digestive action, as witness the fact that it works after being eaten in clover by the animal. From these researches came *dicoumarin* which does the same thing as heparin and can be taken by mouth, as you'd take an aspirin or a dose of soda.

Meanwhile other surgeons had already tackled the heart itself. They hadn't done it as a matter of election. They'd done it as an emergency, to save lives. For civilians don't wait for wars to carry on their own little private conflicts. Some sections of the country are worse than others, of course, and stabbing between the ribs with long slender knives is a fairly common practice in some areas. Usually this habit doesn't produce very bad results. The knife goes into the lung, there is an escape of air and blood into the chest, the collapse of the lung by the air stops the bleeding and escape of air, the patient has a little shortness of breath for a day or so, and maybe a little fever, the whole thing is absorbed, and nothing happens. Every surgeon in a large city hospital has seen dozens, even hundreds of such cases.

But every now and then the wound moves closer to the center of the chest and then there is real trouble. This time the knife, sometimes a bullet, enters the heart itself and blood spurts through the opening with each beat of the heart. Usually the hemorrhage doesn't appear through the wound that enters the skin, for like the wound in the lung, the chest muscles tend to close the opening. What happens is that blood pours out into the tough bag called the "pericardium" which surrounds the heart. As it fills the bag, something has to give way. Usually it is the thing that can least afford to be disturbed in its function, the heart itself. Pressure of blood in the pericardium gradually limits the space in which the heart can beat.

Doctors call this process cardiac tamponade, which means simply an increasing pressure upon the heart by the blood it is pumping out through the opening in its own wall. Tamponade is an emergency that calls for immediate action, or death will ensue at once. Rarely will such an injury occur in a place where the patient can be rushed immediately to an operating room set up and ready for a heart operation. There has to be a period of getting the patient to the hospital, making the diagnosis, and getting him to the operating room. In that time he may very well die unless the emergency is realized and tackled courageously at once.

Staffs of great city hospitals are trained in this matter of heart wounds, trained to recognize from the thready or absent pulse, the distant heart sounds in the stethoscope, the absence of heart movements when the chest is examined with the fluoroscope, the picture of cardiac tamponade. And they get to work at once, with a needle and a syringe, to remove from the pericardium some of the blood pressing on the heart. Meanwhile an emergency operating room is prepared and the anesthetic begun.

The rest is simple. There is nothing particularly difficult about sewing up a heart wound. The most important work has probably been done by the resident or intern who had the sense to shove a needle in and remove the blood from the pericardium. It's easy then to remove a couple of rib ends from the front of the chest wall and expose the heart itself. A suture is usually put through the tip of the heart, the apex, and used as a guy while the wound itself is closed with a few quick strands of silk. There usually isn't much difficulty in this, either, for the heart is thick and muscular, and the stitches hold well. With the wound closed and escape of blood controlled, the operation is over. It's as simple as that and consumes perhaps three-quarters of an hour. No longer is the suture of a heart wound a surgical miracle, to be reported with great éclat in medical journals and newspapers. Surgeons in Richmond, New Orleans, Atlanta, and many other large cities now have long series of successful heart wound operations to their credit.

When war came along the ground work in treating this most dangerous of all injuries had already been done. War wounds of the heart do not often come to treatment in even the front line hospitals, unfortunately. Bullet and shrapnel wounds of this area are much more likely to be fatal than the knife wounds of civilian combat, but if they do reach the operating rooms, the surgical principles for handling them are clear. Every war surgeon is familiar with them, and can put them into application at once. Many lives were saved because of that knowledge.

But the spearheads which have been driven into the wall of this last frontier of heart surgery are only the beginning. Take for example the problem of pericarditis. In some diseases such as severe pneumonia, rheumatic infection, or almost any severe infection produced by the streptococcus, the sac surrounding the heart may become infected also, usually by way of the blood stream in which we now know bacteria travel in large numbers during almost any severe disease caused by micro-organisms. The tough pericardial sac fills up with pus and the effect is very much the same as if it were filled with blood. Pressure interferes with the heart action.

Surgeons have long known that in pericarditis cases they can make a small window through the lower front portion of the chest and allow this pus to drain out, relieving the pressure and allowing the heart room to work. Irrigations, too, can be carried out through this window, decreasing the likelihood of adhesions between the pericardium and the heart, which may later interfere with the operation of that vital blood pump.

A less conspicuous, more chronic inflammation of the pericardium leaves it thick, and tough, sometimes plastered tightly around the heart itself. This chronic form of pericarditis gradually constricts the action of the heart until the circulation can no longer be kept up properly, and the patient begins to show definite signs that the blood isn't being pumped efficiently. These signs are fluid in the abdomen, conspicuous dilation of veins of the skin, signs of oxygen-lack, moisture in the lungs—all evidence of impending fatal heart failure.

Surgeons long ago began to study these cases, many of them children doomed to an early death unless the condition were relieved. They used their trained senses to tell them what had happened, but they didn't stop at that. It wasn't right to subject a patient to an operation of such magnitude unless you could be sure of what had happened. So they took advantage of a peculiarity of the heart. Move around, turn from one side to another and the normal heart moves also, shifts slightly in position. Here take an electrocardiogram—the electric heart picture that tells exactly what is going on in the muscle of the heart itself—and the picture is slightly different in each position. Cardiologists call that a shift of the "electrical axis" of the heart. Such a shift is normal.

With a heart sealed into position by a chronically inflamed, leathery pericardium, a heart so small and contracted that it is unable any longer to do its work efficiently, there is a different picture. The heart can't shift with movement, so the electrocardiogram is the same in all positions, because the electrical axis of the heart can't move. That's the clinc..ing fact in this diagnosis of "chronic constrictive pericarditis."

Once the diagnosis is established the surgeon can tackle the problem with certainty. He makes an incision through the chest, exposing the heart, and goes about the business of removing the whole front portion of the leathery pericardium, sometimes he even has to separate it from the surface of the heart itself. But he keeps on until the heart is free to expand and beat normally. After this operation, a dramatic thing happens. The heart can do its work so the shortness of breath disappears, the color returns to normal, the fluid in the body cavities is absorbed, and the veins lose their distended appearance.

Still another wedge was driven into the frontier of heart surgery when surgeons first had the courage to tackle a strange sort of condition that sometimes happens in children. This is an abnormality which the doctors call a "patent ductus arteriosus."

To understand this one it is necessary to go far back into the development of a child, back into its mother's womb. Here the developing child, of course, has no need for its lungs, since it does not breathe. The lungs are collapsed, and oxygen comes directly to the child from its mother's blood stream. But the child's circulation is functioning, in fact it begins to work while the embryo is little more than a ball-shaped mass of developing cells.

Since blood does not need to go through the child's lungs so long as it is not breathing, nature builds a by-pass between the pulmonary artery from the right side of the heart and the aorta from the left side, so that blood goes directly into the aorta and the general circulation of the body, without going through the lungs. This little by-pass, situated just above the heart between the great arteries going to the lungs and the main blood channel of the aorta, is called the "ductus arteriosus." Normally it closes off as soon as the child is born and begins to breathe for himself, for new blood must go through the lungs and no by-pass is needed.

In a few cases the closing off does not occur and a child is left with an opening between the lung artery and the aorta. The whole circulation is thus thrown out of order. About one out of every four of these children will not live beyond adolescence unless something is done. Most frequent complication of "patent ductus arteriosus" is streptococcic infection of the heart valves called subacute bacterial endocarditis, a condition ordinarily always fatal, but now apparently for the first time controlled by penicillin. But the point is that generally nothing can cure it in one of these cases in which blood rushes through the circulatory by-pass with each beat of the heart, that is so long as the ductus arteriosus remains open.

Surgeons thought a long time before they tackled this problem. The technical difficulties of working between the aorta, the heart, and the lung arteries, when a slip of an instrument meant an uncontrollable hemorrhage from one of them, was enough to frighten the stoutest hearted. But one thing will push surgeons to attempt operations fraught with the greatest hazard, the sight of children doomed to death by one of this group of disturbances called congenital anomalies. To save those children they will try even the apparently impossible.

So skillful surgeons opened the chest in these children, slit the pleura over the great pulsing vessels, located the ductus arteriosus, hardly half an inch in length, and tied it off with heavy strands of silk. Then they cut it in two and to make certain that there would be no bleeding, sewed the ends up carefully. Some cases didn't come through it, that was inevitable. A thing like this can succeed only in a matter of percentages —but the other side is all black, so no matter what the mortality, the surgeon is still ahead with those he saves.

It was a marvelously delicate operation, a great demonstration of surgical skill and technique. And the results were even more startling. Freed of the by-pass, patients threw off their heart infection, and played like normal children.

Even more recent and more dramatic is the work of Dr. Alfred Blalock and his associates at Johns Hopkins with other abnormalities of the heart. Circulation blocks, product of faulty development of the child, often interfere with proper flow of oxygen to the body itself. By a new technique Johns Hopkins surgeons have connected the great arteries and veins around the heart by new channels, called anastomoses, shunting the blood again properly to the lungs and insuring an adequate supply of vital oxygen.

To the older heart sufferer, too, has come a ray of hope for his heart damaged by hardening of the heart arteries themselves. Dr. Beck of Cleveland, the same surgeon who put a patch on the heart, devised, several years ago, an operation which attaches a stalk of muscle from the chest wall to the surface of the heart, bringing new blood vessels to supply a critical need.

It is not unreasonable to believe that soon science and surgery, working together, will find a way to search out the innermost secrets of the heart, operating upon the valves themselves, the site of our most often fatal forms of heart disease.

1946

D. MAN'S MIND

Thinking

JAMES HARVEY ROBINSON

From *The Mind in the Making*

ON VARIOUS KINDS OF THINKING

THE TRUEST AND MOST PROFOUND OBSERVATIONS ON Intelligence have in the past been made by the poets and, in recent times, by story-writers. They have been keen observers and recorders and reckoned freely with the emotions and sentiments. Most philosophers, on the other hand, have exhibited a grotesque ignorance of man's life and have built up systems that are elaborate and imposing, but quite unrelated to actual human affairs. They have almost consistently neglected the actual process of thought and have set the mind off as something apart to be studied by itself. *But no such mind, exempt from bodily processes, animal impulses, savage traditions, infantile impressions, conventional reactions, and traditional knowledge, ever existed,* even in the case of the most abstract of metaphysicians. Kant entitled his great work *A Critique of Pure Reason.* But to the modern student of mind pure reason seems as mythical as the pure gold, transparent as glass, with which the celestial city is paved.

Formerly philosophers thought of mind as having to do exclusively with conscious thought. It was that within man which perceived, remembered, judged, reasoned, understood, believed, willed. But of late it has been shown that we are unaware of a great part of what we perceive, remember, will, and infer; and that a great part of the thinking of which we are aware is determined by that of which we are not conscious. It has indeed been demonstrated that our unconscious psychic life far outruns our conscious. This seems perfectly natural to anyone who considers the following facts:

The sharp distinction between the mind and the body is, as we shall find, a very ancient and spontaneous uncritical savage prepossession. What we think of as "mind" is so intimately associated with what we call "body" that we are coming to realize that the one cannot be understood without the other. Every thought reverberates through the body, and, on the other hand, alterations in our physical condition affect our whole attitude of mind. The insufficient elimination of the foul and decaying products of digestion may plunge us into deep melancholy, where as a few whiffs of nitrous monoxide may exalt us to the seventh heaven of supernal knowledge and godlike complacency. And *vice versa,* a sudden word or thought may cause our heart to jump, check our breathing, or make our knees as water. There is a whole new literature growing up which studies the effects of our bodily secretions and our muscular tensions and their relation to our emotions and our thinking.

Then there are hidden impulses and desires and secret longings of which we can only with the greatest difficulty take account. They influence our conscious thought in the most bewildering fashion. Many of these unconscious influences appear to originate in our very early years. The older philosophers seem to have forgotten that even they were infants and children at their most impressionable age and never could by any possibility get over it.

The term "unconscious," now so familiar to all readers of modern works on psychology, gives offense to some adherents of the past. There should, however, be no special mystery about it. It is not a new animistic abstraction, but simply a collective word to include all the physiological changes which escape our notice, all the forgotten experiences and impressions of the past which continue to influence our desires and reflections and conduct, even if we cannot remember them. What we can remember at any time is indeed an infinitesimal part of what has happened to us. We could not remember anything unless we forgot almost everything. As Bergson says, the brain is the organ of forgetfulness as well as of memory. Moreover, we tend, of course, to become oblivious to things to which we are thoroughly accustomed, for habit blinds us to their existence. So the forgotten and the habitual make up a great part of the so-called "unconscious." . . .

We do not think enough about thinking, and much of our confusion is the result of current illusions in regard to it. Let us forget for the moment any impressions we may have derived from the philosophers, and see what seems to happen in ourselves. The first thing that we notice is that our thought moves with such incredible rapidity that it is almost impossible to arrest any specimen of it long enough to have a look at it. When we are offered a penny for our thoughts we always find that we have recently had so many things in mind that we can easily make a selection which will not compromise us too nakedly. On inspection we shall find that even if we are not downright ashamed of a great part of our spontaneous thinking it is far too intimate, personal, ignoble or trivial to permit us to reveal more than a small part of it. I believe this must be true of everyone. We do not, of course, know what goes on in other people's heads. They tell us very little and we tell them very little. The spigot of speech, rarely fully opened, could never emit more than driblets of the ever renewed hogshead of thought—*noch grösser wie's Heidelberger Fass*. We find it hard to believe that other people's thoughts are as silly as our own, but they probably are.

We all appear to ourselves to be thinking all the time during our waking hours, and most of us are aware that we go on thinking while we are asleep, even more foolishly than when awake. When uninterrupted by some practical issue we are engaged in what is now known as a *reverie*. This is our spontaneous and favorite kind of thinking. We allow our ideas to take their own course and this course is determined by our hopes and fears, our spontaneous desires, their fulfillment or frustration; by our likes and dislikes, our loves and hates and resentments. There is nothing else anything like so interesting to ourselves as ourselves. All thought that is not more or less laboriously controlled and directed will inevitably circle about the beloved Ego. It is amusing and pathetic to observe this tendency in ourselves and in others. We learn politely and generously to overlook this truth, but if we dare to think of it, it blazes forth like the noontide sun.

The reverie or "free association of ideas" has of late become the subject of scientific research. While investigators are not yet agreed on the results, or at least on the proper interpretation to be given to them, there can be no doubt that our reveries form the chief index to our fundamental character. They are a reflection of our nature as modified by often hidden and forgotten experiences. We need not go into the matter further here, for it is only necessary to observe that the reverie is at all times a potent and in many cases an omnipotent rival to every other kind of thinking. It doubtless influences all our speculations in its persistent tendency to self-magnification and self-justification, which are its chief preoccupations, but it is the last thing to make directly or indirectly for honest increase of knowledge. Philosophers usually talk as if such thinking did not exist or were in some way negligible. This is what makes their speculations so unreal and often worthless.

The reverie, as any of us can see for himself, is frequently broken and interrupted by the necessity of a second kind of thinking. We have to

make practical decisions. Shall we write a letter or no? Shall we take the
subway or a bus? Shall we have dinner at seven or half past? Shall we
buy U. S. Rubber or a Government bond? Decisions are easily distinguishable from the free flow of the reverie. Sometimes they demand a good
deal of careful pondering and the recollection of pertinent facts; often,
however, they are made impulsively. They are a more difficult and laborious thing than the reverie, and we resent having to "make up our mind"
when we are tired, or absorbed in a congenial reverie. Weighing a decision, it should be noted, does not necessarily add anything to our knowledge, although we may, of course, seek further information before making it.

RATIONALIZING

A third kind of thinking is stimulated when anyone questions our
belief and opinions. We sometimes find ourselves changing our minds
without any resistance or heavy emotion, but if we are told that we are
wrong we resent the imputation and harden our hearts. We are incredibly
heedless in the formation of our beliefs, but find ourselves filled with an
illicit passion for them when anyone proposes to rob us of their com-
panionship. It is obviously not the ideas themselves that are dear to us,
but our self-esteem, which is threatened. We are by nature stubbornly
pledged to defend our own from attack, whether it be our person, our
family, our property, or our opinion. A United States Senator once
remarked to a friend of mine that God Almighty could not make him
change his mind on our Latin-American policy. We may surrender, but
rarely confess ourselves vanquished. In the intellectual world at least
peace is without victory.

Few of us take the pains to study the origin of our cherished convictions; indeed, we have a natural repugnance to so doing. We like to
continue to believe what we have been accustomed to accept as true, and
the resentment aroused when doubt is cast upon any of our assumptions
leads us to seek every manner of excuse for clinging to them. *The result
is that most of our so-called reasoning consists in finding arguments for
going on believing as we already do.*

I remember years ago attending a public dinner to which the Governor
of the state was bidden. The chairman explained that His Excellency
could not be present for certain "good" reasons; what the "real" reasons
were the presiding officer said he would leave us to conjecture. This
distinction between "good" and "real" reasons is one of the most clarifying
and essential in the whole realm of thought. We can readily give what
seem to us "good" reasons for being a Catholic or a Mason, a Republican

or a Democrat. But the "real" reasons are usually on quite a different plane. Of course the importance of this distinction is popularly, if somewhat obscurely, recognized. The Baptist missionary is ready enough to see that the Buddhist is not such because his doctrines would bear careful inspection, but because he happened to be born in a Buddhist family in Tokio. But it would be treason to his faith to acknowledge that his own partiality for certain doctrines is due to the fact that his mother was a member of the First Baptist Church of Oak Ridge. A savage can give all sorts of reasons for his belief that it is dangerous to step on a man's shadow, and a newspaper editor can advance plenty of arguments against the Reds. But neither of them may realize why he happens to be defending his particular opinion.

The "real" reasons for our beliefs are concealed from ourselves as well as from others. As we grow up we simply adopt the ideas presented to us in regard to such matters as religion, family relations, property, business, our country, and the state. We unconsciously absorb them from our environment. They are persistently whispered in our ear by the group in which we happen to live. Moreover, as Mr. Trotter has pointed out [in *Instincts of the Herd*] these judgments, being the product of suggestion and not of reasoning, have the quality of perfect obviousness, so that to question them

. . . is to the believer to carry skepticism to an insane degree, and will be met by contempt, disapproval, or condemnation, according to the nature of the belief in question. When, therefore, we find ourselves entertaining an opinion about the basis of which there is a quality of feeling which tells us that to inquire into it would be absurd, obviously unnecessary, unprofitable, undesirable, bad form, or wicked, we may know that that opinion is a nonrational one, and probably, therefore, founded upon inadequate evidence.

Opinions, on the other hand, which are the result of experience or of honest reasoning do not have this quality of "primary certitude." I remember when as a youth I heard a group of business men discussing the question of the immortality of the soul, I was outraged by the sentiment of doubt expressed by one of the party. As I look back now I see that I had at the time no interest in the matter, and certainly no least argument to urge in favor of the belief in which I had been reared. But neither my personal indifference to the issue, nor the fact that I had previously given it no attention, served to prevent an angry resentment when I heard *my* ideas questioned.

This spontaneous and loyal support of our preconceptions—this process of finding "good" reasons to justify our routine beliefs—is known to modern psychologists as "rationalizing"—clearly only a new name for a very ancient thing. Our "good" reasons ordinarily have no value in promoting honest enlightenment, because, no matter how solemnly they may be marshaled, they are at bottom the result of personal preference or prejudice, and not of an honest desire to seek or accept new knowledge.

In our reveries we are frequently engaged in self-justification, for we cannot bear to think ourselves wrong, and yet have constant illustrations of our weaknesses and mistakes. So we spend much time finding fault with circumstances and the conduct of others, and shifting on to them with great ingenuity the onus of our own failures and disappointments. *Rationalizing is the self-exculpation which occurs when we feel ourselves, or our group, accused of misapprehension or error.*

All mankind, high and low, thinks in all the ways which have been described. The reverie goes on all the time not only in the mind of the mill hand and the Broadway show girl, but equally in weighty judges and godly bishops. It has gone on in all the philosophers, scientists, poets, and theologians that have ever lived. Aristotle's most abstruse speculations were doubtless tempered by highly irrelevant reflections. He is reported to have had very thin legs and small eyes, for which he doubtless had to find excuses, and he was wont to indulge in very conspicuous dress and rings and was accustomed to arrange his hair carefully. Diogenes the Cynic exhibited the impudence of a touchy soul. His tub was his distinction. Tennyson in beginning his "Maud" could not forget his chagrin over losing his patrimony years before as the result of an unhappy investment in the Patent Decorative Carving Company. These facts are not recalled here as a gratuitous disparagement of the truly great, but to insure a full realization of the tremendous competition which all really exacting thought has to face, even in the minds of the most highly endowed mortals.

And now the astonishing and perturbing suspicion emerges that perhaps almost all that had passed for social science, political economy, politics, and ethics in the past may be brushed aside by future generations as mainly rationalizing. John Dewey has already reached this conclusion in regard to philosophy. Veblen and other writers have revealed the various unperceived presuppositions of the traditional political economy, and now comes an Italian sociologist, Vilfredo Pareto, who, in his huge treatise on general sociology, devotes hundreds of pages to substantiating a similar thesis affecting all the social sciences. This conclusion may be ranked by students of a hundred years hence as one of the several great discoveries of our age. It is by no means fully worked out, and it is so opposed to nature that it will be very slowly accepted by the great mass of those who consider themselves thoughtful. As a historical student I am personally fully reconciled to this newer view. Indeed, it seems to me inevitable that just as the various sciences of nature were, before the opening of the seventeenth century, largely masses of rationalizations to suit the religious sentiments of the period, so the social sciences have continued even to our own day to be rationalizations of uncritically accepted beliefs and customs. . . .

HOW CREATIVE THOUGHT TRANSFORMS THE WORLD

This brings us to another kind of thought which can fairly easily be distinguished from the three kinds described above. It has not the usual qualities of the reverie, for it does not hover about our personal complacencies and humiliations. It is not made up of the homely decisions forced upon us by everyday needs, when we review our little stock of existing information, consult our conventional preferences and obligations, and make a choice of action. It is not the defense of our own cherished beliefs and prejudices just because they are our own—mere plausible excuses for remaining of the same mind. On the contrary, it is that peculiar species of thought which leads us to *change* our mind.

It is this kind of thought that has raised man from his pristine, subsavage ignorance and squalor to the degree of knowledge and comfort which he now possesses. On his capacity to continue and greatly extend this kind of thinking depends his chance of groping his way out of the plight in which the most highly civilized peoples of the world now find themselves. In the past this type of thinking has been called Reason. But so many misapprehensions have grown up around the word that some of us have become very suspicious of it. I suggest, therefore, that we substitute a recent name and speak of "creative thought" rather than of Reason. *For this kind of meditation begets knowledge, and knowledge is really creative inasmuch as it makes things look different from what they seemed before and may indeed work for their reconstruction.*

In certain moods some of us realize that we are observing things or making reflections with a seeming disregard of our personal preoccupations. We are not preening or defending ourselves; we are not faced by the necessity of any practical decision, nor are we apologizing for believing this or that. We are just wondering and looking and mayhap seeing what we never perceived before.

Curiosity is as clear and definite as any of our urges. We wonder what is in a sealed telegram or in a letter in which some one else is absorbed, or what is being said in the telephone booth or in low conversation. This inquisitiveness is vastly stimulated by jealousy, suspicion, or any hint that we ourselves are directly or indirectly involved. But there appears to be a fair amount of personal interest in other people's affairs even when they do not concern us except as a mystery to be unraveled or a tale to be told. The reports of a divorce suit will have "news value" for many weeks. They constitute a story, like a novel or play or moving picture. This is not an example of pure curiosity, however, since we readily identify ourselves with others, and their joys and despair then become our own.

We also take note of, or "observe," as Sherlock Holmes says, things which have nothing to do with our personal interests and make no personal appeal either direct or by way of sympathy. This is what Veblen so well calls "idle curiosity." And it is usually idle enough. Some of us when we face the line of people opposite us in a subway train impulsively consider them in detail and engage in rapid inferences and form theories in regard to them. On entering a room there are those who will perceive at a glance the degree of preciousness of the rugs, the character of the pictures, and the personality revealed by the books. But there are many, it would seem, who are so absorbed in their personal reverie or in some definite purpose that they have no bright-eyed energy for idle curiosity. The tendency to miscellaneous observation we come by honestly enough, for we note it in many of our animal relatives.

Veblen, however, uses the term "idle curiosity" somewhat ironically, as is his wont. It is idle only to those who fail to realize that it may be a very rare and indispensable thing from which almost all distinguished human achievement proceeds. Since it may lead to systematic examination and seeking for things hitherto undiscovered. For research is but diligent search which enjoys the high flavor of primitive hunting. Occasionally and fitfully idle curiosity thus leads to creative thought, which alters and broadens our own views and aspirations and may in turn, under highly favorable circumstances, affect the views and lives of others, even for generations to follow. An example or two will make this unique human process clear.

Galileo was a thoughtful youth and doubtless carried on a rich and varied reverie. He had artistic ability and might have turned out to be a musician or painter. When he had dwelt among the monks at Valambrosa he had been tempted to lead the life of a religious. As a boy he busied himself with toy machines and he inherited a fondness for mathematics. All these facts are of record. We may safely assume also that, along with many other subjects of contemplation, the Pisan maidens found a vivid place in his thoughts.

One day when seventeen years old he wandered into the cathedral of his native town. In the midst of his reverie he looked up at the lamps hanging by long chains from the high ceiling of the church. Then something very difficult to explain occurred. He found himself no longer thinking of the building, worshipers, or the services; of his artistic or religious interests; of his reluctance to become a physician as his father wished. He forgot the question of a career and even the *graziosissime donne*. As he watched the swinging lamps he was suddenly wondering if mayhap their oscillations, whether long or short, did not occupy the same time. Then he tested this hypothesis by counting his pulse, for that was the only timepiece he had with him.

This observation, however remarkable in itself, was not enough to produce a really creative thought. Others may have noticed the same thing and yet nothing came of it. Most of our observations have no assignable results. Galileo may have seen that the warts on a peasant's face formed a perfect isosceles triangle, or he may have noticed with boyish glee that just as the officiating priest was uttering the solemn words, *ecce agnus Dei,* a fly lit on the end of his nose. To be really creative, ideas have to be worked up and then "put over," so that they become a part of man's social heritage. The highly accurate pendulum clock was one of the later results of Galileo's discovery. He himself was led to reconsider and successfully to refute the old notions of falling bodies. It remained for Newton to prove that the moon was falling, and presumably all the heavenly bodies. This quite upset all the consecrated views of the heavens as managed by angelic engineers. The universality of the laws of gravitation stimulated the attempt to seek other and equally important natural laws and cast grave doubts on the miracles in which mankind had hitherto believed. In short, those who dared to include in their thought the discoveries of Galileo and his successors found themselves in a new earth surrounded by new heavens.

On the 28th of October, 1831, three hundred and fifty years after Galileo had noticed the isochronous vibrations of the lamps, creative thought and its currency had so far increased that Faraday was wondering what would happen if he mounted a disk of copper between the poles of a horseshoe magnet. As the disk revolved an electric current was produced. This would doubtless have seemed the idlest kind of an experiment to the stanch business men of the time, who, it happened, were just then denouncing the child-labor bills in their anxiety to avail themselves to the full of the results of earlier idle curiosity. But should the dynamos and motors which have come into being as the outcome of Faraday's experiment be stopped this evening, the business man of to-day, agitated over labor troubles, might, as he trudged home past lines of "dead" cars, through dark streets to an unlighted house, engage in a little creative thought of his own and perceive that he and his laborers would have no modern factories and mines to quarrel about had it not been for the strange practical effects of the idle curiosity of scientists, inventors, and engineers.

The examples of creative intelligence given above belong to the realm of modern scientific achievement, which furnishes the most striking instances of the effects of scrupulous, objective thinking. But there are, of course, other great realms in which the recording and embodiment of acute observation and insight have wrought themselves into the higher life of man. The great poets and dramatists and our modern story-tellers have found themselves engaged in productive reveries, noting and artistically presenting their discoveries for the delight and instruction of those who have the ability to appreciate them.

The process by which a fresh and original poem or drama comes into being is doubtless analogous to that which originates and elaborates so-called scientific discoveries; but there is clearly a temperamental difference. The genesis and advance of painting, sculpture, and music offer still other problems. We really as yet know shockingly little about these matters, and indeed very few people have the least curiosity about them. Nevertheless, creative intelligence in its various forms and activities is what makes man. Were it not for its slow, painful, and constantly discouraged operations through the ages man would be no more than a species of primate living on seeds, fruit, roots, and uncooked flesh, and wandering naked through the woods and over the plains like a chimpanzee. . . .

We have now examined the various classes of thinking which we can readily observe in ourselves and which we have plenty of reasons to believe go on, and always have been going on, in our fellow-men. We can sometimes get quite pure and sparkling examples of all four kinds, but commonly they are so confused and intermingled in our reverie as not to be readily distinguishable. The reverie is a reflection of our longings, exultations, and complacencies, our fears, suspicions, and disappointments. We are chiefly engaged in struggling to maintain our self-respect and in asserting that supremacy which we all crave and which seems to us our natural prerogative. It is not strange, but rather quite inevitable, that our beliefs about what is true and false, good and bad, right and wrong, should be mixed up with the reverie and be influenced by the same considerations which determine its character and course. We resent criticisms of our views exactly as we do of anything else connected with ourselves. Our notions of life and its ideals seem to us to be *our own* and as such necessarily true and right, to be defended at all costs.

We very rarely consider, however, the process by which we gained our convictions. If we did so, we could hardly fail to see that there was usually little ground for our confidence in them. Here and there, in this department of knowledge or that, some one of us might make a fair claim to have taken some trouble to get correct ideas of, let us say, the situation in Russia, the sources of our food supply, the origin of the Constitution, the revision of the tariff, the policy of the Holy Roman Apostolic Church, modern business organization, trade unions, birth control, socialism, the excess-profits tax, preparedness, advertising in its social bearings; but only a very exceptional person would be entitled to opinions on all of even these few matters. And yet most of us have opinions on all these, and on many other questions of equal importance, of which we may know even less. We feel compelled, as self-respecting persons, to take sides when they come up for discussion. We even surprise ourselves by our omniscience. Without taking thought we see in a flash that it is most righteous and expedient to discourage birth control by legislative enactment, or that one who decries intervention in Mexico is clearly wrong, or that big advertising is essential to big business and that big business is the pride of the land. As godlike beings why should we not rejoice in our omniscience?

It is clear, in any case, that our convictions on important matters are not the result of knowledge or critical thought, nor, it may be added, are they often dictated by supposed self-interest. Most of them are *pure prejudices* in the proper sense of that word. We do not form them ourselves. They are the whisperings of "the voice of the herd." We have in the last analysis no responsibility for them and need assume none. They are not really our own ideas, but those of others no more well informed or inspired than ourselves, who have got them in the same careless and humiliating manner as we. It should be our pride to revise our ideas and not to adhere to what passes for respectable opinion, for such opinion can frequently be shown to be not respectable at all. We should, in view of the considerations that have been mentioned, resent our supine credulity. As Trotter has remarked:

"If we feared the entertaining of an unverifiable opinion with the warmth with which we fear using the wrong implement at the dinner table, if the thought of holding a prejudice disgusted us as does a foul disease, then the dangers of man's suggestibility would be turned into advantages. . . .

The "real" reasons, which explain how it is we happen to hold a particular belief, are chiefly historical. Our most important opinions—those, for example, having to do with traditional, religious, and moral convictions, property rights, patriotism, national honor, the state, and indeed all the assumed foundations of society—are, as I have already suggested, rarely the result of reasoned consideration, but of unthinking absorption from the social environment in which we live. Consequently, they have about them a quality of "elemental certitude," and we especially resent doubt or criticism cast upon them. So long, however, as we revere the whisperings of the herd, we are obviously unable to examine them dispassionately and to consider to what extent they are suited to the novel conditions and social exigencies in which we find ourselves to-day.

The "real" reasons for our beliefs, by making clear their origins and history, can do much to dissipate this emotional blockade and rid us of our prejudices and preconceptions. Once this is done and we come critically to examine our traditional beliefs, we may well find some of them sustained by experience and honest reasoning, while others must be revised to meet new conditions and our more extended knowledge. But only after we have undertaken such a critical examination in the light of experience and modern knowledge, freed from any feeling of "primary certitude," can we claim that the "good" are also the "real" reasons for our opinions.

1920

Imagination Creatrix

JOHN LIVINGSTON LOWES

From *The Road to Xanadu*

I

EVERY GREAT IMAGINATIVE CONCEPTION IS A VORTEX into which everything under the sun may be swept. "All other men's worlds," wrote Coleridge once, "are the poet's chaos." In that regard "The Ancient Mariner" is one with the noble army of imaginative masterpieces of all time. Oral traditions—homely, fantastic, barbaric, disconnected—which had ebbed and flowed across the planet in its unlettered days, were gathered up into that marvel of constructive genius, the plot of the *Odyssey*, and out of "a tissue of old *märchen*" was fashioned a unity palpable as flesh and blood and universal as the sea itself. Well-nigh all the encyclopedic erudition of the Middle Ages was forged and welded, in the white heat of an indomitable will, into the steel-knot structure of the *Divine Comedy*. There are not in the world, I suppose, more appalling masses of raw fact than would stare us in the face could we once, through some supersubtle chemistry, resolve that superb, organic unity into its primal elements. It so happens that for the last twenty-odd years I have been more or less occupied with Chaucer. I have tracked him, as I have trailed Coleridge, into almost every section of eight floors of a great library. It is a perpetual adventure among uncharted Ophirs and Golcondas to read after him—or Coleridge. And every conceivable sort of thing which Chaucer knew went into his alembic. It went in *x* —a waif of travel-lore from the mysterious Orient, a curious bit of primitive psychiatry, a racy morsel from Jerome against Jovinian, alchemy, astrology, medicine, geomancy, physiognomy, Heaven only knows what not, all vivid with the relish of the reading—it went in stark fact, "nude and crude," and it came out pure Chaucer. The results are as different from "The Ancient Mariner" as an English post-road from spectre-haunted seas. But the basic operations which produced

630

them (and on this point I may venture to speak from first-hand knowledge) are essentially the same.

As for the years of "industrious and select reading, steady observation, insight into all seemly and generous arts and affairs" which were distilled into the magnificent romance of the thunder-scarred yet dauntless Rebel, voyaging through Chaos and old Night to shatter Cosmos, pendent from the battlements of living sapphire like a star—as for those serried hosts of facts caught up into the cosmic sweep of Milton's grandly poised design, it were bootless to attempt to sum up in a sentence here the opulence which countless tomes of learned comment have been unable to exhaust. And what (in apostolic phrase) shall I more say? For the time would fail me to tell of the *Æneid*, and the *Orlando Furioso*, and the *Faërie Queene*, and *Don Juan*, and even *Endymion*, let alone the cloud of other witnesses. The notion that the creative imagination, especially in its highest exercise, has little or nothing to do with facts is one of the *pseudodoxia epidemica* which die hard.

For the imagination never operates in a vacuum. Its stuff is always fact of some order, somehow experienced; its product is that fact transmuted. I am not forgetting that facts may swamp imagination, and remain unassimilated and untransformed. And I know, too, that this sometimes happens even with the masters. For some of the greatest poets, partly by virtue of their very greatness, have had, like Faust, two natures struggling within them. They have possessed at once the instincts of the scholar and the instincts of the artist, and it is precisely with regard to facts that these instincts perilously clash. Even Dante and Milton and Goethe sometimes clog their powerful streams with the accumulations of the scholar who shared bed and board with the poet in their mortal frames. "The Professor still lurks in your anatomy"—*Dir steckt der Doktor noch im Leib*—says Mephistopheles to Faust. But when, as in "The Ancient Mariner," the stuff that Professors and Doctors are made of has been distilled into quintessential poetry, then the passing miracle of creation has been performed.

II

But "creation," like "creative," is one of those hypnotic words which are prone to cast a spell upon the understanding and dissolve our thinking into haze. And out of this nebulous state of the intellect springs a strange but widely prevalent idea. The shaping spirit of imagination sits aloof, like God as he is commonly conceived, creating in some thaumaturgic fashion out of nothing its visionary world. That and that only is deemed to be "originality"—that, and not the imperial moulding of old matter into imperishably new forms. The ways of creation are wrapt in mystery; we may only marvel, and bow the head.

Now it is true beyond possible gainsaying that the operations which we call creative leave us in the end confronting mystery. But that is the fated terminus of all our quests. And it is chiefly through a deep-rooted reluctance to retrace, so far as they are legible, the footsteps of the creative faculty that the power is often thought of as abnormal, or at best a splendid aberration. I know full well that this reluctance springs, with most of us, from the staunch conviction that to follow the evolution of a thing of beauty is to shatter its integrity and irretrievably to mar its charm. But there are those of us who cherish the invincible belief that the glory of poetry will gain, not lose, through a recognition of the fact that the imagination works its wonders through the exercise, in the main, of normal and intelligible powers. To establish that, without blinking the ultimate mystery of genius, is to bring the workings of the shaping spirit in the sphere of art within the circle of the great moulding forces through which, in science and affairs and poetry alike, there emerges from chaotic multiplicity a unified and ordered world. . . .

Creative genius, in plainer terms, works through processes which are common to our kind, but these processes are superlatively enhanced. The subliminal agencies are endowed with an extraordinary potency; the faculty which conceives and executes operates with sovereign power; and the two blend in untrammelled interplay. There is always in genius, I imagine, the element which Goethe, who knew whereof he spoke, was wont to designate as "the Dæmonic." But in genius of the highest order that sudden, incalculable, and puissant energy which pours up from the hidden depths is controlled by a will which serves a vision—the vision which sees in chaos the potentiality of Form.

III

. . . "The imagination," said Coleridge once, recalling a noble phrase from Jeremy Taylor's *Via Pacis*, ". . . *sees all things in one*." It sees the Free Life—the endless flux of the unfathomed sea of facts and images— but it sees also the controlling Form. And when it acts on what it sees, through the long patience of the will the flux itself is transformed and fixed in the clarity of a realized design. For there enter into imaginative creation three factors which reciprocally interplay: the Well, and the Vision, and the Will. Without the Vision, the chaos of elements remains a chaos, and the Form sleeps forever in the vast chambers of unborn designs. Yet in *that* chaos only could creative Vision ever see *this* Form. Nor without the cooperant Will, obedient to the Vision, may the pattern perceived in the huddle attain objective reality. Yet manifold though the ways of the creative faculty may be, the upshot is one: from the empire of chaos a new tract of cosmos has been retrieved; a nebula has been compacted—it may be!—into a star.

Yet no more than the lesser are these larger factors of the creative process—the storing of the Well, the Vision, and the concurrent operation of the Will—the monopoly of poetry. Through their conjunction the imagination in the field of science, for example, is slowly drawing the immense confusion of phenomena within the unfolding conception of an ordered universe. And its operations are essentially the same. For years, through intense and unremitting observation, Darwin had been accumulating masses of facts which pointed to a momentous conclusion. But they pointed through a maze of baffling inconsistencies. Then all at once the flash of vision came. "I can remember," he tells us in that precious fragment of an autobiography—"I can remember the very spot in the road, whilst in my carriage, when to my joy the solution occurred to me." And then, and only then, with the infinite toil of exposition, was slowly framed from the obdurate facts the great statement of the theory of evolution. The leap of the imagination, in a garden at Woolsthorpe on a day in 1665, from the fall of an apple to an architectonic conception cosmic in its scope and grandeur is one of the dramatic moments in the history of human thought. But in that pregnant moment there flashed together the profound and daring observations and conjectures of a long period of years; and upon the instant of illumination followed other years of rigorous and protracted labour, before the *Principia* appeared. Once more there was the long, slow storing of the Well; once more the flash of amazing vision through a fortuitous suggestion; once more the exacting task of translating the vision into actuality. And those are essentially the stages which Poincaré observed and graphically recorded in his "Mathematical Discovery." And that chapter reads like an exposition of the creative processes through which "The Ancient Mariner" came to be. With the inevitable and obvious differences we are not here concerned. But it is of the utmost moment to more than poetry that instead of regarding the imagination as a bright but ineffectual faculty with which in some esoteric fashion poets and their kind are specially endowed, we recognize the essential oneness of its function and its ways with all the creative endeavours through which human brains, with dogged persistence, strive to discover and realize order in a chaotic world.

For the Road to Xanadu is the road of the human spirit, and the imagination voyaging through chaos and reducing it to clarity and order

is the symbol of all the quests which lend glory to our dust. And the
goal of the shaping spirit which hovers in the *poet's* brain is the clarity
and order of pure beauty. Nothing is alien to its transforming touch.
"Far or forgot to (it) is near; Shadow and sunlight are the same."
Things fantastic as the dicing of spectres on skeleton-barks, and ugly
as the slimy spawn of rotting seas, and strange as a star astray within
the moon's bright tip, blend in its vision into patterns of new-created
beauty, *herrlich, wie am ersten Tag.* Yet the pieces that compose the
pattern are not new. In the world of the shaping spirit, save for its
patterns, there is nothing new that was not old. For the work of the
creators is the mastery and transmutation and reordering into shapes
of beauty of the given universe within us and without us. The shapes
thus wrought are not that universe; they are "carved with figures
strange and sweet, All made out of the carver's brain." Yet in that brain
the elements and shattered fragments of the figures already lie, and
what the carver-creator sees, implicit in the fragments, is the unique
and lovely Form.

1927

The Psychology of Sigmund Freud

A. A. BRILL

PSYCHOANALYSIS WAS UNKNOWN IN THIS COUNTRY until I introduced it in 1908. Ever since then, I have been translating, lecturing and writing on this subject both for physicians and laymen; and I am happy to say that today psychoanalysis, which has encountered so much opposition here, as it did abroad, is firmly established not only in medicine, but also in psychology, sociology, pedagogy and anthropology. It has not only permeated and transvalued the mental sciences, but indirectly also *belles lettres* and the cultural trends of the last generation.

At the beginning of the psychoanalytic movement in this country, its opponents and some of its lukewarm friends predicted that, like so many other discoveries in mental therapy, psychoanalysis was destined to be short-lived. They were poor prophets. The falsity of their prognosis can be seen in the fact that the psychoanalytic terminology, some of which I was the first to coin into English expressions, can now be found in all standard English dictionaries. Words like *abreaction, transference, repression, displacement, unconscious*, which I introduced as Freudian concepts, have been adopted and are used to give new meanings, new values to our knowledge of normal and abnormal behavior. . . .

Sigmund Freud was born in 1856 in Freiberg, Moravia, formerly Austria, now Czechoslovakia. He was brought up in Vienna, having lived there since the age of four. In his autobiography, he states: "My parents were Jews and I remained a Jew."

One of the arguments that has been hurled at psychoanalysis on a few occasions is that its originator was a Jew, implying thereby that the theories expressed by Freud do not apply to the rest of mankind. Such an argument, which, if accepted, would also invalidate Christianity, is too stupid to require refutation. Freud's works had the honor of forming part of the sacred pyre on Hitler's accession to power. The fact that the bulk of this pyre was composed of works of non-Jewish thinkers plainly shows that truth knows no creed or race. I feel, however, that Freud's

Jewish descent—constitution—as well as the environment to which he was subjected because of it—fate—exerted considerable influence on his personality. One might say that only a Jewish genius, forged in the crucible of centuries of persecution, could have offered himself so willingly on the altar of public opprobrium for the sake of demonstrating the truths of psychoanalysis.

Freud tells us that in college he always stood first, and was hardly ever examined. Despite the very straitened financial condition of his family, his father wanted him to follow his own inclination in the selection of a vocation. He had no special love for medicine at that age, nor did he acquire it later, but rather he was stimulated by a sort of inquisitiveness directed to human relations and objects of nature. He was very much attracted to Darwin's theories because they offered the prospect of an extraordinary advance of human knowledge, and he finally decided to enter the medical school after he had read Goethe's beautiful essay, *Die Natur*. . . .

While still in the university, he worked for a number of years in the physiological laboratory of the famous Ernst Brücke, who was his teacher and gave him as his first task the histology of the nervous system. With only a short interruption Freud worked in the Institute from 1876 until 1882. Then, he discovered, that with the exception of psychiatry, the other medical specialties did not attract him. He graduated from the medical school in 1881, and in 1882 he entered Vienna's well known *Allgemeine Krankenhaus* (general hospital). There, he went through the usual routine services, but continued his studies on the anatomy of the brain, in which he became very proficient. It is not generally known that in his early days Freud wrote a number of works on diseases of the nervous system, which were very highly regarded by his contemporaries.

In 1885 he was attracted by the fame of Charcot, who was applying hypnotism to the study and treatment of hysteria and other functional nervous diseases. He remained for a year in Paris as a pupil and translator of this master's works. In 1886 he returned to his native Vienna and "married the girl who waited for me in a far-off city longer than four years." He then entered private practice, but continued as an instructor in the university.

What Freud saw in Charcot's Clinic made a very deep impression on him. While still a student, he also witnessed a performance of the "magnetiser," Hansen, in which a test person became deadly pale when she merged into a cataleptic rigidity, and remained so during the whole duration of the catalepsy. This convinced Freud of the genuineness of hypnotic phenomena, a conviction which remained in him despite the fact that the contemporary professors of psychiatry considered hypnosis fraudulent and dangerous. From Charcot he learned that hypnosis could produce hysterical symptoms as well as remove them, and that hysteria could also occur in men; and from Liébault and Bernheim of the Nancy School he learned that suggestion alone, without hypnotism, was as efficacious as suggestion employed in hypnosis.

When Freud returned to Vienna and demonstrated what he had learned from Charcot, he met with considerable opposition. It was the age of physical therapy, when physicians knew nothing about the psychic factors in disease, when everything was judged by the formula, *Mens sana in corpore sano* (a healthy mind in a healthy body). Every symptom was explained on the basis of some organic lesion, and if nothing physical was discovered, it was assumed that there must be something in the brain to account for the disturbance. The treatment was based on this same deficient understanding; drugs, hydrotherapy, and electrotherapy were the only agents that physicians could use. When the patient was excited, he received some sedative; if he was depressed and felt fatigue, he was given a tonic; and when drugs failed, electricity or cold baths were recommended. All these remedies gave only temporary alleviation, mainly through suggestion. Most of the thoughtful physicians were fully cognizant of this helpless state, but there was nothing else to be done.

During the first few years of his private practice Freud relied mostly on hypnotism and electrotherapy, but he soon realized that the latter failed to benefit the patient, and that the whole idea of electric treatment for functional nervous diseases was fantastic. He had some good results, however, from hypnotic therapy; but he soon found that not every patient could be hypnotized, and that even those who could be, did not remain permanently cured. Attributing such failures to a deficiency in his technique, to an inability on his part to put every patient into a state of somnambulism with its consequent amnesia, he spent some weeks in Nancy with Liébault and Bernheim, to whom he took a recalcitrant patient for treatment. Bernheim made a number of efforts to produce a deep hypnotic state in the patient, but finally had to admit failure. Freud, though disappointed with the technique of hypnotism, learned a great deal from the experiments witnessed there concerning the forceful psychic forces which were still to be investigated. Very soon thereafter, he gradually gave up hypnotism and developed what he called "psychoanalysis." In this connection he makes the following interesting statement: "The importance of hypnotism for the history of the development of psychoanalysis must not be too lightly estimated. Both in theoretic as well as in therapeutic aspects, psychoanalysis is the administrator of the estate left by hypnotism."

In order to give a full account of the development of psychoanalysis, it will be necessary to go back a few years. While Freud still worked in Brücke's laboratory, he made the acquaintance of Dr. Josef Breuer, a prominent general practitioner of high scientific standing. Although Breuer was 14 years older than Freud, they soon became friends and frequently discussed their scientific views and experiences. Knowing Freud's interest in neurology and psychiatry, Breuer gave him an account of a very interesting case of hysteria which he had studied and cured by hypnosis from 1880 to 1882. As this unique case was of the greatest importance to the development of psychoanalysis, it will be worth while to give a few details.

The patient concerned was a young girl of unusual education and talent, who had become ill while nursing her father to whom she was very much attached. Dr. Breuer states that when he took her as a patient she presented a variegated picture of paralyses with contractures, inhibitions and states of psychic confusion. Through an accidental observation Breuer discovered that the patient could be freed from such disturbances of consciousness if she could be enabled to give verbal expression to the affective phantasies which dominated her. Breuer elaborated this experience into a method of treatment. He hypnotized her and urged her to tell him what oppressed her at the time, and by this simple method he freed her from all her symptoms. The significance of the case lay in this fact, that in her waking state the patient knew nothing about the origin of her symptoms, but once hypnotized, she immediately knew the connection between her symptoms and some of her past experiences. All her symptoms were traceable to experiences during the time when she had nursed her sick father. Moreover, the symptoms were not arbitrary and senseless, but could be traced to definite experiences and forgotten reminiscences of that emotional situation.

A common feature of all the symptoms consisted in the fact that they had come into existence in situations in which an impulse to do something had to be foregone because other motives suppressed it. The symptom appeared as a substitute for the unperformed act. As a rule, the symptom was not the result of one single "traumatic" scene, but of a sum of many similar situations. If the patient in a state of hypnosis recalled hallucinatorily the act which she had suppressed in the past, and if she now brought it to conclusion under the stress of a freely generated affect, the symptom was wiped away never to return again. It was remarked that the causes which had given origin to the symptom resembled the traumatic factors described by Charcot in his experimental cases. What was still more remarkable was that these traumatic causes with their concomitant psychic feelings had been entirely lost to the patient's memory, as if they had never happened, while their results—that is, the symptoms, had continued unchanged, as if unaffected by the wear and tear of time, until attacked by Breuer through hypnosis.

Although Breuer, as was mentioned above, told Freud about this wonderful discovery, he did not publish his findings. Freud could not understand why. The discovery seemed to him of inestimable value. But following his return from Nancy in 1889 with the cognition of hypnotic suggestive therapy, Freud decided to test Breuer's method in his own cases, and found ample corroboration of its efficacy during a period of many years. He then urged Breuer to report with him the results of his method, and in 1893 they jointly issued a preliminary communication, *On the Psychic Mechanisms of Hysterical Phenomena.*

As can be seen, Breuer was the spiritual creator of this method of treatment and Freud always gave him full credit for it, although they differed from the very beginning in their basic interpretation of the symptoms. They called their treatment the "cathartic method" because they concluded that the efficacy of it rested on the mental and emotional purging, catharsis, which the patient went through during the treatment. The other conclusion drawn by the authors was that hysteria was a disease of the past, and that, as Freud put it later, the symptom was, as it were, a monument to *some* disagreeable and forgotten (repressed) episode from the patient's life. The patient, however, did not know the meaning of the monument any more than the average German would know the meaning of the Bunker Hill monument. This concept for the first time showed the importance of distinguishing between conscious and unconscious states, which was later amplified and developed by Freud as the psychology of the unconscious. New meaning was given to the affective or emotional factors of life, their fluctuations and dynamism. The symptom was the result of a dammed-up or strangulated affect. The patient could not give vent to the affect because the situation in question made this impossible, so that the idea was intentionally *repressed* from consciousness and excluded from associative elaboration. As a result of this repression, the sum of energy which could not be discharged took a wrong path to bodily innervation, and thus produced the symptom. In other words, the symptom was the result of a conversion of psychic energy into a physical manifestation, such as pain or paralysis. Thus, a pain in the face, diagnosed as neuralgia, might be due to an insult which would ordinarily evoke the thought, "I feel as if he had slapped me in the face." As this insult could not be retaliated against, the strangulated energy remained in a state of repression and gave rise to "neuralgia." The cure or the discharge was effected through what the authors called the process of *abreaction*. The hypnotized patient was led back to the repressed episodes and allowed to give free vent in speech and action to the feelings which were originally kept out of consciousness.

Breuer's and Freud's discoveries were not received as sympathetically as the authors expected. Their psychogenetic views of hysteria were interesting, but too revolutionary to be accepted by their older colleagues. On the other hand, in spite of much discussion, there was as yet, no real antagonism. That did not arise until later, when Freud began to stress the sexual factor in the neuroses. In his report of Anna O., Breuer stated: "The sexual element in her make-up was astonishingly undeveloped." Throughout their book the sexual elements, of which there were many in every case, were treated no differently than the other factors in the patients' lives. How Freud happened to become interested in sex and then stress its importance in the etiology of the neuroses he tells us later.

Very soon after the appearance of the *Studies in Hysteria*, Breuer withdrew from the field. He was, after all, unprepared for this specialty, and inasmuch as he enjoyed a stable and lucrative practice and a high reputation as a family physician, the storm which began to gather as his collaborator advanced deeper into the etiology of the neuroses more or less frightened him. Freud, therefore, continued alone to elaborate and perfect the instrument left by his erstwhile friend and collaborator; and as a result, the cathartic method underwent numerous modifications, the most important of which was the giving-up of hypnotism in favor of *free association*. As pointed out above, not everybody could be hypnotized, and since hypnotism was absolutely indispensable to the cathartic treatment at that time, many a worthy patient had had to be given up just because he or she could not be hypnotized. Freud was also dissatisfied with the therapeutic results of catharsis based on hypnotism. Although cures were often very striking, they were often of very short duration and depended mainly on the personal relation between the patient and physician. Moreover, Freud always entertained a feeling of antipathy to the application of hypnotism and suggestion to patients. Speaking of his visit to Bernheim in 1889, he states: "But I can remember even then a feeling of gloomy antagonism against this tyranny of suggestion. When a patient who did not prove to be yielding was shouted at: 'What are you doing? *Vous vous contresuggestionnez!*', I said to myself that this was an evident injustice and violence."

Yet his visit to Bernheim later helped him out of the dilemma of not being able to hypnotize some patients. He recalled the following experiment which he had witnessed there, the object of which was to overcome the post-hypnotic amnesia: On being awakened, the patient could not remember anything that had transpired during hypnosis, but when he was urged to make an effort to recall what had been said to him, he eventually remembered everything. Freud applied the same method to those patients whom he could not hypnotize. He urged them to tell him everything that came to their minds, to leave out nothing, regardless of whether they considered it relevant or not. He persuaded them to give up all conscious reflection, abandon themselves to calm concentration, follow their spontaneous mental occurrences, and impart everything to him. In this way he finally obtained those *free associations* which lead to the origin of the symptoms. As he developed this method, he found that it was not as simple as he had thought, that these so-called free associations were really not *free*, but were determined by unconscious material which had to be analyzed and interpreted. He therefore designated this new technique *psychoanalysis*. The cathartic method, however, was ever preserved as a sort of nucleus of psychoanalysis despite the expansions and modifications which Freud gradually made as he proceeded with the new technique.

In the course of working with free associations, Freud gained a tremendous amount of insight into the play of forces of the human mind which he could not have obtained through the former therapeutic procedure. The question as to how the patient could have forgotten so many outer and inner experiences, which could be recalled only in a state of hypnosis and which were difficult to bring to consciousness by means of free association, soon became revealed to him. The forgotten material represented something painful, something disagreeable, or something frightful, obnoxious to the ego of the patient, which he did not like to think of consciously. In order to make it conscious, the physician had to exert himself mightily to overcome the patient's *resistance*, which kept these experiences in a state of repression and away from consciousness. The neurosis proved to be the result of a psychic conflict between two dynamic forces, impulse and resistance, in the course of which struggle the ego withdrew from the disagreeable impulse. As a result of this withdrawal, the obnoxious impulse was kept from access to consciousness as well as from direct motor discharge, but it retained its impulsive energy.

This unconscious process actually is a primary defense mechanism, comparable to an effort to fly away from something. But in order to keep the disagreeable idea from consciousness, the ego has to contend against the constant thrust of the repressed impulse which is ever searching for expression. But despite constant exertion by the ego, the repressed, obnoxious impulse often finds an outlet through some by-path, and thus invalidates the intention of the repression. The repressed impulsive energy then settles by this indirect course on some organ or part of the body, and this innervation constitutes the symptom. Once this is established, the patient struggles against the symptom in the same way as he did against the originally repressed impulses.

To illustrate these mechanisms let us consider the case of an hysterical young woman. For some months she was courted by a young man proclaiming his ardent love for her. Suddenly one day he made an unsuccessful sexual assault upon her, and then disappeared, leaving her in a state of deep depression. She could not confide in her mother, because from the very beginning of the affair the mother had forbidden her to see the young man. Three years later I found her suffering from numerous hysterical conversion symptoms, and attacks of an epileptic character which had existed for some two and a half years. Analysis showed that the attacks represented symbolically what had taken place at the time of the abortive sexual assault. Every detail of the so-called epileptiform attack—every gesture, every movement—was a stereotyped repetition of the sexual attack which the patient was reproducing unconsciously. The other symptoms, too, were directly traceable to the love affair.

The whole process of this disease can readily be understood if we bear in mind the various steps of this love situation. The young woman was healthy and, biontically speaking, ready for mating; her primitive instinct of sex was striving for fulfillment. Consciously, she could think of love only in the modern sense of the term, in which the physical elements are deliberately kept out of sight. Her middle-class, religious environment precluded any illicit sexual activity as far as she was consciously concerned. But, behind it all, the sexual impulses were actively reaching out for maternity. She was sincerely in love with the man, but naturally thought of love as marriage, with everything that goes with it. The sudden shock of coming face to face with the physical elements of sex left a terrific impression on her mind: on the one hand, consciously, she rejected vehemently the lover's physical approaches, and on the other hand, unconsciously, she really craved them. For weeks afterwards she vividly lived over in her mind everything that had happened to her, and, now and then, even fancied herself as having yielded—a thought which was immediately rejected and replaced by feelings of reproach and disgust. Last, but not least, she actually missed the love-making, which she had enjoyed for months prior to the attempted assault. As she could not unburden herself to anyone, she tried very hard to forget everything, and finally seemingly succeeded. But a few weeks later she began to show the symptoms which finally developed into the pathogenic picture which was diagnosed as epilepsy or hystero-epilepsy. These symptoms were the symbolization, or, if you will, a dramatization of the conflict between her primitive self and her ethical self, between what Freud now calls the *Id* and the *Ego*.

To make ourselves more explicit, it will be necessary to say something about the elements of the psychic apparatus. According to Freud's formulation the child brings into the world an unorganized chaotic mentality called the *Id*, the sole aim of which is the gratification of all needs, the alleviation of hunger, self-preservation, and love, the preservation of the species. However, as the child grows older, the part of the id which comes in contact with the environment through the senses learns to know the inexorable reality of the outer world and becomes modified into what Freud calls the ego. This ego, possessing awareness of the environment, henceforth strives to curb the lawless id tendencies whenever they attempt to assert themselves incompatibly. The neurosis, as we see it here, was, therefore, *a conflict between the ego and the id*. The ego, aware of the forces of civilization, religion and ethics, refused to allow motor discharge to the powerful sexual impulses emanating from the lawless id, and thus blocked them from attainment of the object towards which they aimed. The ego then defended itself against these impulses by repressing them. The young lady in question seemingly forgot this whole episode. Had the repression continued unabated, she would have remained healthy. But the repressed material struggled against this fate, finally broke through as a substitutive formation on paths over which the ego had no control, and obtruded itself on the ego as symptoms. As a result of this process, the ego found itself more or less impoverished, its integrity was threatened and hurt, and hence it continued to combat the symptom in the same way as it had defended itself against the original id impulses.

This whole process constitutes the picture of the neuroses, or rather of the transference neuroses, which comprise hysteria, anxiety hysteria, and the compulsion neuroses, in contradistinction to the so-called narcistic neuroses, melancholic depressions, and to the psychoses, schizophrenia, paranoid conditions and paranoia proper, in which the underlying mechanisms are somewhat different. In a psychosis, as will be shown later, the illness results from *a conflict between the ego and the outer world*, and in the narcistic neurosis from *a conflict between the ego and the super-ego*. For just as the ego is a modified portion of the id as a result of contact with the outer world, the super-ego represents a modified part of the ego, formed through experiences absorbed from the parents, especially from the father. The super-ego is the highest mental evolution attainable by man, and consists of a precipitate of all prohibitions and inhibitions, all the rules of conduct which are impressed on the child by his parents and by parental substitutes. The feeling of *conscience* depends altogether on the development of the super-ego.

From the description given here of the mechanism of the neurosis, scant as it is, one can already see the great rôle attributed by Freud to the unconscious factor of the mind. Psychoanalysis has been justly called the "psychology of depths" because it has emphasized the rôle of the unconscious mental processes. Unlike those psychologists and philosophers who use such terms as conscious, co-conscious, and sub-conscious in a very loose and confused manner, Freud conceives *consciousness* simply as an organ of perception. One is conscious or aware of those mental processes which occupy one at any given time. In contrast to this, the *unconscious* is utterly unknown and cannot be voluntarily recalled. No person can bring to light anything from his unconscious unless he is made to recall it by hypnosis, or unless it is interpreted for him by psychoanalysis. Midway between conscious and unconscious there is a *fore-conscious* or pre-conscious, which contains memories of which one is unaware, but which one can eventually recall with some effort.

This structure of a conscious fore-conscious, and an actual unconscious, is based on the attempt which Freud made to conceive the psychic apparatus as a composition of a number of forces or systems. It is a theoretical classification, which seems, however, to work well in practice. Bearing in mind these spatial divisions, we can state that whereas *the dream is the royal road to the unconscious*, most of the mechanisms discussed in the *Psychopathology of Everyday Life* belong to the fore-conscious system. This work was written after Freud became convinced that there is nothing arbitrary or accidental in psychic life, be it normal or abnormal. For the very unconscious forces which he found in the neuroses he also found in the common faulty actions of everyday life, like ordinary forgetting of familiar names, slips of the tongue, mistakes in reading or writing, which had hitherto been considered accidental and unworthy of explanation. Freud shows in the *Psychopathology of Everyday Life* that a rapid reflection or a short analysis always demonstrates the disturbing influence behind such slips, and conclusively proves that the same disturbances, differing only in degree, are found in every person, and that the gap between the neurotic and the so-called normal is, therefore, very narrow.

The dream, according to Freud, represents the hidden fulfillment of an unconscious wish. But the wishes which it represents as fulfilled are the very same unconscious wishes which are repressed in neurosis. Dreaming is a normal function of the mind; it is the guardian of sleep in so far as it strives to release tensions generated by unattainable wishes—tensions which, if not removed, might keep the person from sleeping. The dream is not always successful in its efforts; sometimes it oversteps the limits of propriety; it goes too far; and then the dreamer is awakened by the super-ego.

Without going further into the psychology of the dream, enough has been said to show that these twin discoveries—that non-conscious psychic processes are active in every normal person, expressing themselves in inhibitions and other modifications of intentional acts, and that the dreams of mentally healthy persons are not differently constructed from neurotic or psychotic symptoms—gave rise not only to a New Psychology, but to fruitful investigations in many other fields of human knowledge. The ability to interpret the dreams of today made it possible also to interpret the dreams of yesterday. Freudian literature, therefore, abounds in studies throwing new light on mythology, folklore, fairy tales, and ethnology; and psychoanalysis has become as important to the non-medical sciences as to the therapy of the neuroses. . . .

I have always found it hard to understand why Freud's views on sex roused so much opposition. Freud did not enter that realm voluntarily, but was forced by a natural course of events into taking account of the sexual factor in neuroses. Following the discovery of the psychogenesis of hysterical symptoms, first through Breuer's cathartic method and later through the technique of "free association," Freud was led, step by step, to discover and explore the realm of *infantile sexuality*. This discovery was based entirely on empiric material. In probing for the origin of hysterical symptoms, in tracing them back as far as possible, even into childhood, Freud found physical and psychical activities of a definitely sexual nature in the earliest ages of childhood. The necessary conclusion was that the traumas underlying the symptoms were *invariably* of a sexual nature, since all his cases produced similar findings. Finally, therefore, he concluded that sexual activities in childhood could not be considered abnormal, but were on the contrary normal phenomena of the sexual instinct.

In following up these discoveries it was natural that he should also investigate the rôle of sexuality in the extensive syndrome of neurasthenia. To his surprise Freud found that *all* his so-called neurasthenics exhibited some sexual abuses. . . . In the course of these investigations he was able to bring order into the field of neurasthenia—that "garbage can of medicine," as Forel aptly called it—by separating from others those cases which were mainly characterized by anxiety. The results he embodied in his classic paper, *On the Right to Separate from Neurasthenia a Definite Symptom-Complex as "Anxiety Neurosis,"* in which he called attention for the first time to the relation between anxiety and sex. The pursuit of studies in this direction brought him at length to the conviction that all neuroses represent a general disturbance of the sexual functions; that the *actual neuroses* (neurasthenia and anxiety neuroses) result from a direct chemical or toxic disturbance, while the *psychoneuroses* (hysteria and compulsion neuroses) represent the psychic expression of these disturbances. This conclusion, based at first on explorations in the sexual life of adults, but reënforced and confirmed since 1908 through analyses of children, was finally compressed into the famous dictum that "*In a normal sex life no neurosis is possible.*"

Freud was not the first to discover sexual difficulties in man. One need only think of literature throughout the ages to realize that there was abundant material on the subject long before the appearance of *Three Contributions to the Theory of Sex*. Freud's special merit lies in the fact that before him sex had been treated as an isolated phenomenon, or as (more or less) an abnormality, whereas he paid it the respect of considering it as a component of the normal personality. In the words of Dr. James J. Putnam, former professor of neurology at Harvard University, "Freud has made considerable addition to this stock of knowledge, but he has done also something of greater consequence than this. He has worked out, with incredible penetration, the part which the instinct plays in every phase of human life and in the development of human character, and has been able to establish on a firm footing the remarkable thesis that psychoneurotic illnesses never occur with a perfectly normal sexual life." Dr. Putnam wrote those words in his introduction to my first translation (1910) of Freud's three essays on sex, and I can think of no finer estimate of Freud's contribution to sexology.

In his study of sex, Freud kept steadily in mind the total human personality. His formulation of infantile sexuality has opened new fields of interest in the realm of child study and education which already are yielding good results. Another concept which has been enormously helpful to physicians and educators is Freud's *libido* theory. In psychoanalysis libido signifies that quantitatively changeable and not at present measurable energy of the sexual instinct which is usually directed to an outside object. It comprises all those impulses which deal with love in the broad sense. Its main component is sexual love; and sexual union is its aim; but it also includes self-love, love for parents and children, friendship, attachments to concrete objects, and even devotion to abstract ideas.

For those who are unacquainted with Freud's theories of the neuroses, it will not be amiss to add a few remarks on the paths taken by the libido in neurotic states. The homestead of the libido is the ego; in the child the whole libido is centered in the ego, and we designate it as *ego libido*. The child may be said to be purely egoistic at first; but as he grows older and reaches the narcistic stage of development, we speak of *narcistic libido*, because the former ego libido has now become erotically tinged. Still later, when the child has successfully passed through the early phases of development and can transfer his libido to objects outside himself, that is, when he is genitally pubescent, we speak of *object libido*. Libido thus can be directed to outside objects or can be withdrawn back to the ego. A great many normal and pathological states depend on the resulting interchanges between these two forces. The transference neuroses, hysteria and compulsion neuroses, are determined by some disturbance in the give-and-take of object libido, and hence are curable by psychoanalytic therapy, whereas the narcistic neuroses, or the psychoses which are mainly controlled by narcistic libido, can be studied and helped, but cannot as yet be cured by analysis. The psychotic is, as a rule, inaccessible to this treatment because he is unable to transfer sufficient libido to the analyst. The psychotic is either too suspicious or too interested in his own inner world to pay any attention to the physician.

But leaving this problem to the psychoanalytic therapist, one must agree with Freud that by broadening the term sex into love or libido, much is gained for the understanding of the sexual activity of the normal person, of the child, and of the pervert. As will be shown later, the activities of all three spring from the same source, but the manifestations of each depend on the accidental factors to which they have been subjected by their early environments. Moreover, the libido concept loosens sexuality from its close connection with the genitals and establishes it as a more comprehensive physical function, which strives for pleasure in general, and only secondarily enters into the service of propagation. It also adds to the sexual sphere those affectionate and friendly feelings to which we ordinarily apply the term love. To illustrate the application of the libido concept clinically, let us take the case of a nervous child, keeping in mind Freud's dictum that no neurosis is possible in a wholly normal sexual life —a teaching which has aroused more resistances against psychoanalysis than any other utterance of Freud.

An apparently normal girl of about four became very nervous, refused most of her food, had frequent crying spells and tantrums, with consequent loss of weight, malaise, and insomnia, so that her condition became quite alarming. After the ordinary medical measures had been found of no avail, I was consulted. The case was so simple that I could not understand why no one had thought of the cure before I came on the scene. The child had begun to show the symptoms enumerated above, about two months after her mother was separated from her, and she was cured soon after her mother returned to her. I cannot go into the many details of this interesting case, but one can readily see that it differed materially from the case of the young woman mentioned earlier. There we dealt with a disturbance of adult sexuality, here with an emotional disturbance based on a deprivation of mother love in a very sensitive or neurotic child. Nevertheless, it was a disturbance in the child's love life. . . .

. . . *Sublimation*, another term coined by Freud, is a process of deflecting libido or sexual-motive activity from human objects to new objects of a non-sexual, socially valuable nature.

Sublimation gives justification for broadening the concept of sex. Most of our so-called feelings of tenderness and affection, which color so many of our activities and relations in life, originally form part of pure sexuality, and are later inhibited and deflected to higher aims. Thus, I have in mind a number of benevolent people who contributed much of their time and money to the protection and conservation of animals, who were extremely aggressive in childhood and ruthless Nimrods as adults. Their accentuated aggression originally formed a part of their childhood sexuality; then, as a result of training, it was first inhibited and directed to animals, and later altogether repressed and changed into sympathy. Now and then, we encounter cases in which repression and sublimation do not follow each other in regular succession, owing to some weakness or *fixation* which obstructs the process of development. This may lead to paradoxical situations. For example, a man, who was notorious as a great lover of animals, suffered while riding his favorite pony from sudden attacks during which he beat the animal mercilessly until he was exhausted, and then felt extreme remorse and pity for the beast. He would then dismount, pat the horse, appeasing him with lumps of sugar, and walk him home—sometimes a distance of three or four miles. We cannot here go into any analysis of this interesting case; all we can say is that the horse represented a mother symbol, and that the attacks, in which cruelty alternated with compassion, represented the ambivalent feeling of love and hatred which the patient unconsciously felt for his mother.

This patient was entirely changed by analysis, and although he has not given up his interest in animals and still contributes much to their comfort, he is no longer known to the neighborhood boys as "the man who pays a dollar for a sick cat or sick dog." Psychoanalytic literature is rich in clinical material which demonstrates the great benefits accrued from Freud's amplification of the sex concept. It not only gives us an understanding of the broad ramifications of sexual energy hitherto undreamed of, but it has also furnished us with an instrument for treatment and adjustment of many unfortunates who are no more responsible for their perversions than is the victim of infantile paralysis for his malady.

In his effort to understand the mechanism of the expressions observable in those erroneous actions illustrated in the *Psychopathology of Everyday Life*, as well as the distortions in dreams, Freud discerned a remarkable resemblance between these distortions and those found in wit. The following slip of the tongue shows that a slight substitution of one letter not only uncovers the real truth, but also provokes mirth. It was related to me many years ago by one of my patients. She was present at an evening dance of a wealthy, but not too generous, host, which continued until about midnight, when everybody expected a more or less substantial supper. Instead, just sandwiches and lemonade were served. Theodore Roosevelt was then running for President for the second time, under the slogan, "He gave us a square deal." While they were disappointedly consuming this modest repast, the guests were discussing the coming election with the host, and one of them remarked, "There is one fine thing about Teddy; he always gives you *a square meal*."

This *lapsus linguae* not only disclosed unwittingly what the speaker thought of the supper, discharging his hidden disappointment, but it also provoked an outburst of laughter among the guests, for they, through identification with the speaker, found outlet for their own disappointment. But unlike the speaker and the host, who were embarrassed by the mistake, the others experienced a sudden relaxation of the tension generated by disappointment and resentment, which expressed itself in laughter. This slight distortion changed the whole atmosphere of the party. Instead of resentful tension, the majority of the guests now felt relaxed and pleased. There is no doubt that there is a definite connection between faulty actions, dreams and wit. In all of them, the unconscious underlying thoughts are brought to consciousness in some sort of disguise, as if to say, "The truth cannot always be told openly, but somehow it does come out."

. . . Freud's interest in wit was a logical consequence of his free association technique. Once he became convinced that nothing must be ignored —that whatever the patient expressed, be it in mimicry or in sounds, formed part of an effort to release something indirectly because circumstances prevented direct expression—once this fact dawned upon him, it was simply a question of classifying the various forms of distortion and showing in what function of the psychic apparatus they were manifested. The mechanisms of *condensation, displacement, substitution, illogical thinking, absurdity, indirect expressions, elisions,* and *representation through the opposite,* are all present in everyday conversation, but such conventional inaccuracies glide by without any evident impediments. When the thought in question meets with inner resistances, however, a lapse of some kind occurs, which the speaker recognizes and at once excuses by some such expression as "I mean . . ." or "Oh, I made a mistake." The average person readily accepts such excuses, not realizing that by the slip of the tongue the speaker has unconsciously betrayed his resistance to something in the present situation. The disguises seen in the simple lapses of everyday life are even more evident in dreams because *censorship* is more or less abolished during sleep; but fundamentally they are the same. In wit these mental disguises are especially evident, but here they are utilized to produce pleasure. They, too, are products of the unconscious, and show that no matter how much restriction civilization imposes on the individual, he nevertheless finds some way to circumvent it. Wit is the best safety valve modern man has evolved; the more civilization, the more repression, the more need there is for wit. Only relatively civilized people have a sense of humor. The child and the true primitive show no such mechanisms. The child like the savage is still natural and frank. When the child begins to dream, which shows that repressive forces are already at work, he also shows the beginnings of a sense of humor.

The most pronounced psychopathological expressions which point to a deep-seated disturbance are *hallucinations* and *delusions,* which occur in adult psychotics and show a somewhat different kind of disguise. The hallucination as a verbal expression is neither witty nor in any other way distorted. The only thing peculiar about it is that the patient hears, sees, or feels something which is not perceived by anyone else. To be sure, the patient's statements do not concur with the objective facts; yet he is not lying; subjectively speaking, he actually perceives everything he says he does. But we know from Freud that hallucinations represent outward projections of inner feelings. Thus, a woman who has seemingly been living quite contentedly with her husband for five years, hears people say that she is a "bad woman," that her husband is divorcing her, and that she has had illicit relations with a well known movie star. At the same time she complains of peculiar feelings like pin-pricks and electricity in certain parts of her body. These statements could be true, but they are not. We, therefore, call them hallucinatory.

And indeed, the whole picture of the disease in this case showed that the woman suffered from hallucinations of hearing, sight, and sensation. Their meaning became plain when her mother informed me that her son-in-law had been impotent all these years, but that her daughter neverthe-less loved him and would not consider leaving him. The hallucinations depicted the wish to be divorced and be married to a real man as a recom-pense for her drab existence. The annoyance and displeasure caused by "all that talk" and by the peculiar prickling sensations, represented the pangs of conscience, or the feeling of guilt which accompanied her erotic phantasies. The distortion in this whole picture consisted of a fusion of feelings and ideas which had played a part in the conflict in the mind of this sensitive patient. She could not decide one way or the other, so she tore herself entirely away from reality and behaved, as we say, *dereis-tically*. She abandoned all logic and objectified her phantasies in disguised fashion. . . .

It is quite clear that the distortions manifested in the psychoses are shown by the whole behavior of the person rather than through verbal expressions. Verbal distortions as seen in lapses, errors, blunders in speech and action, are immediate responses to a struggle between the ego and the id. No matter how anxious we are to hide our true nature in adjust-ing ourselves to the repressive forces of civilization, repression sometimes fails and our real desires come to the surface. The dream is a hidden ful-fillment of a repressed wish, or a direct attempt to obtain in phantasy what is denied us in reality. Wit is a direct effort to make use of dis-tortions in order to obtain pleasure from otherwise forbidden sources. Both lapses and dreams are momentary illusions which render a very quick and very brief service to the organism. Wit, on the other hand, is a conscious mechanism for the production of pleasure, the highest or latest development of civilization in this direction. We like to tell jokes and listen to them because for the moment we not only forget inexorable reality, but also obtain pleasure at the expense of our hardships.

But in all these phenomena we remain in touch with reality; the mis-take, the dream and the joke amply demonstrate this. The psychosis ex-hibits alone no compromise with reality, turns its back on reality, as it were. Yet, even in a psychosis, symptoms show that there is a constant struggle between fancy and reality. A chronic schizophrenic may remain in a hospital for years in a state of indifference, but now and then he may suddenly act like a rational being. Sometimes a severe shock, such as an accident or illness which threatens his self-preservative instinct, brings the schizophrenic back to reality for a time. The latest form of therapy for schizophrenics is based on this very idea. I am referring to the insulin or, as it is called, the shock therapy, because the patient re-ceives such a shock through the hypoglycemia that for a time at least he gives up his phantasy world. But it matters little whether hypoglycemia ʒures or only produces a transient change; the fact that schizophrenics occasionally return to normality spontaneously and then relapse, and the fact that an accidental or experimental shock can drive them back to reality at least for a time, clearly shows that the psychotic, too, is not altogether detached from reality. . . .

That the world which at first turned its back on him [Freud] has now recognized his great services to science and culture is shown by the many honors that have been showered upon him within the last few years. To mention only one of many: His eightieth birthday was an international event. It was celebrated in Vienna at the *Wiener Konzerthaus* and was attended by distinguished scientists from Vienna and abroad. The birthday oration, which was delivered by Thomas Mann, is a masterpiece which has been translated into many languages.

1938

PART SIX

THE ROCKET AND THE ATOM

Synopsis

A. Rockets, Missiles, Space

IT IS NO EXAGGERATION TO STATE THAT AS OUR FOURTH
Edition appears, a wholly new age, the Age of Space, has arrived in the
history of mankind. With Sputnik, travel to other planets in our solar system,
and perhaps even beyond, has ceased to be a visionary dream and entered the
realm of the practicable. The instrument is the rocket. It is still in its early
stages of development, but already thinking about it plays a major part not
only in the field of travel but in that of warfare as well.

What is the basic principle of rocketry and how does it work? G. Edward
Pendray is one of the earliest pioneers in American rocketry, as well as a
gifted and lucid writer. He explains the fundamentals in Reaction Motors.
As always in science, the steps from theory to practical application are difficult.
Our present working models are exceedingly complex and each working part
must function exactly if a launching is to be a success. There was an unjust
national outcry when our first launching after Sputnik proved a failure.
Hundreds of such launchings, both successful and the reverse, had already
taken place. Time and again the failure of a single component among
thousands had caused disaster. A dramatic example of such a disaster is
described in We Learn a Lesson, by Milton Rosen, a technical expert at the
White Sands Proving Ground.

The step from simple rocket to earth satellite involves a new set of concepts having their basis in fundamental astronomical theory. The average
individual is confused by the problem of what keeps a satellite in its orbit,
neither falling to earth nor escaping into space. With the aid of Newton's
laws and with a minimum of technical detail, the British physicist and

writer Arthur C. Clarke answers the question in A Shot Around the World.

Yet another step remains. We have the knowledge, both theoretical and practical, to get our satellite into position. But this is not to say that we can launch it with living creatures and have them return to earth safely. Our next article is concerned with the problems raised and how they can be solved. From Russia, which made the first great step, comes P. Isakov's Life in Sputnik. A comparison of this article with similar ones written in America re-emphasizes the universality of science.

Is it possible that on one of our voyages into space we will encounter life as we know it or even thinking creatures like ourselves? One of the leading British astronomers, Sir James Jeans, poses the mathematical and biological possibilities in his notable article Is There Life on Other Worlds?

B. The Power of the Atom: An End or a Beginning?

Since the first atomic bomb was exploded over Hiroshima, it has been stated innumerable times that our new knowledge can result either in complete extinction of the human race or in an earthly paradise. In this section we examine some of the factors which bear on both aspects of the subject.

First come definitions, in Atomic Terms and What They Mean, originally issued as a small booklet by the Esso Research and Engineering Company. Next we turn to the military achievements and the radiation hazards involved in fission and fusion. Henry D. Smyth's Atomic Energy for Military Purposes, published shortly after the surrender of Japan, is the definitive work on its subject. The selection from it which is reprinted here catches the excitement of the historic moment when an international group of scientists first caught the implications of the laboratory experiment which proved that atomic fusion had taken place and that the energy of the atom had been released.

From fission to fusion has been a rapid and relatively easy step, whose details continue to be shrouded in military secrecy. But in the historical perspective of Jacob Sacks' Atomic Warfare, Past and Future we learn something of how science discovered a new type of bomb which in theory has no power limitations and in practice is already measured in units thousands of times greater than the first baby atomic bombs.

Explosive power is only one and possibly the least of the dangers inherent in nuclear bombs. A greater danger is that of radiation poisoning and the possible extermination of living things on earth. It is this danger which is the subject of the next articles. The first is the short and dramatic The Death of Louis Slotin by Ralph E. Lapp. Slotin used primitive methods in making his experiments. More important, he failed to heed the warnings given him. He suffered the consequences.

Is humanity now in similar danger on a global scale? Our finest scientific minds are examining this question with increasing concern. Controversy rages. To illuminate it we have chosen two dispassionate articles from authoritative sources. Radiations and the Genetic Threat, which describes a single aspect of the problem, is by Warren Weaver, President of the Rockefeller Foundation. It is based on information collected by the National Academy of Sciences, our foremost scientific society. Next we print a report by the Academy entitled Recommendations for Protection Against Radiation Exposure. The program it suggests is obviously incomplete. It does not take fully into account the possibility of open nuclear warfare designed to eliminate an enemy. Against such an eventuality there seems at present to be no adequate defense.

There is another and brighter side to the coin. Conceivably atomic power, by alleviating want and suffering, can eliminate the basic cause of power struggle and warfare among nations. Nuclear reactors will someday furnish power far greater than that supplied by natural resources like coal and oil. In the space of a decade nuclear products are playing an ever more important role in industry and medicine. These are the developments which are described in Nuclear Power in the Future by J. R. Dunning, Industrial Uses of Isotopes, a Report of the United States Atomic Energy Commission, and Isotopes in Medicine and Biology by Hendrik M. Rozendahl.

The problem of the future of man is not basically scientific in nature. The scientist provides us with the knowledge and the tools. He does not tell us how to use them. The solution, as Raymond B. Fosdick points out in A Layman Looks at Science, rests with all of us. On the wisdom of the present generation may rest the destiny of humanity.

Reaction Motors: How They Work and Some Experiments with Them

G. EDWARD PENDRAY

———

JET PROPULSION IS ROCKET POWER. THERMAL-JET engines, duct engines, jet motors, jet-propelled planes, robot bombs, jet-propelled gliders, war rockets, thrusters and skyrockets—all of these are merely different aspects of rocket power. All of them, as we shall see, operate on exactly the same basic principle: the principle of a motor that *thrusts* or pushes, instead of producing rotary motion in a shaft or wheel.

This is the one simple difference that makes rocket power unique—and incidentally makes it so difficult at first for our wheel-conditioned minds to grasp. A few thousand years ago some person, now unknown and long forgotten, invented the wheel. It was such a successful device, so easily adapted to doing its share of the world's work, that when fuel-burning engines were first developed they naturally were made to be harnessed to it. The reciprocating motion of their pistons was transformed by means of a crank into a rotary movement for only one purpose: to turn wheels. Even when we set the engine to the task of moving us through the air, we did so through the medium of a kind of wheel, the propeller.

To understand the principle of jet propulsion, we must think therefore in terms of an engine that does not turn a wheel; a new kind of engine, working on a totally new principle; differing from all the other engines of the world; an engine that *thrusts*.

Such an engine is known as a reaction motor, and reaction motors of all kinds, whether rocket motors, jet engines or duct engines, produce their thrust by a unique method. They simply jet out a stream of gas or other material at high velocity. The resulting reaction is what provides the push. That is why, of course, the principle of the reaction motor is known as *jet propulsion*.

The first apparatus ever proposed to make use of jet propulsion was described by Heron, or Hero, a philosopher of old Alexandria, about the beginning of the Christian Era. Heron was an ingenious man who also invented a slot machine and a fire engine. In one of his books, the *Pneumatica,* he outlined plans for building a little device called the "aeolipile." It consisted of a hollow sphere mounted on pivots, equipped with two opposed bent metal spouts. Steam under pressure was introduced into the sphere through a pipe in one of the supports. The vapor, spurting from the curved spouts, caused the sphere to spin rapidly. . . .

The skyrocket, which aside from Heron's toylike contrivance was the first artificial device to make use of jet propulsion, was invented more than seven hundred years ago. But neither Heron nor the hundreds of generations of fireworks makers . . . had any real understanding of the principle of jet propulsion. They only knew it worked.

It remained for Sir Isaac Newton, some 265 years ago, to give us the basis for understanding what rocket power really is, and the unique things it can do. Newton, formulating in simple language the three Laws of Motion his mathematics and observation had helped him to discover, wrote out in Latin this observation: "To every action there is always an equal and contrary reaction; the mutual actions of any two bodies are always equal and oppositely directed."

Thus, the hand that pushes a cradle is itself pushed *by* the cradle, to exactly the same degree and in the opposite direction. The foot that thrusts downward on the earth is *thrust upward* by the earth in precisely the same amount. The bullet that is ejected by a gun causes the gun to recoil—and the two actions are not only opposite in direction, but are equal in amount.

This is the statement of Newton's Third Law of Motion. Although it describes a phenomenon we daily experience throughout our lives, few people consider or even recognize the reaction that necessarily is a part of every movement of every object. It is important that we recognize it now, for the Third Law is a complete statement of the principle upon which the reaction motor operates.

In most human activities the *action* is what is wanted; the reaction is thrown away or ignored. In jet propulsion, the "action" is thrown away. The *reaction* is the particular harvest we are seeking.

The simplest form of reaction motor—and the best known—is the one that drives an ordinary skyrocket.

Here is a cross-section drawing of a skyrocket. At the tip is a cone-shaped cap which provides rudimentary streamlining to aid the rapid upward flight of the projectile. Immediately under the cap usually are nested the combustible pellets, the "stars" that cascade brilliantly into the sky at the top of the flight. These are the payload of the skyrocket; they are not a basic part of the rocket itself.

Into the main body of the rocket, usually contained in a heavy paper tube, a quantity of black powder is packed. This is the fuel or *propellant* charge, (*A*). The material is usually a form of ordinary gunpowder, often mixed with extra charcoal or some other material to slow down the rate of combustion. It is squeezed into the rocket under high pressure, thus packed tightly into a solid cake. Because it is solid, the flame cannot permeate the cake, so combustion takes place only at the exposed surface of the cone-shaped *blast chamber, (B)*.

The simple thrust mechanism—or *motor*—of the rocket is completed by constricting the walls of the case below the blast chamber to form a nozzle. Sometimes the throat of the nozzle is reinforced with clay or other hard material to prevent its burning out. A fuse (*D*) and a long stick—a crude balancing device—complete the rocket.

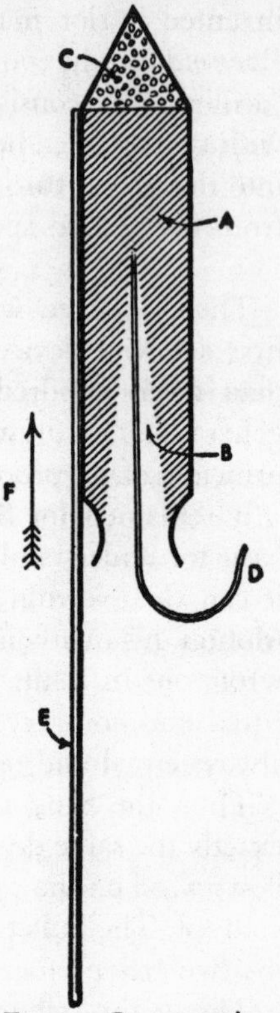

On firing, what happens is this:

Heat from the fuse ignites the surface of the powder on the walls of the cone-shaped blast chamber. The powder does not explode, but a continuous combustion takes place very rapidly, releasing large quantities of gas at high temperature. Considerable pressure builds up instantly in the chamber, since the hot gas is formed at a much faster rate than it can easily escape through the restriction at the nozzle.

Fig. 1. Cross section of a skyrocket.

The net effect is to eject a stream of gas at great velocity, directed backward. This thrusts the rocket forcibly in the opposite direction.

As the fuel burns, the blast chamber rapidly enlarges, but the restriction at the nozzle continues to keep the pressure high and guides the escaping jet. The rocket takes off with a tremendous swish, emitting a stream of sparks and fire, and flies until the fuel is completely consumed. Then an arrangement at the top of the tube fires the "stars" and the bursting charge in which they are packed.

In a jet motor such as that of the skyrocket there are no moving parts—except the stream of escaping gas. It is by no means easy to grasp just how this jet, with nothing to push against, exerts the surprising power that thrusts the whole body of the rocket so violently toward the sky.

The common notion is that the jet does its work by pushing against the air. Superficially this seems reasonable. The air is certainly a resisting medium. But a stream of gas, no matter how rapidly it is moving, or how dense it may be, is no solid connecting rod, capable of pushing against something and transmitting the push back against whatever is adjacent to its starting end. Gas consists of billions upon billions of tiny hard pellets—the molecules of which it is composed. These are not connected together in any way. On the contrary, they are seeking to escape from each other as fast as possible, expanding like a cloud of steam.

The surrounding air similarly consists of random, flying molecules. When a molecule of ejected gas strikes a molecule of air, the collision sends both off in other directions and with altered speeds. But how could such a collision, even when multiplied by the thousands of billions, drive a rocket which is not in any way connected to them? Drive it, moreover, in a specific direction?

The answer, of course, is that they couldn't. The air in no way helps to drive the rocket. It only impedes the action—by getting in the way of the projectile in front, and hindering the rapid, straight-line ejection of the gas behind.

It is something else that drives the rocket—and this brings us back to Newton and his Law of Motion: "To every action there is always an equal and contrary reaction; the mutual actions of any two bodies are always equal and oppositely directed."

Consider the ejected gas as one "body"; the rocket as the other.

The rocket, forcing the gas to escape, pushes it violently toward the earth. The gas, escaping, pushes the rocket as violently toward the sky.

This is jet propulsion, or rocket power, the simple principle of the reaction motor.

It may still not be entirely clear exactly how this mysterious reaction occurs. Here is another drawing that may help in the further understanding of it.

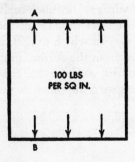

A

100 LBS
PER SQ IN.

B

Fig. 2.

Imagine a hollow box, filled with gas under pressure. For convenience, let us say the pressure is 100 pounds per square inch. This means, of course, that every square inch on the inside of the box will be pushed upon by gas with a steady pressure of 100 pounds. Under these conditions the box itself will not move in any direction, for the total pressure on each side will exactly balance the total pressure on the opposite side.

Now, suppose a hole were to be cut in side

B, exactly (for convenience in doing our mental arithmetic) one square inch in area. At once we have a new condition in the box, as shown in the second diagram. Note that the pressure exerted by the gas on side *B* is now no longer exactly equal to that on side *A.* It is, in fact, 100 pounds less. The box will therefore be pushed in the direction of the arrow *E,* with a force of 100 pounds. The push will continue as long as we bring in fresh supplies of gas or fuel, as at D, to keep the pressure in the box at the established level.

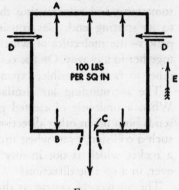

Fig. 3.

In essentials, this is how things go in the reaction motor. An important refinement is the addition of a nozzle at *C,* to direct the escaping gas and control its expansion. This facilitates the movement of the stream and adds to the thrust, often as much as 35 to 50 per cent or more.

The approximate thrust or push of any reaction motor may be calculated by multiplying the area of the orifice of the throat (*C*) by the pressure of the gas in the chamber, and adding about 50 per cent for the additional contribution of the nozzle. The exact value of the thrust will, of course, vary according to several factors, including the fuel used, the pressure of the gas, completeness of combustion and an experimentally determined item rocket engineers call "the constant of the nozzle," which depends upon the nozzle size, shape and other factors.[1] . . .

So far as the basic principles are concerned, all jet-propulsion motors obey the same laws, and in that sense are identical. When it comes to practical application of these laws, it is soon seen that a bewildering number and variety of motors can be contrived, ranging all the way from low-powered water, steam or compressed-air jets to motors that produce a high-speed blast by burning gasoline, alcohol, benzol, hydrogen, or other fuels.

Moreover, there is at least one broad line of division among all the various types of reaction motors, according to the way in which oxygen is obtained for the combustion. If the oxygen is taken from the surrounding atmosphere, by compression of the air or other means, we have the class appropriately called the *airstream engines.*[2] If oxygen is supplied in the

---

[1] The thrust can also be calculated, of course, by applying the formula $T = MV$, where T is thrust, M is the mass ejected per second, and V is the velocity of the jet in feet per second.

[2] Also called *airjet engines,* etc.

form of liquid oxygen or some oxygen-yielding compound, the motor is designated as a *true rocket* or *chemical fuel motor.*

Each of these major groups is further subdivided. There are, for example, at least two basically different types of the true rocket motors, and at least three types, so far, of the airstream engines. Since we shall have frequent occasion to refer to these several types of motors and engines, this table may prove a convenient point of reference:

TYPES AND CLASSES OF REACTION MOTORS

I. *The true rocket, or chemical fuel motors:*
   A. The solid-fuel rocket motor (burns solid fuels such as gunpowder or smokeless powder).
   B. The liquid-fuel motor (burns fuels such as liquid oxygen and gasoline, or liquid oxygen and alcohol).
II. *The airstream engines:*
   A. The thermal jet engine (burns a variety of possible fuels, including gasoline and kerosene, with air delivered into the combustion chamber by means of a rotary compressor).
   B. The intermittent duct engine (burns gasoline or similar fuels with air, compressed into the blast chamber by the ram effect. Action is pulsating or intermittent).
   C. The continuous duct engine (burns the same fuels as the intermittent engine; also depends on atmospheric oxygen compressed by ram effect, but its action is continuous).

From this table we see that there is first of all the simple *solid-fuel rocket motor,* the kind that drives skyrockets and many types of military rockets such as the bazooka, the airplane rockets and the British "Z-gun" anti-aircraft rocket.

Second, there is the *liquid-fuel rocket motor,* which provides power for many types of thrusters, catapults and some types of military rockets, also for such long-range rockets as the German "V-2" rocket weapon. Because of the energy in the fuels it can burn, the liquid-fuel motor is potentially the most powerful type of all. To liquid-fuel motors rocket engineers of the future will turn for power to send sounding rockets high into the atmosphere, to shoot mail and express over long distances, and to serve as auxiliary or even primary power for high-flying, super-fast stratoliners of a coming age.

Among the airstream engines, the best known is the *thermal jet engine,* also called the "turbo-jet engine," the "turbo-jet" or the "swish." . . .

The other types of airstream engines are *duct engines,* much simpler than the jet engine in that they require almost no moving parts, and get along without either air compressors or turbine wheels. They do, however, require that the aircraft or glider to which they are attached be given a rapid preliminary start. Duct engines, having no air compressor of their own, depend at least partly on the compression or "ram effect" of the air during flight to provide them with oxygen to burn their fuels.

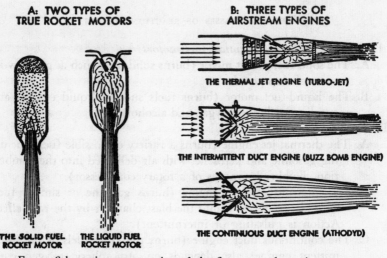

A: TWO TYPES OF
TRUE ROCKET MOTORS

B: THREE TYPES OF
AIRSTREAM ENGINES

THE THERMAL JET ENGINE (TURBO-JET)

THE INTERMITTENT DUCT ENGINE (BUZZ BOMB ENGINE)

THE CONTINUOUS DUCT ENGINE (ATHODYD)

THE SOLID FUEL
ROCKET MOTOR

THE LIQUID FUEL
ROCKET MOTOR

Fig. 4. Schematic representation of the five types of reaction motors.

The earliest successful duct engine was the "buzz-bomb engine," used by the Germans to propel their robot bombs in 1944 against London and southern England. It does not operate with a continuous blast, as does the thermal jet engine and the generally used types of rocket motors,[3] but proceeds by a series of pulses or intermittent explosions, hence the name.

Still under development is the *continuous duct engine,* more usually called the ramjet, which may ultimately serve as auxiliary power for fast-flying aircraft. In principle it is similar to the intermittent type, depending on the ram effect of the air for compression, but at suitable high velocity it will produce a continuous blast of power.

These, then, are the engines for the coming age of rocket power: the solid- and liquid-fuel rocket motors, the two kinds of duct engines, and

---

[3] It should be noted that the true rocket motors may also operate intermittently. An intermittent type of dry-fuel motor was developed by Dr. Robert H. Goddard as early as 1916.

the turbo-jet. Simplest of all, essentially, are the rocket motors, and it is to them we shall turn for the rest of this chapter. . . .

Historically, of course, the solid-fuel rocket motors were the earliest to appear. If we look once more at the skyrocket, the most familiar of the true rocket motors, we will perceive that the motor and the fuel supply are there most ingeniously combined. The fuel is made to provide its own motor, in the form of the cone-shaped blast cavity which rapidly enlarges as the fuel burns away.

This form of rocket motor offers no problems of metallurgy, because there is no metal. There is no problem about the burning out of the walls, for so long as they consist of fuel, burning is what is desired. This rocket motor obviously does very well the job it is designed to do. Unfortunately it does not provide us with a good pattern for rocket motors of more power and utility.

For one thing, the gas pressure is necessarily low, whereas good efficiency requires a relatively high pressure, measured in hundreds of pounds per square inch. Why is the pressure low? Because if it were higher, it would burst the paper tube in which the rocket is contained, or blow out the flimsy nozzle—or more likely still, cause the flame to permeate the powder charge, no matter how tightly packed. This might set the whole fuel supply off at once, resulting in an explosion instead of a flight.

Another problem with the skyrocket motor is that the combustion chamber changes shape and size continually throughout the run. At the beginning it is small. During the burning it rapidly enlarges. But since its enlargement depends both upon the rate and uniformity of the combustion of the fuel, the shape changes, too, along with the size. If for a given fuel, gas pressure, nozzle and other conditions there is only one best shape, the skyrocket can have it, at most, for only a fraction of a second. During the rest of its operation it is bound to be doing a less satisfactory job.

These problems of the skyrocket motor are shared by all forms of solid-fuel motors, though by ingenious methods some have been designed to overcome the worst difficulties.

The first considerable improvement was the application of a metal nozzle, properly shaped to give maximum aid to the escaping gases. Such a nozzle immediately improves the performance of the motor. Pressure can then be increased by substituting smokeless powder or cordite for the fuel, and exchanging metal or strong laminated plastic containers for the paper ones. This, however, may introduce a new problem: the new containers may weigh more than the paper, and if the chamber pressure is to be increased a great deal, we must be careful to see that the extra weight of the stronger jacket does not nullify the gain obtained from a more powerful fuel.

Dr. Robert H. Goddard, whose pioneer work established the modern period of rocket research, gave considerable study at one time to the problem of improving the performance of the solid-fuel motor. He discovered that the average velocity of ejection in an ordinary skyrocket was only about 1,000 feet a second, but when he fired charges of dense smokeless powder in strong steel chambers, with properly shaped smooth tapered nozzles, he obtained velocities of ejection up to nearly 8,000 feet per second. Assuming the masses ejected to be the same, the impulse of the later rocket motor would be eight times as great, with the same weight of fuel, and thus would theoretically drive a rocket not eight but sixty-four times as far—a very considerable reward for thus increasing the jet velocity.

However, it is not possible to add a steel jacket and metal nozzle without adding weight; so as a practical matter the skyrocket and the smokeless powder rocket could hardly start with weights, fuel charges and other factors even. The smokeless powder rocket would have to weigh more, or else carry less fuel or payload at the start.

To get around this it was early suggested by Dr. Goddard that the blast chamber should not be merely a cavity in the fuel supply, but a separate contrivance, into which the fuel could be inserted as needed. Several ingenious ways were suggested for doing this. Dr. Goddard's proposal was to shoot pellets of fuel into the chamber intermittently, like machine-gun bullets.[4] Similar ideas offered by other experimenters include thrusting a solid stick of fuel rapidly into the chamber through an orifice, the speed of insertion being equal to the rate of burning, or powdering the fuel and blowing it in by air or gas, through suitable inlet ports.

If one or another of these ideas were adopted, only the motor chamber (which could be relatively small) would need to be strong enough to withstand the high gas pressure of the blast; the fuel container could be light and flimsy, and thus add very little to the weight.

Unfortunately, any apparatus for shooting pellets into the chamber is likely to be heavy, expensive and cantankerous, full of personal little kinks and problems of its own. Blowing the powder into the chamber with gas pressure is no easy one to handle, either. Likewise, the idea of thrusting a stick of fuel into the chamber through some sort of opening runs into very special headaches, including the difficulty of sealing the edges of the

---

[4] Dr. Goddard patented such an intermittent rocket apparatus in 1914, and brought it to a good state of development during the first World War. He later gave up this line of experiment, however, in favor of liquid-fuel motors.

orifice against back pressure without also making it too hard to push the fuel in. Too, there is the matter of judging to a high degree of accuracy just how fast the fuel will burn—solid fuels being particularly variable in this respect.

The upshot is that while the application of one or another of these ideas might possibly further improve the performance of solid-fuel rockets, experimenters and military experts have preferred to continue using solid-fuel rockets of the simpler sort—taking the disadvantages in exchange for the convenience and general freedom from worry that solid-fuel rockets without internal mechanism can have at the site of battle.

This should not be taken to mean that great advances have not been made, however. The demand for powerful, simple, dependable war rockets of many kinds has put great pressure on technical rocket men. The improvements have been almost countless, and include better metal and plastic jackets, proper metal nozzles—and above all, better fuels.

Practically all of the new fuels are related to cordite, of course.[5] There are now not only many types of these propellants, but the charges are being made in a variety of ways, one of the most interesting being extrusion. In this process the material is made in plastic form and pushed through dies—usually in factories operated by remote control—to produce long rods or tubes of the fuel material of just the right size and shape to fit into the rocket bodies. These need only cutting to proper length and final insertion.

In most modern military rockets the fuel is burned with great rapidity. In the bazooka, for example, the whole charge goes off in a fraction of a second, while the rocket is traversing the length of the eight-foot launching tube.

The quick-burning effect is produced by a process just the reverse of that used in the skyrocket, where the powder is tightly packed to keep the flame from permeating it. In the quick-burning solid-fuel rocket, the charge is specially prepared to encourage the flame to get almost everywhere at once. If gunpowder or smokeless powder is used, the load may be in the form of "doughnuts" or pressed fuel, packed with loose powder to propagate the flame. If it is cordite or some other of the more powerful explosives, the charge may be fluted, hollowed or drilled full of holes, so the flame can eat it quickly, over a large surface.

The effect of this quick burning is to produce a takeoff almost like a cannon shot. The rocket gets away with a quick "ffff-tt." The flame is

[5] This statement is no longer true. By 1958 solid fuels of many different types and bases were being employed, and in many instances solid-fuel rockets were competing actively with their liquid-fuel counterparts for long-range-missile and space-flight uses.

hardly more than a brilliant flash and then gone. The projectile flies almost all of the way to its target on momentum, obeying the same laws of ballistics as an artillery shell.

For such short-range devices as military rockets, the dry-fuel motor does very well; in fact it is the only practical type. But this kind of motor will never give the power and sustained performance needed for high-altitude sounding rockets, for example, or long-range military or trajectory rockets.[6] For these, we must turn to the liquid-fuel motor.

The solid-fuel rocket has obvious limitations which the liquid-fuel motor appears to overcome readily—but in so doing it introduces a host of new problems all its own.

To begin with, it is a device that functions only in the presence of intense heat. The temperature within a liquid-fuel rocket motor is almost always at or above the melting point of the materials of which it is constructed. Moreover, there is an enormous contrast in temperatures from one part of the motor to another. At the point where the fuel enters, the thermometer may register as low as the boiling point of liquid oxygen, −297 degrees Fahrenheit. At the hottest point, the temperature may be at least half that of the surface of the sun.

The burden which these conditions put upon a simple, small and necessarily light structure is enormous. The surprising thing is that a liquid-fuel motor made of metals can operate at all. Yet motors have been developed in this country to give sustained performance for indefinite periods, to provide thrusts from a few pounds to 6,000 pounds or more[7] and weighing for the largest sizes, about 200 pounds, or about ½ ounce per pound of thrust. Smaller ones, capable of yielding thrusts up to 100 pounds, may be nested in the hand, and weigh less than a pound.

The high temperature at which the liquid-fuel motor must be operated to produce suitable results is no mere temporary obstacle which some ingenious trick or discovery may some day solve. Rather, it is inherent in the nature of fuels and jet velocities. It is the principal limiting factor on the operation of any jet motor.

To obtain a jet velocity of between 6,000 and 7,000 feet per second with fuels of the type in general use, the temperature inside the combustion chamber must be around 5,000 degrees Fahrenheit. To obtain a jet velocity of 8,000 feet per second, a blast-chamber temperature of about 8,000 degrees Fahrenheit is required. A jet velocity of 10,000 feet per second will need a

[6] See footnote 5. Solid fuels have undergone very considerable development since this statement was first written in 1944.

[7] The thrust developed by the German "V-2" rocket motor, a liquid-fuel type, is more than 26 tons. Motors used in long-range missiles and for space flight may have thrusts of one million pounds or more.

temperature of 12,200 degrees, and a 12,000 foot-per-second jet can be generated only by operating at a temperature of some 17,300 degrees. No ordinary constructional metals, of course, will stand any of these temperatures, except for very brief periods. . . .

The melting point of aluminum, the most commonly used material for rockets because of its lightness, is 1218 degrees Fahrenheit, or only about a fourth of the temperature required to produce a 6,000 to 7,000 foot-persecond jet. The melting point of steel, which is often used in motor construction is around 2,200 degrees; still well below the temperature of the 6,000 to 7,000 foot motor. . . .

Almost every rocket experimenter has seen motors of the finest steel burn out in less than a second of firing. At these temperatures it is not so much a matter of melting as of erosion. The metal behaves somewhat like an icicle in the flame of a blowtorch. The surface melts or softens. Then the furious blast of the escaping jet carries the softened part away, exposing new material underneath. Almost before the metal of the motor has become hot clear through, it has been cut to pieces by this process. Under such circumstances all ordinary ideas of cooling are futile.

Dr. Robert H. Goddard was the first experimenter on record to tackle the liquid-fuel motor problem, and was also the first to shoot a rocket powered by a liquid-fuel motor. The German experimenters of the *Verein für Raumschiffahrt* (German Rocket Society), however, were quicker than Goddard to report their experiences. Consequently, the history of their early attempts to harness liquid fuels is a well known and highly instructive tale.

Their first idea was to place the blast chamber of the motor directly in the liquid oxygen tank, thus allowing the cold oxygen itself to cool the metal. It was an ingenious scheme, but in the initial design the intense heat of the motor raised such sudden pressure that the oxygen tank ultimately exploded. The motor was cone-shaped; a direct descendant of the cavity in the skyrocket's fuel load. The nozzle, which projected out of the bottom of the oxygen tank, was about three inches long. Blast chamber, nozzle, and oxygen tank were made of an aluminum alloy, chosen for its lightness and the rapidity with which it conducted heat.

In their next attempt, the experimenters produced an oxygen tank which had a larger safety valve, and the motor also was larger. Its performance, however, was very much like the first. In both of these motors the fuels were introduced through separate inlet ports near the throat of the nozzle, and were forcibly injected upward by gas pressure.

The tests taught several lessons, not the least of which was that liquid oxygen is not a very satisfactory coolant. It also became clear that a cone-shaped chamber is not an effective design. The volume of the chamber is too small in relation to the area of its surface, and the sharp corners where the nozzle joins obstruct the rapid flow of the gases.

A later motor developed by these experimenters and demonstrated in 1931 to Mrs. Pendray and me as representatives of the American Rocket Society had many improvements. The motor was cooled by running water. The material was aluminum alloy, and the blast chamber was what the experimenters called "egg shaped," though inspection showed it to be cylindrical, with each end finished off in a hemisphere. The propellants came in through two ports near the throat, directed upward so the streams of liquid oxygen and gasoline would meet near the radius of the upper hemisphere.

This motor was small, weighing about a pound. It produced a thrust of about 20 pounds, at a calculated jet velocity of about 6,000 feet per second.

Perhaps the best known pioneer series of motor experiments ever reported were those made under the auspices of the American Rocket Society between 1932 and the beginning of the Second World War.

The society's first motor was based principally on German designs. I returned to this country with the ideas on which it was constructed following the *Verein für Raumschiffahrt* demonstration in 1931. The motor was not merely a duplication of the German work. Made of cast aluminum alloy, it was considerably heavier than the German motor. The blast chamber was cylindrical, with hemispheric ends, and measured two inches in diameter and three inches in length. The nozzle was three inches long, with a half-inch throat and a taper of about ten degrees.

The inside of the nozzle was carefully machined and the inner surface finished to mirrorlike smoothness. The fuel inlets were bored—after the German fashion—in such a way as to introduce the fuel near the nozzle, in streams directed toward the back of the motor. The theory of this was, simply, that such a position for the inlets would make the fuel travel substantially twice the length of the motor, and thus provide for some cooling effect along the walls as well as better mixing and combustion. It was an excellent theory, but subsequent experiences indicated that it did not work well in practice, and it was later abandoned.

The first test took place at a proving ground near Stockton, New Jersey, on November 12, 1932. The motor was mounted for the test between two pipelike cylindrical tanks, one of which contained liquid oxygen; the other gasoline under nitrogen gas pressure of 300 pounds per square inch. A water jacket surrounded the motor for cooling. The whole contrivance was fastened between two parallel upright wooden bars, on which it was free to slide against the tension of a spring. Previously the spring had been calibrated so that by measuring the distance traveled against its tension, the experimenters would be able to determine the thrust of the motor.

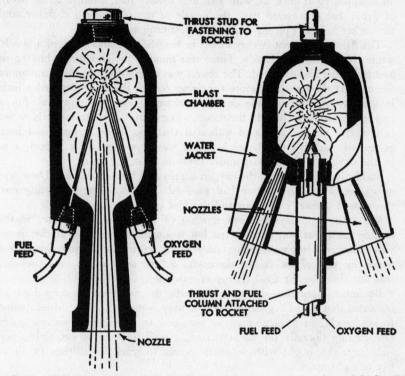

THRUST STUD FOR
FASTENING TO
ROCKET

BLAST
CHAMBER

WATER
JACKET

NOZZLES

FUEL
FEED

OXYGEN
FEED

THRUST AND FUEL
COLUMN ATTACHED
TO ROCKET

FUEL FEED   OXYGEN FEED

NOZZLE

FIG. 5. Two early types of liquid-fuel rocket motors. *Left*—the original ARS motor, designed by the author and H. F. Pierce; *right,* a four-nozzle motor designed by John Shesta for the ARS No. 4 rocket.

The report[8] on the first test, as published in *Astronautics* for November 1932, read in part as follows:

We had previously decided that the fuels should be turned on almost simultaneously, the oxygen first, the gasoline close behind. I judged that the fuse was going properly to light the fuels. About three minutes had passed since the final turning down of the oxygen valve. Enough pressure should have been built up to start the firing. . . .

Mr. Pierce (H. F. Pierce, later president of the society) threw his switches

[8] "The History of the First A.I.S Rocket."

rapidly. The fuse apparatus worked to perfection. For an instant there was a great fire, as the pure oxygen struck the burning fuse.

In an instant the gasoline was also pouring into the rocket. The fuse, the flare, and the uncertainty about the performance of our rocket motor all disappeared at once, as, with a furious hissing roar, a bluish white sword of flame shot downward from the nozzle of the combustion chamber, and the rocket lunged upward against the retaining spring. . . .

The flame was about twenty inches in length, clear and clean, of a bluish-white color, and quite steady. There was none of the chugging, choking or backfiring we had expected. The sound was even and powerful throughout the test. At the last, just before the firing ceased, the noise changed a little in quality—an indescribable change, perhaps a little less powerful. For a moment most of us thought the motor was hot, and about to burst. Now we believe this change in sound indicated that the liquid oxygen had been exhausted, and that the flame thereafter was supported for a second or so by the oxygen which flowed under pressure from the tank.

Suddenly we knew that the oxygen supply had been exhausted. There was an excess of gasoline, as we had planned. This now came spurting out, throwing a shower of fire around the foot of the proving stand. . . .

We made an immediate examination of the rocket. The water in the cooling tank was hot, but not too hot to touch. The nozzle of the motor was clean and bright, showing no sign of scoring or pitting. Inside the narrowest part of the nozzle there was a little soot, which very probably was left there by the final charge of gasoline. . . .

But most important—the marks made by the rocket on the soaped guides indicated that it had registered a lift of sixty pounds. . . . Our fifteen-pound rocket would, in a vacuum, have ascended to a height of sixteen miles. Discounting liberally for air resistance, a well-designed rocket, flying perfectly straight, ought with so much power to reach an altitude in air of five to eight miles.

These enthusiastic comments about the motor turned out, however to be too optimistic.

In subsequent tests it scored badly, and a whole sequence of motors like it, both with and without water jackets, burned out with disheartening regularity when tested against standard conditions on a proving stand especially constructed for the purpose.

The society had phenomenal luck with its first test. It is not known to this day why the motor stood up so well for that first shot or so, and later showed its weakness all too plainly. It was that kindly Providence, no doubt, which is traditionally said to watch over rocket experimenters.

A rocket motor produces so much quick power, and speeds on its way so fast in flight that it does not have to burn very long in any one shot to go a long distance. But more than a few seconds are usually necessary, and the need, except for military rockets, is to develop a motor that can be used repeatedly, for whatever length of time might be desired, without danger of burning out.

Pursuing this objective, the experimental group of the American Rocket Society subsequently gave almost five years (working week ends and evenings principally, since this was an amateur occupation) toward the development of successful motors capable of firing for indefinite periods, and developing high thermal efficiency.

The first step was the construction of a suitable proving stand. To provide a cheap and easy method of getting data on many types and shapes of motors without building completely new models each time, a sectional motor was developed which made it possible to exchange some parts—for example nozzles—without any more trouble than the undoing of a few clamps.

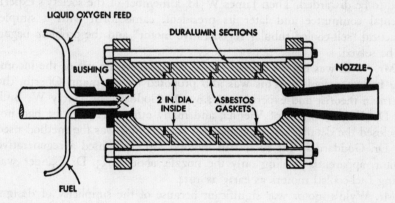

FIG. 6. Sectional liquid-fuel motor used in the American Rocket Society's test stand experiments.

With this proving stand, followed subsequently by bigger ones and additional refinements, it was possible to try a great many types of motors and motor parts. It was possible, too, to prove to the satisfaction of all concerned that simple cooling schemes, such as water jackets, ice bags, dry-ice packs and the like were quite ineffective if the shot were to last more than a few seconds. Air-cooling likewise proved ineffective.

Turning next to metals and materials which it was believed would withstand the heat without special cooling, the experimenters performed tests with ceramics and fire clays of various types, with hard metals such as Stellite, with Nichrome and other heat-resistant metals, and with blocks of pure carbon serving as nozzles. The ceramics and fire clays cracked rapidly under the change in temperatures in the motor. The heat-resistant metals soon proved to lack sufficient heat resistance. The carbon had too little strength; motors made of it burst promptly. All other materials likewise failed with disheartening certainty.

By the end of the first series of tests, it was clear that none of these schemes would produce a permanent non-melting motor. The experimenters next turned to studies of ways in which the incoming fuel or the liquid oxygen could be made to do the cooling. The experiences of the Germans with liquid oxygen as a coolant brought this suggestion into early disrepute. Using the oxygen in this way simply caused it to boil furiously and vaporize before it could get into the blast chamber.

The fuel, however, offered a source of cooling that had possibilities. Most of the suggestions for ways to introduce the fuel around the nozzle— the place of most serious burning—were complex and cumbersome, and had to be discarded. Then James Wyld, a member of the society's experimental committee and later its president, came forth with a simple, practical "self-cooled tubular regenerative motor" and the problem began to be solved.

Mr. Wyld was not, of course, the first to suggest the use of the incoming fuel as a coolant. This was also proposed by Hermann Oberth, the German theorist and experimenter; by Dr. Goddard, by Harry W. Bull, by Dr. Eugen Sanger of Vienna, and many others. Though he had not disclosed the details, it is probable that fuel cooling was the method used by Dr. Goddard in his successful motors.[9] Mr. Bull used a regenerative motor, apparently cooling only the nozzle, about 1933. Dr. Sanger was using fuel-cooled motors as early as 1934.

Mr. Wyld's motor was significant because of the simplicity of design, inherent lightness and practicality. It was a significant accomplishment also because the inventor freely published the design of his motor in *Astronautics* for April, 1938. He made no attempt to patent the device, thus making it available for the advancement of rocket research everywhere.

The Wyld motor was simplicity itself. The blast chamber of the first model consisted of an aluminum tube two inches in diameter and six inches long, to the lower end of which was attached a short, stubby Monel metal nozzle of very thin wall section—one eighth of an inch or less in thickness.

The blast chamber was encased in a second tube, just a trifle larger, so as to leave a cylindrical space about an eighth of an inch in thickness for the passage of the fuel. This double jacketing was carried to the nozzle also,

---

[9] It is now known that Dr. Goddard used the method called "curtain-cooling" rather than the regenerative principle.

but here the permitted thickness of the liquid layer was greater.

In such a motor the fuel comes in near the tip of the nozzle and goes into the coolant chamber surrounding the nozzle with a swirling motion. From there it passes rapidly through the passage surrounding the blast chamber, and thence to a mixing device at the head of the motor. From the mixer it is sprayed through a series of inlet ports, intimately mingled with liquid oxygen which is brought in at the motor head.

When the walls of the motor are thin enough, heat imparted by the escaping jet can readily pass through the metal and into the incoming fuel. The motor is called "regenerative" because it saves heat that would otherwise be wasted through the nozzle and the blast-chamber body, and brings it back inside the motor. . . .

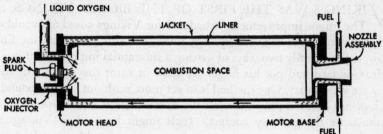

Fig. 7. Cross section of the Wyld regenerative motor as originally presented in *Astronautics*.

In basic principle, the Wyld type of regenerative motor is the motor in use today in many an operation making use of liquid fuels. It works almost equally well with liquid oxygen, nitric acid or other liquid oxidizers. Only the metals used in its construction need be altered to take account of the relative corrosiveness of some of these chemical combinations. To use nitric acid, for example, the inner part of the motor and its connections must be made of stainless steel.

The regenerative motor has a quite pleasing by-product, which arises from its regenerative features, the length of the blast chamber and the general design: its thermal efficiency is excellent.

The efficiencies are now of the order of 40 to 45 per cent in larger motors of this type, corresponding to jet velocities of 6,000 to 7,500 feet per second or better with liquid oxygen and gasoline. This efficiency is still far from the theoretical maximum, but compared with the efficiency of the sky-rocket, at 2 per cent, or the early motors of American experimenters, which were only about 5 per cent efficient, this is enormous.

Edition of 1949
Revised by the author, 1958

We Learn a Lesson

MILTON ROSEN

From *The Viking Rocket Story*

VIKING 8 WAS THE FIRST OF THE BIGGER VIKINGS. . . . The minor improvements scheduled for Vikings 5 and 6* would enable them to reach 125, perhaps 135 miles, but this would be the limit. Now, there are only two ways of getting a substantial improvement in altitude. Goddard had put his finger on them in 1919; they were true then, they are valid today. One method is to get more push out of each pound of fuel, or as Goddard put it, to eject the exhaust gas at higher speed, which is the same thing. More energetic fuels might be used in Viking, but they would require a new power plant and we could not afford one. Our fuels, oxygen and alcohol, were not the best, but they were good enough, and they were easy to handle. Alternatively we could get more push by improving the efficiency of our rocket motor. We tried this, but it was not successful. Reaction Motors who did the work produced a tempting efficiency gain, but at a prohibitive cost. Every time a high-performance motor was run, it emitted a continuous high-pitched, ear-splitting scream. The screaming was hard on observers, but its effect on the motor was more potent. After a few seconds welds cracked open, and if the motor were permitted to run longer, it exploded. We could not possibly use such a motor in Viking.

The other road to higher altitude involves making the fuel a larger portion of the total weight. More fuel means larger tanks, and larger tanks are heavier. The process can be self-defeating unless the increase in tank weight is proportionately less than the weight of additional fuel, or unless weight can be stolen from other parts of the rocket. The Martin designers approached this problem with gusto. They planned and built a Viking that held 3,500 pounds, almost two tons, more fuel without adding one single pound of structure. If the tanks were heavier, and they were,

---

* In a series of tests of Viking rockets at White Sands, New Mexico, each rocket was given a number representing its position in the series.

674

the designers made up the loss by lightening other parts of the rocket, such as the fins. They produced a rocket having 80 per cent of its gross weight in fuel, the highest fuel-to-weight ratio ever achieved. The rocket's appearance was changed. No longer could reporters call it "the slim, pencil-like Viking." It was fatter, but the fat was fuel, and this was very important.

The increase in width from thirty-two to forty-five inches provided an opportunity to rearrange the power plant and control components and to make them more accessible. The peroxide tank was high on the list of parts to be moved. In previous Vikings it had been wound into a large coil just under the skin and enclosed the turbine and all the piping that ran fore and aft through the rocket. We remembered the steam leaks in the early Vikings, when we had tried desperately to tighten the turbine bolts, some of which were so inaccessible that we could hardly get a tool onto them. In the new Viking there was room to place the turbine and the peroxide tank side by side so that both would be fully exposed when the tail section doors were removed.

Previously, Viking had stood on its fins. For static firings, these same robust fins had been bolted to the launching stand, and they had to resist the motor's tremendous push. With the larger diameter, the Martin people said the rocket could be supported at the base of its shell. The fins, then, would have to support only themselves; they would not have to take the weight of the whole rocket or the thrust of the motor. Therefore, they could be built much lighter. The scheme was adopted and, in addition, the fin shape was changed to a triangle, and the fins were made smaller.

Although the rocket was to be supported at four points of the base frame, the Martin designers decided that two of these points would suffice to bolt the rocket to the stand for static firings. While this decision seemed logical when it was made, it was a mistake, one that sowed the seed of disaster.

The original Viking had been tilted forward three degrees on its launching stand and had flown a nearly straight line at a small angle from the vertical. The new Viking would point straight up at takeoff and would bend forward gently during the early part of flight, so that it would land uprange to the north. When the design was finished we were amazed and delighted with the predicted altitude. The bigger Viking with moderate payload and average good performance should reach an elevation of 150 miles; with light payload and optimum efficiency—190 miles. This was a clear advance over Viking 7, but there were new risks. The rocket would be heavily loaded with fuel. If Viking rose slowly before, now it would stagger off the ground. We had to worry about a sudden gust of wind whipping the tail into the launching stand at the instant of takeoff. We had to be sure that the gimbaled motor would keep the airframe erect when it was practically hovering a few feet above the stand. It was a gamble, a good gamble; if it paid off, it would pay well.

The new Viking was two years in the making. There were a few false starts, and I changed my mind several times about various features of the design. It was intended originally that Viking 7 would be the first larger rocket, but at the end of 1950 we saw clearly that we had at least another year's work ahead to finish the new design. Also, after the weird accident to Viking 6, we had another incentive—we wanted to finish the original series with a fully successful flight. Viking 7 was such a flight and we felt rewarded when it broke the V-2 record.

We were a small organization, a few men at the Laboratory and small groups at Martin and RMI. Our funds were very limited and had to be expended with care. We could not afford to try several designs and then choose the best, discarding the others. Our initial decisions had to be weighed carefully, and once committed to a given approach, we had to make the best of it. When the first new tail section was built it was put through structural tests at the Martin plant. The forces that the tail would have to withstand during static firings were applied by hydraulic jacks—the expected force plus a small margin of safety. The design had been close, in order to keep the weight down, and we dared not test beyond this small margin. One part, a column that transmits the motor's force into the shell, failed when the test load was within a few pounds of its final value. The column was strengthened and the test was repeated to full load.

The steering had to be revised to fit a rocket of different weight and shape. When the airframe was fully assembled, it was set up vertically at the Martin plant for tests of the complete steering system: the gyros, the amplifiers, the valves, the servos and the gimbaled motor. Immediately our old enemy struck—vibration in the control system. All our past experience was brought to bear on this problem, and it was solved. During four long months the fully assembled rocket was undergoing tests at the Martin plant—every test that would be made later at White Sands was run again and again in the factory. Finally the rocket was painted and shipped. It arrived at Oro Grande on May 17, 1952, and was unloaded from its express car onto the flat-bed truck that carried it across the desert to the Viking hangar at the Base.

The tests in the hangar were completed without incident. Then on May 30, the rocket was towed to the launching area and erected on its stand. Very soon afterward the rocket had to be covered and lashed to the gantry because of a severe sandstorm that came up suddenly. Work was suspended for the day. Vertical tests began the next day, Saturday, and continued through Sunday and into the following week. First, the threads in the southwest tie-down block were found to be stripped. This was one of the two fittings that were bolted to the launching stand for static firing. Without much ado we decided to ream out the threads of both blocks, to slip through longer bolts, and cap them with nuts. The controls people had some difficulty getting good responses, but traced their trouble to test equipment and eliminated it. On Tuesday when Hardin attempted to pressure test the alcohol tank he could not close the vents. He found both valve actuating motors burned out, and also that the wiring had permitted him to apply both opening and closing currents at the same time. He replaced the motors and changed the wiring to prevent a recurrence of this failure.

On Wednesday we made flow tests of the new peroxide tank. The tank was filled with water, pressure was applied, the valve was opened and the water spurted through a flexible hose into a drum that was being weighed on a platform balance. Youngquist, who was conducting the test, had difficulty keeping the water from splashing out of the drum. He was anxious not to lose any water because the test showed that we were running short. The test was run several times and Johnny was drenched repeatedly. The sailors who stood watching these proceedings laughed at his discomfort. Youngquist figured out that air was breaking through the swirling liquid at the bottom of the tank before it could be completely drained. He suggested installing a baffle at the tank outlet to keep the liquid from swirling, and this turned the trick. These minor difficulties were typical; they were corrected readily and without much concern. Generally speaking, the rocket was in good condition, and we were confident it would perform well—too confident.

Preparations for the static firing began on Thursday. The prestatic tests were conducted in leisurely fashion. Several new experimental devices were installed to be tested in conjunction with the static firing. While we were firing rockets, we were also developing new devices that would improve later models. One of these was a heat exchanger in the turbine exhaust that some day would pressurize the oxygen tank and save another few pounds of weight. Another was a gauge that measured the liquid levels in the fuel tanks and which could be used eventually to control the fuel flow so that both tanks exhausted simultaneously. These devices were still in the early stages of development, but the static firing provided one more chance to get valuable information about their characteristics.

All operations were moving ahead smoothly toward the fifty-second static firing scheduled for 10 A.M., Friday.

I awoke at four-thirty Friday morning, and drove into the launching areas as the rocket crew were starting their final checks. The upper-air scientists, who had worked through the night installing their equipment in the nose, were gone. I had always argued against the practice of testing upper-air equipment in the static, but I had always given in. For the rocket crew the static is an ordeal far more trying than the flight. On a flight firing, when the rocket has lifted one inch off the stand, they are finished; there is nothing more they can do. As the flight proceeds, the men at the telemeter house watch tensely for the first loss of signal, ready to retune their receivers. The radar men at C Station sweat at their dial cranks to keep the echo from the rocket in the range notch. The optical trackers strain to keep the white speck of rocket on the crosshairs in their telescopes; if they lose it once, they never find it again. But the rocket man breathes a sigh of relief and waits for the news, albeit with tense expectation.

On static firings it is different. When the firing button is pushed and the motor ignites, we see through the blockhouse window a chained beast, roaring ominously, straining at its fastenings. Every second is a long second, and we listen to the count, thinking it will never end. That is why I didn't want the upper-air scientists in a static firing. The more equipment in the rocket, the more to worry about. They look at it differently, and naturally so. For a scientist, every test is a valuable test, especially in rocket work, when the equipment must operate that one vital time, during the flight, or all is lost. The static is the closest thing to a flight. The equipment is subjected to severe vibration; if it survives the static, it is odds-on to operate during flight. Once, I pointed out jokingly that some day they could lose their precious equipment in a static firing. They were completely unperturbed; to the man they were willing to take the risk.

We started fueling at 7:30 A.M., thirty minutes late. The controls crew had held up the schedule while they traced a faulty metering circuit between the rocket and the blockhouse. There was no concern about the delay. I set the firing time back one-half hour to 10:30. Alcohol started flowing into the rocket. The hose running from the rocket's tail to the pump cart some twenty-five feet away became taut as the pump came up to speed. Behind the pump cart was the flat-bed truck loaded with alcohol drums. As each drum was emptied, a sailor thrust the suction line into the next full drum.

We had built a new launching stand for Viking 8 and had designed it to incorporate a device that weighed the rocket. I had wanted such a device for a long time. I never trusted the fuel weights we obtained from flow meters or by weighing separate drums before and after they were emptied. The weighing device was simple and foolproof. It consisted of four load cells, one in each leg of the launching table. The load cells gave an electrical signal in proportion to the weight resting on the stand. The cells were connected to a continuous-strip recorder on which a moving pen traced a record of the rocket's weight. It was a simple matter to mark the chart at the start and end of each fueling operation. By subtracting successive chart readings we could tell the exact amounts of alcohol, peroxide and oxygen that were actually inside the rocket.

All the men not engaged in the fueling operations clustered around the weight recorder where Don Cosner officiated with calm assurance. For this static firing the alcohol tank was to be only half full because the static duration was intended to be fifty seconds, whereas a full tank could provide fuel for over a hundred seconds of burning. When the correct weight of liquid was in the rocket, Don signaled the men to stop pumping. They drained and disconnected their hoses and pulled out to make way for the peroxide crew. Peroxide was loaded in less than five minutes, a remarkable feat made possible by Al Niles' newly developed peroxide-loading pump. We checked our time and noticed that we were thirty minutes ahead of our revised schedule. There was no need to advance the firing time so we loafed for a half hour before starting oxygen. We would take on a full tank of oxygen even though we needed only half, so that we wouldn't have to replace the oxygen that would boil away should the firing be delayed. Cosner had calculated how much the new oxygen tank should hold. As the level neared his value, he signaled the pump operator to decrease the flow. The recorder pen moved up slowly, and then Don flipped his finger across his throat and yelled to cut off the flow. One second later the white plumes of vapor shooting out from the oxygen vents showed that the tank was full. Cosner smiled with obvious satisfaction.

We were coming up on X-minus-15-minutes, and everyone was in the blockhouse for the start of firing operations. A few Doppler and Beacon people were standing by to go through the motions of a firing for practice. They did not need to operate for static, and their range stations were not manned. There was activity before the telemeter and cutoff consoles—these were essential to the static. Radio Cutoff, as always, stood ready to shut down the motor if we were unable to do so from the firing desk. Such an emergency had yet to arise, but we would not think of firing without them. This day, Nat Wagner, head of the Cutoff group was in the blockhouse.

As the second hand on the large clock swept through the last minute before X-minus-15, we became quiet. Jim Hartman was at the firing desk, substituting for Hardin who took over the fire-watcher station and was peering at the rocket through binoculars. Mason was at the controls panel; Munnell and I were between the two operators a step behind them. At X-minus-15-minutes Hartman turned on master power and Mason switched the gyros to erect. When after two minutes the gyro meters did not come to zero, Mason requested permission to erect the gyros from the panel controls. Munnell assented. This procedure left some uncertainty about the true position of the gyros, a condition that would never be tolerated for a flight, but could be accepted on static. The count proceeded with a hold. At X-minus-1-minute the rocket was pressurized. Munnell, Hardin and I hung over Jim Hartman at the firing desk as the meter needles swung up, wavered and then stood still.

Forty-five seconds . . . Hardin nodded to Munnell, indicating that he was satisfied with the pressure levels. Ed flicked on his green light. The rocket was cleared for firing.

Thirty-five seconds . . . I turned to the telemeter men and called for recorders. The word was relayed to the telemeter house seven miles up-range. We waited.

Twenty-five seconds . . . The answer came back. Recorders were on. Lieutenant Cooper, the Navy project officer, started the count down in a hushed, tense voice.

Twenty, nineteen, eighteen, seventeen . . . I looked at the men. Their eyes were straight ahead, fixed on their instruments.

Twelve, eleven, ten, nine . . . After one last glance at both rocket panels I concentrated on the ready lights—all green.

Five, four, three, two . . . Fire!

Igniter on . . . plug drop . . . fire light . . . the motor had started. At plus four seconds, the firing panel meters wavered and dropped to lower levels. I looked at Ed to see if he had noticed it. He had and was glancing alternately at the panel meters and the rocket. At nine seconds we heard a dull throbbing sound in the jet blast. The thought flashed through my mind: Should we cut it or let it run longer to get enough time on the record? How long was enough? At thirteen seconds the rocket started heaving almost imperceptibly. Then without warning, before our horrified eyes, it tore loose from the stand and started slowly to rise. We saw the tubes and cables that were connected to the rocket for static snap one by one as the tail moved upward out of our sight. A great cloud of dust billowed toward us as the mighty roar of a flying rocket bore down upon the blockhouse roof.

Takeoff! The rocket has broken loose! The rocket is flying! The alarming words flashed out from the blockhouse. At the telemeter station the men dashed up to the roof to start training their antennas which had been lashed down for the static.

Plus twenty-five seconds . . . Nat Wagner yelled at me across the blockhouse, "Shall we cut it?"

As the seconds slipped away I pondered this deadly question. The rocket was lost—the only consideration now was safety. With only half a tank of alcohol it could not go far, not possibly leave the range. It we cut it too early, it might fall on one of the installations close to the launching area, maybe C Station.

"No!" I shouted back. "Don't cut it. You don't know where the rocket is!"

Thirty-five seconds . . . Wagner was tense, his eyes seemed glazed. He knew he held the safety of the range in his hands. Probably he had visions of the rocket going to El Paso or farther.

Forty-five seconds . . . Nat and I were staring at each other across the blockhouse. I knew he wanted to stop the rocket and I felt it would be a mistake. There was no time to explain the conditions—a tank half full to start, fifteen seconds of fuel burned on the ground.

Fifty-five seconds . . . "We're going to cut it," Nat announced. He waited a few seconds for my reply. I would not try to stop him now. If the rocket had not cleared the immediate area by this time, it never would. He pressed the button. We waited in silence, not knowing whether he had stopped the rocket or whether it had cut itself off previously. We had ceased to hear its sound many seconds before.

Finally, at 120 seconds, we heard a muffled explosion. We looked at each other; that must be impact. We rushed out of the blockhouse and scanned the horizon. To the southeast we saw a gray mushroom of smoke rising slowly against the pale, blue sky. We estimated its distance as four or five miles. I walked toward the launching stand. The two tie-down blocks from the rocket were still in place, bolted to the crossbeams of the stand. Attached to the blocks were a few scraps of structure that had been torn from the rocket when it broke loose. The two shiny stubs of aluminum pointed upward, silent evidence of the rocket's awful power.

I walked back to the blockhouse, found my pickup truck, and drove in the direction of impact. Several other vehicles were close ahead and behind. We took a dirt road that ran parallel to a line of telephone poles. It led finally to a theodolite station on a small mound above the boondocks. The trackers were outside, waving to us and pointing to the southwest. I got out and asked them how far it was to the impact point. They guessed about a mile and cautioned that the terrain was too rough for a pickup, no roads, just boondocks. I parked my truck and hopped into a jeep that was already well loaded. After ten minutes of seesawing through the boondocks, we saw a few parked vehicles and several men standing around a part of the wreckage.

Torn and twisted fragments of the rocket were lying among the boondocks and were scattered over a large area. We learned later from a theodolite film record of the flight that the rocket had torn apart when it was descending a mile above the ground. This film was acquired in a very fortuitous manner. It happened that one of the theodolite men, an Army sergeant, was testing a new lens on his instrument. As the firing time approached he stopped work in order to watch the activity in the launching area three miles away. Knowing the test was a static, he must have been startled when he saw the rocket take off. Without hesitation he switched on the power, put his theodolite in operation and swung it around to track the flying missile. The film he obtained was a valuable and unexpected part of the records we would examine for months after the firing.

I continued walking around the boondocks, looking at parts of the wreckage. The hot noonday sun beat down fiercely on this scene of destruction. Here was the motor half buried in the ground, bent and flattened by the force of impact. Some more of our men were walking around aimlessly, their faces drawn and dejected. Hardly anyone spoke. The events that had transpired in the blockhouse a brief half hour before were now part of the irrevocable past. As I thought about them, it seemed incredible that we had let the rocket get away. Jim Hartman at the firing panel was not to be blamed. Although he had practiced assiduously with the controls, the experience was new to him, and we knew he would take no emergency action without a command. It was up to us—Munnell, Hardin, or me—to give that command. We were the three most experienced men on Viking operations, with ten statics and seven flights to our credit. Many times in the past each one of us had made instant decisions when they were required. Yet, a few moments ago, we had seen impending danger and had not recognized it. We had stood there, mesmerized, betrayed by our confidence that nothing drastic could happen to a Viking.

I came upon the alcohol tank, burst open and smashed out of shape. It is the fate of all high-altitude rockets to end up more or less as wreckage. Is the rocket then to be considered a loss? Not at all. The materials that go to make a rocket, the ton and a half of steel and aluminum, are worth very little. Nor is the work required to fashion a complicated mechanism from basic materials the greatest cost. It is the time and effort of the engineers and scientists that is most expensive and most valuable—for without this essential ingredient the steel and aluminum would never fly. It costs more to design and test a Viking than it does to build one. This effort is never lost, because it is as much a part of the men as it is part of the rocket.

The upper-air people had found the nose. It was in one piece and still sealed, though somewhat dented and flattened at the tip. They were cutting open the skin with a pair of pliers in order to remove a high voltage battery. They had lost. They would discover no secrets of the atmosphere in Viking 8, and even though some of their instruments might be repaired and used again, it was little consolation. When they had finished cutting off the tip they lifted the nose into a jeep and drove away slowly toward the Base.

The tail structure, partially damaged at takeoff, was devastated on impact by the explosion of residual peroxide. The charred and twisted fragments lay scattered about a blackened central area. Was this the structure that had deceived us? No, we had deceived ourselves. We had tested this structure at the factory for normal loads plus a small margin of safety. We would learn later that the tail had been subjected to over twice the normal force, and our small margin was totally inadequate to cope with it. Why didn't we recognize that an abnormal condition existed? It was because we were watching the rocket and trusting our ability to sense its condition. I had always belittled the value of watching the rocket, but like the others, I had always watched it. Viking 8 had proven that we could not trust our senses. Under tension, a man sees what he is prepared to see. A fire would be detected immediately because we were always looking for fire. But not one of us saw the white plumes of vapor issuing from the rocket at X-plus-3-seconds when the oxygen vents opened, because this was completely unexpected. If we had seen them, we would most certainly have stopped the firing. When later we looked at color movies of the firing, and we looked at them hundreds of times, we saw the vents open and we knew they could have been seen from the blockhouse. We had lost a rocket and learned a lesson.

1955

A Shot Around the World

ARTHUR C. CLARKE

From *The Making of a Moon*

THE LAWS GOVERNING THE BEHAVIOR OF SATELLITES are basically simple, but because they involve conditions outside the range of normal human experience many people find it hard to grasp them. Perhaps if we lived on a planet which, like Jupiter, had a dozen natural moons in the sky, the idea of creating a few additional ones would not seem so surprising.

It is "common sense" that it needs force to keep a body in motion, and that if this propulsive force—whatever its origin—is removed the body will sooner or later come to rest. Any kind of vehicle, whether it travels on the sea, the land or in the air, obeys this fundamental law; no one expects an automobile to keep moving indefinitely once the motor is turned off.

Yet common sense—the accumulated experience of all the generations of men—is often a misleading guide. It is so in this case, and it required the genius of Galileo and Sir Isaac Newton to point out the true laws of motion, which here on Earth are disguised and distorted by the confusing effects of friction. The scientific outlook reverses the common sense opinion; it needs *no* force to keep a body moving. The planets circle in their orbits forever, without any help from the angels whom medieval theologians pictured as busily pushing them along.

The development of high-altitude flight has made it common knowledge that great speeds can easily be reached and maintained in the thin air of the upper atmosphere, where frictional drag is reduced to a small fraction of its value at sea level. It requires little effort of imagination to see that where there is no atmosphere at all, the last trace of resistance will also vanish. Once a body in space has been given a certain speed, it can maintain that speed indefinitely.

The only natural force that can affect the motion of a body in space, once it is clear of the atmosphere, is gravity. It is gravity that keeps the Moon chained in its orbit—and it is gravity that will control the new moons we are building now.

No one knows what gravity is: we can merely describe its actions, but that is all that we need do for our present purpose. The movement of bodies in gravitational fields has been the subject of intense study ever since the invention of gunpowder gave birth to the applied (or misapplied) science of ballistics. In a sense, a satellite is no more than a missile of infinite range.

Why this is so may be seen from a very simple argument; the fact that it has become almost a cliché in books on space travel will not deter us from using it again. Imagine a gun, pointed horizontally, standing on the edge of a very high cliff, and consider what will happen if the shell is fired at varying speeds. For the moment, assume that there is no such thing as air resistance.

If it merely trickles out of the barrel (*vide* one of early scenes in Chaplin's *The Great Dictator*) the shell will fall vertically and will hit the bottom of the cliff after a time given by the simple equation $s = \frac{1}{2}gt^2$—which is probably all that most people remember of dynamics after they have left school. It would take just one minute, for example, for the shot to reach the base of a cliff eleven miles high, if such a phenomenon can be imagined.

Now this time of fall is quite independent of the velocity with which the shell is projected, as long as it leaves the gun horizontally. In the very hypothetical case we have assumed, the missile will always reach the plain beneath it one minute after firing, however fast it leaves the gun. However, the distance of the point of impact from the base of the cliff will increase steadily with the speed of projection. If the shell leaves the gun at a mile a second—sixty miles a minute—it will hit the ground sixty miles away at the end of its one-minute fall, and so on.

However, we have ignored one fundamental point. The Earth isn't flat,[1] and as we increase the speed of projection of the missile its range will obviously lengthen more rapidly than simple arithmetic would indicate. At two miles a second, it will hit the ground considerably more than 120 miles away; at four miles a second, much more than 240 miles away, because of the curvature of the Earth's surface.

It is obvious from the diagram what is going to happen next. There will be a certain speed at which the projectile never reaches the Earth at all, because the surface drops away at the same rate as the descending shell.

[1] I am waiting, with considerable interest, for the reactions to the satellite program of the people who still believe that it is.

When this happens, the missile will be in a state of permanent fall around the world, never getting any closer to the surface.

One can get a rough idea of the speed necessary to achieve this state of affairs by the simple geometry of Figure 1. After its one-minute "fall," the projectile must be just as far from the ground as when it started—i.e., it

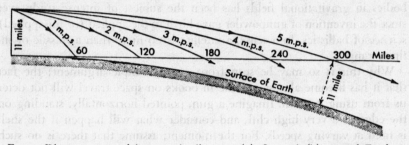

FIG. 1. Distances covered by a projectile over (a) flat and (b) curved Earth.

must still be eleven miles up. The problem may therefore be stated in this form: "How far must one travel before the Earth's surface drops away eleven miles below the horizon?"

This is merely the reverse way of looking at a familiar question, "How far away is the visible horizon from a height of eleven miles?" The answer is approximately three hundred miles, which, therefore, gives us the distance the projectile must cover in one minute. So its launching speed has to be three hundred miles a minute, or five miles a second.

In actual practice, of course, no satellite could be established at such a low altitude, because air resistance would bring it to rest in a few seconds. Even a hundred miles up, a satellite might not be able to complete its 24,000-mile circuit of the globe before being slowed down so seriously that it would fall back to Earth. But from about 150 miles onward, semi-permanent orbits are possible—that is, a satellite would stay up for days or weeks before the faint traces of air resistance brought it spiraling down.

The critical speed of five miles a second—eighteen thousand miles an hour—is known as "circular" or "orbital" velocity, and it is important to realize that it is quite independent of the size or mass of the satellite concerned. If the Earth had a natural moon just outside the atmosphere, this is the speed at which it would have to travel, and since at this speed it takes an hour and a half to go around the world, this would be the duration of the "month."

A permanent satellite can be established at any altitude, as long as it is high enough to avoid atmospheric drag; there is nothing particularly sacrosanct about the eighteen-thousand-miles-per-hour, ninety-minute orbit —except that, being the closest to the Earth, it is the easiest to achieve. At greater distances from the Earth, where the downward pull of gravity begins to weaken, less speed is required to maintain a satellite in its orbit, and the period of revolution is correspondingly increased. For example, 1,075 miles up, the period becomes exactly two hours—one-twelfth of a day —a convenient fraction which may make this particular distance of special importance.

There has been a great deal of popular confusion about the role which the Earth's gravitational field plays in connection with satellites. Indeed, there have been newspaper articles which stated that such satellites maintained themselves in their orbits because they were "beyond the Earth's gravity." This, of course, is utter nonsense; although gravity weakens with increasing distance from the Earth, at the heights where the first satellites will be established it still has 90 per cent of its sea-level value. Without the pull of gravity, in fact, the satellites would at once fly off into space, since there would be no downward force checking their natural tendency to continue moving in a straight line.

At this point it is impossible to avoid another astronautical cliché—the stone-and-string analogy. If you tie a stone on the end of a piece of string, it requires very little effort to keep it whirling around in a circle. The system is in a state of balance because the tension of the string counteracts the tendency of the stone to fly away. One of man's earliest weapons, the sling, depends on this simple application of dynamical laws.

In the case of a satellite, the pull of gravity plays the part of the string. With this analogy in mind, it is obvious that the greater the radius of movement—the longer the string—the more slowly a satellite need move in order to maintain its equilibrium.

Close satellites will revolve around the Earth very much more rapidly than our planet turns on its axis, and as we shall see later this gives rise to some very odd effects. It is necessary to go out to the considerable altitude of 22,000 miles before the orbital period is as much as a day. Figure 2 shows in diagrammatic form the distances which satellites at various altitudes would cover in the same period—in this case, one hour—as compared with the arc through which the Earth itself revolves.

Although we have so far discussed only circular orbits, because these are the simplest and in some ways most useful ones, they really represent a rather exceptional case. In practice, the orbit of a real satellite would not be a perfect circle but an ellipse—perhaps a highly elongated one. To establish an exactly circular orbit would demand an impossible and indeed unnecessary degree of accuracy on the part of the launching rocket.

Circles exist only in geometry books; real planets, comets and satellites (artificial or natural) move round their center of attraction in elliptical paths—a fact which gives them a kind of inherent stability. If a satellite is traveling too slowly at some part of its orbit it will fall inward and thus pick up speed. Conversely, if it were going too fast, it would swing outward.

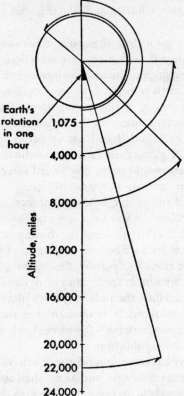

FIG. 2. Arcs covered in one hour by satellites at varying distances from the Earth.

Thus any error—within limits—in the initial launching speed would not prevent the establishment of a satellite. The orbit would automatically adjust its shape to take up the slack, as it were. If the launching speed were too low, at the other end of its orbit the satellite would drop down toward Earth, but that would not matter as long as it remained clear of the atmosphere.

The actual shape of a satellite's orbit is only one of its characteristics; the plane in which it lies is another. From the practical point of view, it is easiest to launch a satellite into the Equatorial plane, because when it takes off it can get the maximum boost from the thousand-mile-an-hour spin of the Earth at the Equator. That is, assuming that it is launched in the west-east direction; if fuel economy were no problem, it would be possible to establish a satellite moving from east to west, against the direction of the Earth's spin. Such an orbit would be termed a "retrograde" one, but there would be no particular purpose in trying to achieve it since it would require an extra two thousand miles an hour of rocket impulse over the "direct" orbit.

Of very great scientific interest, for reasons which will be clear later, is the orbit which passes over the Poles. The Polar and Equatorial orbits represent two extreme cases, but orbits at intermediate angles are equally possible. In fact, the plane of a satellite can lie at *any* angle in space; the only restriction is that it must pass through the center of the Earth. A few of the more interesting possible satellite orbits are shown in Figure 3. For simplicity, only circular orbits are shown.

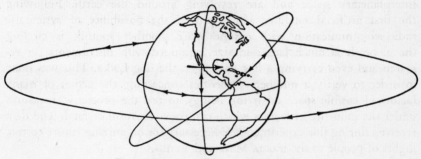

FIG. 3. Some possible satellite orbits.

If our planet were not turning on its axis, any satellite would continually retrace the same path above the Earth's surface, and after completing one revolution would be back over the same spot from which it had started. However, the real situation is not as simple as that; only a satellite above the Equator would forever trace out the same ground track on the globe below. A satellite in an orbit that passed over the Poles would weave out a pattern embracing the entire Earth as it shuttled from north to south and the planet turned beneath it. This kind of behavior is both an advantage and a disadvantage; it means that a satellite can reconnoiter the whole globe several times during a single day—but conversely it will be visible from any given ground station only for a few minutes in each twenty-four hours.

1957

Life in Sputnik

P. ISAKOV

Translation from the Soviet Press

AN EXCEEDINGLY DIFFICULT, EXCEPTIONALLY IMPOR-
tant stage in mastering cosmic space has been attained. For the first
time in the history of our planet man-made devices have penetrated
interplanetary space and are revolving around the earth. Following
the first artificial satellite, which proved the possibility of systematic
radio communication with cosmic space, another sputnik is circling
the globe. It is much larger in size, equipped with instruments for research and even carrying a live passenger, the dog Laika. This was done
in order to verify a number of theories concerning the action of many
factors of cosmic space on living beings, to test the protective measures
under the influence of factors which can prove harmful or fatal. The data
received during this experiment are necessary for organizing future cosmic
flights of people to the moon, Mars and Venus.

WITHOUT ATMOSPHERE

Flight of both animals and man in cosmic space is possible only in
hermetically-sealed chambers in which the air, both in composition and
pressure, is similar to that on earth.

It is known that there is no air, no oxygen in interplanetary space. To
ensure the respiration of an organism in a cosmic apparatus a supply of
oxygen is needed. For this purpose it is expedient to use liquid oxygen.
During the evaporation of one liter of the liquid about 800 liters of gas
are formed. But the use of liquid oxygen is practical for only relatively
short flights. It would be difficult to take a huge supply of liquid oxygen
for flights lasting several months or more. In such cases it would be more
expedient to install hothouses with plants on the space ship as plants
absorb carbon dioxide from the air and give off oxygen.

690

The absence of barometric pressure of the air is an important factor in interplanetary space as compared with the conditions of life on earth. Let us recall that the necessary quantity of oxygen is soluble in blood only at definite barometric pressure. If the barometric pressure is insufficient, even the presence of pure oxygen cannot ensure the organism's being adequately supplied.

However, this does not exhaust the role of barometric pressure. All liquids in the organism, particularly blood, contain dissolved gases—oxygen, nitrogen, carbon dioxide, etc. If the barometric pressure of the air drops, the dissolved gases leave the blood. In case of a sharp drop in barometric pressure such a quantity of gases may escape at once from the liquids in the organism as will involve grave consequences and at times even full derangement of the organism's physiological functions.

The temperature at which liquids boil depends on the surrounding pressure. The lower the pressure, the lower the temperature at which boiling begins. At a pressure of the mercury column of 47 millimeters (corresponding to 19 kilometers above sea level), a liquid begins to boil at 37 degrees Centigrade—the temperature of human blood. The "boiling" of blood inevitably entails grave consequences.

When can such derangement occur? This can happen if the chamber is suddenly no longer airtight. Naturally, it is necessary to take precautionary measures to prevent such accidents.

How can this be done? Firstly, by creating the necessary barometric pressure in the chamber. But such a method is not very reliable, since any breach in the wall, anything making it less than airtight, would cause grave and often irreparable consequences. The second method is to use specially-designed clothing or space suits. The necessary barometric pressure is maintained in the space suit through the stretching of the suit fabric which grips the body tightly.

In practice the two methods are combined: barometric pressure is maintained in the chamber and special space clothing is used. The suit is brought into action when the chamber is no longer airtight.

The flight of animals in a sputnik will make it possible to ascertain how reliably airtight the chambers are, as well as the adequacy of the space suits, to work out the method of feeding and supplying water to organisms under these conditions and a number of other questions.

A suitable environmental temperature is an important condition for the normal existence of human beings. On earth organisms are subjected to a fluctuation of the temperature of the environment in a relatively small range—approximately from +70 degrees to −70 degrees C. However, this does not mean that all animals are adapted to such fluctuations of temperature. Many can withstand only a considerably smaller temperature fluctuation. That is why thorough investigations have to be made of interplanetary space where temperature fluctuation can be immeasurably greater. The first experiment of launching a sputnik with a dog has already shown that Soviet scientists are correctly solving the problem of creating the necessary temperature regime within the sputnik. During the first hours of flight the dog behaved calmly and its general state was satisfactory.

The inhabited satellite is equipped with instruments for studying temperature and pressure.

SUN MEANS NOT ONLY LIFE

It is exceedingly important to study with the help of sputniks the influence of various forms of solar and cosmic radiation on living organisms.

It is known that a small part of the sun's rays reach the surface of our planet. The rest are retained by the earth's atmosphere. Thus, for example, the ultraviolet part of the solar spectrum is almost completely retained by the atmosphere. In the upper layers of the atmosphere, as beyond its bounds, the intensity of ultraviolet radiation is so considerable that it is fatal for living cells. But protection from the action of ultraviolet radiation from the sun is not a difficult matter since most materials, including ordinary glass, keep out this part of the solar spectrum.

But solar radiation also has rays more unpleasant for living organisms. This is so-called X-ray radiation. The action of X-rays, at first entirely imperceptible to the organism, can lead to very undesirable consequences. That is why protection against them must be especially reliable.

There are, however, no grounds for fearing them excessively. On earth, too, workers in some professions have to deal with such radiation. Protective measures have been worked out, reliably safeguarding people from them. There is no reason to assume that these problems will baffle designers of inhabitable space craft.

Cosmic rays, or cosmic particles, as they are more properly called, can be much more dangerous. They consist of nuclei of different chemical elements. Cosmic rays contain hydrogen nuclei to a great extent (about 80 per cent), with less of the heavier nuclei, of iron, for example.

The intensity of cosmic particles is not the same at different altitudes. Landing in the earth's atmosphere, cosmic particles clash with air molecules, and their energy is lost in ionizing the molecules. Only an extremely insignificant number of cosmic rays penetrate the lower layers of the atmosphere. But at an altitude of about 200 kilometers their number increases 150-fold. The intensity of cosmic particles is still greater in inter-planetary space. It is believed that beyond the bounds of the atmosphere the intensity of cosmic particles equals approximately 0.5 particle a second per one square centimeter.

The velocity of cosmic particles is exceedingly great, approaching the speed of light. Possessing tremendous kinetic energy, such particles clashing with molecules of other substances cause their dissociation and disintegration into ions. Ionization of molecules also takes place when cosmic particles penetrate the tissues of an organism, leading to the destruction of cells, to morbid phenomena similar to those caused by gamma-radiation arising from nuclear reaction.

The penetration of one particle into the tissue of an organism is still not dangerous. Even particles of such heavy elements as zinc and iron cause damage to only 15,000 cells approximately. Compared with the total number of cells in an organism, about 1,000,000 million, this of course is infinitesimally small. It is clear that the place where such a particle strikes is also of significance. It is one thing if a particle causes the destruction of fat cells in the subcutaneous layer and an entirely different matter in the case of the nerves of the cardiac muscle, or vitally important centers of the cerebrum.

The question, naturally, arises: How is the organism to be protected from cosmic particles? So far there are no fully completed projects on this score. The published data speak of great difficulty in protection. It is effected on the same principle as protection from nuclear radiation. The presence of nuclei of heavy elements in cosmic particles complicate this task. Even the most powerful artificial sources in laboratories have not yet created particles with energies which could be compared to the energy of heavy nuclei of cosmic radiation. The launching of a sputnik with animals will enable scientists to obtain highly important data on this question.

The task of science is not only to determine the amount of such penetration the tissues of an organism can withstand and to ascertain the intensity of cosmic particles, but also to establish the time in the course of which undesirable consequences may arise. It is known that the so-called latent period, i.e., the time from the moment cosmic particles enter the organism to the moment their action becomes evident can last for weeks and even months. This necessitates prolonged observation of the organism after it has been subjected to the influence of the particles. For this purpose in a number of cases the animals, after staying in the sputnik, will have to be brought back to earth for subsequent study.

The second Soviet artificial earth satellite is equipped with measuring instruments for investigating all the above-mentioned "radiational" influences of cosmic space, short wave ultraviolet and X-ray radiation of the sun and cosmic rays.

It is necessary to say a few words about the so-called meteorite danger.

It is known that more than a ton of meteorites daily penetrates the atmosphere of our planet. Possessing huge velocities of 30-50 and more kilometers per second, they are heated by friction with the air and burn up in the upper layers of the atmosphere. As a rule, meteorites do not penetrate to altitudes lower than 70-100 kilometers. But the higher the altitude, the greater the possibility of a sputnik encountering meteorites. It is important to establish to what extent such a probability depends on the altitude of the orbit, the season of the year, etc.

The first weeks of flight by Sputnik I show it has not been subjected to the action of meteorites of destructive force. The meteorite particles which only make a hole in it are not a serious obstacle for ensuring the life of animals within the satellite. Protection against such particles can be provided either by arranging a metal screen to absorb the energy of these particles at some distance from the shell of the sputnik, or by diverting these particles by electromagnetic radiation or by other means. It is not to be precluded that the probability of clashes with meteorite particles will prove to be no greater than that of motor traffic accidents.

HOW MUCH DOES LAIKA WEIGH IN THE SPUTNIK?

The living space in a sputnik is very rigidly limited, and for that reason the mobility of animals in a satellite has to be greatly restricted. Such restriction causes changes in the psysiological functions of the organism. For example, we know that when a man is confined to bed for a long time it is often necessary to take measures to prevent hemostasis, bedsores, etc. Naturally, such measures have also been devised for animals within a sputnik.

A satellite has to be accelerated to about 8,000 meters per second. Since such speed has to be attained soon after launching, prolonged and considerable acceleration is necessary.

The effects of acceleration or overload, as it is called, on the organisms of animals and humans have been studied intensively in recent years. Large and prolonged acceleration occurs during flight on high-speed planes.

If acceleration acts vertically, from foot to head, then a redistribution of the entire mass of blood in the organism may result. There will be an overabundance in the lower part of the body and a shortage in the upper part. At the time of considerable intensity of acceleration the usual level of blood circulation in the cerebrum may be reduced, leading to a derangement of the functions of the central nervous system, even loss of consciousness.

If acceleration acts horizontally on man's body, it can be withstood much better. Special suits which tightly grip certain parts of the body and do not allow blood to accumulate in them help to fight the overload. These questions also are being studied in experiments with animals.

A few words about the speed of movement which an organism can stand. We know that uniform speed does not exert any effect on the organism. But the greater the speed of movement, the harder it becomes for man to orient himself in space. At a definite speed of movement there comes a time when man's sensory organs are unable to provide the brain with exhaustive information, in veiw of the rapid succession and incompleteness of the sensations. Therefore, the main control of cosmic flight will be from ground stations with the help of electronic comouting machines in accordance with a program drawn up in advance. Thus, in cosmic flight astronauts will be free of directly controlling their flight, since this is literally beyond man's capability.

Let us proceed to the question of the absence of the force of gravity, or zero-g, which cosmic travelers will inevitably encounter. The action of zero-g has been studied both in the case of animals and man in recent years. Although these observations pertain to brief instances of zero-g, lasting no more than some seconds, there is no doubt that the influence of prolonged zero-g may prove to be entirely different. This is exactly what has to be established through the use of sputniks carrying animals.

Weight is a factor in all our movements. For example, in raising our arms we overcome the force of the earth's gravity, while the same force facilitates movement when we lower arms. It may be assumed that if the force of the earth's gravity ceases to exert its influence, the usual coordination of all motions will be upset. The muscular exertion of raising the arm, worked out in the course of the entire preceding life, may prove to be unnecessarily great. And conversely, the lowering of the arm will require unusually great exertion, since its weight which helps to lower the arm will be absent.

Such derangement in the coordination of motions has already been established in experiments with animals and man. At the same time these experiments have revealed the remarkable ability of the nervous system to adapt itself quite quickly to new conditions. After a certain number of experiments, coordination of motions under zero-g conditions begins to improve considerably.

Zero-g (weightlessness) undoubtedly also influences such functions of the organism as respiration, blood circulation, body temperature, etc. We know that the weight of the blood is one of the factors in the regulation of blood circulation. The exclusion of this factor in zero-g conditions may affect the distribution of blood in separate parts of the organism. Observation shows that zero-g causes a certain lowering of blood pressure.

Under the effect of acceleration the gas exchange in the organism increases, the consumption of oxygen and the emission of carbon dioxide rise several times. During zero-g we may expect a lowering of the gas exchange, at least after the organism becomes adapted to the absence of gravity. These data are important for ensuring oxygen to animals and determining the capacities of air-conditioning devices. Naturally, experiments with animals within a sputnik will be quite fruitful in this respect as well.

There is one more important factor necessitating the launching of animal-carrying sputniks. We refer to the saving of a crew of future astronauts. We discussed earlier some protective measures under conditions of cosmic space when the chamber is no longer airtight. But unforeseen circumstances may compel the pilots to leave the space ships. It is necessary to foresee the possibility of saving the people in such cases as well. Naturally, it is expedient to conduct such experiments with animals at first. Moreover, for scientific purposes, also, it would be highly desirable to save the animals after a sputnik finishes traveling along its orbit. Specifically, this is necessary for studying the subsequent state of the animals.

WHERE ARE THE BIOLOGICAL FRONTIERS?

The distance of the orbit from the earth is of significance for flights of sputniks without animals. The greater this distance, the longer the existence of the sputnik. What about animal-carrying sputniks? Is there any reason for seeking to reduce the distance of the orbit from the earth? It turns out that at all altitudes where sputniks can be launched there is no difference as regards providing conditions for the life of animals. It makes no difference whether a sputnik travels within 300 or 1,000 kilometers from the earth. Equal conditions for the life of animals are necessary.

Beginning with very low altitudes, our atmosphere rapidly loses all the properties necessary for maintaining life. The ability of the atmosphere to maintain the normal gas exchange necessary for man extends only to an altitude of about five kilometers. Only a perfectly healthy man can go higher, and then only for a short time.

Insufficient barometric pressure of the atmosphere makes itself felt starting at an altitude of eight or nine kilometers. The appearance of so-called altitude pain, associated with the emission of nitrogen bubbles from the liquids of the organism, is possible at this altitude.

The so-called time reserve, that is, the period when man retains consciousness after the supply of oxygen is exhausted is practically the same, starting at an altitude of 19-20 kilometers. For example, if the supply of oxygen is cut at an altitude of 12 kilometers, a man can take the necessary measures without danger of losing consciousness for approximately 30 seconds. At 15 kilometers the time reserve is shortened to 15 seconds. At an altitude of 19 kilometers, as pointed out above, the time reserve is very small and hardly depends on the further increase of altitude.

At an altitude of 19,200 meters, where the general barometric pressure of the mercury column is 47 millimeters, it will be necessary to take measures for the protection of an organism from the boiling of liquids.

The borderline of absorption of heavy particles of cosmic radiation is at around 36-37 kilometers. Above that altitude serious protection from cosmic particles is necessary. The region where the ultraviolet part of the solar spectrum is equivalent to that in interplanetary space starts at 42-43 kilometers above sea level.

Meteorites usually burn up at an altitude of about 100 kilometers.

The propagation of sound becomes impossible at or above an altitude of 122 kilometers. At this altitude the distance between the air molecules equals approximately the length of sound waves man can hear. Above this border air molecules are even more scattered.

It is approximately at this altitude that the intensity of cosmic particles begins to rise sharply.

As for the region where sputniks can exist for a long time, it is much higher than all these boundaries.

Our times are the times of rapid, ever-accelerating development of science and technology. The launching of sputniks, particularly of Sputnik II with an animal on it, signifies the advent of a new era in the history of science, in the history of man's mastery of cosmic space. At the same time it also signifies the beginning of a systematic advance into the universe. We believe that within the next five to ten years the flight of man into cosmic space, possibly, with the landing on other planets of our solar system, will become a reality.

1957

Is There Life on Other Worlds?

SIR JAMES JEANS

$\mathbb{S}$O LONG AS THE EARTH WAS BELIEVED TO BE THE center of the universe the question of life on other worlds could hardly arise; there were no other worlds in the astronomical sense, although a heaven above and a hell beneath might form adjuncts to this world. The cosmology of the *Divina Commedia* is typical of its period. In 1440 we find Nicholas of Cusa comparing our earth, as Pythagoras had done before him, to the other stars, although without expressing any opinion as to whether these other stars were inhabited or not. At the end of the next century Giordano Bruno wrote that "there are endless particular worlds similar to this of the earth." He plainly supposed these other worlds—"the moon, planets and other stars, which are infinite in number" —to be inhabited, since he regarded their creation as evidence of the Divine goodness. He was burned at the stake in 1600; had he lived only ten years longer, his convictions would have been strengthened by Galileo's discovery of mountains and supposed seas on the moon.

The arguments of Kepler and Newton led to a general recognition that the stars were not other worlds like our earth but other suns like our sun. When once this was accepted it became natural to imagine that they also were surrounded by planets and to picture each sun as showering life-sustaining light and heat on inhabitants more or less like ourselves. In 1829 a New York newspaper scored a great journalistic hit by giving a vivid, but wholly fictitious, account of the activities of the inhabitants of the moon as seen through the telescope recently erected by His Majesty's Government at the Cape.

It would be a long time before we could see what the New York paper claimed to see on the moon—batlike men flying through the air and inhabiting houses in trees—even if it were there to see. To see an object of human size on the moon in detail we should need a telescope of from 10,000 to a 100,000 inches aperture, and even then we should have to wait years, or more probably centuries, before the air was still and clear enough for us to see details of human size.

To detect general evidence of life on even the nearest of the planets would demand far larger telescopes than anything at present in existence, unless this evidence occupied an appreciable fraction of the planet's surface. The French astronomer Flammarion once suggested that if chains of light were placed on the Sahara on a sufficiently generous scale, they might be visible to Martian astronomers if any such there be. If this light were placed so as to form a mathematical pattern, intelligent Martians might conjecture that there was intelligent life on earth. Flammarion thought that the lights might suitably be arranged to illustrate the theorem of Pythagoras (Euclid, 1.47). Possibly a better scheme would be a group of searchlights which could emit successive flashes to represent a series of numbers. If, for instance, the numbers 3, 5, 7, 11, 13, 17, 19, 23 . . . (the sequence of primes) were transmitted, the Martians might surely infer the existence of intelligent Tellurians. But any visual communication between planets would need a combination of high telescopic power at one end and of engineering works on a colossal although not impossible, scale at the other.

Some astronomers—mainly in the past—have thought that the so-called canals on Mars provided evidence of just this kind, although of course unintentionally on the part of the Martians. Two white patches which surround the two poles of Mars are observed to increase and decrease with the seasons, like our terrestrial polar ice. Over the surface of Mars some astronomers have claimed to see a geometrical network of straight lines, which they have interpreted as a system of irrigation canals, designed to bring melted ice from these polar caps to parched equatorial regions. Percival Lowell calculated that this could be done by a pumping system of 4,000 times the power of Niagara. It is fairly certain now that the polar caps are not of ice, but even if they were, the radiation of the summer sun on Mars is so feeble that it could not melt more than a very thin layer of ice before the winter cold came to freeze it solid again. Actually the caps are observed to change very rapidly and are most probably clouds consisting of some kind of solid particles.

The alleged canals cannot be seen at all in the largest telescopes nor can they be photographed, but there are technical reasons why neither of these considerations is conclusive against the existence of the canals. A variety of evidence suggests, however, that the canals are mere subjective illusions—the result of overstraining the eyes in trying to see every detail of a never very brightly illuminated surface. Experiments with school children have shown that under such circumstances the strained eye tends to connect patches of color by straight lines. This will at least explain why various astronomers have claimed to see straight lines not only on Mars, where it is just conceivable that there might be canals, but also on Mercury and the largest satellite of Jupiter, where it seems beyond the bounds of possibility that canals could have been constructed, as well as on Venus, on which real canals could not possibly be seen since its solid surface is entirely hidden under clouds. It may be significant that E. E. Barnard, perhaps the most skilled observer that astronomy has ever known, was never able to see the canals at all, although he studied Mars for years through the largest telescopes.

A more promising line of approach to our problem is to examine which, if any, of the planets is physically suitable for life. But we are at once confronted with the difficulty that we do not know what precise conditions are necessary for life. A human being transferred to the surface of any one of the planets or of their satellites, would die at once, and this for several different reasons on each. On Jupiter he would be simultaneously frozen, asphyxiated, and poisoned, as well as doubly pressed to death by his own weight and by an atmospheric pressure of about a million terrestrial atmospheres. On Mercury he would be burned to death by the sun's heat, killed by its ultra-violet radiation, asphyxiated from want of oxygen, and desiccated from want of water. But this does not touch the question of whether other planets may not have developed species of life suited to their own physical conditions. When we think of the vast variety of conditions under which terrestrial life exists on earth—plankton, soil bacteria, stone bacteria, and the great variety of bacteria which are parasitic on the higher forms of life—it would seem rash to suggest that there are any physical conditions whatever to which life cannot adapt itself. Yet as the physical states of other planets are so different from that of our own, it seems safe to say that any life there may be on any of them must be very different from the life on earth.

The visible surface of Jupiter has a temperature of about $-138°$ C., which represents about 248 degrees of frost on the Fahrenheit scale. The planet probably comprises an inner core of rock, with a surrounding layer of ice some 16,000 miles in thickness, and an atmosphere which again is several thousands of miles thick and exerts the pressure of a million terrestrial atmospheres which we have already mentioned. The only known constituents of this atmosphere are the poisonous gases methane and ammonia. It is certainly hard to imagine such a planet providing a home for life of any kind whatever. The planets Saturn, Uranus, Neptune, and Pluto, being farther from the sun, are almost certainly even colder than

Jupiter and in all probability suffer from at least equal disabilities as abodes of life.

Turning sunward from these dismal planets, we come first to Mars, where we find conditions much more like those of our own planet. The average temperature is about $-40°$ C., which is also $-40°$ on the Fahrenheit scale, but the temperature rises above the freezing point on summer afternoons in the equatorial regions. The atmosphere contains at most only small amounts of oxygen and carbon dioxide, perhaps none at all, so that there can be no vegetation comparable with that of the earth. The surface, in so far as it can be tested by a study of its powers of reflection and polarization, appears to consist of lava and volcanic ash. To us it may not seem a promising or comfortable home for life, but life of some kind or other may be there nevertheless.

Being at the same average distance from the sun as the earth, the moon has about the same average temperature, but the variations around this average temperature are enormous, the equatorial temperature varying roughly from $120°$ C. to $-80°$ C. The telescope shows high ranges of mountains, apparently volcanic, interspersed with flat plains of volcanic ash. The moon has no atmosphere and consequently no water; it shows no signs of life or change of any kind, unless perhaps for rare falls of rock such as might result from the impact of meteors falling in from outer space. A small town on the moon, perhaps even a large building, ought to be visible in our largest telescopes, but, needless to say, we see nothing of the kind.

Venus, the planet next to the earth, presents an interesting problem. It is similar to the earth in size but being nearer the sun is somewhat warmer. As it is blanketed in cloud we can only guess as to the nature of its surface. But its atmosphere can be studied and is found to contain little or no oxygen, so that the planet's surface can hardly be covered with vegetation as the surface of the earth is. Indeed, its surface is probably so hot that water would boil away. Yet no trace of water vapor is found in the atmosphere, so that the planet may well be devoid of water. There are reasons for thinking that its shroud of clouds may consist of solid particles, possibly hydrates of formaldehyde. Clearly any life that this planet may harbor must be very different from that of the earth.

The only planet that remains is Mercury. This always turns the same face to the sun and its temperature ranges from about $420°$ C. at the center of this face to unimaginable depths of cold in the eternal night of the face which never sees the sun. The planet is too feeble gravitationally to retain much of an atmosphere and its surface, in so far as this can be tested, appears to consist mainly of volcanic ash like the moon and Mars. Once again

we have a planet which does not appear promising as an abode of life and
any life that there may be must be very different from our own.

Thus our survey of the solar system forces us to the conclusion that it
contains no place other than our earth which is at all suitable for life at all
resembling that existing on earth. The other planets are ruled out largely
by unsuitable temperatures. It used to be thought that Mars might have
had a temperature more suited to life in some past epoch when the sun's
radiation was more energetic than it now is, and that similarly Venus can
perhaps look forward to a more temperate climate in some future age.
But these possibilities hardly accord with modern views of stellar evolution.
The sun is now thought to be a comparatively unchanging structure, which
has radiated much as now through the greater part of its past life and will
continue to do the same until it changes cataclysmically into a minute
"white dwarf" star. When this happens there will be a fall of temperature
too rapid for life to survive anywhere in the solar system and too great for
new life ever to get a foothold. As regards suitability for life, the earth
seems permanently to hold a unique position among the bodies surrounding our sun.

Our sun is, however, only one of myriads of stars in space. Our own
galaxy alone contains about 100,000 million stars, and there are perhaps
10,000 million similar galaxies in space. Stars are about as numerous in
space as grains of sand in the Sahara. What can we say about the possibilities of life on planets surrounding these other suns?

We want first to know whether these planets exist. Observational astronomy. can tell us nothing; if every star in the sky were surrounded by a
planetary system like that of our sun, no telescope on earth could reveal a
single one of these planets. Theory can tell us a little more. While there is
some doubt as to the exact manner in which the sun acquired its family of
planets, all modern theories are at one in supposing that it was the result of
the close approach of another star. Other stars in the sky must also experience similar approaches, although calculation shows that such events must
be excessively rare. Under conditions like those which now prevail in the
neighborhood of the sun, a star will experience an approach close enough to
generate planets only about once in every million million million years.
If we suppose the star to have lived under these conditions for about 2,000
million years, only one star in 500 million will have experienced the necessary close encounter, so that at most one star in 500 million will be surrounded by planets. This looks an absurdly minute fraction of the whole,
yet when the whole consists of a thousand million million million stars,
this minute fraction represents two million million stars. On this calculation, then two million million stars must already be surrounded by planets

and a new solar system is born every few hours. . . . Detailed calculation shows that the chance of a star's producing planets in this early stage, although not large, would be quite considerable, and suggests, with a large margin to spare, that although planetary systems may be rare in space, their total number is far from insignificant. Out of the thousands or millions of millions of planets that there must surely be in space, a very great number must have physical conditions very similar to those prevailing on earth.

We cannot even guess whether these are inhabited by life like our own or by life of any kind whatever. The same chemical atoms exist there as exist here and must have the same properties, so that it is likely that the same inorganic compounds have formed there as have formed here. If so, we would like to know how far the chain of life has progressed, but present-day science can give no help. We can only wonder whether any life there may be elsewhere in the universe has succeeded in managing its affairs better than we have done in recent years.

1941

Editors' Note:—

This discussion, which appeared in the First Edition of *A Treasury of Science,* remains substantially in accordance with modern scientific opinion. However, in the Preface to the Fourth Edition, the questions of the origin of planetary systems, the number of planets suitable for life as we know it, and the likelihood of the emergence of organisms elsewhere are considered on the basis of researches completed since Sir James Jeans wrote the above account. The reader is also referred to the Editors' Note on page 90, which discusses briefly new theories of stellar origin. These theories have brought the classical theories described by Jeans into question.

B. THE POWER OF THE ATOM: AN END OR A BEGINNING?

Atomic Terms and What They Mean

THE ESSO RESEARCH AND ENGINEERING COMPANY

Accelerator. A device for imparting very high velocity to charged particles such as *electrons** or *protons.* These fast particles can penetrate matter and are known as *radiation.* Fast particles of this type are used in research or to study the structure of the *atom* itself.

Activation. Making a substance artificially *radioactive* in an *accelerator* such as a *cyclotron* or by *bombarding* it with *neutrons.*

Alpha particle (alpha ray, alpha radiation.) A small electrically charged particle of very high velocity thrown off by many *radioactive* materials, including *uranium* and *radium.* It is identical with the *nucleus* of a helium *atom* and is made up of two *neutrons* and two *protons.* Its electric charge is positive and twice as great as that of an *electron.*

Atom. The tiny "building block" of nature. All materials are made of atoms. The *elements,* such as iron, lead and sulfur, differ from each other because they contain different atoms. Atoms are unbelievably small. No one has ever seen one. There are six sextillion (6 followed by 21 zeros) atoms in an ordinary drop of water. The word "atom" comes from the Greek word meaning indivisible. Now we know it can be split and consists of an inner core (*nucleus*) surrounded by *electrons* which rotate around the nucleus like the planets around the sun.

Atomic energy. Energy released in *nuclear reactions.* Of particular interest is the energy released when a *neutron* splits an atom's *nucleus* into smaller pieces (*fission*) or when two nuclei are joined together under millions of degrees of heat (*fusion*). "Atomic energy" is really a popular misnomer. It is more correctly called *"nuclear energy."*

Atomic number. The number of *protons* (positively charged particles) found in the *nucleus* of an *atom.* All *elements* have different atomic numbers. The atomic number of hydrogen is 1, that of oxygen 8, iron 26, lead 82, *uranium* 92.

* *Italics indicate key words defined in this glossary.*

Atomic theory. Since the time of the ancient Greeks man has held the theory that all matter is composed of tiny, invisible particles called *atoms*. It remained for the chemists and physicists of the 19th and 20th centuries to verify the existence of the atom and the validity of the atomic theory.

Atomic weight. The atomic weight is approximately the sum of the number of *protons* and *neutrons* found in the *nucleus* of an atom. The atomic weight of oxygen, for example is approximately 16 (actually it is 16.0044)—it contains 8 neutrons plus 8 protons. Aluminum is 27—it contains 14 neutrons and 13 protons.

Atom smasher. A machine (an *accelerator*) that speeds up atomic and sub-atomic particles so that they can be used as projectiles to literally blast apart the *nuclei* of other *atoms*.

Autoradiography. Self-portraits of *radioactive sources* made by placing the radioactive material next to photographic film. The radiations fog the film leaving an image of the source. It was such self-portraits that led to the discovery of radioactivity.

Background. Background *radiation* is always detected by a counter. It is caused by radiation coming from *sources* other than the *radioactive* material to be measured. This "background" is primarily due to cosmic rays which constantly bombard the earth from outer space.

Beta particle (beta radiation). A small electrically charged particle thrown off by many *radioactive* materials. It is identical with the *electron* and possesses the smallest negative electric charge found in nature. Beta particles emerge from radioactive material at high speeds, sometimes close to the speed of light.

Betatron. A large doughnut-shaped *accelerator* in which *electrons (beta particles)* are whirled through a changing magnetic field gaining speed with each trip and emerging with high energies. Energies of the order of 100 million *electron volts* have been achieved. The betatron produces artificial beta radiation.

Bev. A billion *electron volts*. An *electron* possessing this much energy travels with a speed close to that of light—186,000 miles a second.

Bevatron. A huge circular *accelerator* such as the one located at the University of California. *Protons* are whirled through the 160-foot "doughnut" between the poles of a magnet weighing 13,000 tons. It is designed to produce energies of 10 billion *electron volts*.

Binding energy. The energy which holds the *neutrons* and *protons* of an atomic *nucleus* together.

Bombardment. Shooting *neutrons, alpha particles* and other high energy particles at atomic *nuclei* usually in an attempt to split the nucleus or to form a new *element*.

Breeder. A *reactor* which is producing more atomic fuel than it is consuming. A non*fissionable isotope, bombarded* by *neutrons,* is transformed into a fissionable material, such as *plutonium,* which can be used as fuel. Scientists are working toward the day when all the material burned in reactors will be replaced through this process.

Chain reaction. When a *fissionable nucleus* is split by a *neutron* it releases energy and one or more neutrons. These neutrons split other fissionable nuclei releasing more energy and more neutrons making the reaction self-sustaining.

Charge. The fuel (*fissionable* material) placed in a *reactor* to produce a *chain reaction.*

Cloud chamber. A glass-domed chamber filled with moist vapor. When certain types of atomic particles pass through the chamber they leave a cloud-like track much like the vapor trail of a jet plane. This permits scientists to "see" these particles and study their motion.

Cobalt-60. A *radioactive isotope* of the *element* cobalt. Cobalt-60 is an important source of *gamma radiation* and is used widely in research.

Compton effect. The glancing collision of a *gamma ray* with an *electron.* The gamma ray gives up part of its energy to the electron.

Control rod. A rod used to control the power of a nuclear *reactor.* The reactor functions through the splitting of nuclear fuel by *neutrons.* The control rod absorbs neutrons which would normally split *atoms* of the fuel. Pushing the rod in reduces the release of atomic power. Pulling out the rod increases it.

Converter. A *reactor* which uses one kind of fuel and produces another. For example a converter charged with *uranium isotopes* might consume Uranium-235 and produce *plutonium* from Uranium-238.

Core. The heart of a nuclear *reactor* where the *nuclei* of the fuel *fission* (split) and release energy. The core is usually surrounded by a reflecting material which bounces stray *neutrons* back to the fuel.

Cosmotron. A huge *accelerator,* one of the atomic "guns," located at Brookhaven National Laboratory. It speeds up particles to the billion *electron volt* range. The Brookhaven machine has a magnet weighing 2,200 tons.

Counter. A device for counting nuclear disintegrations to measure *radioactivity.* The signal which announces a disintegration is called a count.

Critical mass. The amount of nuclear fuel necessary to sustain a *chain reaction.* If too little fuel is present too many *neutrons* will stray and the reaction will die out.

Curie. A measure of the rate at which a *radioactive* material throws off particles. The radioactivity of one gram of *radium* is a curie. It is named for Pierre and Marie Curie, pioneers in radioactivity and discoverers of the *elements* radium, radon, and polonium.

Cutie-pie. A portable instrument equipped with a direct reading meter used to determine the level of *radiation* in an area.

Cyclotron. A particle *accelerator.* In this atomic "merry-go-round" atomic particles are whirled around in a spiral between the ends of a huge magnet gaining speed with each rotation in preparation for their assault on the target material.

Decay. When a *radioactive atom* disintegrates it is said to decay. What remains is a different *element.* An atom of polonium decays to form lead, ejecting an *alpha particle* in the process.

Deuterium. Heavy hydrogen. The *nucleus* of heavy hydrogen is a *deuteron.* It is called heavy hydrogen because it weighs twice as much as ordinary hydrogen.

Deuteron. The *nucleus* of an *atom* of *heavy hydrogen* containing one *proton* and one *neutron.* Deuterons are often used as atomic projectiles.

Dosimeter (dose meter). An instrument used to determine the *radiation* dose a person has received.

Electron. A minute atomic particle possessing the smallest amount of negative electric charge found in nature. In an *atom* the electrons rotate around a small *nucleus.* The weight of an electron is so infinitesimal that it would take 500 octillions (500 followed by 27 zeros) of them to make a pound. It is only about a two-thousandth of the mass of a *proton* or *neutron.*

Electron volt (ev). A small unit of energy. An *electron* gains this much energy when it is acted upon by one volt.

Element. A basic substance consisting of a "family" of naturally occurring *isotopes.* For example, hydrogen, lead and oxygen are elements. All *atoms* of an element contain a definite number of *protons* and thus have the same *atomic number.*

Film badge. A piece of masked photographic film worn like a badge by nuclear workers. It is darkened by nuclear *radiation,* and radiation exposure can be checked by inspecting the film.

Fission. The splitting of an atomic *nucleus* into two parts accompanied by the release of a large amount of *radioactivity* and heat. Fission reactions occur only with heavy *elements* such as *uranium* and *plutonium.*

Fissionable. A *nucleus* which undergoes *fission* under the influence of *neutrons,* even of very slow neutrons. *Uranium-235,* an *isotope* of uranium with mass number 235, is fissionable. *Plutonium* is also fissionable.

Fusion. The joining of atomic *nuclei* to form a heavier nucleus, accomplished under conditions of extreme heat (millions of degrees). If two nuclei of light *atoms* fuse, the fusion is accompanied by the release of a great deal of energy. The energy of the sun is believed to be derived from the fusion of hydrogen atoms to form helium.

Gamma rays (gamma radiation). The most penetrating of all *radiations.* Gamma rays are very high energy *X-rays.*

Geiger counter. A gas-filled electrical device which detects the presence of *radioactivity* by counting the formation of *ions.*

Half-life. A means of classifying the rate of *decay* of *radioisotopes* according to the time it takes them to lose half their strength (intensity). Half-lives range from fractions of seconds to billions of year. *Cobalt-60,* for example, has a half-life of 5.3 years. A *radioactive* material loses half its strength when its age is equal to its half-life.

Heavy hydrogen. Same as *deuterium.*

Heavy water. Water which contains *heavy hydrogen (deuterium)* instead of ordinary hydrogen. It is widely used in *reactors* to slow down *neutrons.*

Hot. A colloquial term meaning highly *radioactive.*

Ion. Usually an *atom* which has lost one or more of its *electrons* and is left with a positive electrical charge. There are also negative ions, which have gained an extra electron.

Ionization chamber. A device roughly similar to a *geiger counter* and used to measure *radioactivity.*

Isotope. Two *nuclei* of the same *element* which have the same charge but different masses are called isotopes. They contain the same number of *protons* but a different number of *neutrons. Uranium-238* contains 92 protons and 146 neutrons while the isotope U-235 contains 92 protons and 143 neutrons. Thus the *atomic weight* (atomic mass) of U-238 is three higher than that of U-235.

Kev. Kilo *electron volts* or 1,000 electron volts. A unit of energy.

Kilocurie. 1,000 *curies.* A unit of *radioactivity.*

Linear accelerator. A machine for speeding up charged particles such as *protons.* It differs from other *accelerators* in that the particles move in a straight line at all times instead of in circles or spirals.

Master slave manipulators. Mechanical hands used to handle *hot* materials. They are remotely controlled from behind a protective *shield.*

Meson. A particle which weighs more than the *electron* but generally less than the *proton.* Mesons can be produced artificially. They are also produced by cosmic *radiation* (natural radiation coming from outer space). Mesons are not stable—they disintegrate in a fraction of a second.

Mev. Million *electron volts.*

Milliroentgen. One one-thousandth of a *roentgen.* A unit of *radioactive* dose.

Moderator. A material used to slow *neutrons* in a *reactor.* These slow neutrons are particularly effective in causing *fission.* Neutrons are slowed down when they collide with *atoms* of light *elements* such as hydrogen and carbon, two common moderators.

Molecule. The smallest unit of a compound. A water molecule consists of two hydrogen *atoms* combined with one oxygen atom. Hence the well-known formula, H_2O.

Monitor. A *radiation* detector used to determine whether an area is safe for workers. A *cutie-pie* is a portable monitor.

Neutron. One of the three basic atomic particles. The neutron weighs about the same as the *proton* and, as its name implies, has no electric charge. Neutrons make effective atomic projectiles.

Nuclear bombardment. The shooting of atomic projectiles at *nuclei* usually in an attempt to split the *atom* or to form a new *element.*

Nuclear energy. The energy released in a *nuclear reaction,* such as *fission* or *fusion.* Nuclear energy is popularly, though mistakenly, called *atomic energy.*

Nuclear reaction. Result of the *bombardment* of a *nucleus* with atomic or sub-atomic particles or very high energy *radiation.* Possible reactions are emission of other particles or the splitting of the nucleus (*fission*). The *decay* of a *radioactive* material is also a nuclear reaction.

Nucleonics. The applications of nuclear science and techniques in physics, chemistry, astronomy, biology, industry and other fields.

Nucleus. The inner core of the *atom.* It consists of *neutrons* and *protons* tightly locked together.

Pair production. The conversion af a *gamma ray* into a pair of particles —an *electron* and a *positron.* This is an example of direct conversion of energy into matter according to Einstein's famous formula: $E = mc^2$; (energy) = (mass) × (velocity of light).²

Photoelectric effect. Occurs when an *electron* is knocked out of an *atom* by a light ray or *gamma ray.* This effect is used in an "electric eye." Light falls on a sensitive surface knocking out electrons which can then be detected.

Photon. A bundle (quantum) of *radiation.* Constitutes, for example, *X-rays* and light. In certain processes *gamma rays* behave as photons.

Pig. A container (usually lead) used to ship or store *radioactive* materials. The thick walls protect the person handling the container from *radiation*.

Pile. A nuclear *reactor*. Called a pile because the earliest reactors were "piles" of graphite blocks and *uranium slugs*.

Pitchblende. An ore containing both *uranium* and *radium*. The Curies had to purify tons of pitchblende to obtain a barely visible speck of radium.

Plutonium. A heavy *element* which undergoes *fission* under the impact of *neutrons*. It is a useful fuel in nuclear *reactors*. Plutonium does not occur in nature but can be produced and "burned" in reactors.

Positron. A particle which has the same weight and charge as an *electron* but is electrically positive rather than negative. The positron's existence was predicted in theory years before it was actually detected. It is not stable in matter.

Proton. One of the basic particles of the atomic *nucleus* (the other is the *neutron*). Its charge is as large as that of the *electron*, but positive.

Q-value. The energy liberated or absorbed in a *nuclear reaction*.

Rabbit. A capsule which carries samples in and out of an atomic *reactor* through a pneumatic tube. Purpose is to permit study of the effect of intense *radiation* upon various materials.

Radiation (radioactivity). The emission of very fast atomic particles or rays by *nuclei*. Some *elements* are naturally radioactive while others become radioactive after *bombardment* with *neutrons* or other particles. The three major forms of radiation are *alpha, beta* and *gamma,* named for the first three letters of the Greek alphabet.

Radiochemistry. That phase of chemistry concerned with the properties and behavior of *radioactive* materials.

Radioisotope. A *radioactive isotope* of an *element.* A radioisotope can be produced by placing material in a nuclear *reactor* and *bombarding* it with *neutrons*. Radioisotopes are being used today as *tracers* in many areas of science and industry and are at present the most important peacetime contribution of *atomic energy*.

Radium. One of the earliest known naturally *radioactive elements*. It is far more radioactive than *uranium* and is found in the same ores.

Reactor. An atomic "furnace." In a reactor, *nuclei* of the fuel undergo *fission* under the influence of *neutrons*. The fission produces new neutrons, and hence a *chain reaction*. This releases large amounts of energy. This energy is removed as heat which may be used to make steam for use in generation of electricity.

Roentgen. A unit of *radioactive* dose, or exposure. The Atomic Energy

Commission has established a conservative limit of exposure for the protection of atomic workers.

Scintillation counter. A device for counting atomic particles by means of tiny flashes of light (scintillations) which the particles produce when they strike certain crystals.

Shield. A wall which protects workers from harmful *radiations* released by radioactive materials.

Slug. A "fuel element" for a nuclear *reactor,* a piece of *fissionable* material. The slugs in large reactors consist of *uranium* metal coated with aluminum to prevent corrosion.

Source. Any substance which emits radiation. Usually refers to a piece of radioactive material conveniently packaged for scientific or industrial use.

Synchrotron. An *accelerator* used to achieve higher velocities for atomic particles than is possible in a conventional *cyclotron.*

Thermonuclear reaction. A *fusion* reaction, that is, a reaction in which two light *nuclei* combine to form a heavier *atom,* releasing a large amount of energy. This is believed to be the sun's source of energy. It is called thermonuclear because it occurs only at a very high temperature.

Thorium. A heavy *element.* When *bombarded* with *neutrons* thorium changes into *uranium,* becoming *fissionable* and thus a source of *atomic energy.*

Tracer. A *radioisotope* which is mixed with a stable material. The radioisotope enables scientists to trace the material as it undergoes chemical and physical changes. Tracers are being used widely in science, industry and agriculture today. When *radioactive* phosphorus, for example, is mixed with a chemical fertilizer the radioactive substance can be traced through the plant as it grows.

Tritium. Often called hydrogen three. Extra heavy hydrogen whose *nucleus* contains two *neutrons* and one *proton.* It is three times as heavy as ordinary hydrogen and is *radioactive.*

Unstable. All *radioactive elements* are unstable since they emit particles and *decay* to form other elements.

Uranium. A heavy metal. The two principal *isotopes* of natural uranium are U-235 and U-238. U-235 has the only readily *fissionable nucleus* which occurs in appreciable quantities in nature, hence its importance as nuclear fuel. Only 1 part in 140 of natural uranium is U-235.

Van de Graaff accelerator. An electrostatic generator—a particle *accelerator.* To obtain the voltage, static electricity is picked up at one end of the machine by a rubber belt and carried to the other end where it is stored.

X-ray. Highly penetrating *radiation* similar to *gamma rays.* Unlike gamma rays, X-rays do not come from the *nucleus* of the *atom* but from the surrounding *electrons.* They are produced by electron *bombardment.* When these rays pass through an object they give a shadow picture of the denser portions.

"Z." Symbol for *atomic number.* An *element's* atomic number is the same as the number of *protons* found in one of its *nuclei.* All *isotopes* of a given element have the same *"Z"* number.

1956

Atomic Energy for Military Purposes

HENRY D. SMYTH

From *Atomic Energy for Military Purposes*

FROM CHAPTER I. INTRODUCTION

THE CONSERVATION OF MASS AND OF ENERGY

THERE ARE TWO PRINCIPLES THAT HAVE BEEN cornerstones of the structure of modern science. The first—that matter can be neither created nor destroyed but only altered in form—was enunciated in the eighteenth century and is familiar to every student of chemistry; it has led to the principle known as the law of conservation of mass. The second—that energy can be neither created nor destroyed but only altered in form—emerged in the nineteenth century and has ever since been the plague of inventors of perpetual-motion machines; it is known as the law of conservation of energy.

These two principles have constantly guided and disciplined the development and application of science. For all practical purposes they were unaltered and separate until some five years ago. For most practical purposes they still are so, but it is now known that they are, in fact, two phases of a single principle for we have discovered that energy may sometimes be converted into matter and matter into energy. Specifically, such a conversion is observed in the phenomenon of nuclear fission of uranium, a process in which atomic nuclei split into fragments with the release of an enormous amount of energy. The military use of this energy has been the object of the research and production projects described in this report

THE EQUIVALENCE OF MASS AND ENERGY

One conclusion that appeared rather early in the development of the theory of relativity was that the inertial mass of a moving body increased as its speed increased. This implied an equivalence between an increase in energy of motion of a body, that is, its kinetic energy, and an increase in its mass. To most practical physicists and engineers this appeared a mathematical fiction of no practical importance. Even Einstein could hardly have foreseen the present applications, but as early as 1905 he did clearly state that mass and energy were equivalent and suggested that proof of this equivalence might be found by the study of radioactive substances. He concluded that the amount of energy, E, equivalent to a mass, m, was given by the equation

$$E = mc^2$$

where c is the velocity of light. If this is stated in actual numbers, its startling character is apparent. It shows that one kilogram (2.2 pounds) of matter, if converted entirely into energy, would give 25 billion kilowatt hours of energy. This is equal to the energy that would be generated by the total electric power industry in the United States (as of 1939) running for approximately two months. Compare this fantastic figure with the 8.5 kilowatt hours of heat energy which may be produced by burning an equal amount of coal.

The extreme size of this conversion figure was interesting in several respects. In the first place, it explained why the equivalence of mass and energy was never observed in ordinary chemical combustion. We now believe that the heat given off in such a combustion has mass associated with it, but this mass is so small that it cannot be detected by the most sensitive balances available. . . . In the second place, it was made clear that no appreciable quantities of matter were being converted into energy in any familiar terrestrial processes, since no such large sources of energy were known. Further, the possibility of initiating or controlling such a conversion in any practical way seemed very remote. Finally, the very size of the conversion factor opened a magnificent field of speculation to philosophers, physicists, engineers, and comic-strip artists. For twenty-five years such speculation was unsupported by direct experimental evidence, but beginning about 1930 such evidence began to appear in rapidly increasing quantity. . . .

NUCLEAR BINDING ENERGIES

It is a general principle of physics that work must be done on a stable system to break it up. Thus, if an assemblage of neutrons and protons is stable, energy must be supplied to separate its constituent particles. If energy and mass are really equivalent, then the total mass of a stable nucleus should be less than the total mass of the separate protons and neutrons that go to make it up. This mass difference, then, should be equivalent to the energy required to disrupt the nucleus completely, which is called the binding energy. Remember that the masses of all nuclei were "approximately" whole numbers. It is the small differences from whole numbers that are significant.

Consider the alpha particle as an example. It is stable; since its mass number is four and its atomic number two it consists of two protons and two neutrons. The mass of a proton is 1.00758 and that of a neutron is 1.00893, so that the total mass of the separate components of the helium nucleus is

$$2 \times 1.00758 + 2 \times 1.00893 = 4.03302$$

whereas the mass of the helium nucleus itself is 4.00280. Neglecting the last two decimal places we have 4.033 and 4.003, a difference of 0.030 mass units. This, then, represents the "binding energy" of the protons and neutrons in the helium nucleus. It looks small, but recalling Einstein's equation, $E = mc^2$, we remember that a small amount of mass is equivalent to a large amount of energy. Actually 0.030 mass units is equal to 4.5×10^{-5} ergs per nucleus or 2.7×10^{19} ergs per gram molecule of helium. In units more familiar to the engineer or chemist, this means that to break up the nuclei of all the helium atoms in a gram of helium would require 1.62×10^{11} gram calories or 190,000 kilowatt hours of energy. Conversely, if free protons and neutrons could be assembled into helium nuclei, this energy would be released.

Evidently it is worth exploring the possibility of getting energy by combining protons and neutrons or by transmuting one kind of nucleus into another. . . .

THE NEED OF A CHAIN REACTION

Our common sources of power, other than sunlight and waterpower, are chemical reactions—usually the combustion of coal or oil. They release energy as the result of rearrangements of the outer electronic structures of the atoms, the same kind of process that supplies energy to our bodies. Combustion is always self-propagating; thus lighting a fire with a match releases enough heat to ignite the neighboring fuel, which releases more heat which ignites more fuel, and so on. In the nuclear reactions we have described this is not generally true; neither the energy released nor the new particles formed are sufficient to maintain the reaction. But we can imagine nuclear reactions emitting particles of the same sort that initiate them and in sufficient numbers to propagate the reaction in neighboring nuclei. Such a self-propagating reaction is called a "chain reaction" and such conditions must be achieved if the energy of the nuclear reactions with which we are concerned is to be put to large-scale use.

PERIOD OF SPECULATION

Although there were no atomic power plants built in the thirties, there were plenty of discoveries in nuclear physics and plenty of speculation. A theory was advanced by H. Bethe to explain the heat of the sun by a cycle of nuclear changes involving carbon, hydrogen, nitrogen, and oxygen, and leading eventually to the formation of helium. This theory is now generally accepted. The discovery of a few $(n,2n)$ nuclear reactions (i.e., neutron-produced and neutron-producing reactions) suggested that a self-multiplying chain reaction might be initiated under the right conditions. There was much talk of atomic power and some talk of atomic bombs. But the last great step in this preliminary period came after four years of stumbling. The effects of neutron bombardment of uranium, the most complex element known, had been studied by some of the ablest physicists. The results were striking but confusing. The story of their gradual interpretation is intricate and highly technical. . . .

DISCOVERY OF URANIUM FISSION

As has already been mentioned, the neutron proved to be the most effective particle for inducing nuclear changes. This was particularly true for the elements of highest atomic number and weight where the large nuclear charge exerts strong repulsive forces on deuteron or proton projectiles but not on uncharged neutrons. The results of the bombardment of uranium by neutrons had proved interesting and puzzling. First studied by Fermi and his colleagues in 1934, they were not properly interpreted until several years later.

On January 16, 1939, Niels Bohr of Copenhagen, Denmark, arrived in this country to spend several months in Princeton, N. J., and was particularly anxious to discuss some abstract problems with A. Einstein. (Four years later Bohr was to escape from Nazi-occupied Denmark in a small boat.) Just before Bohr left Denmark two of his colleagues, O. R. Frisch and L. Meitner (both refugees from Germany), had told him their guess that the absorption of a neutron by a uranium nucleus sometimes caused that nucleus to split into approximately equal parts with the release of enormous quantities of energy, a process that soon began to be called nuclear "fission." The occasion for this hypothesis was the important discovery of O. Hahn and F. Strassmann in Germany which proved that an isotope of barium was produced by neutron bombardment of uranium. Immediately on arrival in the United States Bohr communicated this idea to his former student J. A. Wheeler and others at Princeton, and from them the news spread by word of mouth to neighboring physicists including E. Fermi at Columbia University. As a result of conversations between Fermi, J. R. Dunning, and G. B. Pegram, a search was undertaken at Columbia for the heavy pulses of ionization that would be expected from the flying fragments of the uranium nucleus. On January 26, 1939 there was a Conference on Theoretical Physics at Washington, D. C., sponsored jointly by the George Washington University and the Carnegie Institution of Washington. Fermi left New York to attend this meeting before the Columbia fission experiments had been tried. At the meeting Bohr and Fermi discussed the problem of fission, and in particular Fermi mentioned the possibility that neutrons might be emitted during the process. Although this was only a guess, its implication of the possibility of a chain reaction was obvious. . . .

GENERAL DISCUSSION OF FISSION

Consider the suggestion of Frisch and Meitner in the light of the two general trends that had been discovered in nuclear structure:—first, that the proportion of neutrons goes up with atomic number; second, that the binding energy per particle is a maximum for the nuclei of intermediate atomic number. Suppose the U-238 nucleus is broken exactly in half; then, neglecting the mass of the incident neutron, we have two nuclei of atomic number 46 and mass number 119. But the heaviest stable isotope of palladium $(Z=46)$ has a mass number of only 110. Therefore to reach stability each of these imaginary new nuclei must eject nine neutrons, or four neutrons in each nucleus must convert themselves to protons by emitting electrons thereby forming stable tin nuclei of mass number 119 and atomic number 50; or a combination of such ejections and conversions must occur to give some other pair of stable nuclei. Actually, as was suggested by Hahn and Strassmann's identification of barium ($Z=56$, $A=$ 135 to 140) as a product of fission, the split occurs in such a way as to produce two unequal parts of mass numbers about 140 and 90 with the emission of a few neutrons and subsequent radioactive decay by electron emission until stable nuclei are formed. Calculations from binding-energy data show that any such rearrangement gives an aggregate resulting mass considerably less than the initial mass of the uranium nucleus, and thus that a great deal of energy must be released.

Evidently, there were three major implications of the phenomenon of fission: the release of energy, the production of radioactive atomic species and the possibility of a neutron chain reaction. The energy release might reveal itself in kinetic energy of the fission fragments and in the subsequent radioactive disintegration of the products. The possibility of a neutron chain reaction depended on whether neutrons were in fact emitted—a possibility which required investigation.

These were the problems suggested by the discovery of fission, the kind of problem reported in the journals in 1939 and 1940 and since then investigated largely in secret. The study of the fission process itself, including production of neutrons and fast fragments, has been largely carried out by physicists using counters, cloud chambers, etc. The study and identification of the fission products has been carried out largely by chemists, who have had to perform chemical separations rapidly even with sub-microscopic quantities of material and to make repeated determinations of the half-lives of unstable isotopes . . .

SUMMARY

Looking back on the year 1940, we see that all the prerequisites to a serious attack on the problem of producing atomic bombs and controlling atomic power were at hand. It had been proved that mass and energy were equivalent. It had been proved that the neutrons initiating fission of uranium reproduced themselves in the process and that therefore a multiplying chain reaction might occur with explosive force. To be sure, no one knew whether the required conditions could be achieved, but many scientists had clear ideas as to the problems involved and the directions in which solutions might be sought. . . .   *1945*

Atomic Warfare, Past and Future

JACOB SACKS

From *The Atom at Work*

I

T IS ONE OF THE GREATEST IRONIES OF HISTORY THAT the most powerful and destructive weapon that warfare has ever known was produced in the country that is the least military-minded of the great powers. Only in the United States were there the reserves of scientific ability and technical resources of manpower and machinery, to devote two billion dollars to the making of the atomic bomb while furnishing almost limitless amounts of arms and supplies for its own newly created armed forces and those of its allies as well.

Those reserves of scientific ability were not all native products. Among the foremost of the nuclear physicists who were living in the United States in 1939 and who played large parts in the development of the bomb were a number of scientists of European birth who had come here to escape the totalitarianisms that had engulfed their native lands. . . .

It was in March of 1939, before the Nazis had started the war that was to engulf almost the whole world, that the first steps were taken. The group consisting of Fermi, Szilard, Teller, Weisskopf, and Wigner started the move to have the nuclear physicists of the free world stop the publication of their results. With the help of Niels Bohr, the aid of those in the free countries of Europe was enlisted in this effort. The co-operation was obtained, but it took time. During this time there was a great deal published, and so made accessible to the nuclear physicists of Germany.

That was one part of the necessary action. The other was to bring to the attention of the responsible authorities in this country the realization of the possibilities of an atomic bomb, so that experiments could be gotten under way as soon as possible. The first attempt by these same individuals in March of 1939, was made in the accepted way, "through channels."

Dean Pegram of Columbia University arranged a conference between Fermi and representatives of the Navy. They were not impressed, so the attempt to get action by going "through channels" came to nothing. But Szilard and Wigner, both of Hungarian birth, kept at it, and in July of 1939 they approached Einstein. These three took the matter up with Alexander Sachs, an economist who was a personal friend of President Roosevelt. As a result, Einstein wrote a long letter setting forth the situation. This letter was given to Roosevelt by Sachs, and action followed in short order. . . .

There was enough known about nuclear fission by June of 1940, when all publication stopped, so that the lines of investigation that needed to be followed to produce an atomic bomb were pretty well mapped out. There were two obvious lines to be followed; one was to find means of separating the fissionable isotope, U^{235}, from the 140-fold more abundant U^{238}. The other was to determine whether a chain-reacting pile was possible, to produce enough plutonium to make an atomic bomb of this element.

What was needed to follow out the first line, which looked more immediately promising, was a large area in an isolated and sparsely inhabited part of the country that had access to enormous amounts of electric power. That area was found in the hill country of East Tennessee, where the power would come from the dams of the TVA. Thus was Oak Ridge set up under General Leslie R. Groves, in an area of almost 100 square miles that was practically uninhabited.

The only way of making the separation of the two isotopes was to use the differences in the physical properties of their compounds that resulted from the difference in the molecular weights. There were several possibilities. It was hard to tell in advance which one would be the most practical, and there was no time to waste on what would be the orderly progress of an industrial research program. This would be to go from the laboratory to a pilot plant, then to a small-scale production unit, and finally to the large-scale unit, ironing out the "bugs" that developed in each stage before going on to the next one. The jump had to be made from laboratory to full-scale production unit, bypassing the intermediate steps.

One promising method was to use the principle of the mass spectrograph which sorts out the isotopes according to their mass by a combination of an electrical and magnetic field. Dr. A. O. Nier of the University of Minnesota took the one he had been using to study the mechanism by which bacteria can incorporate carbon dioxide into complex organic molecules, and found that he could produce in it 1/30,000,000 of an ounce of U^{235} in a 16-hour day. That was the laboratory stage, and the result was encouraging enough so that E. O. Lawrence converted the 37-inch cyclotron into a large-scale mass spectrograph. He found that he could step up the separation rate to as much in an hour as Nier was able to produce with his small magnet in 16 hours. That was the pilot plant stage. There were "bugs" in it, and when these were worked out a huge plant was built at Oak Ridge to do the job on a production basis. Ordinarily, the tremendous electrical current necessary to operate this would have been carried in copper bus bars. But copper was now a scarce item and could not be spared for the project, since no one could be sure of success. Instead, $400,000,000 worth of the enormous stock of silver which the Treasury had lying idle in the vaults, was borrowed and marked for duty. There was some virtue in this necessity, for silver is a somewhat better conductor of electricity than copper, so less energy is lost as heat. The difference is only a few percent, but the amount of power required was so tremendous that using silver meant a saving of several dollars a day. This plant did turn out a fair amount of U^{235}, but the gaseous diffusion method turned out to be more practical. This electromagnetic separation plant is now used to separate the stable isotopes of other elements from each other, in order to supply material for a study of their properties.

Besides the gaseous diffusion method, which did accomplish the job, there were other methods, possibilities on paper, which were tried out on the laboratory scale, and found wanting. The gaseous diffusion method, which worked so well that an enormous plant with floor space equivalent to half a square mile was built at Oak Ridge to house the operation, consists of passing a gaseous compound through myriads of tiny holes in a solid material, the so-called porous barrier. The method depends on the principle that at any given temperature, the speed with which molecules of a gas move around is inversely proportional to the square root of the molecular weight. That is, if the molecular weight of one compound is 100, and of another 64, then the speeds with which the molecules travel are in the ratio of 8 to 10. By allowing, or forcing, the gas to pass through these minute openings, more of the lighter, faster-moving molecules will appear in the first portion that gets through to the far side of the barrier. This method of separating isotopes had been tried out in the laboratory, by W. D. Harkins and his students at the University of Chicago, in the early twenties. They had worked with chlorine, using it in the form of hydrogen chloride gas. They did not accomplish anywhere near a complete separation, but they did get a fraction which contained a definitely higher percentage of the 35 isotope and less of the 37 isotope than in ordinary chlorine. This was enough to prove the point.

The only gaseous compound of uranium that appeared feasible was uranium hexafluoride, UF_6. At ordinary temperatures this is a solid, but it becomes a gas when heated to 166° Fahrenheit. The difference in molecular weights between $U^{235}F_6$ and $U^{238}F_6$ is very small, and when the square roots are taken the difference becomes smaller still in proportion. That means there is only a very slight difference in the speeds at which the two kinds of molecules travel. This is so small that if only a tiny fraction of the material is allowed to pass through the barrier, the greatest possible enrichment in the lighter isotope is only 43 parts per million. If any worth-while quantity of material is to be obtained as a final product, half the total quantity must be allowed to pass through the barrier, and this reduces the theoretically possible enrichment to 30 parts per million. In actual operation, not even this degree of separation is attained in a single step. But by passing the lighter fraction through a second stage, a further enrichment is obtained, and so on. Many acres of barrier were needed, and each portion of the compound would have to pass through 5,000 such barriers. To get one pound of final product, 100,000 pounds of uranium hexafluoride had to be put through the first stage. In order for the process to work at all, the diameter of the holes had to be less than one-tenth the average distance the molecules of the gas would travel before bumping into each other. That meant holes less than 4/10,000,000 of an inch in diameter, and billions upon billions of such tiny holes. The porous material out of which these barriers were made had to be something that would not clog up and not be acted on chemically by the uranium hexafluoride.

This was a large order to fill, but it was filled. And in filling the order, a whole new set of engineering materials was devised, and new high standards of engineering practice were achieved. Uranium hexafluoride reacts vigorously with water, it corrodes many metals, and its vapors are poisonous. Consequently, new alloy materials had to be found for the pumps, which would resist the corroding action of the material. New lubricants for these pumps had to be found which would be resistant to chemical attack. The lubricants were made by treating certain ordinary products obtained from petroleum with the same fluorine that converted the uranium itself into a gaseous compound. Many of these fluorinated compounds had been known before, as laboratory curiosities. It was known that they are very resistant to chemical change. All these things had to be worked out in the laboratory, on the test tube scale, and then put into large-scale production. The efforts were successful, and the job was done. These engineering materials, and many other products developed for the project, are now being used profitably on a commercial basis, in peacetime uses. Among other things, plastics containing fluorine are on the market, with properties that make them superior for certain purposes to anything that was available before.

While this work on the separation of U^{235} was going on, the first chain-reacting pile had been made in the squash courts at the University of Chicago. This pile served as the laboratory model for the construction of one on a much larger scale at Oak Ridge, which was itself only a pilot plant for the three that were built at Hanford, Washington. The one at Chicago never developed more than a few watts of power, and no provision was necessary for cooling it. At Oak Ridge, the pile eventually got up to a power of about 2,000 kilowatts, and the enormous heat generated had to be disposed of. In this case, the cooling was done by air. At Hanford, the Columbia River supplied the water for cooling the piles.

One of the problems that had to be worked out for plutonium was its chemical separation from the large amount of unchanged uranium and the fission products. The chemistry of plutonium had been worked out by Seaborg at California on the minute fraction of an ounce that one of the large cyclotrons there was able to produce. Working out the chemical properties of pure plutonium was one thing; finding out how to separate the plutonium from the enormously greater amounts of some thirty other elements formed in the fission process was another. Many of the fission products are elements whose chemical properties are similar to those of plutonium, so the separation process is very involved. To protect the chemists from staggering amounts of radioactivity, all the work had to be done by remote control, behind thick walls of concrete, with all the material out of sight. The fission products contained in a single bar of uranium that had been in the pile long enough to be worked up for its plutonium gave out beta particles and gamma rays in thousands of times the number that would come from all the radium that had ever been mined. Only when the plutonium had been obtained as a pure compound did the chemist dare to look upon his handiwork, and then only through a glass. This was safe enough, because the alpha particles from the plutonium are so readily absorbed by matter.

Long before there was even a thousandth part of an ounce of pure U^{235} or plutonium, even before Fermi and his group had brought their first pile up to critical size, a physics research laboratory was started in the vast open spaces of New Mexico, at Los Alamos, to work out the problem of how to put together the atom bomb and make it explode at the right time. There was no time to build the major pieces of equipment needed for this work. A cyclotron was needed, but it would have taken two years to build one. So the one at Harvard University was taken apart, shipped to Los Alamos, and reassembled there. The same thing was done with Van de Graaff generators; two of them were borrowed from the University of Wisconsin. Other equipment was borrowed from many universities which had it.

The bomb and the pile both depend on the neutrons liberated in fission being captured by other atoms of the U^{235} or plutonium and causing fission in them. The pile is a controlled chain reaction, the bomb an uncontrolled one. The fissions in the pile are brought about by neutrons which have been slowed down by the moderator; in the bomb there is no moderator, and the chain reaction is kept going by fissions produced by fast neutrons. In both the pile and the bomb, there is a critical size which must be reached before the chain reaction will keep on. In the pile, the rate of the chain reaction can be controlled by the cadmium or boron control rods. In the bomb, once the critical size has been reached, there is no power that can control it; the explosion is inevitable. There are always stray neutrons around, and even one solitary neutron in a mass of critical size would be enough to start the chain reaction. Some of these come from cosmic rays, some from the reaction of the alpha particles with the minute traces of impurities in the bomb material, and some from the spontaneous fission that takes place in the U^{235} or plutonium.

The critical size had to be calculated, and the calculation had to be accurate. If the critical size was underestimated, there would be no explosion. If it were overestimated, then the explosion might take place while the bomb was being assembled and the whole laboratory would be disintegrated. And another imperative was that the parts of the bomb be brought together to make critical size within a very small fraction of a second. The time it takes for a neutron produced in fission to cause another fission is about $1/100,000,000$ of a second. The explosion will take place in $1/1,000,000$ of a second, long before all the material of the bomb has undergone fission. As soon as the chain reaction starts, an enormous amount of heat is liberated, and the temperature of the mass is raised to millions of degrees, approaching that of the sun. The explosion comes from this heat effect. If the parts of the bomb are brought together slowly, then the heat liberated will cause the explosion to take place too early for greatest effect, and it will be inefficient. So a way had to be found out for shooting the parts together within a very small fraction of a second. The

Army Ordnance Department had the knowledge for designing the means to do this, and their experts were called in. . . .

Six years after Alexander Sachs delivered to President Franklin D. Roosevelt the letter from Albert Einstein that had started the project, the atomic bomb was ready for the test. General Groves had organized well the work of the Manhattan District. There was enough U^{235} from the gaseous diffusion plant at Oak Ridge, there was enough plutonium from the piles at Hanford, there was the mechanism for shooting together the masses that would make the critical size. There was still the question, would it explode? Had the $2,000,000,000 and the years of effort on the part of many of the most eminent physicists and chemists in the country been well spent, or would the bomb turn out to be the most stupendous dud of all time? The date for the test had been set, July 16, 1945, in a remote and isolated section of the Alamogordo Air Base. The few inhabitants of the area had been moved out of range. The final calculations had been checked and checked again. The most secret part of the project, the intricate mechanism for assembling the bomb, for firing the parts together and setting off the explosion, was being assembled in an old ranch house, under Dr. Robert F. Bacher, then professor of physics at Cornell University, later to be appointed the first scientist member of the United States Atomic Energy Commission. Among those present at this operation was Dr. Klaus Fuchs, the German-born nuclear physicist who had fled to England to escape the Nazis.

The time of the test had been set for 4 A.M., but the weather postponed it for an hour and a half. Everyone had been cleared from the area for six miles around the steel tower from which the bomb was to be dropped. The nearest safe point was set up at this distance, behind shelters of timber and earth, in which the controls for the operation had been assembled. The main observation point was ten miles away from the tower and there came those who had taken leading parts in the work. The tension among the scientists and others present was increasing by the minute. The time signals were called out over the loud speaker. "Minus 20 minutes . . . minus 15 minutes . . . minus 5 minutes . . ." At minus 45 seconds, the robot mechanism took control. Each of those seconds must have seemed like hours to the waiting group. Then, in the word of the official statement released by the War Department:

> At the appointed time there was a blinding flash lighting up the whole area brighter than the brightest daylight. A mountain range three miles from the observation point stood out in bold relief. Then came a tremendous sustained roar and a heavy pressure wave which knocked down two men

outside the control center. Immediately thereafter, a huge multi-colored surging cloud boiled up to an altitude of over 40,000 feet. Clouds in its path disappeared. Soon the shifting substratosphere winds dispersed the now grey mass.

The test was over, the project a success.

Three weeks later, on August 6, 1945, the first atomic bomb used on a military objective was dropped on Hiroshima, and on August 9 the second one was dropped on Nagasaki. The awful destruction caused by these bombs gave the militarists who ruled Japan the "out" that let them surrender and end the war in which they had already suffered a military defeat which they were psychologically unwilling to admit.

The explosive force released by the bombs that fell on Hiroshima and Nagasaki is stated to have been equivalent to that from 20,000 tons of T.N.T. How much U^{235} or plutonium was used is still a secret, but it is known that the amount is measured in pounds. Less than one-tenth of one per cent of the mass of the uranium or plutonium is converted to energy in the explosion. . . .

Both the bombs dropped on Japan were exploded several hundred feet in the air. In this way the maximum immediate destruction was achieved, with the minimum of delayed effects. By far the greatest portion of the radioactive isotopes formed went up in the cloud that followed the blast, and so were dissipated over thousands of square miles of the earth's surface. The amount that was deposited on the ground in the immediate area was so small as to be no hazard whatever to the survivors.

In 1946, at Bikini, an atoll in the Pacific Ocean, two more atomic bombs were exploded for test purposes in the Army's "Operation Crossroads." In one of these the bomb was exploded at a low altitude above the surface of the water, and in the other, the explosion took place below the surface. Since then, an atomic weapons proving ground has been established at Eniwetok atoll, and tests have been held there. The veil of secrecy, which was never really lifted from the operations at Bikini, has been clamped down on these further operations.

What is known, or can be surmised, is that ways have been found to make the atomic bombs more destructive than those which were used on Japan, Also, it is known that an atomic bomb set to explode in a city after it had penetrated underground, would cause far less immediate destruction than an air burst, but the radioactivity remaining in the area could be enough to kill those who remained and survived the immediate effects of the explosion. It is quite possible that an area could be made completely uninhabitable by the underground explosion of an atomic bomb.

Terrible as is the atomic bomb, it may still not be the last word in destructiveness. It is within the realm of possibility that man may be able to create a far more powerful weapon out of the energy of the atom. The President of the United States had made public the news that this country is working on the hydrogen bomb, and it would be the height of folly to suppose that the nuclear physicists of Russia are not doing the same thing. The hydrogen bomb depends on nuclear fusion, rather than fission, for the release of energy. It operates on the same type of process that is going on in the sun and the stars: the condensation of hydrogen to helium. The reaction involving only the light isotope, either through the carbon cycle as it takes place in the sun, or directly, as it is supposed to happen in certain of the stars, is extremely slow even at temperatures of millions of degrees. But as soon as one of the heavier isotopes, deuterium or tritium, enters the picture, the reaction speeds up enormously. When only these heavy isotopes are involved, the speed of the process changes from the snail's pace to that of lightning. According to the calculations of the theoretical physicists, these reactions should begin to take place when the temperature is $15,000°$ C., but only slowly. As the temperature is raised to several million degrees, the speed increases enormously, so that it would take less than a millionth of a second.

For the weight of material involved, the energy liberated in fusion is much greater than in fission. When U^{235} or plutonium undergoes fission, only about one-tenth of one per cent of the mass is converted to energy, but in the fusion reaction involving either deuterium or tritium alone, or the one in which they both take part, up to seven-tenths of one per cent of the mass is converted to energy. There are neutrons liberated in the fusion reactions, but there is no way for these neutrons to keep a chain reaction going. There would be no shortage of materials for a fusion bomb, since deuterium is an article of commerce and tritium can be produced readily in the nuclear reactor.

The difference in the power for destruction of the two bombs does not stop with the greater energy released from fusion. The critical size is the "practical" upper limit for the fission bomb, as well as the lower. That is, it is pointless to put more U^{235} or plutonium in a single bomb assembly than just enough over critical size to make sure it will go off. In a larger mass the explosion would be less efficient than that which would take place when a small fraction had undergone fission. But there is no limit, so far as is known, to the amount of *fusionable* material that can be put in one assembly. So long as the mass of exploding material remains at that enormously high temperature, it is possible for the fusion reaction to keep going. So it is conceivable that a hydrogen bomb could be made with a hundred times the capacity for destruction of those dropped on Hiroshima and Nagasaki, or the "improved" ones tested at Bikini and Eniwetok.

How could such a bomb be set off? How is it possible to reach the terrifically high temperature necessary? There is only one way on earth to do it: to use an "ordinary" uranium or plutonium bomb as the trigger. At the instant of the explosion of the fission bomb, the temperature within the mass is probably several million degrees, and any deuterium or tritium there would undergo the fusion reaction, raising still higher the temperature and pouring out vast amounts of energy to add to the enormous forces for destruction. . . .

. . . the "secret" of the atomic bomb. There never was any such thing. The facts of nuclear fission were there for all to read who could. Any nuclear physicist of any competence could have made the calculations and designed the experiments to determine the critical size of both the pile and the bomb. Certainly Russia has nuclear physicists of no mean competence. Any chemist or physicist could have figured out the possible ways of separating U^{235} from U^{238}, and carried out the laboratory experiments to find out which was the best way to make the separation. To appreciate the fact that plutonium is formed in the operation of the pile and that it is fissionable, also required no flash of genius. . . .

The purpose of the secrecy which surrounded the tremendous effort that led to the atomic bomb was military security. This was obviously necessary. Unfortunately, despite all the vigilance within the extensive ramifications of the project, there was one individual who was in a position to reveal important secret information to the Russians, who during the war were untrusted, and as the later events have shown, untrustworthy, allies. This man, Klaus Fuchs, was a nuclear physicist, born in Germany, who fled from the Nazis to England. His talents were such as to give him an important place in the group of theoretical physicists who worked on the bomb, in England and at Los Alamos. But his mind was a split one, so that he was unable to see the complete antithesis between the political systems of his adopted country and the one in which he was a welcome guest, on the one hand, and that of Russia on the other. Of his own choice, not through avarice or cupidity, without thought that he was being a traitor to the country which had given him refuge, he gave the Russians many of the closely guarded secrets.

What he told them did not make the difference between success and failure in their effort to produce an atomic bomb. It would be highly unrealistic to assume that Russian scientists would have remained unable to duplicate what American scientists did. The information Fuchs gave the Russians undoubtedly saved them many years of experimentation, saved them from following the lines that had turned out to be blind alleys, and it shortened by some years the time between Hiroshima and the first atomic explosion in Russia. . . .

1951

The Death of Louis Slotin

RALPH E. LAPP

From *Atoms and People*

ORDINARY OR NATURAL URANIUM IS QUITE HARMLESS for it will not, by itself, sustain chain reaction. Only when it is embodied in an enormous matrix of some light element like graphite or heavy water does it sustain a slow chain reaction. Were this to be allowed to run out of control, it would not in general produce anything like an explosion. Heat would be produced and some inner parts of the reactor might melt, but it would not qualify as a bomb.

Enriched uranium or plutonium is quite different from ordinary uranium. Assemble too much of it in one place, and the chain reaction will automatically run away. Thus, it was rather important for the people at Oak Ridge and at Hanford to know how much was "enough" so that safety precautions could be taken. At Los Alamos the experts refined their calculations as to the size of the critical mass, but it was essential to have experimental measurements.

The man who headed up the "critical assembly" group was a good friend of mine. I knew Louis Slotin while an undergraduate at the University of Chicago and liked him very much for his pleasant manner and friendly advice. He was never too busy to help out a Ph.D. aspirant, and I remember that he gave me valuable pointers on making Geiger counters. On my visits to Los Alamos I used to stop by to see Slotin and give him the news of Chicago. He was a short, wiry youth with dark hair and soft sad eyes. Somehow or other, he always ended up doing jobs nobody else wanted. He never complained, and I respected the cheerful way that Slotin did dirty work.

Slotin had nerves of iron and he needed them for his critical experiments with the "nukes." Here is essentially what he did in making a critical assembly, or in "tickling the dragon's tail," as we called it. He would set up a table with a neutron counter and a rack. On the rack he would place two pieces of bomb stuff, each one being somewhat less than a critical amount. Then he would push the two pieces, often in the form of hemispheres the size of a split baseball, toward each other. As the gap narrowed between the pieces, he would measure the buildup of the chain reaction inside the assembly. He used a small source of neutrons to amplify the effect, rather than waiting for stray neutrons to come from cosmic rays or from the material itself. He determined the tempo of the buildup by listening to the clicks in an amplifier connected to the neutron counter and in watching a recorder trace out a jagged red line on a moving roll of graph paper.

As the hemispheres came closer and closer, more and more of the neutrons would tend to be caught within the bomb stuff and fewer would be lost through the narrowing air gap. The chain reaction would build up, and, just before it was ready to rip, Slotin would calmly stop the experiment, measure the separation and deduce just how big the critical mass was. He grew quite adept at the experiment for he repeated it fifty times or more. His nonchalance amazed Fermi who once warned him, "Keep doing that experiment that way and you'll be dead within a year." Some of Slotin's colleagues tried to get him to build in automatic safety devices, like powerful springs, which could be triggered to hurl the two hemispheres apart when the neutrons built up too fast. He turned aside this suggestion with this retort: "If I have to depend upon safety devices I am sure to have an accident."

Slotin was asked to repeat the experiment "just one more time" to demonstrate the technique to others in the laboratory. So he gathered the group of six people behind him in the sunlit room where he did his work. One man, Dr. Alvin Graves, had his hand almost on his shoulder as Slotin proceeded to demonstrate his technique. He used two hemispheres that he had worked with before and holding a screwdriver he moved the two pieces of bomb material together to form a "nuke" or nuclear core. Slowly, at first, then more quickly the counters clicked away and the red line moved upward on the white paper chart.

Suddenly the counters screamed and the red ink indicators swung off scale. There had been an accident! The chain reaction was running away. Almost as if by reflex action Slotin hurled himself forward and tore the reacting mass apart with his bare hands. The others gasped and, turning around, Slotin, his face whitely reflecting his terror, motioned them to leave the room.

Slotin telephoned the hospital and said that there had been an accident. Then he telephoned his close friend, Phil Morrison. He was nauseated but, always the true scientist, paused in the hallway and drew a pencil sketch of the room and marked everyone's position, putting a big X for himself. Then he scribbled the time, 3:20 P.M., and hustled the group off to the hospital, all of them jamming into two jeeps.

The big question in the mind of everyone was: how much dose did Slotin get? The neutrons and X-rays which flashed through his body before he tore the assembly apart caused biological damage to his body. This we measure in certain units—called roentgens or r-units. A total of about 400 r over the entire body is considered the lethal amount for most people. This deadly amount does not produce immediate effect but takes time . . . weeks . . . or days . . . depending on the dose.

Phil Morrison, gifted theoretical physicist, worked feverishly to reconstruct the accident and to learn how serious was his friend's plight. Slotin's very blood had been made radioactive by the burst of neutrons which riddled his body, and a small sample of his blood gave a clue to the dose. Of course, Slotin was hospitalized and became ill rather soon, but during the first few days he was cheerful and would ask when visited by Morrison, "Well, what's the dose?" Nobody really knew and it took a long time to find out. Before they did, the tide had changed in Slotin's reaction to the radiation. His differential blood cell count told the story—a picture so hopeless that the attending Army nurse, hardened to hospital routine, broke down and sobbed when she saw the results.

Slotin had been most severely irradiated around the hands and arms. These parts of his pain-ridden body swelled grotesquely and the skin sloughed off. The nation's best doctors were flown to the Army hospital at Los Alamos but they could do little for the weakening patient. Nor could we do much more today.

Technicians strung a telephone connection into the bare hospital room and Slotin talked with his mother in Winnipeg, Canada. The next day, his parents were flown to New Mexico by special Army plane, and they stayed at their son's bedside until he breathed his last. The end came early on the morning of the ninth day after the accident.

The man who stood behind Slotin, Dr. Graves, was severely injured by the accident but he recovered and went on to become associate director of Los Alamos in the postwar period. He had this to say of Slotin: "I can perhaps tell you as much about his personality and character as I could in very many words if I merely quote to you his first statement when we were alone together in the hospital room. He said, 'I'm sorry I got you into this. I am afraid that I have less than a fifty-fifty chance of living. I hope you do better than that.'"

Slotin was not destined to be a great or a famous man. He was one of the many scientists who worked devotedly and unselfishly throughout the war. The young scientist gave his life, just as did many of his comrades in arms.

Slotin's experiment was outlawed at Los Alamos. With the development of television and remote-control gadgetry, it became possible to do the critical assembly operations with no one within a quarter of a mile. White-coated technicians, principally women, control the assembly and make all their observations without the slightest danger to themselves.

1956

Radiations and the Genetic Threat

WARREN WEAVER

THE PLOT

WE ALL REMEMBER THAT DICKENS USED TO START some of his novels with two or three chapters which appeared to be wholly unconnected. Then the relationship would gradually and dramatically come to light. Since our common purpose here is clarity rather than suspense, I will tell you at the outset that our plot will, in a way, be similar. Chapter I will be devoted to the villain of the piece—*radiations*. Chapter II will deal with the innocent victim—the *genes*. Chapter III will describe the crime—*mutations*. And Chapter IV will then give the verdict of society—will indicate, at least in modest part, *what we ought to do about this*.

THE VILLAIN—RADIATIONS

What is radiation? It is energy on the move—energy being transmitted from one location in space to another. But this remark requires an immediate modification. For not all energy on the move is radiation. A thrown baseball or the moving stream of water from a hose—these involve moving energy; but these are purely mechanical effects, rather than radiation. So we must be more accurate and say that radiation is *electromagnetic energy* being transmitted. I am not speaking here of electricity in wires, but rather of electromagnetic waves—radio or television waves—moving freely through space, or as we very inaccurately sometimes say "through the air." (This is really a bad phrase, for insofar as the air plays any role at all, it tends to stop such waves rather than transmit them. A century ago scientists used to say that these waves moved through the "aether," but they just invented this word to diminish their worry over the fact that

733

they didn't understand what was happening. We don't either, but we have abandoned the verbal tranquilizer.)

The most familiar instance of an electromagnetic wave is *light,* the visible light which affects our eyes. And fortunately this familiar instance is a completely typical instance, as we will see in just a moment.

Any wave disturbance can be partly characterized by its *wave length.* In the case of a water wave, this wave length is simply the distance from one crest to the next adjacent crest. One can also speak of the *frequency* of a wave motion, this being simply the number of waves which in each second pass a fixed point. Granting a fixed speed for the waves (and this is the case with electromagnetic waves) the longer the wave length, the fewer of them pass a given point. Quantitatively, if you double the wave length, you halve the frequency. It is often useful to speak both of wave length, which is familiar to us from the water-wave case, and of frequency, which is familiar from the case of sound waves. When one speaks of an "octave" on the piano, the frequency of the upper "do" is just twice the frequency of the lower "do"; so using the sound analogy one can speak of two electromagnetic radiations being an "octave" apart, one of them having a frequency twice that of the other.

In these terms (mixing the sound and light cases) we can think of a great "light-piano." Suppose its keyboard covers about seventy octaves. In the center of it, rather less than one octave wide, is the visible light that affects our eyes. To the right stretch out octave after octave of progressively higher frequencies (smaller and smaller wave lengths). First come about eleven octaves of so-called ultraviolet, the light that is bluer than blue. Then come four octaves of the still shorter wave length X-rays, six octaves of so-called gamma rays, and finally, shortest of all in wave length and highest of all in frequency, some sixteen octaves of very high energy gamma rays derived from cosmic rays.

To the left of the central octave of visible light we find about fifteen octaves of infrared light, then about six octaves of radar waves,[1] and finally some twelve octaves of ordinary radio waves.

That is to say, these physical entities with differing names—radio waves, infrared, visible light, ultraviolet light, X-rays, gamma rays, and cosmic rays—are now all known to be electromagnetic radiations which are alike except that they differ in wave length and hence in frequency. They range from the deep base of the radio waves at the left end of our radiation piano, up to the ultra high tenor of the cosmic rays at the right end. The

---

[1] That is to say, waves of wave lengths which are very short when considered as radio waves, although not in the least short from the point of view of the entire electromagnetic spectrum.

only part of this whole spectrum of which we are immediately conscious is the less than one octave of visible light in the middle.

Speaking broadly, the very long wave length radiations tend to flow around any obstacle they meet, while the very short wave lengths tend to penetrate right into an obstacle. Since we are concerned here with radiations which are able to penetrate into our bodies, we see that we are dealing with the tenor half of the radiation piano, namely, with X-rays, the still more penetrating gamma rays, and the most of all penetrating cosmic rays.

At this point it will be useful to take note of the most common source of radiations. Most ordinary atoms are *stable*—their insides stay put. But some atoms are inherently *unstable*. Their insides have a tendency to readjust into a new pattern of arrangement. It is not possible to predict, for one particular atom, when this readjustment will occur. These unstable atoms—they are often called radioactive—are like alarm clocks wound up and set for unknown times. Eventually the alarm goes off, and the inside of that atom readjusts into a more stable arrangement. When that readjustment occurs, the atom sends out a burst of radiant energy, and this process is in fact the commonest origin of radiations.

Although one cannot at all say when one given radioactive atom will pop off, one can give a useful description of the time behavior of a lot of similar radioactive atoms. One does this by specifying the interval of time within which *half* of the atoms will pop off. This interval is called the *half-life*. Starting out with a large number of unpopped atoms of half-life equal to, just as an example, one day, half would be popped by the end of the first day, half of the remaining half of unpopped atoms would then pop in the second day (or a total of three fourths of the original number), again half of the remaining quarter of unpopped atoms in the third day (or a total of seven eighths of the original number), and so on. Some radioactive atoms have half-lives of minutes, hours, or days. There are some so transient that they have half-lives as short as a millionth of a second, and others so nearly stable that they have half-lives of thousands or even millions of years.

To return now to the general subject of this chapter, namely the radiations which are capable of penetrating our bodies, part are furnished by nature, and part are caused by man. The part furnished by nature is often referred to as the *background radiation,* this implying an inevitable and omnipresent base to which is added whatever man causes. Of this background radiation a certain amount comes *up* from the radioactive material in the rocks and soil. In the top layer of depth one foot there exists on the average, per square mile of earth surface, two grams of radium, eight tons of uranium, and twelve tons of thorium: so clearly the earth under our feet is an important and inescapable source of radiation. On the other hand, part of the background radiation comes *down* from the sky. This part is due to cosmic rays, so very penetrating that they can pass through ten centimeters of lead, and so universally present that as you read these lines some two to three hundred bursts are passing through your body each second. These two contributions, up from the soil and down from the sky, add together to form the background radiation.

In addition to this background that has been flooding man throughout the centuries are the radiations which man has recently learned how to produce. In this latter category there are two main kinds. First, there are the X-rays so widely used in medicine for both diagnostic and therapeutic purposes. Second, there are the rays (from our point of view the gamma rays are the important ones) produced in nuclear experiments, in atomic weapons testing, and in nuclear power plants. In addition to these two main kinds there are various other radiations, usually of minor importance or affecting fewer persons, such as are produced by luminous dials, encountered in certain industries, experienced by certain miners, etc.

The advent of atomic weapons has drawn attention to the possible dangers to man from all sorts of radiations. In the explosion of an atom bomb, in fact, there are produced about one hundred and seventy-five kinds of what the physicist calls isotopes—abnormal variants of the ordinary elements. Some of these isotopes from an atom bomb are stable, and the unstable radioactive ones have half-lives which vary from a few seconds to a thousand million years. About one thousand pounds of radioactive material are produced per ten-megaton shot.

In the explosion of an atom bomb there are three discernible stages. The first, involving truly awful destruction from immediate radiation, heat, and blast, lasts for the order of one second and extends out, one supposes, to a ten- to twenty-five-mile radius. The second stage involves a radiation dose due to immediate fallout which is directly dangerous or even lethal to those receiving it. This lasts for a few days, and extends over an area which presumably may be ten thousand, or perhaps in special circumstances even one hundred thousand square miles. The third stage is that of the eventual "fallout." The finely dispersed radioactive material is carried high into the atmosphere, drifts with the winds, settles down at various rates, or is brought down with rain. This stage lasts over months or years, and extends over the entire planet. This third stage is what is usually meant by "fallout," and the word will be used here in this sense.

So now we have met the villain. It consists of blobs of penetrating energy produced by the popping off of wound-up atoms. Some of these atoms nature herself winds up, but many of these the modern physicist has learned how to wind.

Every cell of a person's body contains a great collection, passed down from the parents, the parents' parents, and so on back, of diverse hereditary units called *genes*. These genes singly and in combination control our inherited characteristics.

These genes exist in every cell of the body. But from the point of view of heredity the ordinary "body cells," which make up the body as a whole, are not comparably as important as the "germ cells" which exist in the reproductive organs, and which play the essential roles in the production of children.

Ordinarily a gene is passed on unchanged to children, grandchildren, and more remote descendants, but occasionally they do change. They are changed by certain agents, notably by heat, by some chemicals, and *by radiation*. It is at this point that we begin to see the villain plotting against the innocent victim.

When a gene becomes thus permanently altered, we say it *mutates*. The gene is then duplicated in its altered form in each subsequent cell division. If the mutant gene is in an ordinary body cell it is merely passed along to other body cells. The mutant gene, under these circumstances, is not passed on to progeny, and the effect of the mutant gene is limited to the person in whom the mutation occurred.

However, it cannot safely be assumed that this body-cell effect is a negligible one on the person in whom the mutation occurred. For various kinds of cellular abnormalities are known to be perpetuated within an individual through body-cell divisions; so these effects are genetic in the broad sense. In fact, although the quantitative relations are not yet clear, it is nevertheless clear that certain malignancies such as leukemia, and certain other cellular abnormalities, can be induced by ionizing radiations. There is also some evidence that effects of this sort measurably reduce the life expectancy of the individual receiving the radiation.

But to return to a consideration of the risks which are passed on to progeny, the mutant gene may exist in a sperm or an egg cell as a result of a mutation having occurred either in that cell or at some earlier cell stage. In this case, a child resulting from this sperm or egg will inherit the mutant gene.

We are now in a position to indicate why it is that radiations, such as X-rays or gamma rays, can be so serious from the genetic point of view. For although the genes, as described above, normally remain unchanged as they multiply and are passed on from generation to generation, they do very rarely change, or *mutate;* and *radiation,* as we have already mentioned, *can give rise to such changes or mutations in the genes.* Mutation ordinarily affects each gene independently; and once changed, an altered gene then persists from generation to generation in its new or mutant form.

Moreover, the *mutant genes,* in the vast majority of cases, and in all the species so far studied, *lead to some kind of harmful effect.* In extreme cases the harmful effect is death itself, or loss of the ability to produce offspring, or some other serious abnormality. What in a way is of even greater ultiumate importance, since they affect so many more persons, are those cases that involve much smaller handicaps, which might tend to shorten life, increase disease, reduce fertility, or to be otherwise detrimental.

In assessing the harm done to a population by deleterious genes, it is clear that society would ordinarily consider the death of an early embryo to be of much less consequence than that of a child or young adult. Similarly a mutation that decreases the life expectancy by a few months is clearly less to be feared than one that in addition causes its bearer severe pain, unhappiness, or illness throughout his life. Perhaps most obviously tangible are the instances, even though they be relatively uncommon, in which a child is born with some tragic handicap of genetic origin.

A discussion of genetic damage necessarily involves, on the one hand, certain tangible and imminent dangers, certain tragedies which might occur to our own children or grandchildren; and on the other hand certain more remote trouble that may be experienced by very large numbers of persons in the far distant future.

This is not a suitable occasion on which to go into details. But due to well understood genetic principles, it is possible to state some important conclusions concerning the danger which is inherent in a radiation-mutated gene. First of all, the change produced by mutation is practically always a change for the worse. Second, the amount of mutation varies directly with the amount of radiation. Third, there is no minimum amount of radiation which is genetically safe—all radiation is genetically bad. A little radiation is a little bad, and a lot is a lot bad. Fourth, once exposed to some radiation, this never "wears off": that is to say, the genetically important number of mutations depends on the total dose that one accumulates from his own conception up to the time of conception of his last child. Fifth, the radiation that is important genetically is only that which reaches the gonads—that is to say, the male testicles and the female ovaries. Sixth, what counts from the point of view of society as a whole is the total number of mutated genes. Thus a small radiation dose to a large number of persons is, socio-genetically speaking, equivalent to a large dose to a few.

The resulting damage may, in a small proportion of cases, appear promptly in one's children or grandchildren: or it may be hidden for many generations: but it is usually not *completely* hidden, and almost always imposes some small handicap on all generations. Moreover these small handicaps accumulate, and the mutated gene eventually eliminates itself through disaster—the disaster of a person whose life span is so shortened or whose fertility is so impaired that no progeny is possible, and this particular genetic line dies out.

THE VERDICT OF SOCIETY

Crime, we ordinarily say, does not pay. One's natural inclination, knowing that any and all radiation is genetically bad, is to say, "Let's just eliminate radiation." But we couldn't do that if we really wanted to, and we wouldn't dare if we could.

We couldn't if we wanted to because of the background radiation which comes up from the soil and rocks, and down from the sky. This background is such as to give each person, on the average in the United States, a reproductive lifetime dose (say, over thirty years, from conception to the birth of the "average" child) of about 3 roentgens.[2]

As a practical matter, moreover, it would be virtually impossible to eliminate man-made radiation also; but this is the part that we wouldn't really dare eliminate even if we could. To consider one type of man-made radiation, at the present time a person in the United States receives a reproductive lifetime dose of about 4.5 roentgens from diagnostic and

---

[2] A *roentgen* is the common unit in which radiation dose is measured. You get a gonad dose of about 0.005 roentgen from a dental X-ray, from 0.1 to 1.0 roentgen from a pelvic X-ray, and up to 2 roentgens in a fluoroscopic examination of the pelvis. In the original report of the Genetics Committee of the National Academy of Sciences the background dose was estimated at 4.3 roentgens and the average dose from diagnostic and therapeutic medical X-rays was estimated at about 3 roentgens. A large amount of additional data has now been analyzed, and the result has been to decrease the estimate of the background dose to 3 roentgens, and to increase the estimate of the medical X-ray dose to about 4.5 roentgens. The estimate for the sum of the two thus remains nearly unchanged.

therapeutic medical X-rays. Any of this that could be avoided without interfering with really necessary medical procedures should, of course, be eliminated. But obviously this involves careful and technical judgments in deciding, in each instance, which is the more acceptable risk—the genetic risk or the medical risk which would result in not using the X-rays.

In addition to the substantial doses from background and from medical X-rays there is the dose—up to the present time small—due to the radioactive fallout from atomic tests. And in the future we certainly face the possibility of significant doses from nuclear power installations.

The reproductive lifetime fallout dose has recently been estimated (assuming no increase in number or size of weapons tested) to be about 0.1 roentgen. There is a considerable uncertainty, and fluctuation from place to place, in this figure; and it may be a fifth as large as stated, or on the other hand, may perhaps be five times as large.

When we think of the genetic risk from any of these sources of radiation we should always, of course, think in terms of comparing two risks —the risk from the radiation, and the risk we would incur if we eliminated the radiation. We all have to compare risks every day, even though we usually do not do so explicitly, but rather in a vague and unformulated way which invokes experience.

If a person must go from New York to San Francisco, he could look up the traffic statistics, and could thus compare two actual numbers, representing the traffic deaths per mile of automobile or of air travel. But in the case before us there are reasons which make any attempted comparison of risk very difficult indeed.

We wish to compare Risk A, the genetic risk from radiation, with Risk B, the medical, economic, political, and military risk which might result from decreasing X-rays, from handicapping the development of nuclear power, and from weakening our position of world leadership and our capacity to defend ourselves. Our difficulties result from the very basic facts that we do not as yet know enough about human radiation genetics to give precise and quantitative estimates of the radiation Risk A; that we certainly cannot give any accurate estimates of the medical, economic, political, or military Risk B; and that even if we could describe both Risk A and Risk B, there would be the final and baffling difficulty that these two risks are inherently unlike and hence essentially incomparable.

To speak only of Risk A, we must remember that our knowledge of genetics is very largely derived from experiments with lower forms of life—fruit flies, corn, mice. Large-scale and controlled genetic experiments with human beings are obviously out of the question. Genetics, moreover, is an inherently complicated and subtle subject, almost no quantitative facts concerning radiation harm are known with high precision, and the great but necessary leap from mice to men is one which unavoidably introduces uncertainties. But do not make the mistake of concluding, from these discouraging comments, that the geneticists have little to offer in the way of knowledge and advice. On the contrary, and despite uncertainties about details and exact values, geneticists are in firm agreement on practically all of the really basic points.

Many of you will, at this point, want to make a protest, or will at least want to voice your confusion. If the basic genetic facts are indeed firm and agreed, how can different informed persons, all of whom are clearly intelligent and socially sensitive, appear to hold such diverse views? Take the much publicized case of fallout. How can some be worried about this as a serious menace, while others even refer to it as "harmless" or "negligible"?

The recent report of the National Academy of Sciences suggested that we ought to plan our medical and nuclear affairs so that an average U.S. citizen would receive a reproductive lifetime dose, from man-made radiation, of not more than 10 roentgens. Such an amount would probably not double our present genetic load, in the sense of doubling the long-established and long-tolerated rate of natural mutations from background radiation and from other agents (heat and chemicals) which cause radiations. Thus, the report concluded, perhaps 10 roentgens of man-made radiation will not result in an unreasonable burden to society. Well, if 10 roentgens thus gets enthroned as reasonable,[3] isn't the 0.1 roentgen from fallout negligible?

It is certainly not surprising that some persons, deeply and properly concerned over the military and political importance of nuclear weapons, answer that question in the affirmative. But the geneticists, if I interpret them correctly, answer in the negative. How can this be?

I think that this is to be explained, and that some of the differences in emphasis among the geneticists are also to be explained, in terms of two paradoxes—one numerical, the other temporal.

The numerical paradox is the one which applies most directly to the fallout problem. The paradox arises by virtue of the fact that some persons are impressed by relative figures, some by absolute amounts.

A fallout dose of 0.1 roentgens is, for example, only 1/100 of the 10 roentgens set as "reasonable" by the NAS report. It is only about 1/500 of the dose that would presumably be required to double the natural

---

[3] *Reasonable*, mind you; not *harmless*.

rate of mutation. If I am already running a certain risk (and after all surviving in spite of it) then ultimately to add to this risk by only one part in five hundred doses, when put in this relative way, seems pretty negligible.

But look at the question in other terms. At the present time, roughly 4.5 per cent of the babies born in the United States have serious defects (congenital malformation, mental defectives, epilepsy, cutaneous and skeletal defects, visual and aural defects, etc.). Of these, it seems likely that about half are genetic in origin. Let us roughly assume that 2 per cent of the babies born have defects of mutational origin.

Now all the persons now alive in the world—all the persons who at this moment face this problem—will have, before they are all dead, something of the order of fifteen thousand million babies (1.5×10^9). The immediate genetic risk to this vast set of babies—the world's next set of persons—may well be increased, due to fallout, only by one part in 5000 (2×10^{-4}).[4] The increase in risk is very small; but the increase applies to a vast number of persons. The estimated result, in fact, is 6000 additional handicapped babies. Now what impresses you as more significant —that 6000 is a good many babies to subject to serious handicap, or that 1/5000 is a very small fraction and correspondingly is a very small relative addition to the thirty million babies that, without fallout, will have serious genetic handicaps? And remember that this calculation underestimates the total radiation effect in two ways: it speaks of first-generation damage (whereas there will be increasing amounts of damage in later generations), and it speaks only of gross abnormalities (which, if we accept the evidence from lower forms of life, constitute only a small part of the total genetic damage).

In connection with these remarks about the numerical paradox there is one aspect of the problem of genetic risk which probably deserves some explanation. Increasing some types of risk to individuals by one part in 5000 might just result in each individual person experiencing a small amount of additional harm—each one might, in an average year, say, have a certain type of physical distress for a total of five thousand and one minutes rather than for five thousand minutes, as previously. But genetic harm does not work that way. Mutations differ a great deal in their seriousness, of course. But for a given mutation, it either occurs or it does not occur. Thus when a lot of persons are subjected to a low radiation dose, almost all of them experience no harm whatsoever, but

[4] This factor is the product of 1/500 (a reasonable ratio of fallout to the doubling dose) by 1/10 (a reasonable estimate of the fraction of total damage which would be expressed in the first generation).

in the case of a few persons, mutation will occur. When a mutation occurs it occurs, so to speak, completely. The result for the person in whom it occurs is just the same as though the mutation had been caused by a larger dose of radiation. In other words, a small dose actually affects a small proportion of the exposed population, and a larger dose affects a larger proportion; but those individuals who are affected experience the same result in the two cases.

The temporal paradox is also a difficult one. What impresses you as more important—a relatively little tangible and tragic suffering encountered promptly, by your own children and grandchildren, say; or a great deal more of rather vague and remote suffering to be encountered by the next fifty or one hundred generations?

Some sincere and intelligent persons, including some geneticists, think it is difficult enough to try to play short-range God, without attempting, or worrying about, the problems of a long-range God. These persons, moreover, have a substantial comfort in their confidence that man's intellect will succeed in finding ways out of the long-range difficulties, so that we are justified in trying to deal only with the next few generations.

On the other hand, there are equally sincere and intelligent persons, again including some geneticists, who think that we may well have no greater responsibility than that of protecting the genetic heritage of the future; and that that responsibility does not in the least excuse our committing genetic crimes simply on the grounds that they will not be found out for a long time.

I hope that the statement of these two paradoxes may help you interpret certain statements which might otherwise confuse you, and—worst of all—might lead you to think that this situation is so mixed up that the best thing to do is disregard it. Whatever we do, we must not disregard this problem. A massive discontinuity was introduced into life by the discovery of nuclear fission. We have to learn to live with it, for the alternative is that we do not live.

1957

Recommendations for Protection Against Radiation Exposure

THE NATIONAL ACADEMY OF SCIENCES

IN LIGHT OF THE CONSIDERATIONS WHICH HAVE BEEN reviewed by this Committee: this Committee has several recommendations.

These recommendations should all be interpreted in the light of the basic fact that *any* additional radiation is genetically undesirable. Therefore our society should hold additional radiation exposure as low as it possibly can. If certain figures (such as 10 roentgens) occur in a recommendation, it should most emphatically not be assumed that any exposure less than that figure is, so to speak, "all right": nor should it be for a moment assumed that disaster will suddenly descend if one of these figures is exceeded.

In any case in which a figure is stated, it is with the idea: stay just as far under this as you can; do not consider that this is an amount of radiation which is genetically harmless, for there is no such figure other than zero.

Opposing the fact that any further radiation is genetically bad is the practical fact that further radiation, from certain sources at least, is probably inevitable. The factors which argue for an increase in radiation are not genetic, and should obviously be appraised by a group much more representative than this Committee. Thus our recommendations will have to be evaluated by others, who must decide what decisions society should or must make. As geneticists we say: *keep the dose as low as you can.*

Thus we recommend:

A) That, in view of the fact that total accumulated dose is the genetically important figure, steps be taken to institute a national system of radiation exposure record-keeping, under which there would be maintained for every individual a complete history of his total record of exposure to X-rays, and to all other gamma radiation. This will impose minor burdens on all individuals of our society, but it will, as a compensation, be a real protection to them. We are conscious of the fact that this recommendation will not be simple to put into effect.

B) That the medical authorities of this country initiate a vigorous movement to reduce the radiation exposure from X-rays to the lowest limit consistent with medical necessity; and in particular that they take steps to assure that proper safeguards always be taken to minimize the radiation dose to the reproductive cells.

C) That for the present it be accepted as a uniform national standard that X-ray installations (medical and nonmedical), power installations, disposal of radioactive wastes, experimental installations, testing of weapons, and all other humanly controllable sources of radiations be so restricted that members of our general population shall not receive from such sources an average of more than 10 roentgens, in addition to background, of ionizing radiation as a total accumulated dose to the reproductive cells from conception to age 30.

D) The previous recommendation should be reconsidered periodically with the view to keeping the reproductive cell dose at the lowest practicable level. If it is feasible to reduce medical exposures, industrial exposures, or both, then the total should be reduced accordingly.

E) That individual persons not receive more than a total accumulated dose to the reproductive cells of 50 roentgens up to age 30 years (by which age, on the average, over half of the children will have been born), and not more than 50 roentgens additional up to age 40 (by which time about nine tenths of their children will have been born.)

F) That every effort be made to assign to tasks involving higher radiation exposures individuals who, for age or other reasons, are unlikely thereafter to have additional offspring. Again it is recognized that such a procedure will introduce complications and difficulties, but this committee is convinced that society should begin to modify its procedures to meet inevitable new conditions.

The basic fact is—and no competent persons doubt this—that radiations produce mutations and that mutations are in general harmful. It is difficult, at the present state of knowledge of genetics, to estimate just how much of what kind of harm will appear in each future generation after mutant genes are induced by radiations. Different geneticists prefer differing ways of describing this situation: But they all come out with the unanimous conclusion that the potential danger is great.

This report recommends that the general public of the United States be protected, by whatever controls may prove necessary, from receiving a total reproductive lifetime dose (conception to age 30) of more than 10 roentgens of man-made radiation to the reproductive cells. Of this *reasonable* (not *harmless,* mind you, but *reasonable*) quota of 10 roentgens over and beyond the inevitable background of radiation from natural causes, we are now using on the average some 3 or 4 roentgens for medical X-rays. This is roughly the same as the unavoidable dose received from background radiation. It is really very surprising and disturbing to realize that this figure is so large, and clearly it is prudent to examine this situation carefully. It is folly to incur any X-ray exposure to the gonads which can be avoided without impairing medical service or progress.

The 10 roentgen recommendation applies in an average sense to the population as a whole. We also include a recommendation concerning the upper limit of exposure that any one individual should receive. These limits would of course apply to persons whose occupations involve radiation exposure, but they are intended as broad and uniform regulations which apply to any and every individual.

The fall-out from weapons testing has, so far, led to considerably less irradiation of the population than have the medical uses—and has therefore been less detrimental. So long as the present level is not increased this will continue to be true; but there remains a proper concern to see to it that the fall-out does not increase to more serious levels.

One important lesson which results from this study is the following: The present state of advance in atomic and nuclear physics on the one hand, and in genetics on the other hand, are seriously out of balance. We badly need to know much more about genetics—about all kinds and all levels of genetics, from the most fundamental research on various lowly forms of life to human radiation genetics. This requires serious contributions of time, of brains, and of money. Although brains and time are more important than money, the latter is also essential; and our society should take prompt steps to see to it that the support of research in genetics is substantially expanded and that is is stabilized.

We ought to keep all of our expenditures of radiation as low as possible. Of the upper limit of 10 roentgens suggested in Recommendation C, we are at present spending about one third for medical X-rays. We are at present spending less—probably under one half a roentgen—for weapons testing. We may find it desirable or even almost obligatory that we spend a certain amount on atomic power plants. But we must watch and guard all our expenditures. From the point of view of genetics, they are all bad.

1957

Nuclear Power in the Future

J. R. DUNNING

WHAT ARE THE FUTURE POSSIBILITIES FOR LARGE-scale utilization of nuclear power? This is not an easy question to answer and, indeed, cannot be fully answered at this time, because there are not enough data or experience available. We have a complex series of interdependent factors: raw material availability and costs, fissionable material production costs, as yet incompletely known scientific and engineering questions on nuclear processes, materials of construction, engineering designs, capital investment, maintenance and operating costs, etc.

While some interesting long-range possibilities exist for conversion of fission fragment energies in part directly into electrical energy, all practical methods for nuclear energy utilization considered feasible in the immediate future involve degradation of nuclear energy into heat, and transfer of the heat to some working fluid in one or more steps either (a) to some process heat application or (b) to some more or less conventional prime mover such as a steam or gas turbine. While many people have unfortunately spoken loosely about using nuclear energy in low-temperature form, it is quite clear that, in general, nuclear energy must produce heat available for use at least in the normal temperature ranges commonly used in industrial and power plant practice, or else it cannot be competitive with other methods of producing heat energy (possibly with the exception of a few special purposes). If steam is the final working fluid, temperatures for most purposes must be in the range of 700° to 1000° F. to be really interesting, which means that the nuclear system itself must be appreciably hotter to allow for the necessary heat transfer temperature differentials.

It is now generally agreed—although there were many who disagreed originally—that high-level nuclear reactors feasible for producing practical operating temperatures and over-all economy cannot be based on natural uranium. Concentrated nuclear fuels are necessary, such as U-235 concentrated at least in some degree. It was this strong conviction rather than possible bomb applications which led some physicists in 1940 to press the development of large-scale U-235 separation, since we believed firmly that no nuclear power industry could be developed without having U-235 separation plants as a base or steppingstone. This philosophy was apparently not widely understood, but future events have justified the conclusions.

Large-scale utilization of nuclear fission power in our national economy does not seem possible unless "net gain breeding" of new fissionable material, such as $_{94}Pu$-239 or $_{92}U$-233, is employed.

The possibility of net gain breeding arises because admittedly somewhat more than two secondary neutrons are emitted per fission in some fissionable materials. One neutron per fission is required to maintain a chain reaction. If the over-all "neutron economy" is such that, after allowing for neutron leakage from the nuclear reactor and true parasitic neutron capture processes, more than one net neutron is still available to react with "fertile materials" like U-238 to form Pu-239, or to react with Th-232 to form U-233 in a similar process, then we may be able to produce more new fissionable fuel materials, Pu-239 or U-233, by "conversion" than we burn. If a reactor can be designed from both an engineering and a heat transfer standpoint, with enough margin to produce a net gain of Pu-239 or U-233 and allow for recycling and reprocessing losses, then in principle by recycling nuclear fuel and fertile materials we can look forward eventually to converting an appreciable fraction of the U-238 or Th-232 in the world into high-grade fissionable fuels. The consequent availability of hundreds of times the amount of nuclear fuel as compared with U-235 alone, and the effect of this upon over-all nuclear power economics, are obvious. A practical "net gain power breeder reactor" would be a tremendous step forward, even though one must recognize that a net gain breeder acts like compound interest and that the time required to double the amount of fissionable material will be long, even with net gains of say 10 per cent per cycle.

The initial phases of nuclear development were largely scientific in character. We are now entering a new phase. If large-scale utilization of power is to be achieved, not only must the nuclear scientists contribute, but the metallurgists, chemical engineers, mechanical engineers, electrical engineers, and especially the process engineers, must work together. Future nuclear reactor power plants to be successful must represent, probably more than any other type of undertaking, an integrated approach by all these diverse skills and fields of knowledge. The artificial walls between scientists and engineers must be broken down. . . .

What will a nuclear power plant look like? . . . There are at least four or five basic approaches to reactor design, with many variations that must be designed and tested before it can be said which types are best and for which specific application.

Broadly speaking, reactor types may be characterized in several ways. In terms of effective "neutron spectrum," at one extreme the "thermal reactor" involves the fissionable material with a considerable amount of moderator, so that the neutrons are largely near thermal velocities. Conversely, at the other extreme the fissionable material may have very little or no associated moderator, so that the neutrons are not slowed appreciably and we have therefore a "fast" reactor. With intermediate amounts of moderator, the neutron spectrum will be intermediate between thermal and fast, and we have an "intermediate" type reactor. The fissionable fuel may be U-235, Pu-239, or possibly U-233, or mixtures.

The reactor fuel may be in many forms—metals, compounds, alloys, mixtures, etc. For moderators we have a considerable choice—ordinary water, heavy water, carbon, beryllium, etc. Should the reactor be a breeder, and should U-238 or thorium be used for fertile material? Should the reactor be "homogeneous" with working materials mixed, or should it be "heterogeneous," or of a lattice type with components segregated? To remove the heat for useful purposes a heat transfer medium is necessary; should it be a gas like helium, a liquid like water, or perhaps molten metals, or materials of low melting point like sodium?

From the standpoint of hazards as well as engineering convenience, more than one heat exchange step has advantages in that the final working fluid, say steam, is isolated from direct contact with the reactor by an intermediate coolant. However, this is serious since it increases the temperature gradients from reactor fuel to working fluids, so that the reactor fuel and construction components must operate at higher temperatures to achieve the same end result. . . .

The nuclear reactor shown in Figure 1 indicates one possible type. Solid U-235 rather well concentrated is the fuel, and a material such as beryllium oxide is indicated as the moderator. Helium gas is the heat exchange fluid, while steam as the final working fluid is used to operate a more or less standard turbine and generator system. The reactor here is shown with "negative" control rods made with a neutron absorber such as boron. These control the reproduction factor by introducing sufficient neutron absorption to hold the chain reaction just at "critical."

Another possible type of reactor is shown in Figure 2. Here the nuclear fuel is indicated in a fluid or suspension form, so it may be circulated and processed for cleanup of fission products, which are the "ashes" of nuclear production, and for dynamic control of fuel ratios. Molten

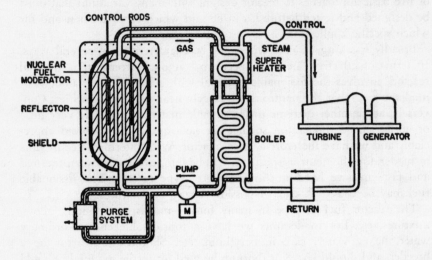

Fig. 1. Schematic nuclear power plant. Uses U-235, solid moderator, helium gas as heat transfer medium, and steam as working fluid to operate conventional power equipment.

metal is indicated as the heat transfer medium, and a gas is shown as the working fluid to operate a gas turbine and associated power equipment. These reactors are, of course, schematic and simply suggestive of the broad range of problems involved.

Clearly, a nuclear reactor is a complex mixture of nuclear physics and process engineering. Underlying all possible designs is the all-important question of materials, for extremely severe limitations are placed on the materials of construction. Not only must they stand the operating temperatures and pressures and corrosion conditions, but their nuclear properties must be such that their parasitic neutron capture is not excessive and, in addition, they must have high "radiation stability." The enormous radiation flux, in which the materials are bombarded with neutrons and gamma rays, is serious since many materials suffer marked deterioration of their physical properties. Fast neutrons knock atoms out of their lattice positions and produce changes in structure. Actual transmutation of the atoms into other types of atoms further changes the character of materials. Some of the best high-temperature alloys developed for ordinary power plant use are useless. This testing of existing materials and the development of new materials, metals, alloys, ceramics, etc., to meet the special problems of nuclear reactors are matters of the utmost importance. Out of this search will come new materials which should be

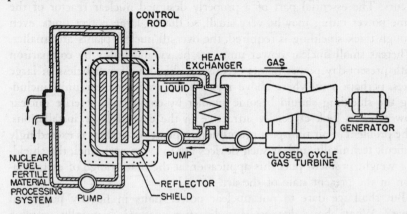

FIG. 2. Integrated nuclear power plant. Schematic diagram showing closed cycle nuclear fuel—fertile material processing system, molten metal as heat transfer medium, gas as a working fluid to operate a closed cycle gas turbine and associated power equipment.

useful in many other fields as well. Materials formerly little used and expensive may find here new applications which will bring their production costs down. Beryllium metal has interesting properties; possibly zirconium may be valuable.

How fast shall we achieve practical nuclear power? Obviously there will be no complete solution to all these diverse problems overnight. Nevertheless, progress will depend upon the effort put into it; in any case, a field with such a range of problems will certainly continue evolving over many years. . . .

It is clear, however, that with uranium fission energy, the radiation shields many feet thick, required for protection of near-by personnel, automatically rule out small mobile power units applicable to such cases as automobiles, even if the capital investment costs in the minimum fissionable material alone were tolerable—admittedly at least pounds of material costing over $10,000 per pound. With a minimum of over fifty tons of shielding, and at least ten feet over-all width, even locomotive use looks impractical.

For large stationary units, as in central power stations, or large mobile units, as on ships where space is not so important, the situation is quite different. One important point arises. Nuclear reactors proper are essentially heat exchange units and can be quite small. Modern coal gas or oil fired boilers in large sizes are enormous, but such a conventional boiler many stories high is actually mostly empty space where the combustion occurs. The essential part of a properly designed nuclear reactor of the same power rating may be very small, so that in large power units, even though thick shielding is required, the over-all nuclear plants are smaller. Whereas small nuclear power units are heavy and bulky by comparison with present-day power plants because of shielding, nevertheless in large sizes, perhaps somewhere above 10,000 horsepower, nuclear units including the shielding should become smaller by comparison. Hence nuclear power plants look especially attractive in the case of large installations. The problem of air transport propulsion in planes or rockets is exceedingly difficult technically and, if such devices are to carry personnel, the shielding weight problem puts this application at the outer range of extrapolation in the present state of the art.

But shall we dare to put nuclear power units in heavily populated areas? What about dangerous radioactive wastes? Naturally extreme caution is being used in the preliminary stages of development. . . . However, with the development of completely enclosed, closed cycle reactors, there should be no dangerous wastes or effluents to spread around. One pound of U-235 "burned" per day means an output larger than any existing power station. The radioactive fission products produced by burning one pound of U-235 weigh just the same, or strictly speaking, 1/10 of 1 per cent less, because of conversion of mass into energy. Handling and disposing of this small quantity of material, less than a handful each day, is a problem which should eventually be solved with full safety and without excessive costs.

What will be the economic justification of atomic power? Certainly current designs for nuclear reactor plants indicate rather larger capital investments compared with those for conventional power units. At present, fuel costs in United States power plants account for only 10 to 25 per cent of the selling price of electrical energy, the difference depending largely on the differing transportation costs for fuel from mine to power plant. Even if the cost of fuel were reduced to zero by substituting nuclear fuel, the cost of electrical energy would not be much reduced. Utopia will certainly not result even from zero-cost fuel. With nuclear power plants costing at least initially somewhat more, with the degree of success of "breeding" new fuels by conversion of U-238 and thorium still uncertain, with comparative operating and maintenance costs yet to be determined, no one can possibly give today a reliable comparative cost analysis of future nuclear power. However, on the basis of the general line of reasoning set forth here, it does seem that there is a fairly good chance of competing with coal at least in high-cost fuel areas. This will mean that, economically, nuclear energy will look more attractive in relatively remote areas and countries where fuel costs are higher than in most of the United States. After further development over ten to twenty-five years, with gradual simplification of nuclear plants, and possibly with the use of more efficient heat engine methods which exploit the enormous temperatures possible with nuclear energy, the balance may shift more favorably to nuclear energy. Ten to twenty years from now, when a new central power station is to be built in any particular area we should be at a point where there will be a real choice between coal, oil, gas, or nuclear "fired" boilers.

Nuclear energy will not bring immediate utopia and, as is usual with new processes, it will almost certainly serve only to supplement rather than displace our present sources of energy. However, where the special properties of nuclear fuel are especially valuable it should find a gradually widening field of application.

1950

Industrial Uses of Isotopes

THE UNITED STATES ATOMIC ENERGY COMMISSION

AS THE ATOMIC ENERGY PROGRAM ENTERED THE year 1950 there were approximately 100 industrial firms exploring the uses of radioisotopes as new industrial tools. Today, nearly 1,200 industrial firms comprise almost 50 per cent of all institutions using radioactive materials. This recent striking growth has seen the use of atomic energy, in the form of radioisotopes, pushed into most major industrial fields. . . .

The nuclear principles involved in most industrial applications are not profound. As a matter of fact some of these uses were conceived toward the end of the last century when radium and X-rays were first discovered. These potential industrial uses spurred the early development of atomic energy and early uses of radiation.

Since there are hundreds of industrial uses of radioisotopes, the various applications are broken down here into several types of use and a few representative examples of each type are discussed.

PENETRATION OF RADIATION

The ability of radiation to penetrate matter has led to the most extensive industrial use of radioisotopes. A part of the radiation is always stopped by the material being irradiated; the amount depends upon the type and energy of the radiation being used and upon the density and thickness of the material and any flaws which may be present.

Radiography

Industrial radiography is one of the large uses of radioisotopes. Its principle is illustrated in Figure 1. Radiography with radium, of course, is a comparatively old method for inspecting metal castings and welds for possible flaws not otherwise detectable. Reactor-produced Cobalt 60,

Cesium 137, and Iridium 192 are now used in much the same way as radium but are much cheaper and more effective. Cobalt 60 equivalent in radiation intensity to $20,000 worth of radium can be purchased for about $100. The radiation from Co–60 will penetrate thicker sections of steel than will the rays from radium.

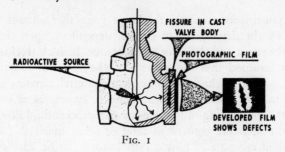

FISSURE IN CAST VALVE BODY

PHOTOGRAPHIC FILM

RADIOACTIVE SOURCE

DEVELOPED FILM SHOWS DEFECTS

FIG. I

In another application of the radiation penetration principle, the transmission-type thickness gage is being used routinely on production lines to help produce more uniform paper, aluminum, copper, tin plate, plastics, rubber, glass, and numerous other items. This continuous, non-contacting method of gaging is especially useful where products are moving rapidly, where temperatures are high, and where products are

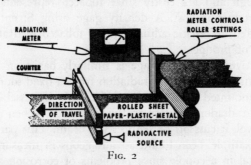

RADIATION METER CONTROLS ROLLER SETTINGS

RADIATION METER

COUNTER

DIRECTION OF TRAVEL

ROLLED SHEET PAPER-PLASTIC-METAL

RADIOACTIVE SOURCE

FIG. 2

soft and may be easily marred. As illustrated in Figure 2, the material whose thickness is to be gaged is passed between a source of radiation and a radiation detector which is connected to an amplifier and recording device. In many cases, the signal caused by the radiation transmitted through the material is used to make automatic corrections in the production process.

Nuclear gages have taken many interesting and ingenious forms. To control ink distribution during lithographic printing, for example, a special built-in thickness gage was developed in which the inking rollers, themselves, serve as radiation sources. A small amount of the low-energy beta emitter Nickel 63 was electroplated on the rollers and "flashed" with a thin protective layer of copper. Detectors near the rollers recorded the beta particles penetrating the 4- to 6-micron thicknesses of ink. By this means, ink film thicknesses were determined on all rollers under dynamic conditions.

In the transmission type of thickness gage the amount of radiation picked up by the detector is, of course, dependent upon the amount of material between it and the radioactive source. In such thickness measurements it is assumed that the density of the material remains constant. Conversely, if the thickness or size of a material remains constant, the same gage may be used to measure density. Examples of such an application are the monitoring of the density of a process fluid flowing through a pipe or the moisture content of sand or other material. . . .

An excellent example of how a radioisotope can be adapted to a high-speed packaging problem is illustrated by a recent development in the cigarette industry. Over the past years this industry has expended considerable effort to improve production quality control with respect to cigarette weight. The average weight of a cigarette is an important factor in cigarette quality. A light-weight cigarette burns both fast and hot, whereas cigarettes that contain more tobacco than necessary are hard to draw through and are costly since tobacco represents about 90 per cent of the production cost. A density gage using Strontium 90 as the source, permitted automatic adjustment of tobacco feed and contributed to uniformity of product. . . .

The radioactive liquid-level gage is similarly based on measuring the change in intensity of a beam of radiation from a fixed source. The source is sometimes mounted on one side of the tank or vessel containing the liquid and the radiation detector on the other side. When the liquid rises to a certain level, it cuts off or reduces the beam. This particular adaptation has, for example, been found advantageous in measuring the height of molten metal in a cupola since problems of corrosion and heat damage can be eliminated.

REFLECTION OF RADIATION

When a beam of radiation is directed toward a material, some of the radiation is reflected. The amount depends upon the type of energy of radiation and upon the composition, density, and thickness of the material.

Radiation reflection is serving a useful industrial purpose in the accurate measurement of thickness of coatings laid over a base metal. For example, it is possible to measure the thickness of gold plated over copper or rubber over steel. . . .

In this technique the beta particles, or electrons, from a radioisotope strike the base metal and the intensity of the reflected beam is measured. The metal is then coated with a different material (either metal or non-metal), and the reflected radiation is again measured. The change in reflection is proportional to the thickness of the coating, up to a certain limiting value, and can be measured directly in micro-inches. Variations in coating thickness can be measured with good accuracy in most cases, and automatic adjustments can be made without stopping or cutting the sheet of moving stock.

The cost for the radioisotope included in such a gage is quite small, usually below $50. The associated electronic equipment is more expensive and may amount to several hundred dollars.

The applicability of the radioactive thickness gage is attested to by the number and variety of industries using them. A number of companies that started out initially with one gage in one plant now have many similar installations in other plants.

Soil-density and soil-moisture gages for use in the field are other industrial applications of the radiation reflection principle. These gages eliminate the delays incident to laboratory determinations. They have been used in the selection of suitable sites for aircraft runways, highway roadbeds, and hydroelectric dams.

Each apparatus uses a radioactive source, a radiation detector, and an electronic recorder. The source and detector are housed in a probe which can be lowered through a one-inch diameter steel tube driven into the ground. The soil density probe utilizes a Cobalt-60 source inserted in the tip of the probe. Gamma rays from the cobalt bombard the soil surrounding the tube and are scattered by it. Some return to the geiger counter which is mounted in the top of the probe and shielded against direct radiation from the Cobalt 60. The amount of reflected radiation can be translated directly into soil density in pounds per cubic foot.

The soil-moisture probe utilizes a neutron source activated either by alpha or gamma rays. Neutrons are strongly affected by the hydrogen atoms in soil moisture. When fast neutrons strike hydrogen atoms they are slowed down and after several such collisions some are reflected back to the vicinity of the probe. The top of the probe contains a geiger counter surrounded by a silver foil and shielded against direct radiation from the neutron source. When a reflected slow neutron strikes the foil, a short-lived radioisotope of silver is formed. The radiation from this rapidly decaying radioisotope is measured by the counter, which is insensitive to the neutrons themselves, and can be translated directly into moisture content of the soil.

The principle of the soil-density and moisture gage is illustrated in Figure 3.

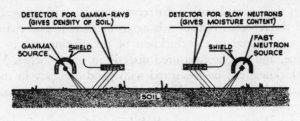

DETECTOR FOR GAMMA-RAYS (GIVES DENSITY OF SOIL) DETECTOR FOR SLOW NEUTRONS (GIVES MOISTURE CONTENT)

GAMMA SOURCE SHIELD SHIELD FAST NEUTRON SOURCE

SOIL

FIG. 3

LUMINESCENCE

The ability of radiation to cause certain materials to emit light, or to luminesce, is a long-known and long-used principle. As a matter of fact, the science of radioactivity is a direct outgrowth of early interest in luminescence. Before the turn of the century, Jean Poincaré postulated an intimate connection between luminescence and the new X-rays found by Roentgen and the mysterious emanations from uranium found by Becquerel.

Luminescence is now a well-developed science with many promises for the future. Many special compounds emit a variety of light rays when struck by atomic particles. These self-luminous markers can be invaluable in emergency situations and have vitally important military applications. Routine applications include such uses as illuminating dials and clocks and providing photometric light standards.

A number of companies have investigated the possibility of using reactor-produced materials in place of naturally occurring radium and polonium in the manufacture of luminescent materials. Reactor-produced radio-isotopes offers several advantages: first, pure beta-ray emitters reduce the health hazards involved; second, reactor-produced isotopes are usually easier to work with; and third, beta radiation has been found to cause less deterioration than the alpha particles of natural radioisotopes, leading to a more constant level of light output and longer life.

IONIZATION

The ability of atomic radiation to ionize most of the materials it strikes can be put to many benefical industrial uses. For example, static electricity in industry is a menacing problem to production and personnel and occurs quite generally whenever products manufactured possess insulating properties. Through their ability to ionize the air at selected points along the moving stock and thus "ground" the static electricity, radioisotopes help to meet this problem.

The electron tube industry also is profiting from the ionizing ability of radioisotopes. A small amount of radioactivity inside certain specialized tubes keeps the gases in a partial state of ionization, allowing more dependable operation of the tubes. The use of radioisotopes as stabilizing agents for spark gaps in ignition systems is also being developed.

ACTIVATION OF CHEMICAL REACTIONS

Activation of chemical reactions is another industrial use of atomic energy that holds many possibilities. It has already been demonstrated that beneficial chemical and physical reactions may occur when certain materials are subjected to the proper amount of radiation. Many new compounds and, especially, some superior plastics have already been made in research operations.

The possibility of producing crosslinked, degraded, and formed materials under accurately controlled conditions by a purely physical process has valuable commercial possibilities. These will depend on the cost of irradiation, the enhanced value of the material, and the comparative cost of competitive chemical processes if they are available.

Irradiation increases the melting point of polyethylene from 70° to 190° centigrade. Irradiated polyethylene drug bottles and other containers can be sterilized without harm.

STERILIZATION

Gamma radiation in large enough doses can destroy bacteria and enzymes in a material without raising its temperature significantly. Many papers have been written since 1920 concerning the effects of ionizing radiation on all types of organisms. The recent availability of large sources of radiation from reactors has caused extensive interest in radiation sterilization.

The absence of high temperatures is quite necessary in the processing of many items such as antibiotics and certain other drugs. Large-scale sterilization or pasteurization of perishable food stuffs such as meats, bananas, potatoes, and beverages holds interesting possibilities. Indeed, cold radiation sterilization has great potential importance.

The success of radiation sterilization and pasteurization will be determined by the enhanced value of products treated. If the irradiation process results in improved or longer lasting products, radiation treatment of many present day items should become profitable.

In the drug industry, radiation sterilization presents fewer problems. Side effects such as occur in many foods, are usually not important. It may be possible to utilize this type of sterilization in many pharmaceutical processes.

Radiation sterilization offers the first promising new principle of food sterilization since Nicholas Appert discovered the art of canning in 1809. Today, more than 40 institutions, including food industries, universities, research institutions, government laboratories, and the military, are actively engaged in radiation processing research. The activities of these many groups are being coordinated in the Quartermaster Food and Container Institute Radiation Sterilization Program. Many believe that this research will lead to the changing of food containers, preparation and processing methods, and distribution and marketing practices of food products.

Sterilization or pasteurization of foods by irradiation presents several problems as well as many promising aspects. Irradiation of some foods may cause changes in texture, color, taste, odor, or nutritional value. Intensive research is now being done to learn why unwanted changes occur and to devise ways to reduce or prevent them.

Irradiation of potatoes to delay sprouting and rotting is now being studied. Routine pasteurization of meats and beverages may be feasible within a few years. In these applications, a comparatively small amount of radiation extends the shelf life without causing the undesirable effects mentioned above.

VOLTAGE PRODUCTION

There are several methods for direct production of electricity from the energy released in the decay of radioactive atoms. This energy is extremely minute compared with that from power reactors, but can be used for certain special applications requiring tiny amounts of power. The first of these methods utilizes a basic principle of physics. When a piece of dry plastic or hard rubber is stroked with a wool cloth, for example, the cloth sweeps off electrons from the surface of the dielectric material and leaves it with a positive charge. The wool cloth, of course, holds the negative charge.

Similarly, beta rays ejected from an insulated radioactive source leave it with a positive charge; this is the principle of the Moseley generator developed in 1913. The useful industrial application of this principle has been realized in the development of one type of atomic battery.

Another battery takes advantage of the ion multiplication principle to produce electricity from radioisotopes. The electricity is generated by the high-energy beta particles emitted from Strontium 90. These high-energy electrons are used to bombard a pea-sized silicon P-N junction, the merging of two specialized types of silicon. The P-N junction, in turn, releases about 200,000 slow-moving electrons for each high-speed electron striking it. About one-millionth of a volt is produced, strong enough to cause an audible signal in a telephone receiver. The battery is about the size of a thimble and has a life expectancy of more than 20 years.

Another very recent development has resulted in an atomic battery which uses a series of thermocouples to convert the heat from the decay of a radioisotope into electricity. The battery in its present form contains several curies of Polonium 210 sealed in a small capsule. The polonium is in contact with the hot junction of 40 thermocouples while the cold junction is located outside the container. The temperature difference of about 450° F. thus produced between the hot and cold junctions causes a current to flow through the device. This first model was found to be 0.2 percent efficient in transforming the energy from atomic decay into electricity.

A fourth type of atomic battery utilizes a radioactive source to ionize the filling gas between two electrodes of dissimilar metallic properties. Still another utilizes a radioisotope-activated luminescent source to energize a photoelectric cell, thus producing a small electric current.

TRACING ATOMS

Tracing atoms is perhaps the most important industrial use of radioisotopes. A few examples of the many ways in which the tracer principle is being used should illustrate its importance.

Prior to World War II cyclotron-produced Phosphorus 32, added to the metal mix, was used to study the wear of piston rings. Today, conventional piston rings are made radioactive by subjecting them to neutron bombardment in reactors.

In such a bombardment, only one atom of iron in approximately one billion is converted from stable Iron 58 to radioactive Iron 59. The radioactive ring is fitted to the piston, using proper shielding and monitoring techniques. The engine is assembled, the lubricating oil is added, and the motor is started. Radioactive iron atoms are worn off the ring along with others and are easily detected in the oil. The sensitivity of the radioisotope method is so high that the wear of the ring can be detected in the first few minutes of running time.

The first such experiments were made primarily to determine engine wear as a function of the type of lubricating oil used, and have led to the production of oils that stand up better under severe operating conditions. It should be noted that it is not necessary to dismantle the engine to make the measurements. Both the rate and total wear can be measured readily. One company conducting such a study has indicated it was able to find out in 4 years for $35,000 what would have required 60 years and cost $1 million by older methods.

One of the simplest and most practical examples of the use of radiation to trace material is the determination of catalyst circulation in a catalytic cracking refinery. The catalyst, in the form of small porous beads, passes slowly down through the cracker, then to a furnace where the accumulated carbon is burned off, and finally back to the top of the cracker. The efficiency of this continuous operation is very dependent upon the rate of catalyst circulation, but it is extremely difficult to measure and thus to control this rate. Until recently it was determined by measuring temperature surges at various points in the cracker, even though this method required 2 man-days and did not give dependable results.

The isotopes technique now used for measuring the rate of catalyst circulation depends on impregnating a half-dozen or so of the few billion beads with radioactive zirconium, and noting the time required for a radioactive bead to pass between two rings of counters fastened at each end of a pipe between the gas lift and cracker. By knowing the weight of the catalyst in the pipe between the two points and the time interval between the two peak radiation readings, the operator can quickly calculate the catalyst circulation rate in tons per hour.

In its first application, this one simple test procedure eliminated the necessity for a $100,000 shutdown of a refinery. Today, this radioisotope procedure is used in a number of refineries for routine plant control. A chart in the control room keeps a continuous record of the flow and circulation of the catalyst. . . .

In another application in the petroleum industry, radioisotopes are used to mark the interface or boundary between two different petroleum products flowing through an overland pipeline. As illustrated in Figure 4 the location of the interface must be known in order to route different products to different take-off points and terminals along the line. The exactness with which the interface can be located determines the volume of product which must be considered as waste to assure that two unlike grades will not be mixed in the consumer product.

The radioisotope method is based on injecting into the line a small amount of radioactive material just at the interface as a different product is added. Geiger counters detect and record the passage of radioactivity in the interface at various points along the line. The isotope technique, which is now being used by a number of petroleum companies, has made it possible to reduce the volume of waste product at the final take-off point by one-third as compared to other methods for determining the location of the interface. The isotope technique has also proved helpful in determining the degree of mixing of various products as they pass through the pipeline.

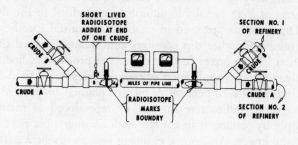

F<small>IG</small>. 4

Further, the technique has been used as a safety feature to start pumps operating automatically as the interface approaches, and thereby avoid the possibility of different products, say gasoline and stove oil, becoming mixed because of holdup in an idle pump. . . .

Somewhat related to flow indication and also to a test procedure is the use of radioisotope markers or tracers in leak detection. Perhaps the simplest application is the use of radiosodium or radioiodine in detecting leaks in water lines.

In this case a small quantity of the radioisotope is introduced into the line and the path of its radiation followed until it reaches the spot where the radiation reading drops off. In a number of instances these tests have made it possible to find and repair leaks in buildings with a minimum disruption of the structure. Furthermore, the test gives quick and reliable results where other techniques fail. . . .

Radioisotopes have been used as a "moving marker" to trace pirate colors. They provide a means of preventing what is called color soiling in multicolor textile printing operations. This occurs whenever one color is carried forward by the fabric from one printing roller to the next, and may jeopardize the sale of many hundreds of yards of valuable fabric.

Any color is in danger of being contaminated by the preceding colors—especially by the immediately preceding one. It is not always possible to arrange the color sequence for printing such that the most sensitive colors are applied first. Frequent replacing of dye solutions is costly; hence, constant efforts must be made to prevent or reduce color contamination.

Many solutions to the problem were tried in the past but without practical success. However, radioisotopes now offer the ideal solution since the offending or so-called pirate color can be labeled with radioactivity and its gradual invasion of a sensitive color dye box carefully and continuously monitored.

It is not necessary to synthesize a costly radioactive dye for this use. A few millicures of P-32 as soluble phosphate are added to the dye bath in question. Dip counters are used to establish the initial specific activity of the pirate color and other dip counters continuously record the level of contamination in dye boxes further down the production line.

A recently developed application of radioisotopes in the field of fine arts may have industrial significance. A picture painted or printed with sufficiently long-lived radioactive ink can be reproduced as many times as desired simply by placing it in contact with photographic paper and then developing the image. An isotope emitting low-energy beta particles, such as Nickel 63, produces clear, sharp reproductions. On the other hand, a softened, diffused effect is obtained with the high-energy beta particles of Phosphorus 32, which can reach the photographic emulsion at an appreciable distance. Tones from light gray to black are obtained by repeated applications of the ink or with inks of different radioactive concentration.

The radioisotope technique has also been used for measuring the wear of gears, the contact wear of distributor points, and the wear of tire tread as a function of vehicle velocity. Similar techniques have been used for measuring the wear and life of machine cutting tools, for studying carbon brush wear during commutation of a direct-current motor, and for determining the wear of floor waxes.

The radioisotope technique is also adaptable to the study of wear caused by corrosion rather than by friction. For example, radiosulfur has been used to study the corrosion of gas-fired thermoelectric generators, radiosodium has been used to test the corrosion of refractories by molten glass, and radiocobalt has been used in determining the wear of fire brick in the lining of blast furnaces.

Space does not permit listing additional applications. However, the use of radioisotopes in most tracing problems is a "natural" and awaits only the application of the technique to the problem at hand.

FUTURE INDUSTRIAL ASPECTS

There can be no doubt that radioisotopes hold many keys to present-day industrial problems. Many believe that radioactivity and the capabilities of the industrial atom will soon be as familiar to industrialists as electricity is today.

Recent developments in low-level radiation counting (counting just above the normal radiation level in nature) hold considerable promise for industrial use of radioisotopes. Using these very sensitive methods, tracer tests could be done during actual processing in an industrial plant and the products reaching the general public would contain such small amounts of radioactivity above the natural level that their handling and use would be completely safe.

Special electronic circuits that cancel out the natural radiation background permit easy measurement of harmless levels of radioactivity. Samples for measurement are usually placed directly into the counter gas or scintillation fluid.

Nature has herself shown how useful radioisotopes can be. For example, it is possible to distinguish recently living wood from wood long dead by means of the radiocarbon produced through the action of cosmic rays on nitrogen in the air. Organic chemicals derived from living materials can be distinguished from those derived from coal and oil. In a similar way, rainwater can be distinguished from groundwater by the radioactivity of naturally occurring radiohydrogen, or tritium.

Many tons of naturally occurring radiocarbon are distributed throughout the world in soil, atmosphere, water, etc. Growing things absorb and use the radioisotope along with stable carbon. At death, absorption stops. Using the decay of naturally occurring radioisotopes as timing devices, ages of things long dead can be accurately determined.

Low-level counting has not been explored to a great extent by industry. Techniques for measurements at these levels are well known, however, and need only industrial development.

1956

Isotopes in Medicine and Biology

HENDRIK M. ROZENDAAL

ISOTOPES FOR SCIENTIFIC USE CONSTITUTE THE FIRST great contribution of the development of atomic energy to peacetime welfare. And it is a contribution which has been particularly exciting for physicians and biologists, because it has given them the most useful new research tool since the invention of the microscope in the seventeenth century and of the X-ray machine some fifty years ago.

Before proceeding, let us define terms. These isotopes, which are now so freely available, are elements identical in chemical properties, but differing slightly in atomic weight. For example, carbon has five isotopes; that is to say, there are five different kinds of carbon atoms all chemically the same because their nuclei carry the same electrical charge, but they differ in their weight. The five kinds of carbon atoms weigh approximately 10, 11, 12, 13, and 14 times as much as the hydrogen nucleus. These weight differences are also responsible for differences in stability; that is to say, two of the five carbon isotopes are natural and stable; three are man-made and unstable. Sooner or later these change into stable isotopes by giving off radiant energy. These radiations are able to penetrate solid matter and the effect by which they are produced is commonly referred to as radioactivity.

When one injects a mixture of these carbon isotopes into the body, it will utilize these substances in identical fashion—that is, the carbon atoms, stable or radioactive, will participate in the same chemical processes. By means of special instruments, such as the Geiger Counter, the investigator will be able to locate and measure the presence of the radioactive atoms throughout the body. This example of carbon isotopes can be extended to many other elements whose isotopes are of particular interest to the medical profession, elements such as hydrogen, nitrogen, oxygen, phosphorus, iodine, sulfur, cobalt, iron, and zinc.

Not only may such radioactive isotopes be used as so-called tracer elements or "tagged" atoms to aid in medical research, but when injected into the body, they can serve as an internal source of radiation, and thus aid in the treatment of diseases which may respond to radiation therapy.

Up until now, by far the most important applications are as tracer elements; and we may look forward to great advances in our knowledge of the physiology and chemistry of the human body because of the ready availability of these materials since the development of atomic energy. Prior to the facilities of the reactor at Oak Ridge, one unit of carbon 14 produced by using a cyclotron would cost approximately one million dollars; the same amount manufactured in the atomic piles of Oak Ridge is now being sold at fifty dollars. More than three hundred laboratories and hospitals in this country and abroad are now engaged in research projects in which isotopes are being used, and this may be said to be only the beginning.

Important tracer investigations in medicine include the study of the mechanisms, reactions, and pathways of elements and chemical compounds in the body during the process of digestion and metabolism. The hundreds of different life materials consisting of carbohydrates, fats, and proteins are formed of relatively few source elements in the diet such as carbon, nitrogen, oxygen, hydrogen, phosphorus, sulfur, and iodine. Isotopes provide labels for these elements, thus making it possible to trace them through the body. Also, it is possible to label drugs and study their localization and mode of action upon organs and bacteria.

Tracing life processes by the use of stable and radioactive isotopes, we have now learned that all components of the body—the muscles, bones, and teeth, as well as the blood, secretions, and food stores—are in a constant state of breaking down and renewal. The multitude of life compounds involved in this process go through continuous and rapid chemical reactions, many of them reversible. Those not serving at any given moment as part of the fixed structure, and not excreted from the body, are combined into a metabolic pool of life ingredients available for use anywhere in the body.

The most surprising fact revealed has been the extreme rapidity with which these processes take place. It has been shown, for instance, the tagged salt injected into the vein is transported to the sweat glands, converted into sweat and carried to the surface of the body in less than one minute's time.

There are many other experiments being carried out. For example, radioactive iron is used to learn more about the mechanism of iron absorption in red blood cells in normal and anemic conditions; radioactive calcium is used to study bone and tooth formation; and radioactive phosphorus and radio potassium to study nerve tissue. One can safely say that the function of every important organ, both in health and in disease, is presently being investigated by means of this new research tool.

It is not possible to carry out such experiments without adequate equipment and a thorough knowledge of the possible dangers of these radioactive materials. We really are only in the very early stages of the development of this important field, but the promises for the future are great and our understanding of the complicated processes of life should increase rapidly.

In clinical medicine, radioactive isotopes are being used to diagnose various circulatory disorders and to locate obstructions in blood vessels. Some malignant, abnormally growing tissues absorb certain elements in the body, such as phosphorus and iodine, faster than the normal tissue. Cancer specialists are taking advantage of this fact and are using radioactive isotopes to help locate tumors and to distinguish between benign and malignant growths. I must emphasize, however, that these studies are still in the experimental stage and do *not* replace or surpass any of the time-tested methods of cancer diagnosis.

Already much has been written about the possibilities of treating disease with radioactive isotopes. For a long time it has been known that certain types of cancer and a number of blood diseases can be arrested at least temporarily by means of X-radiation or radium. Now radioactive isotopes make it possible to apply this radiation internally. We can, for instance, inject radioactive phosphorus into the blood stream and thus produce direct radiation effects upon blood cells and bone marrow. This form of treatment is used in certain cases of leukemia, a cancer of the white blood cells. Because the thyroid gland picks up nearly all of the iodine in the body, we can treat cancer of the thyroid gland with radioactive iodine, again concentrating the radioactive material in the diseased tissue.

Dramatic as this may sound, we must not forget that this form of treatment really does not differ greatly from externally applied radiation, and we are keenly aware that radiation treatment is not the solution to the cancer problem. It is obvious, therefore, that the medical profession is more interested in the research possibilities and applications of atomic energy than in its immediate use in the treatment of disease. We can expect important progress in the knowledge of the basic processes of life, and with this progress there will come more satisfactory ways of treatment of diseases which at present are still beyond our understanding.

1951

A Layman Looks at Science

RAYMOND B. FOSDICK

AUGUST 6, 1945—THE DAY THE ATOMIC BOMB WAS dropped on Hiroshima—brought home to all of us in dramatic fashion the significance of science in human life. The impact of that bomb has left us stunned and confused. Certainly we laymen are frightened by science as we never were before. And certainly, too, we are bewildered by the power which science has suddenly placed in our laps—bewildered and humbled by our realization of how unequipped we are, in terms of ethics, law, and government, to know how to use it.

That, I think, is the first reaction of a layman to the stupendous repercussion of that bomb on Hiroshima. And the first question that comes to his mind is this: What use are radios and automobiles and penicillin and all the other gifts of science if at the same time this same science hands us the means by which we can blow ourselves and our civilization into drifting dust? We have always been inclined to think of research and technology as being consciously related to human welfare. Now, frankly, we are not so sure, and we are troubled, deeply troubled, by the realization that man's brain can create things which his will may not be able to control.

To the layman it seems as if science were facing a vast dilemma. Science is the search for truth, and it is based on the glorious faith that truth is worth discovering. It springs from the noblest attribute of the human spirit. But it is this same search for truth that has brought our civilization to the brink of destruction; and we are confronted by the tragic irony that when we have been most successful in pushing out the boundaries of knowledge we have most endangered the possibility of human life on this planet. The pursuit of truth has at last led us to the tools by which we can ourselves become the destroyers of our own institutions and all the bright hopes of the race. In this situation what do we do—curb our science or cling to the pursuit of truth and run the risk of having our society torn to pieces?

It is on the basis of this dilemma that serious questions are forming in the public mind. Unless research is linked to a humane and constructive purpose should it not be subject to some kind of restraint? Can our scientists afford to be concerned solely with fact and not at all with value and purpose? Can they legitimately claim that their only aim is the advancement of knowledge regardless of its consequences? Is the layman justified in saying to the scientist: "We look to you to distinguish between that truth which furthers the well-being of mankind and that truth which threatens it"?

One of the scientists who played a leading role in the development of the atomic bomb said to the newspapermen: "A scientist cannot hold back progress because of fears of what the world will do with his discoveries." What he apparently implied was that science has no responsibility in the matter and that it will plunge ahead in the pursuit of truth even if the process leaves the world in dust and ashes.

Is that the final answer? Is there no other answer? Frankly, as a layman I do not know. Offhand, this disavowal of concern for the social consequences of science seems callous and irresponsible. But we may be facing a situation where no other answer is realistic or possible. To ask the scientist to foresee the use—the good or evil of the use—to which his results may be put is doubtless beyond the realm of the attainable. Almost any discovery can be used for either social or antisocial purposes. The German dye industry was not created to deal with either medicine or weapons of war; and yet out of that industry came our sulfa drugs and mustard gas. When Einstein wrote his famous transformation equation in 1905 he was not thinking of the atomic bomb, but out of that equation came one of the principles upon which the bomb was based.

Willard Gibbs was a gentle spirit whose life was spent in his laboratory at Yale University and who never dreamed that his work in mathematical physics might have even a remote relationship to war; and yet it is safe to say that his ideas gave added power to the armaments of all nations in both World War I and World War II.

I suspect that the way out of the dilemma is not as simple as the questions now being asked seem to imply. The good and the evil that flow from scientific research are more often than not indistinguishable at the point of origin. Generally they are by-products, or they represent distortions of original purpose, none of which could have been foreseen when the initial discovery was made. We are driven back to a question of human motives and desires. Science has recently given us radar, jet propulsion and power sources of unprecedented magnitude. What does society want to do with them? It can use them constructively to increase the happiness of mankind, or it can employ them to tear the world to pieces. There is scarcely a scientific formula or a process or a commodity which cannot be used for war purposes, if that is what we elect to do with it. In brief, the gifts of science can be used by evil men to do evil even more obviously and dramatically than they can be used by men of good will to do good.

I fear there is no easy way out of our dilemma. I would not absolve the scientists from some measure of responsibility, for they are men of superior training and insight and we are entitled to look to them for help and leadership—more help and leadership, I venture to add, than have thus far been given. However, I note that a considerable number of the scientists who were connected with the atomic bomb project have publicly expressed their apprehension of the consequences of their own creation. "All of us who worked on the atomic bomb," said Dr. Allison of the University of Chicago, "had a momentary feeling of elation when our experiment met with success; but that feeling rapidly changed to a feeling of horror, and a fervent desire that no more bombs would be dropped."

Nevertheless in the long run I do not believe that we shall be successful in making science the arbiter of its own discoveries. Somehow or other society itself must assume that responsibility. The towering enemy of mankind is not science but war. Science merely reflects the social forces by which it is surrounded. When there is peace, science is constructive; when there is war, science is perverted to destructive ends. The weapons which science gives us do not necessarily create war; they make war increasingly more terrible until now it has brought us to the doorstep of doom.

Our main problem, therefore, is not to curb science but to stop war—to substitute law for force and international government for anarchy in the relations of one nation with another. That is a job in which everybody must participate, including the scientists. But the bomb on Hiroshima suddenly woke us up to the fact that we have very little time. The hour is late and our work has scarcely begun. Now we are face to face with this urgent question: "Can education and tolerance and understanding and creative intelligence run fast enough to keep us abreast with our own mounting capacity to destroy?"

That is the question which we shall have to answer one way or the other in this generation. Science must help us in the answer, but the main decision lies within ourselves.

1947

Acknowledgments

For arrangements made with various authors and publishing firms whereby certain copyrighted material was permitted to be reprinted, and for the courtesies extended by them, the following acknowledgments are gratefully made:

THE WONDER OF THE WORLD from *Life: Outlines of General Biology* by Sir J. Arthur Thomson and Patrick Geddes, reprinted by permission from Harper & Brothers.

WE ARE ALL SCIENTISTS from *Darwiniana* by T. H. Huxley, reprinted by permission from D. Appleton-Century Company, Inc.

SCIENTISTS ARE LONELY MEN by Oliver La Farge, reprinted by permission from *Harper's Magazine* and from Oliver La Farge.

TURTLE EGGS FOR AGASSIZ by Dallas Lore Sharp, reprinted by permission from *The Atlantic Monthly*.

ADDRESS BEFORE STUDENT BODY, CALIFORNIA INSTITUTE OF TECHNOLOGY by Albert Einstein, reprinted by permission from Albert Einstein and from the *Sigma Xi Quarterly*.

ICARUS IN SCIENCE from *Stars and Atoms* by Sir Arthur Eddington, reprinted by permission from Yale University Press.

BIOLOGY AND MEDICINE by Alan Gregg, from *Atomic Energy and the Life Sciences,* the July, 1949, Report of the United States Atomic Energy Commission.

THE ORDERLY UNIVERSE by Forest Ray Moulton, from *The World and Man: As Science Sees Them,* edited by Forest Ray Moulton, copyright, 1937, reprinted by permission from Doubleday, Doran & Company, Inc.

THE MILKY WAY AND BEYOND reprinted by permission from Sir Arthur Eddington.

RADIO STARS by A. C. B. Lovell, copyright 1953 by *Scientific American* and reprinted by their permission.

GEOLOGICAL CHANGE by Sir Archibald Geike, Presidential Address before British Association for the Advancement of Science, 1892, reprinted by permission from the British Association for the Advancement of Science. The original article carried no title.

EARTHQUAKES—WHAT ARE THEY? by the Reverend James B. Macelwane, S.J., reprinted by permission from *The Scientific Monthly* and from Father Macelwane.

LAST DAYS OF ST. PIERRE from *Disaster Fighters* by Fairfax Downey, reprinted by courtesy of G. P. Putnam's Sons.

PIN-POINTING THE PAST WITH THE COSMIC CLOCK by Richard Foster Flint, copy-

773

right 1951 by The American Museum of Natural History, reprinted by permission of *Natural History Magazine.*

WHAT MAKES THE WEATHER by Wolfgang Langewiesche, reprinted by permission from *Harper's Magazine.*

MATHEMATICS, THE MIRROR OF CIVILIZATION from *Mathematics for the Million* by Lancelot Hogben, published by W. W. Norton & Company, Inc., and reprinted by their permission.

EXPERIMENTS AND IDEAS by Benjamin Franklin, from *The Ingenious Dr. Franklin* edited by Nathan Goodman, reprinted by permission from The University of Pennsylvania Press.

EXPLORING THE ATOM from *The Universe Around Us* by Sir James Jeans, reprinted by permission from The Macmillan Company, publishers.

THE DISCOVERY OF RADIUM from *Madame Curie: A Biography,* by Eve Curie, copyright, 1937, by Doubleday, Doran and Company, Inc., reprinted by permission from Doubleday, Doran and Company, Inc.

ELECTRONICS EVERYWHERE by A. M. Low, reprinted by permission from the John Day Company. Copyright 1951 by A. M. Low.

GIANT BRAINS by Edmund Callis Berkeley, reprinted by permission from John Wiley & Sons, Inc. Copyright 1949 by Edmund Callis Berkeley.

MACHINES THAT THINK from *Giant Brains,* by Edmund Callis Berkeley, reprinted by permission from John Wiley & Sons, Inc. Copyright 1949 by Edmund Callis Berkeley.

SOME EARLY PIONEERS IN CHEMISTRY from *Chemistry, Matter and Life* by Stephen Miall and L. M. Miall, reprinted by permission from Edward Arnold.

THE FOUNDATIONS OF CHEMICAL INDUSTRY by Robert E. Rose, from *Chemistry in Industry,* edited by H. E. Howe, reprinted by permission from The Chemical Foundation and from Robert E. Rose.

MAN'S SYNTHETIC FUTURE by Roger Adams, reprinted by permission from The American Association for the Advancement of Science.

SPACE, TIME AND EINSTEIN by Paul R. Heyl, reprinted by permission from *The Scientific Monthly* and from Paul R. Heyl.

THE CHARACTERISTICS OF ORGANISMS from *Life: Outlines of General Biology* by Sir J. Arthur Thomson and Patrick Geddes, reprinted by permission from Harper & Brothers.

LEEUWENHOEK: FIRST OF THE MICROBE HUNTERS, condensed from *Microbe Hunters,* copyright, 1926, by Paul de Kruif, reprinted by permission from Harcourt, Brace and Company, Inc.

THE ORIGIN OF LIFE by George Wald, copyright 1954 by *Scientific American* and reprinted by their permission.

ON BEING THE RIGHT SIZE from *Possible Worlds* by J. B. S. Haldane, reprinted by permission from Harper & Brothers.

PARASITISM AND DEGENERATION from *Evolution and Animal Life* by David Starr Jordan and Vernon Lyman Kellogg, reprinted by permission from D. Appleton-Century Company, Inc.

FLOWERING EARTH from *Flowering Earth* by Donald Culross Peattie, reprinted by courtesy of G. P. Putnam's Sons.

A LOBSTER; OR, THE STUDY OF ZOOLOGY from *Discourses Biological and Geological,* by T. H. Huxley, reprinted by permission from D. Appleton-Century Company, Inc.

THE LIFE OF THE SIMPLEST ANIMALS from *Animal Life* by David Starr Jordan and Vernon Lyman Kellogg, reprinted by permission from D. Appleton-Century Company, Inc.

SECRETS OF THE OCEAN from *The Log of the Sun* by William Beebe, reprinted by permission from Henry Holt and Company, Inc.

THE WARRIOR ANTS from *Of Ants and Men* by Caryl P. Haskins, reprinted by permission from Prentice-Hall, Inc., 70 Fifth Avenue, New York.

THE VAMPIRE BAT by Raymond L. Ditmars and Arthur M. Greenhall, reprinted in condensed form from *Zoologica, Scientific Contributions of the New York Zoological Society*, by permission from the New York Zoological Society.

ANCESTORS by Gustav Eckstein, reprinted by permission from *Harper's Magazine* and from Gustav Eckstein.

DARWIN AND "THE ORIGIN OF SPECIES" by Sir Arthur Keith, an Introduction to the Everyman's Library edition of *The Origin of Species* by Charles Darwin, reprinted by permission from E. P. Dutton and Company.

GREGOR MENDEL AND HIS WORK by Hugo Iltis, reprinted by permission from *The Scientific Monthly* and from Hugo Iltis.

THE COURTSHIP OF ANIMALS from *Man Stands Alone* by Julian Huxley, reprinted by permission from Harper & Brothers.

MAGIC ACRES by Alfred Toombs, reprinted by permission from *The American Magazine* and Alfred Toombs.

THE UPSTART OF THE ANIMAL KINGDOM by Earnest A. Hooton, reprinted by permission from *The American Scholar*.

EVOLUTION REVISED, reprinted from *Man, Time and Fossils* by Ruth Moore by permission of Alfred A. Knopf, Inc. Copyright 1953 by Ruth Moore.

LESSONS IN LIVING FROM THE STONE AGE by Vilhjalmur Stefansson, reprinted by permission from *Harper's Magazine*.

RACIAL CHARACTERS OF THE BODY from *Man: A History of the Human Body* by Sir Arthur Keith, reprinted by permission from the Oxford University Press.

BIOGRAPHY OF THE UNBORN, a *Reader's Digest* condensation of the book *Biography of the Unborn* by Margaret Shea Gilbert, reprinted by permission from *The Reader's Digest* and from The Williams & Wilkins Company.

HOW THE HUMAN BODY IS STUDIED from *Man: A History of the Human Body* by Sir Arthur Keith, reprinted by permission from the Oxford University Press.

VARIATIONS ON A THEME BY DARWIN by Julian Huxley, originally titled "Man as a Relative Being," from *Science in a Changing World* edited by Mary Adams, reprinted by permission from George Allen and Unwin, Ltd., and from D. Appleton-Century Company, Inc.

HIPPOCRATES, THE GREEK—THE END OF MAGIC from *Behind the Doctor* by Logan Clendening, reprinted by permission of and special arrangement with Alfred A. Knopf, Inc. Copyright 1933 by Alfred A. Knopf, Inc.

LOUIS PASTEUR AND THE CONQUEST OF RABIES from *The Life of Pasteur* by René Vallery-Radot, reprinted by permission from Doubleday, Doran & Company, Inc.

CHEMOTHERAPY from *Chemotherapy: Yesterday, Today, Tomorrow,* by Alexander Fleming, reprinted by permission from the Cambridge University Press.

THE NEW SCIENCE OF SURGERY by Frank G. Slaughter, reprinted by permission from Julian Messner, Inc. Copyright 1946 by Frank G. Slaughter.

THINKING from *The Mind in the Making* by James Harvey Robinson, reprinted by permission from Harper & Brothers.

IMAGINATION CREATRIX from *The Road to Xanadu* by John Livingston Lowes, reprinted by permission from Houghton Mifflin Company.

THE PSYCHOLOGY OF SIGMUND FREUD by A. A. Brill, an Introduction to *The Basic Writings of Sigmund Freud,* reprinted by permission from The Modern Library and A. A. Brill.

REACTION MOTORS from *The Coming Age of Rocket Power* by Edward Pendray, copyright 1945, 1947 by Harper & Brothers, and reprinted by their permission.

WE LEARN A LESSON from *The Viking Rocket Story* by Milton W. Rosen, copyright 1955 by Milton W. Rosen and reprinted by permission of Harper & Brothers.

A SHOT AROUND THE WORLD from *The Making of a Moon,* copyright © 1957, 1958 by Arthur Charles Clarke and reprinted by permission of Harper & Brothers.

LIFE IN SPUTNIK by P. Isakov, reprinted by permission of the Am-Rus Literary and Music Agency.

IS THERE LIFE ON OTHER WORLDS? by Sir James Jeans, an afternoon lecture of the Royal Institution of Great Britain, reprinted by permission from Sir James Jeans.

ATOMIC TERMS AND WHAT THEY MEAN, reprinted by permission of the Esso Research and Engineering Foundation, Linden, N. J.

ATOMIC ENERGY FOR MILITARY PURPOSES by Henry D. Smyth, reprinted by permission from the Princeton University Press.

ATOMIC WARFARE, PAST AND FUTURE from *The Atom at Work,* by Jacob Sacks, copyright 1951 by the Ronald Press Company and reprinted by their permission.

THE DEATH OF LOUIS SLOTIN from *Atoms and People* by Ralph E. Lapp, copyright © 1956 by Ralph Lapp and reprinted by permission of Harper & Brothers.

RADIATIONS AND THE GENETIC THREAT by Warren Weaver, reprinted by permission of the author.

NUCLEAR POWER IN THE FUTURE by J. R. Dunning, reprinted by permission from *The American Scientist.*

ISOTOPES IN MEDICINE AND BIOLOGY by Hendrik M. Rozendahl, from *Science Marches On,* edited by James Stokeley, copyright 1951 by Ives Washburn, Inc., and reprinted by their permission.

A LAYMAN LOOKS AT SCIENCE by Raymond B. Fosdick, from *The Scientists Speak,* edited by Warren Weaver, copyright 1947 by Boni & Gaer, Inc. Reprinted by permission from the U. S. Rubber Company.